CHARACTERISTIC
FUNCTIONS

CHARACTERISTIC FUNCTIONS

EUGENE LUKACS

Professor of Mathematics
The Catholic University of America
Washington, D.C.

Second Edition
Revised and enlarged

1970
HAFNER PUBLISHING COMPANY
NEW YORK

CHARLES GRIFFIN & COMPANY LIMITED
42 DRURY LANE, LONDON, W.C.2

Copyright © 1970

All rights reserved

First published in 1960
Second edition   1970

Large Medium 8vo, x + 350 pages

Made and printed in Great Britain by
Butler & Tanner Ltd., Frome and London

PREFACE TO SECOND EDITION

The first edition of this book appeared in the series "Griffin's Statistical Monographs and Courses". The general aims and the arrangement of the book remain unchanged in this second edition; however, it seemed desirable to expand the treatment so as to include not only recent developments but also certain parts of the theory of characteristic functions which were known when the first edition was written but for various reasons had to be omitted.

The original section on stable distributions contained a number of results which were stated without proof. The part of Chapter 5 which deals with stable distributions has now been greatly extended; and material on series expansions and on the analytic properties of stable densities has been added, together with detailed proofs. Asymptotic expansions of stable densities and the demonstration of the unimodality of stable distributions have also been included. Chapter 9 is entirely new and deals with infinitely divisible distributions which have no indecomposable factor. Most theorems concerning this class have been obtained during the last few years; the first highly significant results were announced, mostly without proofs, by Yu. V. Linnik in *Doklady* when the manuscript of the first edition was almost completed. It was therefore only possible to state some of the results in the first edition, but the present edition gives a detailed account of these developments. Chapter 10 contains new material on α-decompositions, while Chapter 11 treats of boundary characteristic functions; the latter concept, introduced by J. Marcinkiewicz, has received little attention until quite recently. The topics listed above do not exhaust the additions; there are a number of new sections such as 3.7 (infinite convolutions), 4.4 (non-negative definite functions), and 4.5 (unimodal distributions), as well as many changes and much supplementary matter throughout the book.

I have received many communications from readers and friends which I greatly appreciated and have used in this revision. I am particularly indebted to Dr. R. Cuppens who read the manuscript of the second edition with great care and offered many valuable suggestions.

Thanks are also due to Dr. R. Mureika, Dr. B. Ramachandran, Dr. V. K. Rohatgi, to my wife who helped me with the proof-reading, and to Mrs. A. Miller and Mrs. P. Spathelf for the accurate and speedy typing of the manuscript.

Finally, I wish to express my appreciation to the Publishers for meeting my wishes concerning the appearance of the book.

EUGENE LUKACS

WASHINGTON, D.C.
November 1969

PREFACE TO FIRST EDITION

Characteristic functions and generating functions were originally developed as a tool for the solution of problems in Probability Theory and admit many important applications in this branch of mathematics as well as in Mathematical Statistics. In the present monograph we study characteristic functions for their intrinsic mathematical interest and are not concerned with their possible applications. This statement could be taken as an admission that this book does not properly fit into a series of statistical monographs and courses. However, a mathematical statistician needs a good background in pure mathematics, and the methods discussed in a considerable part of this monograph should be contained in his tool chest.

The literature of the subject is widely scattered over many periodicals, and a substantial part of the important results can be found in Russian and French journals. This part of the literature is often not easily accessible and its use is made even more difficult by the language barrier. A reasonably complete account of the subject is only possible if the foreign literature is adequately covered. The author hopes that such a coverage is provided in this monograph and that this feature will increase its usefulness for students of the subject.

Certain parts of the theory, primarily those discussed in sections 8.2 and 8.5, are the areas in which major advances are being made at present. Important new results had been announced without proof shortly before the manuscript was completed. It was only possible to mention some of these advances (for example theorem 8.2.7) in order to indicate the direction in which research is proceeding at present.

Most of the theorems discussed in this book are given with detailed proofs; occasionally it was possible only to state some results and to refer the reader to the literature for the proofs. The monograph does not contain a complete bibliography; we give selected references for readers who wish either to find the proofs not given in the book or who desire to study some background material. The book can therefore not be used to decide questions of priority. The author to whom a particular result is due is often not even mentioned. If it is customary to associate the name of a particular mathematician with a theorem, then this is done, but the paper in which this result was published is not necessarily listed in the References. An article is included in the list of references only if it contains material which is mentioned in the monograph but not discussed in sufficient detail.

I should like to express my thanks to Dr. R. G. Laha, Dr. I. R. Savage and Dr. S. Vajda for reading the manuscript. The author is particularly indebted to Dr. R. G. Laha for valuable comments and advice. Thanks are also due to the Catholic University for providing clerical help; to Miss I. Christensen, Dr. R. G. Laha, Mrs. E. C. Lukacs, and Mr. B. Ramachandran who read the proofs; and to Mrs. K. Winner who typed the manuscript. The book was written with the partial support of the National Science Foundation under grant NSF–G–4220 which is gratefully acknowledged here.

EUGENE LUKACS

WASHINGTON, D.C.
December 1958

CONTENTS

1 INTRODUCTION

It is now universally recognized that probability theory is a branch of measure theory. Thus probability is defined as a bounded and normed measure. An important part of probability theory is devoted to the study of finite and measurable functions, the random variables. The probability that the value of a random variable belongs to a given set is of interest; this probability is a set function and is called the "probability function" of the random variable. It is known that this set function determines a point function—the distribution function of the random variable. Many of the most important problems concerning random variables can be expressed in terms of distribution functions. This part of probability theory can be studied independently of its measure-theoretic foundation and of theorems of purely measure-theoretic character. The methods of classical analysis provide an efficient approach to problems of this sort.

The present monograph deals with one of the most powerful tools used for the investigation of distribution functions, namely characteristic functions. Before defining characteristic functions it is necessary to summarize briefly some important concepts.

1.1 Distribution functions

In this section, in which we discuss some of the basic properties of distribution functions, we will confine ourselves mostly to the listing of definitions and theorems. Proofs will be only given if they are short, otherwise the reader is referred to standard texts such as the books of Cramér (1946) and Loève (1963). The lack of proofs in this chapter should not impede the reader in using this monograph. In fact, it will be possible to follow the discussion in the subsequent chapters if one takes for granted the statements made in this introduction. Familiarity with proofs which are omitted is not required.

For the sake of brevity we introduce the following notation. Let $F(x)$ be a function of the real variable x; we then write:

$$(1.1.1) \quad \begin{cases} F(+\infty) = \lim_{x \to \infty} F(x) \\ F(-\infty) = \lim_{x \to -\infty} F(x) \\ F(x+0) = \lim_{h \downarrow 0} F(x+h) \\ F(x-0) = \lim_{h \downarrow 0} F(x-h). \end{cases}$$

Here $h \downarrow 0$ means that h tends to zero from above, assuming only positive values.

A function $F(x)$ of a real variable x is called a distribution function if it satisfies the following three conditions:—

    (i) $F(x)$ is non-decreasing, that is $F(x+h) \geqslant F(x)$ if $h > 0$;
    (ii) $F(x)$ is right-continuous, i.e. $F(x+0) = F(x)$;
    (iii) $F(+\infty) = 1$, $F(-\infty) = 0$.

Thus distribution functions are by definition bounded and monotone and many of their basic properties follow from this fact. For instance a distribution function can have only discontinuities of the first kind.[*] A point x is called a discontinuity point of the distribution function $F(x)$ if $F(x+0) = F(x) \neq F(x-0)$; if $F(x) = F(x-0)$ then z is called a continuity point of $F(x)$. The quantity

$$(1.1.2) \qquad p_x = F(x+0) - F(x-0) = F(x) - F(x-0)$$

is called the saltus (jump) of $F(x)$ at the point x. The saltus of a distribution function is positive at its discontinuity points and zero at its continuity points. An interval is called a continuity interval for the distribution function $F(x)$ if both its endpoints are continuity points of $F(x)$. A point x is called a point of increase of the distribution function $F(x)$ if $F(x+\varepsilon) - F(x-\varepsilon) > 0$ for any $\varepsilon > 0$.

Let $F(x)$ be a distribution function and k be a positive integer. Denote by D_k the set of discontinuity points of $F(x)$ with saltus contained in the half open interval

$$\left(\frac{1}{k+1}, \frac{1}{k} \right];$$

this set contains at most $k+1$ points. The set of all discontinuity points of $F(x)$ is the union of all sets D_k ($k = 1, 2, \ldots$) and is therefore at most enumerable. We have therefore proved

Theorem 1.1.1. *The set of discontinuity points of a distribution function is at most enumerable.*

Remark. It follows that the set of continuity points of a distribution function is always dense in the set of real numbers. However, it can happen that the set of discontinuity points is also dense. Let for example $\{r_k\}$ be the enumerable but dense set of all rational numbers and assign to r_k ($k = 1, 2, \ldots$) the saltus $p_k = 2^{-k}$. Then $F(x) = \sum_{r_k < x} p_k$ is a distribution function whose discontinuity points form a dense set.

Let $\{x_\nu\}$ be the set of discontinuity points of the distribution function

---

(*) See E. W. Hobson (1927), pp. 301, 318.

$F(x)$ and write $p_{x_\nu} = F(x_\nu + 0) - F(x_\nu - 0)$ for the saltus of $F(x)$ at the point x_ν. We define the function

$$(1.1.3) \qquad \Phi(x) = \sum_{x_\nu \leqslant x} p_{x_\nu};$$

the summation is here extended over all discontinuity points not exceeding x. The function $\Phi(x)$ increases only by jumps, at points of the sequence $\{x_\nu\}$, and is constant in every closed interval not containing an x_ν. Such a function is called a "step-function". The saltus of $\Phi(x)$ at x_ν is p_{x_ν}. We form also a second function

$$(1.1.4) \qquad \psi(x) = F(x) - \Phi(x).$$

The function $\psi(x)$ is continuous, while $\Phi(x)$ is only continuous from the right; both functions are non-decreasing and satisfy the relations

$$\Phi(-\infty) = \psi(-\infty) = 0, \qquad \Phi(+\infty) = a_1 \leqslant 1, \qquad \psi(+\infty) = b \leqslant 1.$$

It is therefore possible to define two distribution functions by normalizing $\Phi(x)$ and $\psi(x)$.

The functions $F_d(x) = (1/a_1)\Phi(x)$ and $F_c(x) = (1/b)\psi(x)$ are both distribution functions; $F_d(x)$ is a step function while $F_c(x)$ is continuous for all x. According to (1.1.4) we have

$$(1.1.5) \qquad F(x) = \Phi(x) + \psi(x)$$

and therefore also

$$(1.1.6) \qquad F(x) = a_1 F_d(x) + b F_c(x) \qquad (a_1 \geqslant 0,\ b \geqslant 0,\ a_1 + b = 1).$$

The decomposition (1.1.5) and therefore also the decomposition (1.1.6) are unique. Suppose that there are two decompositions

$$F(x) = \Phi(x) + \psi(x) = \Phi_1(x) + \psi_1(x).$$

Then

$$\Phi(x) - \Phi_1(x) = \psi_1(x) - \psi(x).$$

The right-hand side is a continuous function while the left-hand side is the difference of two step functions. Therefore both sides must vanish identically and we obtain

Theorem 1.1.2.   Every distribution function $F(x)$ can be decomposed according to

$$F(x) = a_1 F_d(x) + b F_c(x).$$

Here $F_d(x)$ and $F_c(x)$ are both distribution functions. $F_c(x)$ is continuous for all x while $F_d(x)$ is a step function. The coefficients a_1 and b satisfy the relations $0 \leqslant a_1 \leqslant 1,\ 0 \leqslant b \leqslant 1,\ a_1 + b = 1$.

$F_d(x)$ is called the discontinuous (discrete) part, and $F_c(x)$ is called the continuous part of $F(x)$. We note an immediate consequence of theorem 1.1.1: There exists an enumerable set D such that $\int_D dF_d(x) = 1$. Here and in the following the integral is a Lebesgue–Stieltjes integral. The function $F_c(x)$ is continuous but has not necessarily a derivative at all points; however, every distribution function has a derivative almost everywhere (in the sense of Lebesgue measure). A further decomposition can be obtained by means of more powerful tools of analysis. Applying Lebesgue's decomposition theorem [see Loève (1963)] one can show that it is possible to determine two distribution functions $F_{ac}(x)$ and $F_s(x)$ such that

$$(1.1.7) \qquad F_c(x) = b_1 F_{ac}(x) + b_2 F_s(x)$$

where $b_1 \geqslant 0$, $b_2 \geqslant 0$, $b_1 + b_2 = 1$.

The function $F_{ac}(x)$ can be represented as the integral of its derivative,
$F_{ac}(x) = \int_{-\infty}^x F'_{ac}(y)\,dy$. Moreover $\int_N dF_{ac}(x) = 0$ if N is a set of Lebesgue measure zero. Such a distribution function is said to be absolutely continuous. The distribution function $F_s(x)$ is a continuous function whose derivative is almost everywhere equal to zero; moreover there exists a set N of Lebesgue measure zero such that $\int_N dF_s(x) = 1$. A distribution function with this property is called a singular distribution. Combining (1.1.7) and (1.1.6) we obtain the following

Theorem 1.1.3. *Every distribution function $F(x)$ can be decomposed uniquely according to*

$$(1.1.8) \qquad F(x) = a_1 F_d(x) + a_2 F_{ac}(x) + a_3 F_s(x).$$

Here $F_d(x)$, $F_{ac}(x)$, $F_s(x)$ are three distribution functions. The functions $F_{ac}(x)$ and $F_s(x)$ are both continuous; however $F_{ac}(x)$ is absolutely continuous while $F_s(x)$ is singular and $F_d(x)$ is a step function. The coefficients a_1, a_2, a_3 satisfy the relations $a_1 \geqslant 0$, $a_2 \geqslant 0$, $a_3 \geqslant 0$, $a_1 + a_2 + a_3 = 1$.

The distribution functions $F_d(x)$, $F_{ac}(x)$, $F_s(x)$ are called the discrete, the absolutely continuous, and the singular parts, respectively, of $F(x)$.

A distribution function is said to be pure if one of the coefficients in the representation (1.1.8) equals 1. For pure distributions we will use the expressions discrete distribution if $a_1 = 1$, absolutely continuous distribution if $a_2 = 1$, and singular distribution if $a_3 = 1$. In applications one almost inevitably encounters either discrete or absolutely continuous distributions. Singular distributions are interesting from a theoretical viewpoint but hardly ever occur in practical work. This is the reason why statistical texts frequently refer to absolutely continuous distributions as continuous distributions and seemingly ignore the existence of singular distributions.

Let $F(x)$ be an absolutely continuous distribution function. Then

$$(1.1.9) \qquad F(x) = \int_{-\infty}^{x} F'(y)\,dy$$

where the integral is supposed to be a Lebesgue integral. The derivative $p(x) = F'(x)$ is called the frequency function(*) of the distribution $F(x)$. From the definition of a distribution function it follows that every function $p(x)$ which satisfies the conditions

$$(1.1.10) \qquad \begin{cases} p(x) \geqslant 0 & \text{for all } x, \\ \int_{-\infty}^{\infty} p(x)\,dx = 1 \end{cases}$$

is the frequency function of an absolutely continuous distribution function which is given by (1.1.9).

1.2 Examples of distribution functions

In this section we list a number of important distributions which occur frequently in practical work. For the sake of brevity we refrain from describing mathematical models which lead to these distributions.

(*I*) *Discrete distributions.* The simplest discrete distribution function is a function which has a single saltus of magnitude 1 at the origin. We denote this function by

$$(1.2.1) \qquad \varepsilon(x) = \begin{cases} 0 & \text{for } x < 0 \\ 1 & \text{for } x \geqslant 0. \end{cases}$$

Let ξ be an arbitrary fixed real number; the function $\varepsilon(x-\xi)$ is then a distribution function. It has a single discontinuity point at $x = \xi$ and the magnitude of the saltus at this point is 1. The distributions $\varepsilon(x-\xi)$ are called "degenerate" (or "improper") distributions.

The most general purely discrete distribution function is determined by the location of its discontinuity points and by the magnitude of the corresponding jumps. Let $\{\xi_j\}$ be a sequence which contains all discontinuity points of $F(x)$ and let p_j be the saltus at the point ξ_j. The corresponding distribution function is then given by

$$(1.2.2) \qquad F(x) = \sum_j p_j \varepsilon(x-\xi_j).$$

Here the ξ_j are real numbers and the p_j satisfy the relations

$$(1.2.3) \qquad p_j \geqslant 0, \qquad \sum_j p_j = 1.$$

In Table 1 we present some discrete distribution functions. The Pascal distribution as well as the geometric distribution are particular cases of the

---

(*) The expression "probability density function" or "density function" is often used for "frequency function".

negative binomial distribution. The Pascal distribution is obtained if r is a positive integer, the geometric distribution if $r = 1$.

In the examples given in Table 1 the discontinuity points are consecutive non-negative integers.

Table 1

Discrete distributions

Name	Discontinuity point ξ_j	Saltus at ξ_j	Conditions on parameters
Binomial	$\xi_j = j$ $j = 0, 1, 2, \ldots, n$	$\binom{n}{j} p^j q^{n-j}$	n positive integer $0 < p < 1, q = 1-p$
Hypergeometric	$\xi_j = j$ $j = 0, 1, 2, \ldots,$ $\min(M, n)$	$\dfrac{\binom{M}{j}\binom{N-M}{n-j}}{\binom{N}{n}}$	N, M, n positive integers $N > M$ $N > m$
Geometric	$\xi_j = j$ $j = 0, 1, 2, \ldots,$ ad. inf.	$p\, q^j$	$0 < p < 1, q = 1-p$
Pascal	$\xi_j = j$ $j = 0, 1, 2, \ldots,$ ad. inf.	$p^r \binom{-r}{j}(-q)^j$	r positive integer $0 < p < 1, q = 1-p$
Negative binomial	$\xi_j = j$ $j = 0, 1, 2, \ldots,$ ad. inf.	$p^r \binom{-r}{j}(-q)^j$	r real, $r > 0$ $0 < p < 1, q = 1-p$
Poisson	$\xi_j = j$ $j = 0, 1, 2, \ldots,$ ad. inf.	$e^{-\lambda}\dfrac{\lambda^j}{j!}$	$\lambda > 0$

A discrete distribution is called a "lattice distribution" if its discontinuity points form a (proper or improper) subset of a sequence of equidistant points. We sometimes refer to the discontinuity points of such a distribution as lattice points. They have the form $a+jd$ (a, d constant, $d > 0$; j integer). The constant d is called a "span" of the lattice distribution. The distributions of Table 1 are all lattice distributions which have the origin as a lattice point.

(*II*) *Absolutely continuous distributions.* These distributions are determined by their frequency function $p(x)$. The distribution function can be obtained by integration:

$$(1.2.4) \quad F(x) = \int_{-\infty}^{x} p(y)\, dy.$$

The function $p(y)$ satisfies the relations (1.1.10) which correspond to (1.2.3).

In Table 2 we list a few frequency functions.

The normal distribution is often called the Gaussian distribution. In the French literature it is referred to as the "law of Gauss–Laplace" or "the law of de Moivre–Laplace" or the "second law of Laplace". This last terminology is used to distinguish it from the "first law of Laplace" which is called the "Laplace distribution" in Table 2.

Table 2

Frequency functions

Name of Distribution	Frequency function $p(x)$	Conditions on parameters
Rectangular distribution (Uniform distribution)	$1/2r$ if $\|x-a\| \leqslant r$ 0 if $\|x-a\| > r$	a, r real $r > 0$
Triangular distribution (Simpson's distribution)	$(r-\|x-a\|)/r^2$ if $\|x-a\| \leqslant r$ 0 if $\|x-a\| > r$	a, r real $r > 0$
Laplace distribution	$\frac{1}{2}e^{-\|x\|}$ or more generally $\frac{1}{2\sigma} \exp\left[-\|x-\mu\|/\sigma\right]$ $-\infty < x < \infty$	$\ldots$ μ, σ real $\sigma > 0$
Normal distribution	$(1/\sqrt{2\pi})e^{-x^2/2}$ or more generally $\frac{1}{\sigma\sqrt{2\pi}} \exp\left[-\frac{(x-\mu)^2}{2\sigma^2}\right]$ $-\infty < x < \infty$	$\ldots$ μ, σ real $\sigma > 0$
Student's distribution (with n degrees of freedom)	$\frac{1}{\sqrt{n\pi}} \cdot \frac{\Gamma[(n+1)/2]}{\Gamma(n/2)}\left[1+\frac{x^2}{n}\right]^{-(n+1)/2}$ $-\infty < x < \infty$	$n \geqslant 1$ integer
Cauchy distribution	$1/[\pi(1+x^2)]$ or more generally $\frac{\theta}{\pi[\theta^2+(x-\mu)^2]}$ $-\infty < x < \infty$	$\ldots$ θ, μ real $\theta > 0$
Gamma distribution	$\frac{\theta^\lambda}{\Gamma(\lambda)}x^{\lambda-1}e^{-\theta x}$ for $x > 0$ 0 for $x < 0$	θ, λ real $\theta > 0, \lambda > 0$
Beta distribution	$\frac{\Gamma(p+q)}{\Gamma(p)\,\Gamma(q)} x^{p-1}(1-x)^{q-1}$ for $0 < x < 1$ 0 otherwise	p, q real $p > 0, q > 0$

Two particular cases of the gamma distribution are of interest: for $\lambda = 1$ one obtains the exponential distribution, while the choice $\theta = \frac{1}{2}$, $\lambda = n/2$ (n integer) yields the chi-square distribution with n degrees of freedom which is of great importance in mathematical statistics. We note also that the Cauchy distribution is a particular case ($n = 1$) of Student's distribution. The Beta distribution with parameters $p = q = \frac{1}{2}$ is called the Arc sine distribution.

(*III*) *Singular distributions.*   We give only one example of a singular distribution; this example is closely related to Cantor's ternary set defined over the closed unit interval $V = [0, 1]$. The Cantor set T is constructed by means of a step-by-step procedure. In the first step we remove from V the open interval $(\frac{1}{3}, \frac{2}{3})$. In the second step two open intervals $(\frac{1}{9}, \frac{2}{9})$ and $(\frac{7}{9}, \frac{8}{9})$ are removed from V. From each of the remaining 4 closed intervals the middle (open) interval of length $(\frac{1}{3})^3$ is deleted in the third step and this process is continued indefinitely. Let each of the $(k-1)$ numbers $c_1, c_2, \ldots, c_{k-1}$ assume either the value 0 or the value 1; we denote by $A_{2c_1, 2c_2, \ldots, 2c_{k-1}}$ the open interval with initial point

$$\sum_{j=1}^{k-1} \frac{2}{3^j} c_j + \frac{1}{3^k}$$

and terminal point

$$\sum_{j=1}^{k-1} \frac{2}{3^j} c_j + \frac{2}{3^k}.$$

Our procedure consists then in removing in the kth step the 2^{k-1} open intervals $A_{2c_1, 2c_2, \ldots, 2c_{k-1}}$ of length $(\frac{1}{3})^k$. The Cantor set T is obtained from the closed interval V by removing a denumerable number of open intervals. It is easily seen that the points of T can be characterized in the following manner. Write each number x, $0 \leqslant x \leqslant 1$, in the triadic system

$$x = a_1/3 + a_2/3^2 + \ldots + a_n/3^n + \ldots;$$

the set T consists of all numbers x which can be written in at least one way in the form of a triadic fraction whose digits are only zeros or twos. The points of T therefore have triadic expansions

$$2c_1/3 + 2c_2/3^2 + \ldots + 2c_n/3^n + \ldots$$

where $c_1, c_2, \ldots, c_n, \ldots$ is a sequence of "0" and "1".

We introduce the function

$$g(x) = \begin{cases} \frac{1}{2} & \text{if } \frac{1}{3} < x < \frac{2}{3} \\ \sum_{j=1}^{k-1} \frac{c_j}{2^j} + \frac{1}{2^k} & \text{if } x \in A_{2c_1, \ldots, 2c_{k-1}} \end{cases}$$

Finally we define the function

$$
(1.2.5) \qquad F(x) = \begin{cases} 0 & \text{if } x < 0 \\ g(x) & \text{if } x \in V - T \\ \sum_j \dfrac{c_j}{2^j} & \text{if } x = \sum_j \dfrac{2c_j}{3^j} \in T \\ 1 & \text{if } x \geqslant 1. \end{cases}
$$

It is easily seen that $F(x)$ is a continuous distribution function; moreover its derivative is zero at all points of $V - T$ while it is not differentiable in the points of T. The points of T are the only points of increase of $F(x)$ and form a set of measure zero. Thus $F(x)$ is a singular distribution function.

The singular distribution which we have just discussed has the property that it is constant in the open intervals $A_{2c_1, \ldots, 2c_{k-1}}$. This is, however, by no means typical for singular distribution functions. R. Salem (1943) gave a simple example of a singular distribution function which is strictly increasing.

1.3 The method of integral transforms

In this section we introduce a procedure which is very useful in the study of distribution functions. It is frequently advisable to consider, instead of a distribution function $F(x)$, expressions which are derived from this function. These expressions are usually defined as integral transforms using a suitable kernel $K(t, x)$ which is a function of the variable x and contains also a parameter t. The parameter t can be either discrete—for instance integer-valued—or can have a continuous domain of variation.

The integral transform is defined by

$$
(1.3.1) \qquad \int_{-\infty}^{\infty} K(t, x) \, dF(x),
$$

provided that the integral (1.3.1) exists as a Lebesgue–Stieltjes integral. The conditions for the existence of this integral are of course always of great interest.

We now list a few possibilities for the choice of $K(t, x)$ which are useful in the study of distribution functions.

(A) $K(t, x) = x^t$

(B) $K(t, x) = |x|^t$

(C) $K(t, x) = x^{(t)} = x(x-1)\ldots(x-t+1)$ with $x^{(0)} = 1$.

In the preceding three examples the parameter t is restricted to non-negative integers.

(D) $K(t, x) = e^{tx}$

(E) $K(t, x) = t^x$

(F) $K(t, x) = e^{itx}$ where $i = \sqrt{-1}$.

In cases (D), (E), (F) the parameter is a real-valued and continuous variable.

To emphasize the discrete character of the parameter in cases (A), (B) and (C) we write $k(k = 0, 1, 2, \ldots)$ instead of t. The transforms (A), (B) and (C) then transform the distribution function $F(x)$ into sequences (provided that the integrals exist). We call

$$(1.3.2) \qquad \alpha_k = \int_{-\infty}^{\infty} x^k \, dF(x)$$

the algebraic moment of order k of $F(x)$, or more briefly the kth moment of $F(x)$. Similarly

$$(1.3.3) \qquad \beta_k = \int_{-\infty}^{\infty} |x|^k \, dF(x)$$

is called the kth absolute moment of $F(x)$. We do not intend to use the kernel (C); it leads to the factorial moments $\int_{-\infty}^{\infty} x^{(k)} \, dF(x)$.

The kernels (D), (E) and (F) transform the distribution function $F(x)$ into functions of the real variable t. The function

$$(1.3.4) \qquad M(t) = \int_{-\infty}^{\infty} e^{tx} \, dF(x)$$

is obtained by means of the kernel (D) and is called the moment generating function of $F(x)$. The kernel (E) is used only when $F(x)$ is a purely discontinuous distribution which has all its jumps at non-negative integer values of the variable x. In this case we get the probability generating function

$$(1.3.5) \qquad P(t) = \int_{-\infty}^{\infty} t^x \, dF(x) = \sum_{j=0}^{\infty} t^j p_j$$

where

$$p_j \geqslant 0, \qquad \sum_{j=0}^{\infty} p_j = 1.$$

Here p_j is the saltus of $F(x)$ at the point $x = j$ (j non-negative integer). Probability generating functions were introduced by Laplace; we will use these functions only rarely (in Section 6.3) and mention them here mainly because they were the first integral transforms systematically used in probability theory.

Finally we substitute the kernel (F) into (1.3.1); this yields

$$(1.3.6) \qquad f(t) = \int_{-\infty}^{\infty} e^{itx} \, dF(x).$$

This transform is called the characteristic function[(*)] of the distribution function $F(x)$, and its study is the object of this monograph.

It is known [Cramér (1946) p. 70] that every bounded and measurable function is integrable with respect to any distribution function over $(-\infty, +\infty)$. This assures the existence of the characteristic function (1.3.6) for every distribution function. We introduced the probability generating function only for a special class of lattice distributions. For this class $P(t)$ exists, provided $|t| \leqslant 1$. The existence of the moment generating function is not assured for all distributions. We say that the moment generating function $M(t)$ of a distribution exists if the integral (1.3.4) is convergent for all values of t belonging to an interval (finite or infinite) which contains the origin. The existence of $M(t)$ must be established before it is used. Suppose for the moment that we consider a distribution function for which $M(t)$ exists. We will see later [Section 7.1] that it is then connected to the characteristic function by the relation

(1.3.7) $M(it) = f(t)$.

We conclude this introductory chapter by discussing in somewhat greater detail some properties of algebraic and absolute moments which will be needed later.

1.4 Moments

We first note that moments are defined as Lebesgue–Stieltjes integrals. It is known that for these integrals the concepts of integrability and absolute integrability are equivalent [see Loève (1963) pp. 119 ff.]. We apply this general property of the Lebesgue–Stieltjes integral to the expressions defining the moments and formulate it as

Theorem 1.4.1.   The algebraic moment of order k of a distribution function $F(x)$ exists if, and only if, its absolute moment of order k exists.

From the properties of the integral and from (1.3.2) and (1.3.3) we see immediately that for any positive integer k

(1.4.1) $\alpha_{2k} = \beta_{2k}$
            $\alpha_{2k-1} \leqslant |\alpha_{2k-1}| \leqslant \beta_{2k-1}$

while $\alpha_0 = \beta_0 = 1$.

Theorem 1.4.2.   Let $F(x)$ be a distribution function and suppose that its moment α_k of order k exists. Then the moments α_s and β_s exist for all orders $s \leqslant k$.

(*) Formula (1.3.6) indicates that characteristic functions are the Fourier transforms of distribution functions.

According to Theorem 1.4.1, $\beta_k = \displaystyle\int_{-\infty}^{\infty} |x|^k \, dF(x)$ exists. Clearly

$$\beta_k \geqslant \int_{|x|>1} |x|^k \, dF(x) \geqslant \int_{|x|>1} |x|^s \, dF(x) \quad \text{if } s \leqslant k.$$

Since the integral $\displaystyle\int_{|x|<1} |x|^s \, dF(x)$ is always finite, it follows that β_s and α_s exist for all $s \leqslant k$.

The moments of a distribution function do not always exist; we give now an example for a distribution which has moments only up to a certain order.

The function

$$F(x) = \begin{cases} 0 & \text{for } x < 1 \\ 1 - x^{-m} & \text{for } x > 1 \end{cases}$$

is for $m > 0$ an absolutely continuous distribution function. An elementary computation shows that $\alpha_k = \beta_k = m/(m-k)$ if $k < m$, while the moments of order equal or greater than m do not exist.

As another example we mention Student's distribution. This distribution has moments up to order $(n-1)$. For $n = 1$ this shows that the Cauchy distribution does not possess any moments.

It is of interest to know whether a given sequence of real numbers can be the sequence of the moments of a distribution. The discussion of this difficult problem is beyond the scope of this monograph, and we refer the reader to the book of J. A. Shohat–J. D. Tamarkin (1943). However, we remark that a moment sequence does not necessarily determine a distribution function uniquely. It may happen that two different distributions have the same set of moments. As an illustration we give the following example. The function

$$(1.4.2) \qquad p_1(x) = \begin{cases} C \exp\left[-x^\mu \cos m\pi\right] & \text{if } x > 0 \\ 0 & \text{if } x < 0 \end{cases}$$

where

$$C = \frac{\mu(\cos \mu\pi)^{1/\mu}}{\Gamma(1/\mu)}$$

and $0 < \mu < \tfrac{1}{2}$ is a frequency function. The moments of the corresponding distribution are

$$(1.4.3) \qquad \alpha_n = \frac{\Gamma[(n+1)/\mu]}{\Gamma(1/\mu)} (\cos \mu\pi)^{-n/\mu} \qquad (n = 0, 1, 2, \ldots).$$

Let

$$(1.4.4) \qquad p_2(x) = \begin{cases} C\left[1 + \sin\left(x^\mu \sin \mu\pi\right)\right] \exp\left[-x^\mu \cos \mu\pi\right] & \text{if } x > 0 \\ 0 & \text{if } x < 0. \end{cases}$$

It is known [see Pólya–Szegö (1925), vol. 1, pp. 114 and 286] that for $0 < \mu < \frac{1}{2}$

(1.4.5) $\displaystyle\int_0^\infty x^n \sin (x^\mu \sin \mu\pi) \exp [-x^\mu \cos \mu\pi]\, dx = 0 \quad (n = 0, 1, \ldots).$

This shows that $p_2(x)$ is also a frequency function and is different from $p_1(x)$, but that

$$\alpha_n = \int_0^\infty x^n p_1(x)\, dx = \int_0^\infty x^n p_2(x)\, dx$$

for all non-negative integers n.

The existence of the moments of a distribution function depends on the behaviour of this function at infinity. We give here, without proof, a sufficient condition for the existence of moments.

Theorem 1.4.3.   Let $F(x)$ be a distribution and assume that for some integer k

$$1 - F(x) + F(-x) = O(x^{-k}) \qquad as\ x \to \infty.$$

Then the moments of any order $s < k$ exist.

For the meaning of the symbol O we refer the reader to Appendix A. A proof of theorem 1.4.3 may be found in Cramér (1946).

Table 3
Moments

Name of distribution	Formula for moments α_k and β_k
Rectangular distribution with $a = 0$	$\alpha_{2k-1} = 0,\ \alpha_{2k} = \dfrac{r^{2k}}{2k+1},\quad \beta_k = \dfrac{r^k}{k+1}$
Laplace distribution	$\alpha_{2k-1} = 0,\ \alpha_{2k} = (2k)!,\ \beta_k = k!$
Exponential distribution	$\alpha_k = \beta_k = \theta^{-k} k!$
Gamma distribution	$\alpha_k = \beta_k = \theta^{-k} \lambda(\lambda+1) \ldots (\lambda+k-1)$
Normal distribution with $\mu = 0,\ \sigma = 1$	$\alpha_{2l-1} = 0,\ \alpha_{2l} = \dfrac{(2l)!}{2^l\, l!} = \beta_{2l}$ $\beta_{2l-1} = \dfrac{1}{\sqrt{2\pi}}\, 2^l (l-1)!$
Student's distribution (n degrees of freedom)	$\alpha_{2v-1} = 0,\ \alpha_{2v} = \dfrac{1\cdot 3\cdot \ldots (2v-1)n^v}{(n-2)(n-4)\ldots(n-2v)}$ $(2v < n)$ $\beta_{2v-1} = \dfrac{2^v n^{v-1/2}\,(v-1)!\, \Gamma[(n+1)/2]}{(n-1)(n-3)\ldots(n-2v+1)\,\Gamma(\frac{1}{2})\,\Gamma(n/2)}$ $(2v-1 < n)$

We give several inequalities for absolute moments which supplement the relations (1.4.1). Suppose that the kth moment of a distribution exists, then

(1.4.6) $\beta_{k-1}^2 \leqslant \beta_{k-2}\,\beta_k.$

This inequality follows almost immediately from Schwarz's inequality [see Appendix B or Cramér (1946)]. By elementary operations we obtain finally from (1.4.6) the inequalities

(1.4.7) $\beta_{k-1}^{1/(k-1)} \leqslant \beta_k^{1/k}$

or

(1.4.8) $\beta_1 \leqslant \beta_2^{\frac{1}{2}} \leqslant \beta_3^{\frac{1}{3}} \leqslant \ldots \leqslant \beta_k^{1/k}.$

For a rather wide class of discrete distributions one can obtain recurrence relations for the moments. This class was discussed by Noack (1950) and contains many important distribution functions such as the binomial, Poisson and negative binomial distributions. Recurrence formulae for the moments of singular distributions (especially for the distribution function described in Section 1.2) were given by G. C. Evans (1957). On the preceding page we list in Table 3 formulae for the moments of a few common absolutely continuous distributions.

2 PRELIMINARY STUDY OF CHARACTERISTIC FUNCTIONS

2.1 Elementary properties of characteristic functions

In the preceding chapter we denoted distribution functions by capital letters, as $F(x)$, and the characteristic function of $F(x)$ by the corresponding small letter, as $f(t)$. We adhere to this notation throughout this monograph; if subscripts are used on the symbol for a distribution function then the same subscript is attached to its characteristic function.

We defined the characteristic function $f(t)$ of a distribution function $F(x)$ by

(1.3.6) $$f(t) = \int_{-\infty}^{\infty} e^{itx} \, dF(x).$$

The properties of characteristic functions, stated in theorem 2.1.1, follow immediately from this formula.

Theorem 2.1.1. Let $F(x)$ be a distribution function with characteristic function $f(t)$. Then

(i) $f(0) = 1$

(ii) $|f(t)| \leqslant 1$

(iii) $f(-t) = \overline{f(t)}$.

We use here the horizontal bar atop of $f(t)$ to denote the complex conjugate of $f(t)$.

Theorem 2.1.2. Every characteristic function is uniformly continuous on the whole real line.

It follows from (1.3.6) that

$$|f(t+h) - f(t)| \leqslant \int_{-\infty}^{\infty} |e^{ixh} - 1| \, dF(x) = 2 \int_{-\infty}^{\infty} |\sin(xh/2)| \, dF(x)$$

so that

$$|f(t+h) - f(t)|$$
$$\leqslant 2 \int_{-\infty}^{-A} \left| \sin \frac{xh}{2} \right| dF(x) + 2 \int_{-A}^{B} \left| \sin \frac{xh}{2} \right| dF(x) + 2 \int_{B}^{+\infty} \left| \sin \frac{xh}{2} \right| dF(x).$$

We note that the right-hand side of this inequality is independent of t; it is possible to make the first and the third integral on the right arbitrarily small by choosing $A > 0$, $B > 0$ sufficiently large. Moreover, the second integral on the right can be made arbitrarily small by selecting $h > 0$ sufficiently small, so that the statement is proved.

Let $F(x)$ be a distribution function and let a and b be two real numbers and suppose that $a > 0$. Then

$$(2.1.1) \qquad G(x) = F\left(\frac{x-b}{a}\right)$$

is also a distribution function.

We say that two distribution functions F and G belong to the same type if they are connected by relation (2.1.1) (with $a > 0$).

More generally, we consider a distribution function $F(x)$ and two real numbers a and b and suppose only that $a \neq 0$. We define

$$(2.1.1a) \qquad G(x) = \begin{cases} F\left(\dfrac{x-b}{a}\right) & \text{if } a > 0 \\ 1 - F\left(\dfrac{x-b}{a} - 0\right) & \text{if } a < 0. \end{cases}$$

Then $G(x)$ is also a distribution function. A simple change of the variable under the integral defining $g(t)$ shows that

$$(2.1.2) \qquad g(t) = e^{itb} f(at).$$

For $a = -1$ and $b = 0$ we see that $g(t) = f(-t)$ is a characteristic function whenever $f(t)$ is a characteristic function.

Let $a_1, \ldots, a_n$ be n real numbers such that

$$a_j \geqslant 0, \qquad \sum_{j=1}^{n} a_j = 1$$

and let $F_1(x), \ldots, F_n(x)$ be n distribution functions. Then

$$G(x) = \sum_{j=1}^{n} a_j F_j(x)$$

is also a distribution function; the corresponding characteristic function is

$$g(t) = \sum_{j=1}^{n} a_j f_j(t).$$

Theorem 2.1.3. *Suppose that the real numbers* $a_1, \ldots, a_n$ *satisfy the conditions*

$$a_j \geqslant 0, \qquad \sum_{j=1}^{n} a_j = 1$$

and that $f_1(t), \ldots, f_n(t)$ *are characteristic functions. Then*

$$g(t) = \sum_{j=1}^{n} a_j f_j(t)$$

is also a characteristic function.

As a particular case we obtain the following corollary.

Corollary to theorem 2.1.3. Let f(t) be a characteristic function; then f(t) as well as Re *f(t) are characteristic functions. Here*

$$\text{Re } f(t) = \tfrac{1}{2}[f(t)+\overline{f(t)}] = \int_{-\infty}^{\infty} \cos tx \, dF(x)$$

is the real part of f(t).

We showed in the preceding chapter that any purely discrete distribution can be written in the form

(1.2.2) $\quad F(x) = \sum_j p_j \varepsilon(x-\xi_j)$

where the ξ_j are real while the p_j satisfy the relations

(1.2.3) $\quad p_j \geqslant 0, \qquad \sum_j p_j = 1.$

The Lebesgue–Stieltjes integral with respect to the distribution function (1.2.2) reduces to a sum, so that the characteristic function $f(t)$ of $F(x)$ becomes

(2.1.3) $\quad f(t) = \sum_j p_j e^{it\xi_j}.$

If, in particular, $F(x)$ is a lattice distribution then we can write

(2.1.4) $\quad \xi_j = a+jd$

where a and d are real numbers. The characteristic function of a lattice distribution therefore has the form

(2.1.5) $\quad f(t) = e^{ita} \sum_j p_j e^{itjd},$

where the p_j satisfy (1.2.3). It is immediately seen that

$$\left| f\left(\frac{2\pi}{d}\right) \right| = |e^{[i(2\pi a/d)]}| = 1.$$

Every lattice distribution $F(x)$ therefore has the following property: there exists a real number $t_0 \neq 0$ such that the modulus of its characteristic function $f(t)$ assumes the value 1 for $t = t_0$. We show next that this property characterizes lattice distributions. Suppose that the characteristic function $f(t)$ of a distribution function $F(x)$ has this property. We assume therefore that there exists a $t_0 \neq 0$ such that $|f(t_0)| = 1$. This means that $f(t_0) = e^{it_0\xi}$ for some real ξ or

$$\int_{-\infty}^{\infty} e^{it_0 x} dF(x) = e^{it_0\xi}.$$

It is then easily seen that $F(x)$ satisfies the relation

(2.1.6) $\quad \int_{-\infty}^{\infty} [1-\cos t_0(x-\xi)] dF(x) = 0.$

Since the function $1-\cos t_0(x-\xi)$ is continuous and non-negative, (2.1.6) can hold only if $F(x)$ is a purely discontinuous distribution whose discontinuity points are contained in the set of zeros of the function $1-\cos t_0(x-\xi)$. The discontinuity points of $F(x)$ have then necessarily the form $\xi+(2\pi/t_0)s$ (s integer) so that $F(x)$ is a lattice distribution. We therefore have the following result.

Theorem 2.1.4. A characteristic function $f(t)$ is the characteristic function of a lattice distribution if, and only if, there exists a real $t_0 \neq 0$ such that $|f(t_0)| = 1$.

Table 4 (*)

Characteristic functions

Name of distribution function $F(x)$	Characteristic function $f(t) = \int_{-\infty}^{\infty} e^{itx}\, dF(x)$
Degenerate distribution $\epsilon(x-\xi)$	$e^{it\xi}$
Binomial distribution	$(q+p\, e^{it})^n$
Negative binomial distribution	$\{p[1-q\, e^{it}]^{-1}\}^r$
Poisson distribution	$\exp\{\lambda(e^{it}-1)\}$
Rectangular distribution	$e^{ita}\dfrac{\sin tr}{tr}$
Laplace distribution	$\dfrac{1}{1+t^2}$
Normal distribution	$\exp\left[i\mu t-\dfrac{\sigma^2 t^2}{2}\right]$
Cauchy distribution	$e^{-|t|}$ or more generally $\exp[i\mu t-\theta|t|]$.
Gamma distribution	$\left(1-\dfrac{it}{\theta}\right)^{-\lambda}$
Beta distribution(†)	${}_1F_1(p,p+q,it) = \dfrac{\Gamma(p+q)}{\Gamma(p)}\displaystyle\sum_{j=0}^{\infty}\dfrac{\Gamma(p+j)}{\Gamma(p+q+j)\Gamma(j+1)}(it)^j$

(*) The conditions on the parameters are stated in Table 2 for discrete distributions and in Table 3 for absolutely continuous distributions. We denote here e^A by exp [A].

(†) ${}_1F_1(a, b, z)$ is the confluent hypergeometric function.

Theorem 2.1.4 implies that $|f(t)| < 1$ almost everywhere, provided that $f(t)$ is the characteristic function of a non-degenerate distribution. Suppose that $a < 0$, then $[f(t)]^a$ cannot be a characteristic function. This remark leads to the following corollary.

Corollary 1 to theorem 2.1.4. The only characteristic functions whose reciprocals are also characteristic functions belong to degenerate distributions.

We obtain easily from theorem 2.1.4 the following corollary:

Corollary 2 to theorem 2.1.4. If a characteristic function $f(t)$ has the property that for two incommensurable real values t_1 and t_2 the relations $|f(t_1)| = |f(t_2)| = 1$ hold, then $|f(t)| \equiv 1$.

On the preceding page we listed in tabular form the characteristic functions of some of the distributions given in Tables 1 and 2.

In Section 1.2 we constructed [see (III)] a singular distribution function. It can be shown that the characteristic function of this distribution is given by

$$(2.1.7) \qquad f(t) = e^{it/2} \lim_{n \to \infty} \prod_{j=1}^{n} \cos \frac{t}{3^j}.$$

For details and further examples of characteristic functions of singular distributions we refer the reader to papers by B. Jessen–A. Wintner (1935), A. Wintner (1936), R. Kershner (1936), and the thesis of M. Girault (1954).

2.2 Lebesgue decomposition of characteristic functions

The decomposition theorem 1.1.3 induces immediately a decomposition of the characteristic function. Every characteristic function $f(t)$ can be written in the form

$$(2.2.1) \qquad f(t) = a_1 f_d(t) + a_2 f_{ac}(t) + a_3 f_s(t)$$

with $a_1 \geqslant 0$, $a_2 \geqslant 0$, $a_3 \geqslant 0$ and $a_1 + a_2 + a_3 = 1$. Here $f_d(t)$, $f_{ac}(t)$ and $f_s(t)$ respectively are characteristic functions of (purely) discrete, absolutely continuous and singular distributions. For a pure distribution one of the coefficients a_1, a_2, a_3 is equal to 1 while the other two are zero. We add a few remarks concerning characteristic functions of a pure type.

(A) If $a_1 = 1$ then $f(t)$ is the characteristic function of a (purely) discrete distribution. It follows from (2.1.3) that $f(t)$ is almost periodic[*] so that

$$\lim_{|t| \to \infty} \sup |f(t)| = 1.$$

(B) If $a_2 = 1$ then $f(t)$ belongs to an absolutely continuous distribution. It follows from the Riemann–Lebesgue lemma [see Titchmarsh (1939) p. 403] that

$$\lim_{|t| \to \infty} f(t) = 0.$$

_____

(*) See H. Bohr (1932), (1947).

(C) If $a_3 = 1$ then $f(t)$ is the characteristic function of a singular distribution. In this case $f(t)$ does not necessarily go to zero as $|t|$ tends to ∞. Thus

$$L = \limsup_{|t| \to \infty} |f(t)|$$

may be any number between zero and 1. In fact, examples are known where L assumes the value zero [Girault (1954)]. An example[*] of a characteristic function of a singular distribution for which $L = 1$ was communicated to the author by A. Wintner. Another example is due to C. G. Esseen (1944). Singular distributions for which L equals 1 or 0, or a number between 0 and 1, were given by L. Schwartz (1951).

The behaviour of the characteristic function at infinity permits therefore some inference concerning its type. For instance, if

$$\limsup_{|t| \to \infty} |f(t)| = 0,$$

then $f(t)$ belongs to a continuous distribution.

2.3   Characteristic functions and moments

There is a close connection between characteristic functions and moments. In order to discuss this relation we introduce the following notation.

Let $h(y)$ be an arbitrary function; we define its first (central) difference with respect to an increment t by

$$\Delta_1^t h(y) = \Delta^t h(y) = h(y+t) - h(y-t)$$

and the higher differences by

$$\Delta_{k+1}^t h(y) = \Delta^t \Delta_k^t h(y),$$

for $k = 1, 2, \ldots$. It can be shown by induction that

$$(2.3.1) \qquad \Delta_n^t h(y) = \sum_{k=0}^{n} (-1)^k \binom{n}{k} h[y + (n - 2k)t].$$

In particular, for the function $h(y) = e^{ixy}$ we have

$$(2.3.2) \qquad \Delta_n^t e^{ixy} = e^{ixy}(e^{ixt} - e^{-ixt})^n = e^{ixy}[2i \sin xt]^n.$$

Theorem 2.3.1.   Let $f(t)$ be the characteristic function of a distribution function $F(x)$, and let

$$\frac{\Delta_{2k}^t f(0)}{(2t)^{2k}}$$

(*) Let $f(t) = \prod_{n=1}^{\infty} \cos (t/n!)$; it follows from a result of B. Jessen–A. Wintner (1935) [theorem 11] that $f(t)$ belongs to a purely singular distribution. Moreover, for integer k it is easily seen that $1 - f(2\pi k!) = O(\sum_{n=k+1}^{\infty} k!^2/n!^2) = o(1)$ as $k \to \infty$, so that $\limsup_{|t| \to \infty} |f(t)| = 1$. (For the meaning of the symbols O and o see Appendix A.)

be the (2k)th (central) difference quotient of f(t) at the origin. Assume that

$$M = \liminf_{t \to 0} \left| \frac{\Delta_{2k}^t f(0)}{(2t)^{2k}} \right| < \infty.$$

Then the (2k)th moment α_{2k} of F(x) exists, as do all the moments α_s of order $s < 2k$. Moreover the derivatives $f^{(s)}(t)$ exist for all t and for $s = 1, 2, \ldots, 2k$ and

$$f^{(s)}(t) = i^s \int_{-\infty}^{\infty} x^s e^{itx} \, dF(x) \qquad (s = 1, 2, \ldots, 2k)$$

so that

$$\alpha_s = i^{-s} f^{(s)}(0).$$

From the assumptions of the theorem it is seen that there exists a finite constant M such that

(2.3.3) $\qquad \displaystyle \liminf_{t \to 0} \left| \frac{\Delta_{2k}^t f(0)}{(2t)^{2k}} \right| = M.$

It follows from (2.3.2) that

$$\Delta_{2k}^t f(y) = \int_{-\infty}^{\infty} e^{iyx} (2i \sin xt)^{2k} \, dF(x).$$

The difference quotient at the origin is then

$$\left| \frac{\Delta_{2k}^t f(0)}{(2t)^{2k}} \right| = \int_{-\infty}^{\infty} \left(\frac{\sin xt}{t} \right)^{2k} dF(x).$$

We see therefore from (2.3.3) that

$$M = \liminf_{t \to 0} \int_{-\infty}^{\infty} \left(\frac{\sin xt}{t} \right)^{2k} dF(x)$$

and hence that

$$M \geqslant \liminf_{t \to 0} \int_{-a}^{b} \left(\frac{\sin xt}{t} \right)^{2k} dF(x) = \int_{-a}^{b} x^{2k} \, dF(x)$$

for any finite a and b. It follows then that the (2k)th moment

$$\alpha_{2k} = \int_{-\infty}^{\infty} x^{2k} \, dF(x)$$

exists and that $M \geqslant \alpha_{2k}$. Let s be a positive integer such that $s < 2k$; then it follows from theorem 1.4.2 that the moments β_s and α_s exist for $s = 1, 2, \ldots, 2k$.

From the existence of the moments α_s ($s = 1, 2, \ldots, 2k$) we see immediately that $\int_{-\infty}^{\infty} x^s e^{itx} \, dF(x)$ exists and converges absolutely and uniformly for all real t and $s \leqslant 2k$. It follows from a well-known theorem [see for instance Cramér (1946), pp. 67–68] that all derivatives up to order $2k$ exist and are obtained by differentiating under the integral sign. This proves theorem 2.3.1.

If a characteristic function has a derivative of even order, then the conditions of theorem 2.3.1 are satisfied and we obtain

Corollary 1 to theorem 2.3.1.   *If the characteristic function of a distribution $F(x)$ has a derivative of order k at $t = 0$, then all the moments of $F(x)$ up to order k exist if k is even, or up to order $k - 1$ if k is odd.*

The following example, due to A. Zygmund (1947), shows that the result cannot be improved.

Let $C = \sum\limits_{j=2}^{\infty} \dfrac{1}{j^2 \log j}$.

Then

$$F(x) = C^{-1} \sum_{j=2}^{\infty} \frac{1}{2j^2 \log j} [\varepsilon(x-j) + \varepsilon(x+j)]$$

is a distribution function whose characteristic function is

$$f(t) = C^{-1} \sum_{j=2}^{\infty} \frac{\cos jt}{j^2 \log j}.$$

It can be shown that $f'(t)$ exists and is continuous for all values of t, in particular for $t = 0$. However, the first moment of $F(x)$ is infinite.

Corollary 2 to theorem 2.3.1.   *If the moment α_s of order s of a distribution function $F(x)$ exists then the characteristic function $f(t)$ of $F(x)$ can be differentiated s times and*

$$f^{(s)}(t) = i^s \int_{-\infty}^{\infty} x^s e^{itx} \, dF(x).$$

Corollary 2 follows immediately from the argument used in the last part of the proof of theorem 2.3.1.

Theorem 2.3.1 also yields another result:

Theorem 2.3.2.   *Let $f(t)$ be the characteristic function of a distribution $F(x)$ and assume that for an infinite sequence of even integers $\{2n_k\}$*

$$M_k = \liminf_{t \to 0} \left| \frac{\Delta_{2n_k}^t f(0)}{(2t)^{2n_k}} \right|$$

is finite (but not necessarily bounded) for $k = 1, 2, \ldots$ Then all moments α_s of the distribution function $F(x)$ exist and $f(t)$ can be differentiated for real t any number of times, with

$$f^{(s)}(t) = i^s \int_{-\infty}^{\infty} x^s e^{ixt} \, dF(x).$$

Corollary to theorem 2.3.2.   *Let $f(t)$ be the characteristic function of $F(x)$; if all the derivatives of $f(t)$ exist at the origin then all the moments of $F(x)$ exist.*

It is worthwhile to note that a characteristic function may be nowhere differentiable. As an example we mention the Weierstrass function

$$f(t) = \sum_{k=0}^{\infty} \frac{1}{2^{k+1}} e^{it5^k}.$$

This is the characteristic function of the purely discrete distribution

$$F(x) = \sum_{k=0}^{\infty} \frac{1}{2^{k+1}} \varepsilon(x - 5^k).$$

Let us assume that the first n moments of a distribution function $F(x)$ exist and denote by $f(t)$ its characteristic function. Then $f(t)$ has the Maclaurin expansion

$$f(t) = \sum_{j=0}^{n-1} \frac{f^{(j)}(0)}{j!} t^j + R_n(t)$$

where (*)

$$R_n(t) = \frac{f^{(n)}(0)}{n!} t^n + o(1) \quad \text{as } t \to 0.$$

It follows from theorem 2.3.1 that

$$f(t) = \sum_{j=0}^{n} \frac{\alpha_j}{j!} (it)^j + o(t^n) \quad \text{as } t \to 0.$$

This connection is precisely described in the following manner:

Theorem 2.3.3. *Let $F(x)$ be a distribution function and assume that the nth moment of $F(x)$ exists. Then the characteristic function $f(t)$ of $F(x)$ admits the expansion*

$$(2.3.4) \qquad f(t) = 1 + \sum_{j=1}^{n} c_j (it)^j + o(t^n) \quad \text{as } t \to 0.$$

Conversely, suppose that the characteristic function $f(t)$ of a distribution $F(x)$ has an expansion (2.3.4). Then the distribution function $F(x)$ has moments up to the order n if n is even, but only up to the order $(n-1)$ if n is odd. Moreover $c_j = \alpha_j/j!$ for $j = 1, \ldots, n$ if n is even but only for $j = 1, 2, \ldots, (n-1)$ if n is odd.

We have already established the first part of the theorem. To prove its second part we compute $\Delta_n^t f(0)$ according to formula (2.3.1) using the assumption (2.3.4). This yields an expansion in powers of t; it is easily seen that the constant term of this expansion vanishes and one obtains

---

(*) The remainder term used here is a modification of Lagrange's form for the remainder. This follows from a seldom used form of the remainder term [see Hardy (1963) 151, p. 290].

B

$$(2.3.5) \qquad \Delta_n^t f(0) = \sum_{j=1}^{n} i^j c_j A_j t^j + o(t^n) \qquad\qquad \text{as } t \to 0$$

where
$$A_j = \begin{cases} 0 & \text{if } j+n \text{ is odd} \\ \sum_{k=0}^{n} (-1)^k \binom{n}{k}(n-2k)^j & \text{if } j+n \text{ is even.} \end{cases}$$

We can prove by induction that

$$(2.3.6) \qquad \sum_{k=0}^{n} (-1)^k \binom{n}{k} k^s = \begin{cases} 0 & \text{if } 1 \leqslant s < n \\ (-1)^n n! & \text{if } s = n. \end{cases}$$

From (2.3.5) and (2.3.6) one sees easily that $\Delta_n^t f(0) = i^n c_n t^n 2^n n! + o(t^n)$ so that

$$(2.3.7) \qquad \left| \frac{\Delta_n^t f(0)}{(2t)^n} \right| = c_n n! + o(t^n) \qquad\qquad \text{as } t \to 0.$$

If n is even we can conclude therefore from theorem 2.3.1 that the moment of order n of $F(x)$ exists. If n is odd we see that the validity of (2.3.4) implies the possibility of an expansion

$$f(t) = 1 + \sum_{j=1}^{n-1} c_j (it)^j + o(t^{n-1}) \qquad\qquad \text{as } t \to 0.$$

The argument just used proves therefore that the moment of order $(n-1)$ of $F(x)$ exists. The last part of the theorem follows immediately from (2.3.7).

An expression for the remainder term in formula (2.3.5) was given by E. J. G. Pitman (1961).

To illustrate the situation described by theorem 2.3.3 we give an example, due to A. Wintner (1947).

It is easily seen that the function

$$(2.3.8) \qquad p(x) = \begin{cases} 0 & \text{if } |x| < 2 \\ \dfrac{C}{x^2 \log |x|} & \text{if } |x| > 2 \end{cases}$$

is a frequency function, provided that C is determined so as to make $\int_{-\infty}^{\infty} p(x)\, dx = 1$. From

$$\int_2^A \frac{dx}{x \log x} = \log \log A - \log \log 2$$

it follows that the distribution determined by (2.3.8) does not have any moments. The characteristic function $f(t)$ of $p(x)$ is given by the integral

$$f(t) = 2C \int_2^\infty \frac{\cos tx}{x^2 \log x}\, dx.$$

Then

$$\frac{1-f(t)}{2C} = \int_2^\infty \frac{1-\cos tx}{x^2 \log x}\, dx = \int_2^{1/t} \frac{1-\cos tx}{x^2 \log x}\, dx + \int_{1/t}^\infty \frac{1-\cos tx}{x^2 \log x}\, dx$$

so that $1-f(t)$ is a real, non-negative and even function of t. For any real z one has $0 \leqslant 1-\cos z \leqslant \mathrm{Min}\,(2, z^2)$ so that $[1-f(t)]$ has as a majorant a constant multiple of

$$t^2 \int_2^{1/t} \frac{dx}{\log x} + 2 \int_{1/t}^\infty \frac{dx}{x^2 \log x} = O(-t/\log t) = o(t) \quad \text{as } t \to 0.$$

Thus $f(t) = 1 + o(t)$ admits an expansion of the form (2.3.4) with $n = 1$, $c_1 = 0$, even though the first moment does not exist.

If the moments α_n of $F(x)$ exist for all orders n and if

$$\limsup_{n \to \infty} (|\alpha_n|/n!)^{1/n} = L$$

is finite, then the characteristic function $f(t)$ of $F(x)$ is regular at the origin and has the power series expansion

$$f(t) = \sum_{j=0}^\infty \frac{\alpha_j}{j!}(it)^j$$

and $\rho = 1/L$ is the radius of convergence of this series.

It is possible to define symmetric moments

$$(2.3.9) \qquad (s\alpha)_k = \lim_{A \to \infty} \int_{-A}^A x^k\, dF(x).$$

Symmetric moments may exist for distributions which do not possess moments; the connection between the existence of symmetric moments and symmetric kth derivatives

$$\lim_{t \to 0} \frac{\Delta_k^t f(0)}{(2t)^k}$$

of the characteristic function was investigated by A. Zygmund (1947). We mention here only the simplest case:

Theorem 2.3.4. *Suppose that the characteristic function $f(t)$ of a distribution function $F(x)$ satisfies the "smoothness condition"$\Delta_2^t f(0) = o(t)$ as $t \to 0$, then a necessary and sufficient condition for the existence of $f'(0)$ is the existence of the symmetric moment of order 1, and*

$$(s\alpha)_1 = \lim_{A \to \infty} \int_{-A}^A x\, dF(x) = -if'(0).$$

Zygmund's "smoothness condition" is expressed in terms of the characteristic functions. E. J. G. Pitman (1956) replaced it by a condition on the distribution function.

R. P. Boas (1967) studied the related problem of the behaviour of a distribution function whose characteristic function satisfies a Lipschitz condition of order α $(0 < \alpha \leqslant 1)$.

It is also possible to express the absolute moments of a distribution function $F(x)$ in terms of its characteristic function $f(t)$. To do this we use the well-known fact that

$$(2.3.10) \qquad \frac{1}{\pi} \lim_{A \to \infty} \int_{-A}^{A} \frac{\sin ux}{x} \, dx = \operatorname{sgn} u = \begin{cases} +1 & \text{if } u > 0 \\ 0 & \text{if } u = 0 \\ -1 & \text{if } u < 0 \end{cases}$$

Since absolute moments of even order are identical with the algebraic moments of the same order, we have only to consider absolute moments of odd order. Let r be an odd integer, then

$$\begin{aligned}
\beta_r &= \int_{-\infty}^{\infty} |u|^r \, dF(u) = \int_{-\infty}^{\infty} u^r (\sin u) \, dF(u) \\
&= \frac{1}{\pi} \int_{-\infty}^{\infty} u^r \left[\lim_{A \to \infty} \int_{-A}^{A} \frac{\sin ux}{x} \, dx \right] dF(u) \\
&= \frac{1}{\pi} \lim_{A \to \infty} \int_{-\infty}^{\infty} \int_{-A}^{A} u^r \frac{\sin ux}{x} \, dx \, dF(u) \\
&= \frac{1}{\pi} \lim_{A \to \infty} \int_{-A}^{A} \frac{1}{x} \left[\frac{1}{2i} \int_{-\infty}^{\infty} u^r \left(e^{iux} - e^{-iux} \right) dF(u) \right] dx \\
&= \frac{1}{2\pi i} \int_{-\infty}^{\infty} \left[i^{-r} f^{(r)}(x) - (-i)^{-r} f^{(r)}(-x) \right] \frac{dx}{x}
\end{aligned}$$

so that

$$(2.3.11) \qquad \beta_r = \frac{1}{2\pi i^{r+1}} \int_{-\infty}^{\infty} \left[f^{(r)}(x) + f^{(r)}(-x) \right] \frac{dx}{x}.$$

2.4   The second characteristic

We have shown that every characteristic function $f(t)$ is continuous and that $f(0) = 1$. Therefore there exists a neighbourhood of the origin in which $f(t)$ is different from zero; let $|t| < \Delta$ be this neighbourhood. The function $\phi(t) = \log f(t)$ can be defined uniquely for $|t| < \Delta$, provided we understand by $\log f(t)$ the principal branch of the logarithm of the characteristic function, i.e. that determination of $\log f(t)$ which is continuous and vanishes at $t = 0$. The function $\phi(t)$ is called the second characteristic of the distribution function $F(x)$. We will consistently denote the second characteristic by the Greek letter corresponding to the small letter used for the characteristic function.

Let us again assume that the first n moments of $F(x)$ exist. We obtain then from the Maclaurin series for $\log(1+z)$ and from (2.3.4) the development

$$(2.4.1) \qquad \phi(t) = \sum_{j=1}^{n} \frac{\kappa_j}{j!}(it)^j + o(|t|^n) \qquad \text{as } t \to 0.$$

The coefficients κ_j of this expansion are called the cumulants (or semi-invariants) of $F(x)$. Clearly

$$(2.4.2) \qquad \kappa_j = i^{-j}\phi^{(j)}(0).$$

On account of the relation (2.4.1) one sometimes calls the function $\phi(t)$ the cumulant generating function of $F(x)$. This terminology is however somewhat awkward since $\phi(t)$ exists (in $|t| < \Delta$) even if cumulants and moments do not exist. For this reason we prefer the name "second characteristic" used in the French literature.

The relations between cumulants and moments can be found easily by means of Faà di Bruno's formula [see Jordan (1950), pp. 33–34]. This formula gives an explicit expression for the pth derivative of a function of a function. Suppose that the moment α_n of $F(x)$ of order n exists; then we get

$$(2.4.3) \qquad \kappa_p = \sum (-1)^{k-1} \frac{(k-1)!\,p!}{i_1!(k_1!)^{i_1} \dots i_s!(k_s!)^{i_s}} \alpha_{k_1}^{i_1} \dots \alpha_{k_s}^{i_s}$$

and

$$(2.4.4) \qquad \alpha_p = \sum \frac{p!}{i_1!(k_1!)^{i_1} \dots i_s!(k_s!)^{i_s}} \kappa_{k_1}^{i_1} \dots \kappa_{k_s}^{i_s}$$

for $p = 1, 2, \dots, n$. The summation is extended over all partitions of p which satisfy

$$i_1 + i_2 + \dots + i_s = k$$
$$i_1 k_1 + i_2 k_2 + \dots + i_s k_s = p.$$

3. FUNDAMENTAL PROPERTIES OF CHARACTERISTIC FUNCTIONS

In Sections 3.1–3.6 we discuss the most significant theorems which describe the connection between characteristic functions and distribution functions. These properties account for the importance of characteristic functions in the theory of probability.

3.1 The uniqueness theorem

Theorem 3.1.1. Two distribution functions $F_1(x)$ and $F_2(x)$ are identical if, and only if, their characteristic functions $f_1(t)$ and $f_2(t)$ are identical.

We see immediately from (1.3.6) that the identity of the distribution functions $F_1(x)$ and $F_2(x)$ implies the identity of their characteristic functions; therefore we must only prove the converse proposition. Suppose therefore that the characteristic functions of the distributions $F_1(x)$ and $F_2(x)$ satisfy the relation

$$(3.1.1) \qquad f_1(t) \equiv f_2(t).$$

We denote $F_1(x) - F_2(x)$ by $\beta(x)$ and write (3.1.1) in the form

$$(3.1.2) \qquad \int_{-\infty}^{\infty} e^{itx} \, d\beta(x) \equiv 0.$$

The function $\beta(x)$ is the difference of two monotone increasing functions and is therefore a function of bounded variation. Moreover we see from (3.1.2) that $\beta(x)$ satisfies the relation

$$(3.1.3) \qquad \int_{-\infty}^{\infty} h(x) \, d\beta(x) = 0$$

for all functions $h(x) = e^{itx}$ where t is an arbitrary real constant. Therefore (3.1.3) also holds for any trigonometric polynomial

$$(3.1.4) \qquad h(x) = \sum_{v=-n}^{n} a_v e^{ix\lambda v},$$

where λ is an arbitrary real constant. The relation (3.1.3) is therefore also valid for any function which is the uniform limit of trigonometric polynomials (3.1.4).

We conclude then from Weierstrass' approximation theorem [see Appendix C] that (3.1.3) holds if $h(x)$ is a continuous periodic function.

Let $g(x)$ be a continuous function which vanishes outside a fixed bounded interval J and choose $m > 0$ so large that the half open interval $(-m, m]$

contains J. We then define $h_m(x)$ as a continuous periodic function of period $2m$ such that $h_m(x) = g(x)$ for $-m < x \leqslant m$. Then (3.1.3) holds for the function $h_m(x)$. Since $\beta(x)$ is a function of bounded variation it is possible to choose m so large that the variation of $\beta(x)$ for $|x| \geqslant m$ becomes arbitrarily small; the integral $\int_{-\infty}^{\infty} h_m(x) \, d\beta(x)$ therefore approaches $\int_{-\infty}^{\infty} g(x) \, d\beta(x)$ as m tends to infinity. Hence

$$\int_{-\infty}^{\infty} g(x) \, d\beta(x) = \int_{J} g(x) \, d\beta(x) = 0$$

for every continuous function which vanishes outside a fixed interval J. It follows easily from the uniform boundedness of $g(x)$ that

$$\int_{a}^{b} g(x) \, d\beta(x) = 0,$$

provided that a and b are continuity points of $\beta(x)$ and that $g(x)$ is continuous for $a \leqslant x \leqslant b$. But then $\beta(x)$ must be constant on the set of its continuity points so that $F_1(x)$ and $F_2(x)$ must agree in all continuity points and are therefore identical.

We would emphasize here that two characteristic functions $f_1(t)$ and $f_2(t)$ must agree for *all values of t* in order to assure that the corresponding distribution functions $F_1(x)$ and $F_2(x)$ should be identical. This requirement can only be weakened in a trivial way: one could suppose that the functions $f_1(t)$ and $f_2(t)$ agree for t-values which form a set which is dense on the positive real axis. It follows then from theorem 2.1.1 (condition iii) that they must agree for a set dense on the whole real axis, and one can conclude from theorem 2.1.2 that $f_1(t) \equiv f_2(t)$. Agreement over a finite interval is, in general, not sufficient for the identity of the corresponding distribution functions. In fact, it is not difficult to construct a pair of characteristic functions which belong to different distributions and which agree over a finite interval. It is also possible to show that a pair of different characteristic functions can agree everywhere with the exception of two symmetrically located intervals. We will give these examples in Section 4.3.

Let $F(x)$ be an arbitrary distribution function. It is then easily seen that the function $1 - F(-x-0)$ is also a distribution function. This function is called the conjugate distribution of $F(x)$ and is denoted by

(3.1.5) $\tilde{F}(x) = 1 - F(-x-0).$

Let $f(t)$ be the characteristic function of the distribution $F(x)$; an elementary computation shows that the characteristic function of the conjugate distribution $\tilde{F}(x)$ is

(3.1.6) $\displaystyle\int_{-\infty}^{\infty} e^{itx} \, d\tilde{F}(x) = f(-t) = \overline{f(t)}.$

A distribution function is said to be symmetric if it is equal to its conjugate.

The following characterization of symmetric distributions is easily established.

Theorem 3.1.2.   A distribution function is symmetric if, and only if, its characteristic function is real and even.

The necessity of the condition follows from (3.1.6) while the sufficiency is a consequence of the uniqueness theorem.

Moreover, we see from (3.1.6) that

$$(3.1.7) \quad f(t) = \int_{-\infty}^{\infty} \cos tx \, dF(x).$$

This formula can be used to establish the following property of symmetric distributions.

Theorem 3.1.3.   Let $F(x)$ be a symmetric distribution with characteristic function $f(t)$ and suppose that the moments α_j $(j = 1, 2, \ldots, 2k)$ of $F(x)$ exist. Then

$$f^{(2j-1)}(t) = (-1)^j \int_{-\infty}^{\infty} x^{2j-1} \sin tx \, dF(x) \quad (j = 1, \ldots, k)$$

$$f^{(2j)}(t) = (-1)^j \int_{-\infty}^{\infty} x^{2j} \cos tx \, dF(x) \quad (j = 1, \ldots, k).$$

The theorem is a consequence of formula (3.1.7) and the corollary to theorem 2.3.1.

Corollary to theorem 3.1.3. Let $F(x)$ be a symmetric distribution with characteristic function $f(t)$ and suppose that the moments $\alpha_j (j = 1, \ldots, 2k)$ of $F(x)$ exist. Then

(i) $\alpha_{2j-1} = 0$ $\qquad\qquad\qquad (j = 1, 2, \ldots, k)$

(ii) $\lim\limits_{t \to 0} \dfrac{f^{(2j-1)}(t)}{t} = (-1)^j \alpha_{2j}$ $\quad (j = 1, 2, \ldots, k)$

(iii) $\lim\limits_{t \to 0} \dfrac{f^{(2j)}(t) - f^{(2j)}(0)}{t^2} = 2(-1)^{j+1} \lim\limits_{t \to 0} \int_{-\infty}^{\infty} x^{2j} \dfrac{\sin^2(tx/2)}{t^2} \, dF(x)$

$$= \frac{(-1)^{j+1}}{2} \alpha_{2j+2} \quad (j = 1, 2, \ldots, k-1).$$

The corollary follows immediately from theorem 3.1.3.

3.2   Inversion formulae

Theorem 3.1.1 of the preceding section establishes a one-to-one correspondence between characteristic functions and distribution functions. However, theorem 3.1.1 does not give a method for the determination of the distribution function belonging to a given characteristic function. The theorems discussed in the present section deal with this problem.

Theorem 3.2.1 (the inversion theorem). *Let f(t) be the characteristic function of the distribution function F(x). Then*

$$(3.2.1) \qquad F(a+h) - F(a) = \lim_{T \to \infty} \frac{1}{2\pi} \int_{-T}^{T} \frac{1 - e^{-ith}}{it} e^{-ita} f(t) \, dt,$$

provided that a and a+h (with h > 0) are continuity points of F(x).

For the proof of the inversion theorem we need the following well-known lemma.

Lemma 3.2.1. *The integral $\int_0^x (\sin y)/y \, dy$ is bounded for x > 0 and approaches $\pi/2$ as x tends to infinity.*

The first part of the lemma is easily proved by dividing the range of integration into segments of length π; the second statement is obtained by contour integration.[*]

Let

$$\lambda(h, T) = \frac{1}{\pi} \int_0^T \frac{\sin hy}{y} \, dy = \frac{1}{\pi} \int_0^{hT} \frac{\sin x}{x} \, dx.$$

From this definition and from lemma 3.2.1 it is seen that $\lambda(h, T)$ is bounded for all h and all T and that

$$\lambda(-h, T) = -\lambda(h, T)$$

while

$$(3.2.2) \qquad \lim_{T \to \infty} \lambda(h, T) = \begin{cases} \tfrac{1}{2} \text{ if } h > 0 \\ 0 \text{ if } h = 0 \\ -\tfrac{1}{2} \text{ if } h < 0. \end{cases}$$

We now introduce the integral

$$J_T = \frac{1}{2\pi} \int_{-T}^{T} \frac{e^{-ita} - e^{-it(a+h)}}{it} f(t) \, dt.$$

We substitute here for $f(t) = \int_{-\infty}^{\infty} e^{itx} \, dF(x)$ and note that the absolute value of the integrand does not exceed h. Hence the order of integration may be reversed and one obtains

$$J_T = \frac{1}{2\pi} \int_{-\infty}^{\infty} \left[\int_{-T}^{T} \frac{e^{-it(a-x)} - e^{-it(a+h-x)}}{it} dt \right] dF(x).$$

---

[*] See Titchmarsh (1937), Section 3.122.

We replace the exponentials in the inner integral by trigonometric functions and obtain

$$(3.2.3) \qquad J_T = \frac{1}{\pi} \int_{-\infty}^{\infty} \left[\int_0^T \frac{\sin t(x-a) - \sin t(x-a-h)}{t} \, dt \right] dF(x).$$

We write

$$g(x, T) = \lambda(x-a, T) - \lambda(x-a-h, T)$$

and conclude from the boundedness of $\lambda(x, T)$ and from (3.2.2) that $g(x, T)$ is also bounded for all x and all T and that

$$(3.2.4) \qquad \lim_{T \to \infty} g(x, T) = \begin{cases} 0 & \text{if } x < a \\ \frac{1}{2} & \text{if } x = a \\ 1 & \text{if } a < x < a+h \\ \frac{1}{2} & \text{if } x = a+h \\ 0 & \text{if } x > a+h. \end{cases}$$

Moreover, (3.2.3) can be written as

$$(3.2.5) \qquad J_T = \int_{-\infty}^{\infty} g(x, T) \, dF(x).$$

Let $\varepsilon > 0$ be an arbitrary positive number. We assumed that a and $a+h$ are continuity points of $F(x)$ and we have shown that $g(x, T)$ is bounded. Therefore it is possible to select a $\delta > 0$ which is so small that the three inequalities

$$(I_1) \qquad \left| \int_{a-\delta}^{a+\delta} g(x, T) \, dF(x) \right| \leqslant \varepsilon$$

$$(I_2) \qquad \left| \int_{a+h-\delta}^{a+h+\delta} g(x, T) \, dF(x) \right| \leqslant \varepsilon$$

$$(I_3) \qquad \left| \int_{a+\delta}^{a+h-\delta} dF(x) - \int_a^{a+h} dF(x) \right| \leqslant \varepsilon$$

hold simultaneously.

Moreover, we conclude from (3.2.4) that T can be chosen so large that the relations

$$(I_4) \qquad \left| \int_{a+\delta}^{a+h-\delta} g(x, T) \, dF(x) - \int_{a+\delta}^{a+h-\delta} dF(x) \right| \leqslant \varepsilon$$

and

$$(I_5) \qquad \left| \int_{-\infty}^{a-\delta} g(x, T) \, dF(x) \right| + \left| \int_{a+h+\delta}^{\infty} g(x, T) \, dF(x) \right| \leqslant \varepsilon$$

are both satisfied. We decompose the range of integration of the integral (3.2.5) into the five intervals $(-\infty, a-\delta)$, $(a-\delta, a+\delta)$ $(a+\delta, a+h-\delta)$, $(a+h-\delta, a+h+\delta)$ and $(a+h+\delta, \infty)$ and obtain, using (I_1), (I_2) and (I_5),

$$(I_6) \qquad \left| J_T - \int_{a+\delta}^{a+h-\delta} g(x, T) \, dF(x) \right| \leqslant 3\varepsilon.$$

We see then from (I_6), (I_4) and (I_3) that

$$\left| J_T - \int_a^{a+h} dF(x) \right| \leqslant 5\varepsilon$$

if T is sufficiently large. This is equivalent to (3.2.1), so that the proof of the inversion theorem is completed.

An inversion formula expressing $F(x)$ [instead of its increment $F(x+h) - F(x)$] in terms of an integral involving the characteristic function of $F(x)$ was given by J. Gil-Pelaez (1951).

We remark that the uniqueness theorem could easily have been obtained from the inversion theorem. Such an approach would have shortened the presentation; however, it is of some methodological interest to distinguish between these two theorems.

The inversion formula can be written in a more symmetrical form by putting $a = x - \delta$ and $h = 2\delta$. In this way we obtain

$$(3.2.6) \qquad F(x+\delta) - F(x-\delta) = \lim_{T \to \infty} \frac{1}{\pi} \int_{-T}^{T} \frac{\sin t\delta}{t} e^{-itx} f(t) \, dt$$

provided that $x - \delta$ and $x + \delta$ are continuity points of $F(x)$. The last formula can also be written as

$$\frac{F(x+\delta) - F(x-\delta)}{2\delta} = \lim_{T \to \infty} \frac{1}{2\pi} \int_{-T}^{T} \frac{\sin t\delta}{t\delta} e^{-itx} f(t) \, dt.$$

Let us now assume that $f(t)$ is absolutely integrable over $(-\infty, +\infty)$, the integrand is then dominated by the absolutely integrable function $f(t)$ and converges to $e^{-itx} f(t)$ as δ tends to zero. Hence one may go to the limit under the integral sign; one sees that $F'(x)$ exists for all x and one obtains the following result.

Theorem 3.2.2. *If a characteristic function $f(t)$ is absolutely integrable over $(-\infty, +\infty)$ then the corresponding distribution function $F(x)$ is absolutely continuous and the formula*

$$p(x) = F'(x) = \frac{1}{2\pi} \int_{-\infty}^{\infty} e^{-itx} f(t) \, dt$$

expresses its density function $p(x)$ in terms of the characteristic function. The density function $p(x)$ is continuous.

We have already proved the absolute continuity of the distribution corresponding to $f(t)$ and must still show that $p(x)$ is continuous. We see easily that

$$| p(x+h) - p(x) | \leqslant \frac{1}{\pi} \int_{-A}^{A} | \sin (th/2) | | f(t) | \, dt$$

$$+ \frac{1}{\pi} \int_{|t| > A} | \sin (th/2) | | f(t) | \, dt.$$

We choose A so large that the second integral becomes arbitrarily small and can then make the first integral as small as we wish by selecting h sufficiently small. This completes the proof of the theorem.

We note that this inversion formula is here not derived for all absolutely continuous distributions but only for absolutely continuous distribution functions which have absolutely integrable characteristic functions. We will give later [p. 85] examples of characteristic functions which belong to absolutely continuous distributions but which are not absolutely integrable. However, we will see that under certain conditions the inversion formula is still valid.

It is also possible to derive an inversion formula which is valid for arbitrary absolutely continuous distributions, even if they are not absolutely integrable. As the proof of this formula requires results of the next section, we give it in Section 3.3 (see corollary 3 to theorem 3.3.2).

Let again $f(t)$ be the characteristic function of an arbitrary distribution $F(x)$. We consider the integral

$$(3.2.7) \qquad I_T = \frac{1}{2T} \int_{-T}^{T} e^{-itx} f(t)\, dt.$$

We write in (3.2.7) $f(t) = \int_{-\infty}^{\infty} e^{itz}\, dF(z)$ and see easily that the order of the two integrations may be exchanged, so that

$$I_T = \int_{-\infty}^{\infty} \frac{\sin T(z-x)}{T(z-x)}\, dF(z)$$

$$= \int_{|y|<h} \frac{\sin Ty}{Ty}\, d_y F(y+x) + \int_{|y|>h} \frac{\sin Ty}{Ty}\, d_y F(y+x).$$

Here h is a positive number to be chosen later.

Let $\varepsilon > 0$ be an arbitrary positive number and denote the saltus of $F(x)$ at the point x by p_x, that is $p_x = F(x) - F(x-0)$. It is then possible to choose a value $h_0 > 0$ which is so small that the inequality

$$(3.2.8) \qquad \left| \int_{|y|<h_0} d_y F(y+x) - p_x \right| \leqslant \varepsilon$$

holds.

The integral

$$\int_{|y|>h_0} \frac{\sin Ty}{Ty}\, d_y F(y+x)$$

converges to zero as T tends to infinity, since the integrand is dominated by $+1$ and converges to zero as $T \to \infty$. We can therefore choose T so large that

$$(3.2.9) \qquad \left| \int_{|y|>h_0} \frac{\sin Ty}{Ty}\, d_y F(y+x) \right| \leqslant \varepsilon.$$

Let now h_1 be a number such that

(3.2.10) $\qquad h_0 > h_1 > 0$.

It follows from (3.2.8) that

$$p_x - \varepsilon \leqslant \int_{|y| < h_1} d_y F(y+x) \leqslant \int_{|y| < h_0} d_y F(y+x) \leqslant p_x + \varepsilon$$

so that

(3.2.11) $\qquad \begin{cases} \left| \int_{|y| \leqslant h_1} d_y F(y+x) - p_x \right| \leqslant \varepsilon \\ \text{while} \\ 0 \leqslant \int_{h_1 \leqslant |y| < h_0} d_y F(y+x) \leqslant 2\varepsilon. \end{cases}$

We are still free to choose h_1, subject only to the restriction (3.2.10). We select h_1 so small that

$$1 - \varepsilon \leqslant \frac{\sin Ty}{Ty}$$

for $|y| < h_1$. According to the law of the mean there exists a real $\theta(|\theta| < 1)$ such that

$$\int_{|y| < h_1} \frac{\sin Ty}{Ty} d_y F(x+y) = \frac{\sin T\theta h_1}{T\theta h_1} \int_{|y| < h_1} d_y F(x+y)$$

$$= (1 - \theta_1 \varepsilon) \int_{|y| < h_1} d_y F(x+y)$$

where $0 \leqslant \theta_1 \leqslant 1$. From this we see immediately that

$$\int_{|y| < h_1} \frac{\sin Ty}{Ty} d_y F(x+y) - p_x = \int_{|y| < h_1} d_y F(x+y) - p_x - \theta_2 \varepsilon$$

with $0 \leqslant \theta_2 \leqslant 1$. Hence we conclude from (3.2.11) that

(3.2.12) $\qquad \left| \int_{|y| < h_1} \frac{\sin Ty}{Ty} d_y F(x+y) - p_x \right| \leqslant 2\varepsilon$.

Since $\left| \dfrac{\sin Ty}{Ty} \right| \leqslant 1$, we see from the second formula (3.2.11) that

$$\left| \int_{h_1 \leqslant |y| < h_0} \frac{\sin Ty}{Ty} d_y F(y+x) \right| \leqslant \int_{h_1 \leqslant |y| < h_0} d_y F(y+x) \leqslant 2\varepsilon.$$

We combine the last inequality with (3.2.9) and (3.2.12) and obtain

(3.2.13) $\qquad |I_T - p_x| \leqslant 5\varepsilon$

if T is sufficiently large. Thus we have proved the following statement:

Theorem 3.2.3. Let $f(t)$ be an arbitrary characteristic function. For every real x the limit

$$p_x = \lim_{T \to \infty} \frac{1}{2T} \int_{-T}^{T} e^{-itx} f(t) \, dt$$

exists and is equal to the saltus of the distribution function of $f(t)$ at the point x.

Corollary 1 to theorem 3.2.3.   The characteristic function of a continuous (singular or absolutely continuous) distribution cannot be an almost periodic function.

Let $f(t)$ be the characteristic function of a continuous distribution. We see immediately from theorem 3.2.3 that

$$(3.2.14) \qquad \lim_{T \to \infty} \frac{1}{2T} \int_{-T}^{T} e^{-itx} f(t)\, dt = 0$$

for all real x. We give an indirect proof for the corollary and suppose that $f(t)$ is almost periodic. Formula (3.2.14) means then that all Fourier coefficients of $f(t)$ vanish; we conclude from the uniqueness theorem for almost periodic functions [H. Bohr (1932), (1947), English edition, p. 60] that $f(t) \equiv 0$, which contradicts the assumption that $f(t)$ is a characteristic function.

Corollary 2 to theorem 3.2.3.   A distribution function is purely discrete if, and only if, its characteristic function is almost periodic.

The necessity of the condition follows from our remarks in Section 2.2. To prove the sufficiency we note that an almost periodic characteristic function $f(t)$ necessarily satisfies the relation

$$\limsup_{|t| \to \infty} |f(t)| = 1;$$

in view of corollary 1 to theorem 3.2.3 $f(t)$ must then belong to a purely discrete distribution.

3.3   The convolution theorem

We consider next two distribution functions $F_1(x)$ and $F_2(x)$ and their characteristic functions $f_1(t)$ and $f_2(t)$ respectively. We form the function

$$(3.3.1) \qquad F(z) = \int_{-\infty}^{\infty} F_1(z-x)\, dF_2(x).$$

The function $F_1(z-x)$ is bounded so that the integral (3.3.1) exists. Moreover it is easily seen that $F(z)$ is a distribution function; this follows from the fact that the necessary passages to the limit can be carried out under the integral sign.

We wish to determine the characteristic function $f(t)$ of $F(z)$. Clearly,

$$f(t) = \int_{-\infty}^{\infty} e^{izt}\, dF(z).$$

We consider first the integral $\int_{a}^{b} e^{izt}\, dF(z)$ (where a and b are finite) and write it as a limit of generalized Darboux sums.[*] We use a sequence of subdivisions $\{z_j^{(n)}\}$ of decreasing modulus

$$a = z_1^{(n)} < z_2^{(n)} < \ldots < z_n^{(n)} < z_{n+1}^{(n)} = b$$

of the closed interval $[a, b]$. In this manner we get

$$\int_a^b \exp(izt)\,dF(z) = \lim_{n\to\infty} \sum_{j=1}^n \exp(itz^{(n)})\,[F(z_{j+1}^{(n)}) - F(z_j^{(n)})].$$

In view of (3.3.1) this can be written as

$$\int_a^b \exp(izt)\,dF(z)$$

$$= \lim_{n\to\infty} \int_{-\infty}^\infty \sum_{j=1}^n \exp[it(z_j^{(n)} - x)]\,[F_1(z_{j+1}^{(n)} - x) - F_1(z_j^{(n)} - x)]\exp(itx)\,dF_2(x).$$

From this it follows that

$$\int_a^b e^{izt}\,dF(z) = \int_{-\infty}^\infty \left[\int_{a-x}^{b-x} e^{ity}\,dF_1(y)\right] e^{itx}\,dF_2(x).$$

We take the limit as $a \to -\infty$ and $b \to \infty$ and obtain

(3.3.2) $f(t) = f_1(t)\,f_2(t)$.

Suppose conversely that a characteristic function $f(t)$ is the product (3.3.2) of two characteristic functions. According to the uniqueness theorem relation (3.3.1) holds between the corresponding distribution functions.

Formula (3.3.1) defines an operation between distribution functions; it indicates how a new distribution F can be obtained from two given distributions F_1 and F_2. This operation is called *convolution* (sometimes composition or Faltung) and F is called the convolution of F_1 and F_2 and is written as a symbolic product

$$F = F_1 * F_2.$$

It is seen from (3.3.2) that the convolution is a commutative and associative operation.

We summarize our results as

Theorem 3.3.1 (*Convolution theorem*). *A distribution function F is the convolution of two distributions F_1 and F_2, that is*

$$F(z) = \int_{-\infty}^\infty F_1(z-x)\,dF_2(x) = \int_{-\infty}^\infty F_2(z-x)\,dF_1(x) = F_1 * F_2$$

if, and only if, the corresponding characteristic functions satisfy the relation

$$f(t) = f_1(t)\,f_2(t).$$

Hence the genuine multiplication of the characteristic functions and the

---

symbolic multiplication of the distribution functions correspond to each other uniquely.

The following corollaries follow almost immediately from the convolution theorem.

Corollary 1 to theorem 3.3.1. The product of two characteristic functions is a characteristic function.

Corollary 2 to theorem 3.3.1. If $f(t)$ is a characteristic function, $|f(t)|^2$ is also a characteristic function.

This follows from theorem 2.1.1 and formula (3.1.6).

We mention some properties of the convolution operation which follow easily from its definition.

Theorem 3.3.2. Let $F = F_1*F_2$ be the convolution of two distributions F_1 and F_2. If one of the components of F is a continuous distribution, then the symbolic product is also a continuous distribution. If one of the components of F is absolutely continuous then F is also absolutely continuous.

Remark 1. Let $F = F_1*F_2$ be the convolution of two distributions F_1 and F_2 and suppose that F is a discrete distribution. Then both components F_1 and F_2 are also discrete distributions.

Remark 2. It is, however, not possible to conclude from the assumptions (i) $F = F_1*F_2$, (ii) F is absolutely continuous, that at least one of the distribution functions F_1 and F_2 is absolutely continuous. This will be seen from a representation of the rectangular distribution as the convolution of two singular distributions. This example will be given on page 189.

Corollary 1 to theorem 3.3.2. If $f(t)$ is the characteristic function of a continuous (respectively absolutely continuous) distribution then $|f(t)|^2$ also belongs to a continuous (respectively absolutely continuous) distribution.

Corollary 2 to theorem 3.3.2. Let $F_1(x)$ and $F_2(x)$ be two absolutely continuous distribution functions and denote by $p_1(x)$ and $p_2(x)$ their frequency functions. Let $F = F_1*F_2$ and $p(x) = F'(x)$ be the density of $F(x)$; then

$$p(z) = \int_{-\infty}^{\infty} p_1(z-x)\, p_2(x)\, dx.$$

We are now in a position to derive an inversion formula which is valid for arbitrary frequency functions.

Let $F(x)$ be an arbitrary, absolutely continuous distribution function and denote its frequency function by $p(x) = F'(x)$. We note that the characteristic function $f(t)$ of $F(x)$ is not necessarily absolutely integrable. Let $G(x)$ be an absolutely continuous distribution function and write $g(t)$ for its characteristic function and $q(x) = G'(x)$ for its frequency function. Suppose that $G(x)$ satisfies the following conditions:

   (i) $g(t)$ is absolutely integrable over $(-\infty, \infty)$,
   (ii) $q(x) = O(x^{-2})$ as $|x| \to \infty$.

It follows from theorem 3.2.2 that

$$q(x) = \frac{1}{2\pi} \int_{-\infty}^{\infty} e^{-itx} g(t)\, dt.$$

For any $T > 0$ the function $g_T(t) = g(t/T)$ is an absolutely integrable characteristic function; the corresponding frequency function is

$$q_T(x) = Tq(Tx).$$

We consider the function

(3.3.3) $\qquad h_T(t) = f(t)g_T(t) = f(t)g\left(\frac{t}{T}\right).$

We see from corollary 1 to theorem 3.3.1 that $h_T(t)$ is a characteristic function which is absolutely integrable over $(-\infty, \infty)$. It belongs therefore to an absolutely continuous distribution function $H_T(x)$, and the density of this distribution can be determined from theorem 3.2.2 and is given by

(3.3.4) $\qquad H_T'(x) = \frac{1}{2\pi} \int_{-\infty}^{\infty} e^{-itx} g\left(\frac{t}{T}\right) f(t)\, dt.$

On the other hand we see from corollary 2 to theorem 3.3.2 that

$$H_T'(x) = \int_{-\infty}^{\infty} p\left(x - \frac{y}{T}\right) q(y)\, dy.$$

Therefore we see that

$$|H_T'(x) - p(x)| = \left| \int_{-\infty}^{\infty} \left[p\left(x - \frac{y}{T}\right) - p(x) \right] q(y)\, dy \right|.$$

Let a be a positive number to be chosen later, and write

$$I_1 = \int_{|y| \leqslant a} \left| p\left(x - \frac{y}{T}\right) - p(x) \right| q(y)\, dy$$

$$I_2 = \int_{|y| > a} p\left(x - \frac{y}{T}\right) q(y)\, dy$$

$$I_3 = p(x) \int_{|y| > a} q(y)\, dy,$$

then

(3.3.5) $\qquad |H_T'(x) - p(x)| \leqslant I_1 + I_2 + I_3.$

We write

(3.3.6) $\qquad \omega(x, h) = \sup_{|v| \leqslant h} |p(x + v) - p(x)|$

and

(3.3.7a) $I_1 \leqslant \omega\left(x, \dfrac{a}{T}\right).$

It follows from property (ii) of $q(y)$ that for y sufficiently large,

$$q(y) \leqslant Ay^{-2}.$$

Therefore we have for sufficiently large values of a

(3.3.7b) $I_2 \leqslant \dfrac{A}{a^2} \displaystyle\int_{-\infty}^{\infty} p\left(x - \dfrac{y}{T}\right) dy = \dfrac{AT}{a^2}$

and

(3.3.7c) $I_3 \leqslant \dfrac{2A}{a} p(x).$

We put

$$a = T^{2/3}$$

and conclude from (3.3.7a), (3.3.7b), (3.3.7c) and (3.3.5) that

(3.3.8) $|H'_T(x) - p(x)| \leqslant \omega(x, T^{-1/3}) + AT^{-1/3} + 2Ap(x)T^{-2/3}.$

Let x be a continuity point of $p(x)$, then $\lim_{T\to\infty} \omega(x, T^{-1/3}) = 0$ and we see from (3.3.8) that

$$\lim_{T\to\infty} H'_T(x) = p(x).$$

It follows therefore from (3.3.4) that

$$p(x) = \lim_{T\to\infty} \frac{1}{2\pi} \int_{-\infty}^{\infty} e^{-itx} g\left(\frac{t}{T}\right) f(t)\, dt.$$

We have therefore obtained the following result.

Corollary 3 to theorem 3.3.2.   Let $g(t)$ be a characteristic function which is absolutely integrable over $(-\infty, \infty)$ and suppose that the corresponding frequency function $q(x)$ satisfies the condition $q(x) = O(x^{-2})$ as $|x| \to \infty$. Let $f(t)$ be the characteristic function of an arbitrary absolutely continuous distribution function $F(x)$; the frequency function $p(x)$ of $F(x)$ is then given by

$$p(x) = F'(x) = \lim_{T\to\infty} \frac{1}{2\pi} \int_{-\infty}^{\infty} e^{-itx} g\left(\frac{t}{T}\right) f(t)\, dt,$$

provided x is a continuity point of $p(x)$.

Remark.   This result could also be formulated by stating that the inversion formula of theorem 3.2.2 remains valid for characteristic functions which are not absolutely integrable if the integration in the inversion formula is considered in the sense of a summability method with summability factor $g(t/T)$. If we use $g(t) = 1 - |t|$ for $|t| \leqslant 1$ and $g(t) = 0$ for $|t| \geqslant 1$, we obtain

$$p(x) = \lim_{T\to\infty} \int_{-T}^{T} e^{-itx} \left(1 - \frac{|t|}{T}\right) f(t)\, dt,$$

that is, the integral is taken in the sense of $(C, 1)$-summability. For $g(t) = e^{-|t|}$, the integration is in the sense of Abel summability.

We consider next the convolutions of two purely discrete distributions.

Theorem 3.3.3. Let $F_1(x)$ and $F_2(x)$ be two purely discrete distributions with discontinuity points $\{\xi_\nu\}$ and $\{\eta_\mu\}$ respectively. Then $F = F_1 * F_2$ is also purely discrete and the discontinuity points of F are the points of the sequence $\{\xi_\nu + \eta_\mu\}$. Moreover, let a_ν be the saltus of F_1 at ξ_ν and b_μ be the saltus of F_2 at η_μ and suppose that ξ is a discontinuity point of F. The saltus of F at ξ is then

$$\sum_{\xi_\nu + \eta_\mu = \xi} a_\nu b_\mu.$$

The characteristic functions $f_1(t)$ and $f_2(t)$ of $F_1(x)$ and $F_2(x)$ respectively are

$$f_1(t) = \sum_\nu a_\nu \exp{(it\xi_\nu)}$$

$$f_2(t) = \sum_\mu b_\mu \exp{(it\eta_\mu)}.$$

The characteristic function $f(t)$ of $F(x)$ is, according to the convolution theorem,

$$(3.3.9) \qquad f(t) = f_1(t) f_2(t) = \sum_\nu \sum_\mu a_\nu b_\mu \exp{[it(\xi_\nu + \eta_\mu)]}.$$

Theorem 3.3.3 follows immediately from this formula.

Suppose that $F_1(x)$ and $F_2(x)$ are two purely discrete distribution functions and that at least one of these has infinitely many discontinuity points. It follows then from (3.3.9) that $F(x) = F_1(x) * F_2(x)$ also has infinitely many discontinuity points.

Assume next that each of the purely discrete distributions $F_1(x)$ and $F_2(x)$ has only finitely many discontinuity points, then (3.3.9) becomes

$$(3.3.10) \qquad f(t) = f_1(t) f_2(t) = \sum_{\nu=1}^{n} \sum_{\mu=1}^{m} a_\nu b_\mu \exp{[it(\xi_\nu + \eta_\mu)]}$$

where n and m are the numbers of discontinuity points of $F_1(x)$ and $F_2(x)$ respectively. The last formula indicates that $F = F_1 * F_2$ also has a finite number, say N, of discontinuity points. Let us consider the set $\{\xi_\nu + \eta_\mu\}(\nu = 1, \ldots, n; \mu = 1, \ldots, m)$. Then it is no restriction to assume that the $\xi_1, \xi_2, \ldots, \xi_n$ and $\eta_1, \eta_2, \ldots, \eta_m$ are arranged in increasing order. The set of discontinuity points of $F(x)$ contains at most nm elements, while it is seen immediately that the $n+m-1$ numbers $\xi_1 + \eta_1, \xi_2 + \eta_1,$ $\ldots, \xi_n + \eta_1, \xi_n + \eta_2, \ldots, \xi_n + \eta_m$ are distinct. We formulate this result in the following manner.

Corollary to theorem 3.3.3. Let $F = F_1 * F_2$ be the convolution of two purely discrete distributions F_1 and F_2. The distribution function $F(x)$ has *a finite number of discontinuity points if, and only if, each of the functions F_1 and F_2 has finitely many discontinuity points. Denote by N, n and m the number of discontinuity points of $F(x)$, $F_1(x)$ and $F_2(x)$; then*

$$n+m-1 \leqslant N \leqslant nm.$$

Next let $F(x)$ be an arbitrary distribution function. If $F(x)$ has a discontinuity at the point $x = \xi_j$ with saltus p_j then the conjugate distribution function $\tilde{F}(x)$ of $F(x)$ has a discontinuity at $x = -\xi_j$ with the same saltus p_j. According to theorem 3.3.3 the convolution $F * \tilde{F}$ has the saltus $\sum_j p_j^2$ at the point $x = 0$. On the other hand one can determine the saltus of $F * \tilde{F}$ at $x = 0$ from theorem 3.2.3 and we obtain the following result.

Theorem 3.3.4. Let $F(x)$ be a distribution function and $f(t)$ its characteristic function. Then

$$\lim_{T \to \infty} \frac{1}{2T} \int_{-T}^{T} |f(t)|^2 dt = \sum p_j^2$$

where the p_j are the saltus of $F(x)$ and where the summation on the right is to be taken over all discontinuity points of $F(x)$.

We conclude this section by stating the connection between the existence of the moments of a convolution and the moments of its components.

Theorem 3.3.5. Let F_1 and F_2 be two distributions and suppose that the moments of order k exist for F_1 as well as for F_2. The same is then true for $F = F_1 * F_2$.

This follows easily from the elementary inequality

$$|x+y|^k \leqslant 2^{k-1}(|x|^k + |y|^k).$$

3.4   Limits of distribution functions

In this section we study sequences of distribution functions and their limits and we introduce a specific definition for the convergence of such sequences. In order to motivate this definition we consider first two examples.

Example 1.   Let

$$F_n(x) = \begin{cases} 0 & \text{if } x < -n \\ \dfrac{n+x}{2n} & \text{if } -n \leqslant x < n \\ 1 & \text{if } x \geqslant n \end{cases}$$

$(n = 1, 2, \ldots)$ be a sequence of rectangular distribution functions. This sequence converges for all x and

$$\lim_{n \to \infty} F_n(x) = \tfrac{1}{2}.$$

We note that the limiting function of this sequence of distribution func-· tions is not a distribution function.

Example 2. Let

$$F_n(x) = \frac{n}{\sqrt{2\pi}} \int_{-\infty}^{x} \exp(-n^2 y^2/2)\, dy \quad (n = 1, 2, \ldots)$$

be a sequence of normal distributions. It is easily seen that

$$\lim_{n\to\infty} F_n(x) = \lim_{n\to\infty} \frac{1}{\sqrt{2\pi}} \int_{-\infty}^{nx} e^{-z^2/2}\, dz = \begin{cases} 0 & \text{if} \quad x < 0 \\ \frac{1}{2} & \text{if} \quad x = 0 \\ 1 & \text{if} \quad x > 0. \end{cases}$$

If we look at the graphs of the functions $F_n(x)$ we might expect in-tuitively that the sequence $F_n(x)$ should converge to the degenerate distribution $\varepsilon(x)$. This agrees also with the fact that

$$\lim_{n\to\infty} F_n(x) = 0 \text{ if } x < 0 \text{ and } \lim_{n\to\infty} F_n(x) = 1 \text{ if } x > 0.$$

However, we have

$$\lim_{n\to\infty} F_n(0) = \tfrac{1}{2} \text{ while } \varepsilon(0) = 1.$$

We observe therefore that it seems to be too restrictive to require that a sequence of distribution functions should converge at all points to a limiting distribution function. Example 2 suggests that exceptions should be permitted for the discontinuity points of the limiting distribution. Moreover, we see from Example 1 that a sequence of distribution functions may converge at all points but that the limiting function is not necessarily a distribution function. In view of the situation revealed by these two examples the following definitions seem to be appropriate.

A sequence of functions $\{h_n(x)\}$ is said to converge weakly to a limiting function $h(x)$ if

$$\lim_{n\to\infty} h_n(x) = h(x)$$

for all continuity points x of $h(x)$. We write then

$$\operatorname{Lim}_{n\to\infty} h_n(x) = h(x),$$

that is, we use the symbol "Lim" for weak convergence to distinguish it from "lim" used for ordinary convergence.

Using this terminology we introduce the following definition.

A sequence $\{F_n(x)\}$ of distribution functions is called a convergent sequence if there exists a non-decreasing function $F(x)$ such that

$$\operatorname{Lim}_{n\to\infty} F_n(x) = F(x).$$

We note (see Example 1) that the weak limit of a sequence of distri-bution functions is not necessarily a distribution function. However, the (weak) limit is always a bounded and non-decreasing function. We are primarily interested in obtaining a necessary and sufficient condition for the weak convergence of a sequence of distribution functions to a limiting distribution. In order to obtain this condition we need some results which are also of independent interest. These will be given in the next section.

3.5   The theorems of Helly

We first prove the following lemma:

Lemma 3.5.1.   *Let $\{F_n(x)\}$ be a sequence of non-decreasing functions of the real variable x and let D be a set which is dense on the real line. Suppose that the sequence $\{F_n(x)\}$ converges to some function $F(x)$ in all points of the set D; then*

$$\operatorname*{Lim}_{n\to\infty} F_n(x) = F(x).$$

Let x be an arbitrary continuity point of $F(x)$ and choose two points $x' \varepsilon D$, $x'' \varepsilon D$ so that $x' \leqslant x \leqslant x''$. Then $F_n(x') \leqslant F_n(x) \leqslant F_n(x'')$; hence

$$\lim_{n\to\infty} F_n(x') \leqslant \liminf_{n\to\infty} F_n(x) \leqslant \limsup_{n\to\infty} F_n(x) \leqslant \lim_{n\to\infty} F_n(x'').$$

From the assumption of the lemma we conclude that

$$F(x') \leqslant \liminf_{n\to\infty} F_n(x) \leqslant \limsup_{n\to\infty} F_n(x) \leqslant F(x'').$$

Since D is dense on the real line we have

$$F(x-0) \leqslant \liminf_{n\to\infty} F_n(x) \leqslant \limsup_{n\to\infty} F_n(x) \leqslant F(x+0).$$

From this relation one immediately obtains the lemma.

Theorem 3.5.1 (Helly's First Theorem).   *Every sequence $\{F_n(x)\}$ of uniformly bounded non-decreasing functions contains a subsequence $\{F_{n_k}(x)\}$ which converges weakly to some non-decreasing bounded function $F(x)$.*

The theorem is proved by the standard diagonal method and uses the fact that the set of rational numbers is enumerable and can be arranged in a sequence $\{r_j\}$.

We form first the sequence $\{F_n(r_1)\}$. This is a bounded sequence of real numbers and has therefore at least one accumulation point. Thus it is possible to select a convergent subsequence $\{F_{1,n}(r_1)\}$. Let

$$\lim_{n\to\infty} F_{1,n}(r_1) = \Phi(r_1).$$

In the second step we consider the sequence of functions $\{F_{1,n}(x)\}$. We select again from the bounded sequence of real numbers $\{F_{1,n}(r_2)\}$ a convergent subsequence $\{F_{2,n}(r_2)\}$ and write

$$\lim_{n\to\infty} F_{2,n}(r_2) = \Phi(r_2).$$

The sequence of functions $\{F_{2,n}(x)\}$ is a subsequence of the original sequence $\{F_n(x)\}$ which converges for $x = r_1$ and $x = r_2$. We continue this procedure and obtain a sequence of subsequences of $\{F_n(x)\}$

$$F_{1,1}(x), F_{1,2}(x), F_{1,3}(x), \ldots, F_{1,n}(x), \ldots$$
$$F_{2,1}(x), F_{2,2}(x), F_{2,3}(x), \ldots, F_{2,n}(x), \ldots$$
$$\cdots\cdots\cdots\cdots\cdots\cdots\cdots\cdots\cdots$$
$$\cdots\cdots\cdots\cdots\cdots\cdots\cdots\cdots\cdots$$
$$F_{m,1}(x), F_{m,2}(x), F_{m,3}(x), \ldots, F_{m,n}(x), \cdot$$
$$\cdots\cdots\cdots\cdots\cdots\cdots\cdots\cdots\cdots$$
$$\cdots\cdots\cdots\cdots\cdots\cdots\cdots\cdots\cdots$$

These sequences are selected in such a manner that each sequence is a subsequence of the preceding sequence; moreover the mth sequence

$$F_{m,1}(x), F_{m,2}(x), F_{m,3}(x), \ldots, F_{m,n}(x), \ldots$$

converges at the first m rational points $r_1, r_2, \ldots, r_m$ and we denote

$$\lim_{n\to\infty} F_{m,n}(r_k) = \Phi(r_k), \quad k = 1, 2, \ldots, m.$$

We form the diagonal sequence $\{F_{n,n}(x)\}$ and conclude that

$$\lim_{n\to\infty} F_{n,n}(r_k) = \Phi(r_k)$$

for all rational arguments r_k. The functions $\{F_{n,n}(x)\}$ are non-decreasing and uniformly bounded, so that the function $\Phi(r_k)$, defined for all rational values of the argument, is also bounded and non-decreasing. We introduce now

$$F(x) = \text{g.l.b.}_{r_k > x} \Phi(r_k).$$

The function $F(x)$ is defined for all real x and agrees with $\Phi(x)$ for rational values of the argument. The function $F(x)$ is bounded and non-decreasing and we see from lemma 3.5.1 that

$$(3.5.1) \qquad \operatorname*{Lim}_{n\to\infty} F_{n,n}(x) = F(x),$$

q.e.d.

The limiting function $F(x)$ is not necessarily right continuous; however it is always possible to change the values of $F(x)$ at its discontinuity points in such a manner that it becomes right continuous. Such a change obviously does not affect the validity of the relation (3.5.1).

Theorem 3.5.2 (Helly's Second Theorem). Let $f(x)$ be a continuous function and assume that $\{F_k(x)\}$ is a sequence of uniformly bounded, non-decreasing functions which converge weakly to some function $F(x)$ at all points of a continuity interval $[a, b]$ of $F(x)$, then

$$\lim_{k\to\infty} \int_a^b f(x)\, dF_k(x) = \int_a^b f(x)\, dF(x).$$

Since $f(x)$ is continuous it is possible to construct a subdivision $a = x_0 < x_1 < \ldots < x_N = b$ of $[a, b]$ which is so fine that

(3.5.2) $\quad |f(x) - f(x_j)| \leqslant \varepsilon \quad$ for $x_j \leqslant x \leqslant x_{j+1}$.

Here ε is an arbitrary positive constant. Moreover, the subdivision points can be selected so that they are all continuity points of $F(x)$. Hence $|F_k(x_j) - F(x_j)|$ can be made arbitrarily small if k is sufficiently large. Let $M = \max_{a \leqslant x \leqslant b} f(x)$ and choose K so large that

(3.5.3) $\quad |F_k(x_j) - F(x_j)| \leqslant \dfrac{\varepsilon}{MN} \quad$ for $k \geqslant K$.

We define a step function $f_\varepsilon(x)$ in the interval $[a, b]$ by

(3.5.4) $\quad f_\varepsilon(x) = f(x_j) \quad$ for $x_j \leqslant x < x_{j+1}$

and see from (3.5.2) that $|f(x) - f_\varepsilon(x)| \leqslant \varepsilon$. Clearly we have

(3.5.5) $\quad \left| \displaystyle\int_a^b f(x)\, dF(x) - \int_a^b f(x)\, dF_k(x) \right|$

$$\leqslant \left| \int_a^b f(x)\, dF(x) - \int_a^b f_\varepsilon(x)\, dF(x) \right|$$
$$+ \left| \int_a^b f_\varepsilon(x)\, dF(x) - \int_a^b f_\varepsilon(x)\, dF_k(x) \right|$$
$$+ \left| \int_a^b f_\varepsilon(x)\, dF_k(x) - \int_a^b f(x)\, dF_k(x) \right|.$$

We rewrite the first term on the right of (3.5.5) and see that

$$\left| \int_a^b [f(x) - f_\varepsilon(x)]\, dF(x) \right| \leqslant \varepsilon \int_a^b dF(x) = C_1 \varepsilon.$$

In the same manner we get an estimate for the last term in (3.5.5)

$$\left| \int_a^b f_\varepsilon(x)\, dF_k(x) - \int_a^b f(x)\, dF_k(x) \right| \leqslant C_1 \varepsilon;$$

the existence of the constant C_1 is assured by the assumption of uniform boundedness of the $F_k(x)$. Finally it follows from (3.5.3) and (3.5.4) that

$$\left| \int_a^b f_\varepsilon(x)\, dF(x) - \int_a^b f_\varepsilon(x)\, dF_k(x) \right|$$
$$= \left| \sum_{j=0}^{N-1} f(x_j)[F(x_{j+1}) - F(x_j)] - \sum_{j=0}^{N-1} f(x_j)[F_k(x_{j+1}) - F_k(x_j)] \right|$$
$$\leqslant N\left[M\frac{\varepsilon}{MN} + \frac{M\varepsilon}{MN} \right] = 2\varepsilon.$$

The last three inequalities and (3.5.5) yield the estimate

(3.5.6) $\quad \left| \displaystyle\int_a^b f(x)\, dF(x) - \int_a^b f(x)\, dF_k(x) \right| \leqslant 2(1 + C_1)\varepsilon = C\varepsilon \quad$ if $k \geqslant K$.

But this means that

$$\lim_{k\to\infty} \int_a^b f(x)\,dF_k(x) = \int_a^b f(x)\,dF(x),$$

which is the statement of the theorem.

Corollary to theorem 3.5.2 (extension of Helly's Second Theorem). Let $f(x)$ be continuous and bounded in the infinite interval $-\infty < x < \infty$ and let $\{F_k(x)\}$ be a sequence of non-decreasing, uniformly bounded functions which converges weakly to some function $F(x)$. Suppose that

$$\lim_{k\to\infty} F_k(-\infty) = F(-\infty) \quad and \quad \lim_{k\to\infty} F_k(+\infty) = F(+\infty),$$

then

$$\lim_{k\to\infty} \int_{-\infty}^{\infty} f(x)\,dF_k(x) = \int_{-\infty}^{\infty} f(x)\,dF(x).$$

To prove the corollary we consider the three expressions

$$J_1 = \left| \int_{-\infty}^a f(x)\,dF_k(x) - \int_{-\infty}^a f(x)\,dF(x) \right|$$

$$J_2 = \left| \int_a^b f(x)\,dF_k(x) - \int_a^b f(x)\,dF(x) \right|$$

$$J_3 = \left| \int_b^{\infty} f(x)\,dF_k(x) - \int_b^{\infty} f(x)\,dF(x) \right|$$

where $a < 0 < b$.

Clearly

$$\left| \int_{-\infty}^{\infty} f(x)\,dF_k(x) - \int_{-\infty}^{\infty} f(x)\,dF(x) \right| \leqslant J_1 + J_2 + J_3.$$

Since $f(x)$ is bounded there exists a constant $M > 0$ such that

$$|f(x)| \leqslant M.$$

Let $\varepsilon > 0$; as a consequence of the uniform boundedness of the sequence $\{F_k(x)\}$ it is possible to determine $|a|$ and $|b|$ so large that $J_1 \leqslant \varepsilon$ and $J_3 \leqslant \varepsilon$. From theorem 3.4.2 we see that there exists a K so large that $J_2 \leqslant C\varepsilon$ for $k \geqslant K$. Therefore

$$\left| \int_{-\infty}^{\infty} f(x)\,dF_k(x) - \int_{-\infty}^{\infty} f(x)\,dF(x) \right| \leqslant (C+2)\varepsilon \quad \text{for } k \geqslant K$$

so that the corollary is proved.

A statement, analogous to the corollary, holds if the range of the integration is a semi-infinite interval.

3.6 The continuity theorem

In this section we derive necessary and sufficient conditions for the weak convergence of a sequence of distribution functions to a limiting distribution. The theorems of the preceding section will serve as tools; we need,

however, one more lemma which we deduce next from the inversion formula
and the convolution theorem.

Lemma 3.6.1.   *Let $F(x)$ be a distribution function with characteristic function
$f(t)$, then*

$$\int_0^h F(y)\,dy - \int_{-h}^0 F(y)\,dy = \frac{1}{\pi} \int_{-\infty}^\infty \frac{1-\cos ht}{t^2} f(t)\,dt$$

for any real positive h.

We denote by $R(x)$ the uniform distribution over the interval $(-a, +a)$;
the characteristic function (see Table 4) of $R(x)$ is then

$$r(t) = \frac{\sin ta}{ta}.$$

Let $F(x)$ be an arbitrary distribution function and consider the distribution
$H(x) = F(x) * R(x)$; clearly

$$(3.6.1) \qquad H(x) = \frac{1}{2a} \int_{-a}^a F(x-y)\,dy = \frac{1}{2a} \int_{x-a}^{x+a} F(u)\,du$$

while

$$h(t) = f(t)\frac{\sin ta}{ta}.$$

We apply (3.2.6) and obtain

$$H(x+a) - H(x-a) = \lim_{T\to\infty} \frac{1}{\pi} \int_{-T}^T \frac{\sin^2 at}{at^2} e^{-itx} f(t)\,dt.$$

Using (3.6.1) we see that

$$\int_0^{2a} [F(x+v) - F(x-v)]\,dv = \lim_{T\to\infty} \frac{1}{\pi} \int_{-T}^T \frac{1-\cos 2at}{t^2} e^{-itx} f(t)\,dt.$$

The function $(1-\cos 2at)/t^2$ is absolutely integrable over $(-\infty, +\infty)$ so
that the integral on the right converges absolutely. We write $h = 2a$ and go
to the limit so that

$$\int_0^h [F(x+v) - F(x-v)]\,dv = \frac{1}{\pi} \int_{-\infty}^\infty \frac{1-\cos ht}{t^2} e^{-itx} f(t)\,dt.$$

We finally put $x = 0$ and transform the integral on the left and obtain the
formula of the lemma.

We now proceed to the main theorem of this section.

Theorem 3.6.1 (*Continuity theorem*).   *Let $\{F_n(x)\}$ be a sequence of distribution functions and denote by $\{f_n(t)\}$ the sequence of the corresponding characteristic functions. The sequence $\{F_n(x)\}$ converges weakly to a distribution
function $F(x)$ if, and only if, the sequence $\{f_n(t)\}$ converges for every t to a*

function $f(t)$ which is continuous at $t = 0$. The limiting function is then the characteristic function of $F(x)$.

This theorem indicates that the one-to-one correspondence between distribution functions and characteristic functions is continuous.

The necessity of the condition follows immediately from the extension of Helly's second theorem (corollary to theorem 3.5.2). To prove the sufficiency we assume that the sequence $f_n(t)$ converges for all t to a function $f(t)$ which is continuous at $t = 0$. Let $\{F_n(x)\}$ be the sequence of distribution functions corresponding to the sequence $\{f_n(t)\}$ of characteristic functions. According to Helly's first theorem we can select a subsequence $\{F_{n_k}(x)\}$ such that

$$\underset{k \to \infty}{\text{Lim}}\, F_{n_k}(x) = F(x)$$

where $F(x)$ is a non-decreasing and bounded function which is continuous to the right. Since the $F_{n_k}(x)$ are distribution functions we conclude that the limiting function $F(x)$ satisfies the inequality $0 \leqslant F(x) \leqslant 1$. In order to show that $F(x)$ is a distribution function we must only show that

$$F(\infty) - F(-\infty) = 1.$$

We apply lemma 3.6.1 to the functions $F_{n_k}(x)$ and find that

$$\int_0^h F_{n_k}(y)\,dy - \int_{-h}^0 F_{n_k}(y)\,dy = \frac{1}{\pi}\int_{-\infty}^\infty \frac{1-\cos ht}{t^2} f_{n_k}(t)\,dt.$$

It is easily seen that the passage to the limit, $k \to \infty$, can be carried out under the integral signs so that

$$\frac{1}{h}\int_0^h F(y)\,dy - \frac{1}{h}\int_{-h}^0 F(y)\,dy = \frac{1}{\pi}\int_{-\infty}^\infty \frac{1-\cos y}{y^2} f(y/h)\,dy.$$

The expression on the left of this equation tends to $F(\infty) - F(-\infty)$ as $h \to \infty$. Since we assumed that $f(t)$ is continuous at $t = 0$ we see that

$$\lim_{h \to \infty} f(t/h) = f(0) = \lim_{n \to \infty} f_n(0) = 1.$$

Moreover, it is again permissible to carry out the passage to the limit under the integral sign so that

$$F(\infty) - F(-\infty) = \frac{1}{\pi}\int_{-\infty}^\infty \frac{1-\cos y}{y^2}\,dy.$$

It is well known[*] that

$$\int_0^\infty \frac{1-\cos y}{y^2}\,dy = \frac{\pi}{2}$$

[*] We integrate by parts and see that

$$\int_0^\infty \frac{1-\cos y}{y^2}\,dy = \int_0^\infty \frac{\sin y}{y}\,dy.$$

For the last integral see Titchmarsh (1937), Section 3.122.

so that $F(\infty) - F(-\infty) = 1$. The limiting function $F(x)$ of the subsequence $F_{n_k}(x)$ is therefore a distribution function. The argument just used applies to every convergent subsequence of $\{F_n(x)\}$. It follows then from the uniqueness theorem that every convergent subsequence of $\{F_n(x)\}$ converges weakly to the same limiting distribution $F(x)$. This means however that

$$\text{Lim}_{n\to\infty} F_n(x) = F(x).$$

Corollary 1 to theorem 3.6.1. If a sequence $\{f_n(t)\}$ of characteristic functions converges to a characteristic function $f(t)$ then the convergence is uniform in every finite t-interval $[-T, T]$.

Denote by $F_n(x)$ and $F(x)$ the distribution function of $f_n(t)$ and $f(t)$ respectively. Then

$$(3.6.2) \qquad |f_n(t) - f(t)| \leqslant \left| \int_a^b e^{itx} dF_n(x) - \int_a^b e^{itx} dF(x) \right|$$
$$+ [1 - F_n(b) + F_n(a)] + [1 - F(b) + F(a)].$$

Let ε be an arbitrary positive number and select for a and b two continuity points of $F(x)$, taking $|a|$ and b so large that

$$1 - F(b) + F(a) < \varepsilon.$$

Since

$$\text{Lim}_{n\to\infty} F_n(x) = F(x)$$

we have, for sufficiently large values of n,

$$1 - F_n(b) + F_n(a) \leqslant 1 - F(b) + F(a) + \varepsilon < 2\varepsilon.$$

The inequality (3.6.2) can then be written as

$$(3.6.3) \qquad |f_n(t) - f(t)| \leqslant \left| \int_a^b e^{itx} dF_n(x) - \int_a^b e^{itx} dF(x) \right| + 3\varepsilon.$$

We wish to estimate the difference of the two integrals on the right of (3.6.3) for values of t from the interval $[-T, T]$. To do this we subdivide the interval $[a, b]$ by means of the subdivision points

$$a = x_0 < x_1 < \ldots < x_N = b.$$

It is here no restriction to assume that all subdivision points are continuity points of $F(x)$ and that

$$m = \max_{1 \leqslant k \leqslant N} (x_k - x_{k-1}) < \varepsilon/T.$$

We note that

$$\left| \int_a^b e^{itx} \, dF_n(x) - \int_a^b e^{itx} \, dF(x) \right|$$

$$\leqslant \left| \sum_{k=1}^N \left[\int_{x_{k-1}}^{x_k} e^{itx_k} \, dF_n(x) - \int_{x_{k-1}}^{x_k} e^{itx_k} \, dF(x) \right] \right|$$

$$+ \left| \sum_{k=1}^N \left\{ \int_{x_{k-1}}^{x_k} (e^{itx_k} - e^{itx}) \, dF_n(x) - \int_{x_{k-1}}^{x_k} (e^{itx_k} - e^{itx}) \, dF(x) \right\} \right|.$$

It is easily seen that for $|t| \leqslant T$

$$\left| \int_{x_{k-1}}^{x_k} (e^{itx_k} - e^{itx}) \, dF_n(x) \right| \leqslant mT \int_{x_{k-1}}^{x_k} dF_n(x) < \varepsilon \int_{x_{k-1}}^{x_k} dF_n(x);$$

this inequality remains valid if $F_n(x)$ is replaced by $F(x)$. It follows then from the preceding relation that

$$\left| \int_a^b e^{itx} \, dF_n(x) - \int_a^b e^{itx} \, dF(x) \right| \leqslant \sum_{k=1}^N \left| \int_{x_{-1}}^x dF_n(x) - \int_{x_{k-1}}^{x_k} dF(x) \right| + 2\varepsilon.$$

The sum on the right-hand side of this inequality will not exceed 3ε if n is sufficiently large, hence (3.6.3) becomes

$$|f_n(t) - f(t)| \leqslant 6\varepsilon$$

for all $t \in [-T, T]$, provided that n is chosen sufficiently large. This is the statement of the corollary.

Corollary 2 to theorem 3.6.1. Let $\{f_n(t)\}$ be a sequence of characteristic functions and suppose that this sequence converges for all values of t to a limit function $f(t)$. Assume that $f(t)$ is continuous at $t = 0$; then $f(t)$ is also a characteristic function.

We remark that the limit of a sequence of characteristic functions is necessarily continuous for all t if it is continuous for the particular value $t = 0$. The continuity at $t = 0$ is, however, an essential requirement of theorem 3.6.1 and cannot be relaxed. As an illustration we consider once more the sequence of rectangular distributions, discussed in Example 1 of Section 3.4. We saw there that the distribution functions $F_n(x)$ converge for all values of x; however,

$$\lim_{n \to \infty} F_n(x) = \tfrac{1}{2}$$

so that the limiting function is not a distribution. The characteristic function $f_n(t)$ of $F_n(x)$ is

$$f_n(t) = \frac{\sin tn}{tn},$$

therefore

$$\lim_{n \to \infty} f_n(t) = \begin{cases} 1 & \text{for } t = 0 \\ 0 & \text{for } t \neq 0 \end{cases}$$

so that the limiting function is not continuous for $t = 0$.

The following corollary is a generalization of the continuity theorem. It applies to bounded non-decreasing functions and will be used in Chapter 5.

Corollary 3 to theorem 3.6.1.   Let $\{F_n(x)\}$ be a sequence of bounded non-decreasing functions such that $F_n(-\infty) = 0$ and denote by

$$f_n(t) = \int_{-\infty}^{\infty} e^{itx} \, dF_n(x)$$

their Fourier–Stieltjes transforms. The sequence $\{F_n(x)\}$ converges weakly to a bounded, non-decreasing function $F(x)$ and

$$\lim_{n \to \infty} \{F_n(\infty) - F_n(-\infty)\} = F(\infty) - F(-\infty)$$

if, and only if, the sequence $\{f_n(t)\}$ converges to a function $f(t)$ which is continuous at $t = 0$.

We prove first the sufficiency of the condition and write $V_n = f_n(0) = \int_{-\infty}^{\infty} dF_n(y)$ for the total variation of $F_n(x)$. Then

$$\lim_{n \to \infty} V_n = f(0).$$

Consider first the case $f(0) \neq 0$. Then the sequence of distribution functions $F_n(x)/V_n$ converges weakly (according to theorem 3.6.1) to a distribution $H(x)$ and

$$\operatorname{Lim}_{n \to \infty} F_n(x) = H(x) f(0).$$

If $f(0) = 0$, then

$$\operatorname{Lim}_{n \to \infty} F_n(x) = 0$$

so that the corollary holds in this case also. The necessity of the condition is an immediate consequence of theorem 3.6.1.

Corollary 4 to theorem 3.6.1.   Let $\{f_n(t)\}$ be a sequence of characteristic functions and suppose that it converges uniformly to a limiting function $f(t)$ in every finite t-interval $[-T, T]$. Then the function $f(t)$ is continuous at the point $t = 0$.

To prove the corollary, we note that

$$(3.6.4) \qquad |f(t) - f(0)| \leqslant |f(t) - f_n(t)| + |f_n(t) - f_n(0)| + |f_n(0) - f(0)|.$$

Let ε be an arbitrary positive number; we first choose n so large that

$$|f(t) - f_n(t)| \leqslant \frac{\varepsilon}{3}$$

and for $|t| \leqslant 1$

$$|f_n(0) - f(0)| \leqslant \frac{\varepsilon}{3}.$$

Then we choose t so small that

$$|f_n(t) - f_n(0)| \leqslant \frac{\varepsilon}{3},$$

so that

$$|f(t) - f(0)| \leqslant \varepsilon.$$

The last inequality proves the statement of the corollary.

We are now in a position to modify somewhat the statement of the continuity theorem.

Theorem 3.6.2 (second version of the continuity theorem). Let $\{F_n(x)\}$ be a sequence of distribution functions and denote by $\{f_n(t)\}$ the sequence of the corresponding characteristic functions. The sequence $\{F_n(x)\}$ converges weakly to a distribution function $F(x)$ if, and only if, the sequence $\{f_n(t)\}$ converges uniformly to a limiting function $f(t)$ in every finite t-interval $[-T, +T]$. The limiting function $f(t)$ is then the characteristic function of $F(x)$.

The statement of theorem 3.6.2 follows immediately from the continuity theorem and from the corollaries 1 and 4.

We conclude this section with two remarks concerning the weak convergence of a sequence of distribution functions to a limiting distribution function.

Remark 1. It is possible that a sequence $\{F_n(x)\}$ of distribution functions converges weakly to a limit $F(x)$ but that the moments of the $F_n(x)$ do not converge to the moments of $F(x)$. Let, for instance, $F_n(x)$ be given by $F_n(x) = \frac{1}{n} R_n(x) + \left(1 - \frac{1}{n}\right)\varepsilon(x)$, where $R_n(x)$ is the uniform distribution over the interval $[0, n]$. Since the characteristic function of $F_n(x)$ is

$$f_n(t) = \frac{1}{n} \frac{e^{itn} - 1}{nit} + \left(1 - \frac{1}{n}\right)$$

we see that $\operatorname*{Lim}_{n \to \infty} F_n(x) = \varepsilon(x)$. Moreover, it is easily seen that the moment

$$\alpha_k^{(n)} = \int_{-\infty}^{\infty} x^k \, dF_n(x) = \frac{n^{k-1}}{k+1}.$$

Therefore $\lim_{n \to \infty} \alpha_k^{(n)} = \infty$, while the moments of the limiting distribution $\varepsilon(x)$ are all zero.

Remark 2. The weak convergence of a sequence $\{F_n(x)\}$ of absolutely continuous distribution functions to an absolutely continuous distribution function $F(x)$ does not imply the convergence of the density functions $F_n'(x)$ to $F'(x)$. Define, for example, $F_n(x)$ by

$$F_n(x) = \begin{cases} 0 & \text{if } x < 0 \\ x\left(1 - \dfrac{\sin 2n\pi x}{2n\pi x}\right) & \text{if } 0 \leqslant x < 1 \\ 1 & \text{if } x \geqslant 1. \end{cases}$$

Then $F_n(x)$ converges weakly to the uniform distribution over $[0, 1]$ but $p_n(x) = 1 - \cos 2\pi n x$ does not converge to the rectangular density.

The continuity theorem suggests the expectation that two distribution functions whose characteristic functions do not differ much are close to each other in some sense. This idea was stated in a precise way by C. G. Esseen (1944) [see also B. V. Gnedenko–A. N. Kolmogorov (1954), pp. 196 ff.]. Esseen obtained the following results:

Theorem 3.6.3. *Let A, T and ε be arbitrary positive constants, $F(x)$ a non-decreasing function and $G(x)$ a real function of bounded variation. Let $f(t)$ and $g(t)$ be the Fourier–Stieltjes transforms of $F(x)$ and $G(x)$ respectively. Suppose that*

(i) $F(-\infty) = G(-\infty), \quad F(+\infty) = G(+\infty)$

(ii) $\displaystyle\int_{-\infty}^{\infty} |F(x) - G(x)|\, dx < \infty$

(iii) $G'(x)$ *exists for all x and* $|G'(x)| \leqslant A$

(iv) $\displaystyle\int_{-T}^{T} \left| \frac{f(t) - g(t)}{t} \right| dt = \varepsilon.$

Then to every $k > 1$ there corresponds a finite, positive $c(k)$ depending only on k, such that

$$|F(x) - G(x)| \leqslant k\,\frac{\varepsilon}{2\pi} + c(k)\,\frac{A}{T}.$$

Theorem 3.6.4. *Let A, T and ε be arbitrary positive constants, $F(x)$ a non-decreasing purely discrete function, and $G(x)$ a real function of bounded variation. Let $f(t)$ and $g(t)$ be the Fourier–Stieltjes transforms of $F(x)$ and $G(x)$ respectively. Suppose that*

(i) $F(-\infty) = G(-\infty); \quad F(+\infty) = G(+\infty)$

(ii) $\displaystyle\int_{-\infty}^{\infty} |F(x) - G(x)|\, dx < \infty$

(iii) $\displaystyle\int_{-T}^{T} \left| \frac{f(t) - g(t)}{t} \right| dt = \varepsilon$

(iv) *the functions $F(x)$ and $G(x)$ have discontinuities only at the points x_v ($v = 0, \pm 1, \pm 2, \ldots$; $x_{v+1} > x_v$) and there exists a constant $L > 0$ such that* $\mathrm{Inf}\, (x_{v+1} - x_v) \geqslant L$

(v) $|G'(x)| \leqslant A$ *for all* $x \neq x_v$ ($v = 0, \pm 1, \pm 2, \ldots$).

Then to every number $k > 1$ there correspond two finite positive numbers $c_1(k)$ and $c_2(k)$, depending only on k, such that

$$|F(x) - G(x)| \leqslant k\frac{\varepsilon}{2\pi} + c_1(k)\frac{A}{T},$$

provided that $TL \geqslant c_2(k)$.

The limit theorems of probability theory give approximations for the distributions of normalized sums of random variables. Esseen's theorems provide an important tool for the study of the error terms of these approximations.

3.7 Infinite convolutions[*]

In this section we define and study convergent infinite convolutions and their characteristic functions. It is not our intention to present here an exhaustive discussion. We wish to give only a few results which will permit the construction of certain interesting examples.

In Section 3.3 we defined the convolution of two distributions and regarded it as a symbolic multiplication of distribution functions. It is clearly possible to extend this operation to more than two factors, and it is easily seen that the convolution of a finite number of distribution functions is a commutative and associative operation. Therefore the convolution of a finite number of distribution functions determines uniquely a distribution which is independent of the order in which the factors are taken.

Before defining convergent infinite convolutions we introduce a suitable notation and define certain sets which are useful in studying convolutions. The concepts and notations introduced are also convenient in connection with finite convolutions.

Let $F_1, F_2, \ldots, F_n$ be n distribution functions. We write

(3.7.1) $$\prod_{k=1}^{n} {}^* F_k(x) = \prod_{k=1}^{n} {}^* F_k = F_1 * F_2 * \ldots * F_n$$

for their convolution and use the symbol $\prod^*$ to denote convolution products. The convolution of a finite number of distribution functions is again

---

[*] This section deals with a special topic; familiarity with this subject is not required for an understanding of the rest of the book.

We deal in Section 3.7 with certain sets of real numbers and use the customary set-theoretic notations. We designate sets by Latin italic capitals and their elements by lower-case Latin italic letters. Thus $x \in A$ means that the number x belongs to A; $A \subseteq B$ (or $B \supseteq A$) means that A is contained in B (or B contains A); $\bar{A}$ is the closure; A^c is the complement of A. The empty set is denoted by $\emptyset$.

c

a distribution function; the characteristic function of (3.7.1) is, according to the convolution theorem, given by the product $\prod_{k=1}^{n} f_k(t)$ of the corresponding characteristic functions.

In this section we shall need several lemmas which state simple properties of characteristic functions and of sequences of characteristic functions.

Lemma 3.7.1. *Let $F(x)$ be a distribution function and $f(t)$ its characteristic function. Then* $\mathrm{Re}\,[1-f(t)] \geqslant \tfrac{1}{4}\,\mathrm{Re}\,[1-f(2t)]$.

Since $\mathrm{Re}\,[1-f(t)] = \int_{-\infty}^{\infty} (1-\cos tx)\,dF(x)$ we obtain the statement of the lemma from the elementary relation,

$$1 - \cos tx = 2\sin^2\frac{tx}{2} \geqslant 2\sin^2\frac{tx}{2}\cos^2\frac{tx}{2} = \tfrac{1}{2}\sin^2 tx = \tfrac{1}{4}(1-\cos 2tx).$$

Lemma 3.7.2. *Let $\{F_n(x)\}$ be a sequence of distribution functions and $\{f_n(t)\}$ the corresponding sequence of characteristic functions. Suppose that* $\lim_{n\to\infty} f_n(t) = 1$ *for* $|t| < t_0$, *then* $\mathrm{Lim}_{n\to\infty} F_n(x) = \varepsilon(x)$.

It follows from lemma 3.7.1 that the relation $\lim_{n\to\infty} f_n(t) = 1$ is also valid in the interval $|t| < 2t_0$ and therefore—by iteration—for all real t, so that we can conclude that $\mathrm{Lim}_{n\to\infty} F_n(x) = \varepsilon(x)$.

Lemma 3.7.3. *Let $\{F_n(x)\}$ and $\{G_n(x)\}$ be two sequences of distribution functions and suppose that there exists a distribution $F(x)$ such that*

$$\mathrm{Lim}_{n\to\infty} F_n(x) = F(x) \text{ and } \mathrm{Lim}_{n\to\infty} (F_n * G_n) = F;\ then\ \mathrm{Lim}_{n\to\infty} G_n(x) = \varepsilon(x).$$

It follows from the assumptions of the lemma and from the continuity theorem that

(3.7.2a) $\lim_{n\to\infty} f_n(t) = f(t)$

and

(3.7.2b) $\lim_{n\to\infty} f_n(t)g_n(t) = f(t)$.

Since $f(t)$ is a characteristic function we know that $f(0) = 1$, and we conclude from (3.7.2a) that there necessarily exists a neighbourhood $|t| < t_0$ of the origin such that $|f_n(t)| \geqslant \tfrac{1}{2}$ for n sufficiently large and $|t| < t_0$. Using (3.7.2a) and (3.7.2b), it is then seen easily that $\lim_{n\to\infty} g_n(t) = 1$ for $|t| < t_0$. The statement follows immediately from lemma 3.7.2.

Let $F(x)$ be a distribution function; the spectrum S_F of $F(x)$ is the set of all points of increase of $F(x)$. It is easily seen that S_F is closed, not empty, and that $\int_{S_F} dF(x) = 1$.

We give a second, similar definition. The point spectrum D_F of a distribution function $F(x)$ is the set of all its discontinuity points. Clearly, D_F is an at most denumerable (proper or improper) subset of S_F. D_F need not be closed, and can be empty; in fact $D_F = \emptyset$ if, and only if, F is a continuous distribution.

Let A and B be two, not necessarily disjoint, sets on the real line. We define the vectorial sum $A (+) B$ of the sets A and B as the set of all real numbers x which can be written in at least one way in the form $x = a+b$, where $a \in A$ and $b \in B$. We agree to say that $A (+) B = \emptyset$ if either A or B is empty. If both A and B are one-point sets, $A = \{a\}$ and $B = \{b\}$, then the vectorial addition is equivalent to ordinary addition. If the set B contains only the single point b, $B = \{b\}$, then $A (+) B = A (+) \{b\}$ is obtained from the set A by the translation b. The vectorial addition of sets is commutative and associative. The vectorial sum of two closed sets is not necessarily closed; however, if A and B are closed and bounded sets then $A (+) B$ is also closed.

Remark. The vectorial sum of two sets must not be confused with their set-theoretic union.

We shall need in Chapter 9 a notation for the vectorial sum of n identical summands A, and write $(1)A = A$ and $(n)A = (n-1)A (+) A$ for $n = 2, 3, \ldots$.

Lemma 3.7.4. Let $F_1(x)$ and $F_2(x)$ be two distribution functions and let $F = F_1 * F_2$ be their convolution. Then $S_F = \overline{S_{F_1} (+) S_{F_2}}$ while

$$D_F = D_{F_1} (+) D_{F_2}.$$

Let $y \in S_{F_1}$ and $z \in S_{F_2}$ and put $w = y+z$. We select an arbitrary positive number δ and conclude from the assumptions of the lemma that

$$F(w+\delta) - F(w-\delta) = \int_{-\infty}^{\infty} [F_1(w+\delta-u) - F_1(w-\delta-u)] \, dF_2(u)$$

$$\geqslant [F_1(w-z+2\delta) - F_1(w-z-2\delta)] \int_{z-\delta}^{z+\delta} dF_2(u)$$

$$= [F_1(y+2\delta) - F_1(y-2\delta)][F_2(z+\delta) - F_2(z-\delta)] > 0.$$

Therefore $w = y+z \in S_F$ so that $S_{F_1} (+) S_{F_2} \subseteq S_F$. Since S_F is a closed set, we have also $\overline{S_{F_1} (+) S_{F_2}} \subseteq S_F$.

We still have to prove the relation $\overline{S_{F_1} (+) S_{F_2}} \supseteq S_F$. We give an indirect proof and assume that there exists a point w which belongs to S_F but not to $\overline{S_{F_1}(+) S_{F_2}}$. Since $w \in S_F$ we have for any $\delta > 0$

$$F(w+\delta) - F(w-\delta) = \int_{-\infty}^{\infty} [F_1(w+\delta-u) - F_1(w-\delta-u)] \, dF_2(u) > 0.$$

But this is only possible if there exists a point $u_0 \in S_{F_2}$ such that

$$[F_1(w+\delta-u_0) - F_1(w-\delta-u_0)] > 0.$$

Put $v_0 = w - u_0$; then $v_0 \in S_{F1}$ and $w \in \overline{S_{F_1}(+) S_{F_2}}$ which is a contradiction, so that the first statement of the lemma is proved. In a similar way one can also prove the statement concerning the point spectrum.

We also need another lemma which is of some independent interest:

Lemma 3.7.5. Let $F(x)$ be a distribution function with characteristic function $f(t)$. Then $t^2 \int_{-r}^{r} x^2 \, dF(x) \leqslant 3\,|1-f(t)|$ for $|t| \leqslant \dfrac{1}{r}$ where r is an arbitrary positive number.

Since $\operatorname{Re}[1-f(t)] = \int_{-\infty}^{\infty} (1-\cos tx) \, dF(x) \leqslant |1-f(t)|$ we see immediately that

$$\int_{-r}^{r} (1-\cos tx) \, dF(x) \leqslant |1-f(t)|.$$

The statement of the lemma then follows easily from the fact that $x^2 \leqslant 3(1-\cos x)$ for $|x| \leqslant 1$.

Let $\{F_k\}$, $k = 1, 2, \ldots$, be an infinite sequence of distribution functions. In a purely formal manner we can introduce the infinite convolution(†)

$$\prod_{k=1}^{\infty}{}^{*} F_k = F_1 * F_2 * \ldots * F_k * \ldots$$

of the distributions of the sequence. In order to give this infinite convolution a definite meaning, we form for each positive integer n the finite convolution

$$P_n(x) = \prod_{k=1}^{n}{}^{*} F_k(x).$$

The infinite convolution $\prod_{k=1}^{\infty}{}^{*} F_k$ is said to be convergent if there exists a distribution function $F(x)$ such that $\underset{n \to \infty}{\operatorname{Lim}} P_n(x) = F(x)$. We write then

$$(3.7.3) \qquad F(x) = \prod_{k=1}^{\infty}{}^{*} F_k(x) \quad (= \underset{n \to \infty}{\operatorname{Lim}} P_n(x)).$$

The characteristic function of $P_n(x)$ is the finite product $p_n(t) = \prod_{k=1}^{n} f_k(t)$,

---

(†) In dealing with convolutions it is often convenient to omit the variable and to write F instead of $F(x)$.

and we conclude from theorem 3.6.2 that the necessary and sufficient condition for the convergence of the infinite convolution (3.7.3) is that the sequence $p_n(t)$ should converge uniformly in every finite t-interval to a limit $f(t)$. This limit is then the characteristic function of $F(x)$ and is given by the infinite product $f(t) = \prod_{k=1}^{\infty} f_k(t)$.

Let $\prod_{k=1}^{\infty} f_k(t)$ be the characteristic function of a convergent convolution.

We next show that $\prod_{k=1}^{\infty} f_k(t)$ is uniformly convergent in the sense of the theory of infinite products.(†) Since $\lim_{n \to \infty} p_n(t) = f(t)$ is a characteristic function (namely of the convergent infinite convolution), there exists an interval $|t| < t_0$ such that $f(t)$, and therefore also the factors $f_k(t)$, do not vanish for $|t| < t_0$. The infinite product is then uniformly convergent (in the sense of the theory of infinite products) in this interval. It follows that $\lim_{k \to \infty} f_k(t) = 1$ uniformly in $|t| < t_0$, and we see from lemma 3.7.2 that $\lim_{n \to \infty} f_n(t) = 1$ uniformly in every fixed bounded t-interval. There exists therefore, for every bounded interval, an N such that $f_n(t)$ does not vanish on the interval if $n > N$; this means that the infinite product which represents $f(t)$ is uniformly convergent.

We now derive criteria for the convergence of infinite convolutions.

Theorem 3.7.1. *The infinite convolution* $F(x) = \prod_{k=1}^{\infty} {}^{*} F_k$ *is convergent if,*

and only if, $\text{Lim}_{n \to \infty} \prod_{k=n+1}^{n+p} {}^{*} F_k = \varepsilon(x)$.

We write $G_{n,p} = \prod_{k=n+1}^{n+p} {}^{*} F_k$ and $P_n = \prod_{k=1}^{n} {}^{*} F_k$ so that $P_n * G_{n,p} = P_{n+p}$.

To prove the necessity of the condition, we assume that the infinite convolution is convergent and note that $\text{Lim}_{n \to \infty} P_{n+p} = \text{Lim}_{n \to \infty} P_n = F$. We conclude from lemma 3.7.3 that $\text{Lim}_{n \to \infty} G_{n,p}(x) = \varepsilon(x)$. Conversely, if $\text{Lim}_{n \to \infty} G_{n,p}(x) = \varepsilon(x)$ then $g_{n,p}(t) = \prod_{k=n+1}^{n+p} f_k(t)$ converges uniformly to 1 in every finite t-interval, so that $f(t) = \prod_{k=1}^{\infty} f_k(t)$ also converges uniformly in every finite interval.

(†) See E. C. Titchmarsh (1939), A. I. Markushevich, vol. I (1965).

Theorem 3.7.2. Let $F = \prod\limits_{k=1}^{\infty}{}^{*} F_k$ be a convergent infinite convolution. Then

the infinite convolution $R_n = \prod\limits_{k=n+1}^{\infty}{}^{*} F_k$ is also convergent and

$$\underset{n\to\infty}{\text{Lim}}\, R_n(x) = \varepsilon(x).$$

The convergence of $R_n(x)$ follows immediately from theorem 3.7.1;

moreover, $F = P_n * R_n$ (where again $P_n = \prod\limits_{k=1}^{n}{}^{*} F_k$) and $\underset{n\to\infty}{\text{Lim}}\, P_n(x) = F(x)$,

so that necessarily $\underset{n\to\infty}{\text{Lim}}\, R_n(x) = \varepsilon(x)$.

We next derive a sufficient condition for the convergence of an infinite convolution.

Theorem 3.7.3. Let $\{F_k\}$ be a sequence of distribution functions and assume that the second moment $\alpha_{2,k}$ of F_k exists and that the first moment $\alpha_{1,k}$ of F_k

is zero. Suppose that the sum $\sum\limits_{k=1}^{\infty} \alpha_{2,k}$ converges; the infinite convolution

$\prod\limits_{k=1}^{\infty}{}^{*} F_k$ is then convergent.

It follows from the assumptions and from Taylor's theorem that the characteristic function $f_k(t)$ of $F_k(x)$ can be written in the form

$$(3.7.4) \qquad f_k(t) = 1 + \frac{t^2}{2} f_k''(\vartheta_k t) \quad (|\vartheta_k| \leqslant 1).$$

Let $F(x)$ be a distribution function with finite moments of second order; then its characteristic function satisfies the inequality

$$|f''(t)| \leqslant \int_{-\infty}^{\infty} x^2\, dF(x).$$

We see therefore from (3.7.4) that

$$|1 - f_k(t)| \leqslant \tfrac{1}{2} t^2 \alpha_{2,k}$$

and conclude that the infinite product $\prod\limits_{k=1}^{\infty} f_k(t)$ is uniformly convergent in

every finite t-interval, so that the statement is proved.

Corollary to theorem 3.7.3. Let $\{F_k\}$ be a sequence of distribution functions

and assume that the integral $M_k^{\delta} = \int_{-\infty}^{\infty} |x|^{\delta}\, dF_k(x)$ exists for some δ such

that $0 < \delta \leqslant 1$. Suppose further that $\sum\limits_{k=1}^{\infty} M_k^{\delta} < \infty$; then the infinite con-

volution $\prod\limits_{k=1}^{\infty}{}^{*} F_k$ is convergent.

We note that for $0 < \delta \leqslant 1$ the inequality

$$\frac{|\sin z|}{|z|^\delta} \leqslant 1$$

holds for real z. Therefore

$$|e^{itx} - 1| = 2\left|\sin\frac{tx}{2}\right| \leqslant 2^{1-\delta}|tx|^\delta < 2|tx|^\delta$$

so that

$$|f_n(t) - 1| = \left|\int_{-\infty}^{\infty} (e^{itx} - 1)\, dF_k(x)\right| < 2|t|^\delta M_k^\delta.$$

We conclude in the same way, as in the proof of theorem 3.7.3, that the convergence of the series $\sum_{k=1}^{\infty} M_k^\delta$ implies the convergence of the infinite convolution.

We next give a necessary and sufficient condition for the convergence of an infinite convolution.

Theorem 3.7.4. Let $\{F_k\}$ be a sequence of distribution functions and assume that the first moment $\alpha_{1,k}$ of F_k is zero. Suppose further that the spectra S_{F_k} are uniformly bounded. The infinite convolution $\prod_{k=1}^{\infty}{}^* F_k$ is convergent if, and only if, the series $\sum_{k=1}^{\infty} \alpha_{2,k}$ is convergent.(†)

The sufficiency of the condition follows from theorem 3.7.3, so that we need prove only that it is necessary.

Let $F = \prod_{k=1}^{\infty}{}^* F_k$ be a convergent convolution of distributions which satisfy the conditions of the theorem; write $\tilde{F}_k$ for the distribution function conjugate to F_k, and put $G_k = F_k * \tilde{F}_k$. Let $\alpha_{1,k}^s$ and $\alpha_{2,k}^s$ be the first and second moment respectively of G_k. Then

$$\alpha_{1,k}^s = 0$$

while

(3.7.5) $\qquad \alpha_{2,k}^s = 2\alpha_{2,k}.$

We conclude from the convergence of $\prod_{k=1}^{\infty}{}^* F_k$ that $\prod_{k=1}^{\infty}{}^* \tilde{F}_k$ and therefore also $\prod_{k=1}^{\infty}{}^* G_k$ are convergent. Let $f_k(t)$ and $g_k(t)$ be the characteristic functions of $F_k(x)$ and $G_k(x)$ respectively. The convergence of the infinite

---

(†) The uniform boundedness of the spectra ensures the existence of the second moments.

convolution $\prod_{k=1}^{\infty}{}^{*}G_k$ implies the convergence of the infinite product $\prod_{k=1}^{\infty}g_k(t)$. Since $g_k(t) = |f_k(t)|^2$ is real and positive, we see that the product $\prod_{k=1}^{\infty}g_k(t)$ is absolutely convergent. Therefore the series $\sum_{k=1}^{\infty}|1-g_k(t)| < \infty$. It then follows from lemma 3.7.5 that

$$(3.7.6) \qquad \sum_{k=1}^{\infty}\int_{-r}^{r} x^2\,dG_k(x) < \infty$$

for any real r. Since the spectra S_{F_k} are, by assumption, uniformly bounded, this is also true for the spectra $S_{\bar{F}_k}$ of the conjugate distributions, and we conclude from lemma 3.7.4 that the spectra S_{G_k} are also uniformly bounded. Therefore there exists a value r such that $G_k(x)$ is constant for $|x| > r$ and all k. It follows from (3.7.6) that

$$\sum_{k=1}^{\infty}\alpha_{2,k}^s < \infty.$$

In view of (3.7.5) we have then

$$\sum_{k=1}^{\infty}\alpha_{2,k} < \infty,$$

so that the condition of the theorem is necessary.

We also need some properties of the spectra of convergent infinite convolutions. For this purpose it is convenient to introduce the following terminology.

The closed limit inferior (†) of a sequence $\{A_n\}$ of sets is the set of all points x which have the property that every neighbourhood of x contains at least one point of almost all sets A_n (i.e. all sets A_n with n sufficiently large). We write $\mathrm{Li}\,A_n$ for the closed limit inferior of the sequence $\{A_n\}$. The statement $x \in \mathrm{Li}\,A_n$ means therefore that there exists a sequence of points $\{x_n\}$ such that $x_n \in A_n$ and $\lim_{n\to\infty} x_n = x$. We note that

$$\mathrm{Li}\,A_n = \mathrm{Li}\,\overline{A}_n = \overline{\mathrm{Li}\,A_n}$$

is a closed set.

Theorem 3.7.5. *Let* $F = \prod_{k=1}^{\infty}{}^{*}F_k$ *be a convergent infinite convolution; then*

$$S_F = \mathrm{Li}\,[S_{F_1}(+)\ldots(+)S_{F_n}] = \mathrm{Li}\,S_{P_n}.$$

For the proof of this theorem we need the following lemma:

(†) F. Hausdorff (1927), pp. 146, 147, uses the term "untere abgeschlossene limes". See also C. Kuratowski (1952), p. 241. This is the closure of the inferior limit of the sequence as defined by P. Halmos (1950).

Lemma 3.7.6.   Let $G_n(x)$ $(n = 1, 2, \ldots)$ and $G(x)$ be distribution functions and suppose that $\underset{n\to\infty}{\mathrm{Lim}}\, G_n(x) = G(x)$. Then $S_G \subseteq \mathrm{Li}\, S_{G_n}$.

Let $x \in S_G$ and select h so that $x+h$ and $x-h$ are continuity points of $G(x)$. Then

$$G(x+h) - G(x-h) = \lim_{n\to\infty} [G_n(x+h) - G_n(x-h)] > 0$$

so that $G_n(x+h) - G_n(x-h) > 0$ for sufficiently large n, say $n > N$, that is $x \in S_{G_n}$ and therefore $x \in \mathrm{Li}\, S_{G_n}$, so that the lemma is proved.

We proceed to prove theorem 3.7.5. Let $F = \prod_{k=1}^{\infty}{}^* F_k$ be a convergent infinite convolution. We write again $P_n = \prod_{k=1}^{n}{}^* F_k$ and $R_n = \prod_{k=n+1}^{\infty}{}^* F_k$ so that $F = P_n * R_n$ and $\underset{n\to\infty}{\mathrm{Lim}}\, P_n = F$, while—according to theorem 3.7.2— $\underset{n\to\infty}{\mathrm{Lim}}\, R_n = \varepsilon(x)$. It follows from lemma 3.7.6 that $S_F \subseteq \mathrm{Li}\, S_{P_n}$ so that we have only to show that $S_F \supseteq \mathrm{Li}\, S_{P_n}$. Let $x_0 \in \mathrm{Li}\, S_{P_n}$ and let η be an arbitrary positive number. The open interval $(x_0 - \eta, x_0 + \eta)$ then contains points of all the sets S_{P_n}, provided n is sufficiently large, say $n > N_1$. This means that

(3.7.7a) $P_n(x_0 + \eta) - P_n(x_0 - \eta) > 0$ $(n > N_1)$.

Since $\underset{n\to\infty}{\mathrm{Lim}}\, R_n(x) = \varepsilon(x)$, there exists an integer N_2 such that

(3.7.7b) $R_n(+\eta) - R_n(-\eta) > 0$ for $n > N_2$.

We select $n > N_0 = \max (N_1, N_2)$ and note that $F = P_n * R_n$, so that

$$F(x_0 + 2\eta) - F(x_0 - 2\eta) = \int_{-\infty}^{\infty} [P_n(x_0 + 2\eta - y) - P_n(x_0 - 2\eta - y)]\, dR_n(y)$$

$$\geqslant [P_n(x_0 + 3\eta) - P_n(x_0 - 3\eta)] \int_{-\eta}^{\eta} dR_n(y)$$

$$\geqslant [P_n(x_0 + \eta) - P_n(x_0 - \eta)][R_n(+\eta) - R_n(-\eta)] > 0;$$

this follows immediately from (3.7.7a) and (3.7.7b). Therefore $x_0 \in \mathrm{Li}\, S_{P_n}$ implies that $x_0 \in S_F$, so that the theorem is proved.

We mention without proof two interesting results concerning infinite convolutions.

Theorem 3.7.6.   Let $F = \prod_{k=1}^{\infty}{}^* F_k$ be a convergent infinite convolution and denote by p_k the maximum jump (saltus) of the distribution function $F_k(x)$. The point spectrum $D_F = \emptyset$ if, and only if, the infinite product $\prod_{k=1}^{\infty} p_k$ diverges to zero.

This result is due to P. Lévy (1931).

Theorem 3.7.7. *Let* $F = \prod\limits_{k=1}^{\infty}{}^* F_k$ *be a convergent infinite convolution of purely discrete distribution functions* F_k. *Then* F *is pure, that is,* F *is either purely discrete or purely singular or purely absolutely continuous.*

For the proof we refer the reader to B. Jessen–A. Wintner (1935) [theorem 35] or Wintner (1947) [No. 148].

We next discuss a particular case, i.e. the purely discrete distribution function $B(x)$ which has two discontinuity points at $x = +1$ and $x = -1$ and a saltus of $\frac{1}{2}$ at each of these points,

$$B(x) = \tfrac{1}{2}[\varepsilon(x+1)+\varepsilon(x-1)].$$

The corresponding characteristic function is

$$b(t) = \cos t.$$

Let $\{r_k\}$ be a sequence of positive numbers. In the following we shall use the sequence of distribution functions

$$(3.7.8)\qquad F_k(x) = B\!\left(\frac{x}{r_k}\right).$$

The infinite convolution

$$\prod_{k=1}^{\infty}{}^* B\!\left(\frac{x}{r_k}\right)$$

is called a *symmetric Bernoulli convolution.* Let $\alpha_{1,k}$, $\alpha_{2,k}$ be the first- and second-order moments, respectively, of $F_k(x)$. It is easily seen that $\alpha_{1,k} = 0$ and $\alpha_{2,k} = r_k^2$, while the characteristic function $f_k(t) = \cos r_k t$. The spectrum $S_{F_k} = D_{F_k}$ consists of the two points r_k and $-r_k$. Suppose now that

$$(3.7.9)\qquad \sum_{k=1}^{\infty} r_k^2 < \infty.$$

Then the conditions of theorem 3.7.3 are satisfied and

$$(3.7.10)\qquad F(x) = \prod_{k=1}^{\infty}{}^* F_k(x) = \prod_{k=1}^{\infty}{}^* B\!\left(\frac{x}{r_k}\right)$$

is a convergent infinite convolution. Condition (3.7.9) is therefore sufficient to assure the convergence of a symmetric Bernoulli convolution. Conversely, if we suppose that a symmetric Bernoulli convolution is convergent, then we can conclude from theorem 3.7.1 that $\mathrm{Lim}\, F_k(x) = \varepsilon(x)$; hence $\lim\limits_{k\to\infty} f_k(t)$ $= \lim\limits_{k\to\infty} \cos r_k t = 1$, so that $\lim\limits_{k\to\infty} r_k = 0$. The spectra S_{F_k} are therefore uniformly bounded, and we see from theorem 3.7.4 that condition (3.7.9) is also necessary for the convergence of the symmetric Bernoulli convolution (3.7.10). We next study its spectrum S_F. A point x is in the spectrum S_F if, and only if, it is possible to choose for every n the sign of r_n in such a way that x becomes the sum of a convergent series of the form $\sum_{n=1}^{\infty} \pm r_n$. In the case where $\sum_{n=1}^{\infty} r_n < \infty$, say $A = \sum_{n=1}^{\infty} r_n$, this means that $S_F \subseteq [-A, A]$ and that $-A$ and $+A$ are, respectively, the smallest and greatest values contained in S_F. If $\sum_{n=1}^{\infty} r_n$ is divergent, then it is possible to represent any real number x as the sum of a conditionally convergent series of the form $x = \sum_{n=1}^{\infty} \pm r_n$, so that S_F is the whole real line. We next show that the point spectrum of F is empty, i.e.

$$(3.7.11) \qquad D_F = \emptyset.$$

Let again $P_n = \prod_{k=1}^{n} {}^* F_k$ and write $G_n = P_{n-1}{}^* \left(\prod_{k=n+1}^{\infty} {}^* F_k \right)$, so that $F = G_n {}^* F_n$ or

$$F(x) = \int_{-\infty}^{\infty} G_n(x-y)\, dF_n(y).$$

It then follows from (3.7.8) that

$$(3.7.12) \qquad F(x) = \tfrac{1}{2}[G_n(x-r_n) + G_n(x+r_n)].$$

Let $s(y)$ and $s_n(y)$ be the saltus of $F(x)$ and of $G_n(x)$, respectively, at the point $x = y$. It follows from (3.7.12) that

$$s(y) = \tfrac{1}{2}[s_n(y-r_n) + s_n(y+r_n)]$$

and it is easily seen that

$$(3.7.13) \qquad s(x+2r_n) + s(x-2r_n) \geqslant s(x).$$

We give an indirect proof for (3.7.11) and assume therefore that there exists a point $x_0 \in D_F$. Then $s(x_0) > 0$, and it is possible to choose a positive integer p such that

$$s(x_0) > \frac{1}{p}.$$

We next determine p positive integers $n_1, n_2, \ldots, n_p$ such that $r_{n_1} > r_{n_2} > \ldots > r_{n_p}$. This is always possible since the r_n tend to zero. The $2p$ numbers $x_0 \pm r_{n_j}$ $(j = 1, 2, \ldots, p)$ are then distinct and we see from (3.7.13) that

$$s(x_0 + 2r_{n_j}) + s(x_0 - 2r_{n_j}) \geqslant s(x_0) \quad (j = 1, 2, \ldots, p).$$

Hence

$$\sum_{j=1}^{p} [s(x_0 + 2r_{n_j}) + s(x_0 - 2r_{n_j})] \geqslant p\, s(x_0) > 1.$$

But this is impossible; hence $D_F = \emptyset$.

This result is also a consequence of theorem 3.7.6, but we preferred to give here a direct proof. We also note that we can conclude from theorem 3.7.7 that a convergent symmetric Bernoulli convolution is either purely singular or (purely) absolutely continuous.

We summarize these results in the following statement:

Theorem 3.7.8. *The necessary and sufficient condition for the convergence of the symmetric Bernoulli convolution* $F(x) = \prod\limits_{k=1}^{\infty}{}^{*} B\left(\dfrac{x}{r_k}\right)$ *is the convergence of the sum* $\sum\limits_{k=1}^{\infty} r_k^2$. *The characteristic function of* $F(x)$ *is then given by the infinite product* $f(t) = \prod\limits_{k=1}^{\infty} \cos r_k t$. *The spectrum* S_F *is a bounded set if the series* $\sum\limits_{k=1}^{\infty} r_k$ *converges, but is the whole real line if* $\sum\limits_{k=1}^{\infty} r_k$ *diverges. The point spectrum of an infinite symmetric Bernoulli convolution is always empty, and* $F(x)$ *is either purely singular or absolutely continuous.*

We next consider briefly the case where the r_k form a geometric series, $r_k = a^k$.

Corollary to theorem 3.7.8. *The function* $f(t) = \prod\limits_{k=1}^{\infty} \cos a^k t$ *is the characteristic function of a convergent symmetric Bernoulli convolution*

$$F(x) = \prod_{k=1}^{\infty}{}^{*} B(xa^{-k})$$

if, and only if, $0 < a < 1$.

We finally mention, without proof, another interesting result concerning symmetric Bernoulli convolutions with bounded spectrum. We consider a convolution

$$(3.7.14) \qquad F(x) = \prod_{k=1}^{\infty}{}^{*} B\left(\frac{x}{r_k}\right),$$

where the series $\sum\limits_{k=1}^{\infty} r_k$ converges, and write $\rho_n = \sum\limits_{k=n+1}^{\infty} r_k \ (n = 0, 1, 2, \ldots)$ for the remainder of this series.

Theorem 3.7.9. *Suppose that* $r_n > \rho_n$ *(or equivalently* $\rho_n > 2\rho_{n+1}$*) for all* n. *Then*

$$L(S_F) = 2 \lim_{n \to \infty} 2^n r_n.$$

Here S_F *is the spectrum of the convolution* (3.7.14), *while* $L(S_F)$ *is the Lebesgue measure of* S_F.

For the proof of theorem 3.7.9 we refer the reader to R. Kershner–A. Wintner (1935) or to A. Wintner (1947). Theorem 3.7.9 permits us to decide whether a convolution of the form (3.7.9) is singular. We consider a particular case.

Corollary to theorem 3.7.9. Let $0 < a < \frac{1}{2}$, then the symmetric Bernoulli convolution $F(x) = \prod\limits_{k=1}^{\infty}{}^{*} B(xa^{-k})$ is purely singular.

We conclude this section by giving a few examples.

(I) Let $r_n = \dfrac{1}{n!}$; then $f(t) = \prod\limits_{n=1}^{\infty} \cos\left(\dfrac{t}{n!}\right)$ is the characteristic function mentioned in the footnote to page 20.

(II) Let $r_n = k^{-n}$ $(k = 3, 4, \ldots)$; then $f(t) = \prod\limits_{n=1}^{\infty} \cos(k^{-n} t)$ belongs to a singular distribution with a bounded spectrum, and it can be shown that $\limsup\limits_{|t|\to\infty} |f(t)| > 0$.

(III) If a is a rational number, $0 < a < \frac{1}{2}$, but not the reciprocal of an integer, then R. Kershner (1936) has shown that the singular characteristic function $f(t) = \prod\limits_{k=1}^{\infty} \cos(a^k t)$ satisfies a relation $|f(t)| = O[(\log|t|)^{-\gamma}] = o(1)$ as $|t| \to \infty$ $(\gamma > 0)$; therefore we have in this case $\limsup\limits_{|t|\to\infty} |f(t)| = 0$.

(IV) If $r_n = 3^{-n}$ we obtain, except for a factor $e^{it/2}$, the characteristic function (2.1.7).

(V) If $r_n = 2^{-n}$ then $f(t) = \prod\limits_{n=1}^{\infty} \cos\dfrac{t}{2^n}$. We can then show by an elementary computation (given in section 6.3) that $f(t) = \dfrac{\sin t}{t} = r(t)$. This is the characteristic function of the rectangular distribution and is therefore absolutely continuous and has the interval $[-1, +1]$ as its spectrum.

(VI) For $r_n = 4^{-n}$ we obtain the singular characteristic function

$$f(t) = \prod_{k=1}^{\infty} \cos\left(\frac{t}{4^k}\right)$$

which we shall need later.

Additional examples can be found in B. Jessen–A. Wintner (1935), R. Kershner (1936), A. Wintner (1947) and A. Wintner (1938). The first of these references also contains examples which show that the spectrum of a singular as well as of an absolutely continuous symmetric Bernoulli convolution can be bounded or the full real line.

4 CRITERIA FOR CHARACTERISTIC FUNCTIONS

It is frequently of interest to decide whether a given complex-valued function of a real variable is, or is not, the characteristic function of some probability distribution. The inversion formulae provide a method to answer this question. While this approach is theoretically always possible it is often not practicable. We therefore develop in Sections 4.1–4.4 criteria which can be used to decide whether a given function is a characteristic function. Section 4.5 deals with an essential property of characteristic functions; knowledge of this property helps us to realize that the characteristic functions are practically a unique tool for simplifying the analytical treatment of certain probability problems.

4.1 Necessary conditions

Theorems 2.1.1 and 2.1.2 assert that every characteristic function $f(t)$ satisfies the relations $|f(t)| \leqslant f(0) = 1$ and $f(-t) = \overline{f(t)}$, and is uniformly continuous. Thus, these theorems already provide useful necessary conditions which a function must satisfy in order to be a characteristic function. However, these conditions are not sufficient. To show this we first prove the following theorem and use it to construct an example.

Theorem 4.1.1. *The only characteristic function which has the form* $f(t) = 1 + o(t^2)$ *as* $t \to 0$ *is the function* $f(t) \equiv 1$.

Let $f(t)$ be a characteristic function and assume that $f(t) = 1 + o(t^2)$ as $t \to 0$. It follows then from theorem 2.3.3 that $\alpha_1 = \alpha_2 = 0$. Since $\alpha_2 = \int_{-\infty}^{\infty} x^2 \, dF(x)$ [where $F(x)$ is the distribution function corresponding to $f(t)$] it is seen that $F(x)$ must be constant over every interval which does not contain the point $x = 0$; that is $F(x) = \varepsilon(x)$ and $f(t) \equiv 1$.

The function $f(t) = e^{-t^4}$ satisfies the conditions of the theorems 2.1.1 and 2.1.2, but $e^{-t^4} = 1 + o(t^2)$. Therefore we see from theorem 4.1.1 that e^{-t^4} is not a characteristic function. This example shows that the necessary conditions stated in theorems 2.1.1 and 2.1.2 are not sufficient.

Corollary to theorem 4.1.1. *Let* $w(t) = o(t)$ *as* $t \to 0$ *and suppose that* $w(-t) = -w(t)$. *Then the only characteristic function of the form* $f(t) = 1 + w(t) + o(t^2)$, *as* $t \to 0$, *is the function* $f(t) \equiv 1$.

We know [corollary 2 to theorem 3.3.1] that $f(t)f(-t)$ is a characteristic function. Under the assumptions of the corollary $f(t)f(-t)$

$= [1 + w(t) + o(t^2)][1 - w(t) + o(t^2)] = 1 + o(t^2)$, hence according to theorem 4.1.1 $|f(t)|^2 = f(t)f(-t) \equiv 1$ or $f(t) = e^{iat}$ (a real). Therefore $f(t) = 1 + iat - \frac{1}{2}a^2 t^2 + o(t^2)$ and this has the form $1 + w(t) + o(t^2)$ (with $w(t) = o(t)$) only if $a = 0$ so that $f(t) \equiv 1$.

We next discuss an inequality which every characteristic function must satisfy and which can therefore also be regarded as a necessary condition for characteristic functions. This inequality is also of some independent interest.

Let $F(x)$ be a distribution function and $f(t)$ its characteristic function. Then the inequality

$$(4.1.1) \qquad \int_{|x| < 1/u} x^2 \, dF(x) \leqslant 3u^{-2}[1 - \mathrm{Re}\, f(u)]$$

is valid for $u > 0$.

We note that

$$1 - \mathrm{Re}\, f(u) = \int_{-\infty}^{\infty} (1 - \cos ux) \, dF(x)$$

$$\geqslant \int_{|x| < 1/u} \frac{u^2 x^2}{2}\left(1 - \frac{u^2 x^2}{12}\right) dF(x) \geqslant \frac{11u^2}{24} \int_{|x| < 1/u} x^2 \, dF(x),$$

so that (4.1.1) holds.

We have, according to lemma 3.7.1,

$$(4.1.2) \qquad \mathrm{Re}\, [1 - f(t)] \geqslant \tfrac{1}{4} \mathrm{Re}\, [1 - f(2t)].$$

By induction we obtain easily the following condition:

Theorem 4.1.2. Let n be a non-negative integer; then the inequality

$$\mathrm{Re}\, [1 - f(t)] \geqslant \frac{1}{4^n} \mathrm{Re}\, [1 - f(2^n t)]$$

is satisfied for every characteristic function.

We now consider a characteristic function which has the property that

$$(4.1.3) \qquad |f(t)| \leqslant A < 1 \quad \text{if} \quad |t| \geqslant B.$$

From theorem 4.1.2, applied to the function $|f(t)|^2$, we see that

$$1 - |f(t)|^2 \geqslant \frac{1}{4^n}[1 - |f(2^n t)|^2].$$

Let t be a fixed value such that $|t| < B$, and choose n so that

$$\frac{B}{2^n} \leqslant |t| < \frac{B}{2^{n-1}}.$$

Then—according to (4.1.3)—

$$|f(2^n t)|^2 \leqslant A^2 \quad \text{while} \quad \frac{1}{4^n} > \frac{t^2}{4B^2}.$$

Hence we obtain from theorem 4.1.2 the inequality

$$1-|f(t)|^2 > \frac{t^2}{4B^2}(1-A^2).$$

A slight modification yields the following corollary:

Corollary to theorem 4.1.2. *Let* $f(t)$ *be a characteristic function which satisfies* (4.1.3); *then*

$$|f(t)| < 1-\frac{t^2(1-A^2)}{8B^2}$$

for all t such that $0 < |t| < B$.

We next discuss another important property of characteristic functions.

Theorem 4.1.3. *Let* $f(t)$ *be a characteristic function and let N be an arbitrary positive integer. Denote by*

$$S = \sum_{j=1}^{N} \sum_{k=1}^{N} f(t_j-t_k)\xi_j\,\bar{\xi}_k$$

where $t_1, t_2, \ldots, t_N$ *are arbitrary real and* $\xi_1, \xi_2, \ldots, \xi_N$ *are arbitrary complex numbers. Then S is real and non-negative for any choice of* $N, t_1, t_2, \ldots, t_N$, $\xi_1, \xi_2, \ldots, \xi_N$.

Let $F(x)$ be the distribution function which corresponds to $f(t)$. Then

$$S = \sum_{j=1}^{N} \sum_{k=1}^{N} \xi_j\,\bar{\xi}_k \int_{-\infty}^{\infty} \exp\left[i(t_j-t_k)x\right] dF(x)$$
$$= \int_{-\infty}^{\infty} \left(\sum_{j=1}^{N} \xi_j e^{it_j x}\right)\left(\sum_{k=1}^{N} \bar{\xi}_k e^{-it_k x}\right) dF(x)$$
$$= \int_{-\infty}^{\infty} \left|\sum_{j=1}^{N} \xi_j e^{it_j x}\right|^2 dF(x).$$

The last expression is real and non-negative.

4.2 Necessary and sufficient conditions

The property of characteristic functions which is described by the last theorem suggests the introduction of a concept which is useful in formulating necessary and sufficient conditions for characteristic functions.

A complex-valued function $f(t)$ of the real variable t is said to be *non-negative definite* for $-\infty < t < +\infty$ if the following two conditions are satisfied:

(i) $f(t)$ is continuous;

(ii) for any positive integer N and any real $t_1, \ldots, t_N$ and any complex $\xi_1, \ldots, \xi_N$ the sum

$$S = \sum_{j=1}^{N} \sum_{k=1}^{N} f(t_j-t_k)\xi_j\,\bar{\xi}_k$$

is real and non-negative.

We establish next a few properties of non-negative definite functions.

Theorem 4.2.1. Let $f(t)$ be non-negative definite. Then

(a) $f(0)$ *is real and* $f(0) \geqslant 0$

(b) $f(-t) = \overline{f(t)}$

(c) $|f(t)| \leqslant f(0)$.

Proof of (a). Put $N = 1$, $t_1 = 0$, $\xi_1 = 1$; then (ii) implies (a).

Proof of (b). Put $N = 2$, $t_1 = 0$, $t_2 = t$ and choose arbitrary ξ_1 and ξ_2. Then $S = f(0)[|\xi_1|^2 + |\xi_2|^2] + f(-t)\xi_1\bar{\xi_2} + f(t)\xi_2\bar{\xi_1}$. It follows therefore from (a) and (ii) that $f(-t)\xi_1\bar{\xi_2} + f(t)\xi_2\bar{\xi_1}$ is real for any ξ_1 and ξ_2. We write $f(-t) = \alpha_1 + i\beta_1$, $f(t) = \alpha_2 + i\beta_2$, $\xi_1\bar{\xi_2} = \gamma + i\delta$. Then

$$(\alpha_1 + i\beta_1)(\gamma + i\delta) + (\alpha_2 + i\beta_2)(\gamma - i\delta)$$

is real, so that $(\beta_1 + \beta_2)\gamma + (\alpha_1 - \alpha_2)\delta = 0$ for any γ and δ. This is only possible if $\beta_1 + \beta_2 = 0$ and $\alpha_1 - \alpha_2 = 0$, so that (b) is satisfied.

The property (b) is sometimes expressed by stating that the function $f(t)$ is "Hermitian".

Proof of (c). We again put $N = 2$, $t_1 = 0$, $t_2 = t$ but choose $\xi_1 = f(t)$, $\xi_2 = -|f(t)|$. Using (ii) and (b) we see that

$$S = 2f(0)|f(t)|^2 - 2|f(t)|^3 \geqslant 0.$$

In the case where $|f(t)| > 0$ this inequality immediately yields (c). Since [by (a)] $f(0) \geqslant 0$, relation (c) holds in a trivial way if $|f(t)| = 0$.

We can now formulate a criterion for characteristic functions.

Theorem 4.2.2 (Bochner's theorem). A complex-valued function of a real variable t is a characteristic function if, and only if,

(i) $f(t)$ *is non-negative definite*

(ii) $f(0) = 1$.

The necessity of the conditions is established by theorems 2.1.1 and 4.1.3 so that we need prove only their sufficiency. We therefore assume that $f(t)$ is a non-negative definite function and choose positive integers n and N and a real number x and put $t_j = j/n$, $\xi_j = e^{-ijx}$. It follows then from the definition of non-negative definiteness that

$$\mathfrak{P}_N^n(x) = \frac{1}{N} \sum_{j=0}^{N-1} \sum_{k=0}^{N-1} f\left(\frac{j-k}{n}\right) \exp[-i(j-k)x] \geqslant 0$$

for all x. The difference $j - k = r$ occurs in $N - |r|$ terms of this sum; here r is an integer between $-N+1$ and $N-1$. We collect these terms and write

(4.2.1) $\qquad \mathfrak{P}_N^n(x) = \sum_{r=-N}^{N} \left(1 - \frac{|r|}{N}\right) f(r/n) e^{-irx} \geqslant 0$.

Therefore

$$\int_{-\pi}^{\pi} e^{isx} \mathfrak{P}_N^n(x)\, dx = 2\pi \left(1 - \frac{|s|}{N}\right) f\left(\frac{s}{n}\right)$$

or

(4.2.2) $\left(1-\dfrac{|s|}{N}\right)f\left(\dfrac{s}{n}\right) = \dfrac{1}{2\pi}\displaystyle\int_{-\pi}^{\pi} e^{isx}\,\mathfrak{P}_N^n(x)\,dx.$

We now introduce the function

(4.2.3) $F_N^{(n)}(x) = \begin{cases} 0 & \text{for } x < -\pi \\[2mm] \dfrac{1}{2\pi}\displaystyle\int_{-\pi}^{x}\mathfrak{P}_N^n(y)\,dy & \text{for } -\pi \leqslant x < \pi \\[2mm] 1 & \text{for } x \geqslant \pi \end{cases}$

then (4.2.2) can be written as

(4.2.4) $\left(1-\dfrac{|s|}{N}\right)f\left(\dfrac{s}{n}\right) = \displaystyle\int_{-\pi}^{\pi} e^{isx}\,dF_N^{(n)}(x).$

We see from (4.2.1) and (4.2.3) that $F_N^{(n)}(x)$ is a non-decreasing, right continuous function and conclude from (4.2.4) and assumption (ii) that $\displaystyle\int_{-\infty}^{\infty} dF_N^{(n)}(x) = f(0) = 1$ so that $F_N^{(n)}(x)$ is a distribution function. We consider next, for a fixed n, the sequence $\{F_N^{(n)}(x)\}$ of distribution functions. According to Helly's first theorem there exists a subsequence

$$\{F_{N_k}^{(n)}(x)\} \quad (\text{with } \lim_{k\to\infty} N_k = \infty)$$

which converges weakly to a non-decreasing, bounded function $F^{(n)}(x)$. This limiting function is a distribution function since for any N and any $\varepsilon > 0$ we have $F_N^{(n)}(-\pi-\varepsilon) = 0$ while $F_N^{(n)}(\pi+\varepsilon) = 1$. We see from (4.2.4) that

$$f(s/n) = \lim_{k\to\infty}\left(1-\frac{|s|}{N_k}\right)f(s/n) = \lim_{k\to\infty}\int_{-\pi}^{\pi} e^{isx}\,dF_{N_k}^{(n)}(x).$$

Applying Helly's second theorem we obtain

(4.2.5) $f(s/n) = \displaystyle\int_{-\pi}^{\pi} e^{isx}\,dF^{(n)}(x)$

for all integers s. We introduce the distribution functions

$$F_n(x) = F^{(n)}(x/n).$$

The points of increase of the distribution function $F_n(x)$ are all located in the interval $(-n\pi, +n\pi)$; the characteristic function of $F_n(x)$ is

$$f_n(t) = \int_{-\pi n}^{\pi n} e^{itx}\,dF_n(x) = \int_{-\pi}^{+\pi} e^{itny}\,dF^{(n)}(y).$$

It follows from (4.2.5) that for any integer k

(4.2.6) $f_n(k/n) = f(k/n).$

Let t be an arbitrary real number. It is then possible to determine a sequence $k = k(t, n)$ such that

(4.2.7) $0 \leqslant t - (k/n) < (1/n)$.

We write $\theta = t - (k/n)$; then $0 \leqslant \theta < (1/n)$ and

$$|f_n(t) - f_n(k/n)| = \left| \int_{-\pi n}^{\pi n} e^{i(k/n)x}(e^{i\theta x} - 1)\, dF_n(x) \right| \leqslant \int_{-\pi n}^{+\pi n} |e^{i\theta x} - 1|\, dF_n(x).$$

We apply Schwarz's inequality (see Appendix B) to the last integral and obtain

$$|f_n(t) - f_n(k/n)| \leqslant \left[2 \int_{-\pi n}^{\pi n} (1 - \cos \theta x)\, dF_n(x) \right]^{1/2}$$

$$= \left[2 \int_{-\pi}^{\pi} (1 - \cos n\theta z)\, dF^{(n)}(z) \right]^{1/2}.$$

Since $n\theta < 1$ we have $1 - \cos n\theta z \leqslant 1 - \cos z$ for $|z| \leqslant \pi$; hence

$$|f_n(t) - f_n(k/n)| \leqslant [2 \int_{-\pi}^{\pi} (1 - \cos z)\, dF^{(n)}(z)]^{1/2}$$

$$= \{2[1 - \operatorname{Re} f_n(1/n)]\}^{1/2} = \{2[1 - \operatorname{Re} f(1/n)]\}^{1/2}.$$

By assumption, $f(t)$ is a continuous function such that $f(0) = 1$, and the right-hand member of this inequality can be made arbitrarily small by selecting n sufficiently large; this means that

(4.2.8) $\lim\limits_{n \to \infty} |f_n(t) - f_n(k/n)| = 0$.

Moreover, we see from (4.2.6) and (4.2.7) that

(4.2.9) $f(t) = \lim\limits_{n \to \infty} f(k/n) = \lim\limits_{n \to \infty} f_n(k/n)$.

Since

$$\lim_{n \to \infty} f_n(t) = \lim_{n \to \infty} \{[f_n(t) - f_n(k/n)] + f_n(k/n)\}$$

we see from (4.2.8) and (4.2.9) that for all t

$$\lim_{n \to \infty} f_n(t) = f(t).$$

The continuous function $f(t)$ is therefore the limit of the sequence $\{f_n(t)\}$ of characteristic functions and is therefore (corollary 2 to theorem 3.6.1) also a characteristic function. This completes the proof of Bochner's theorem.

We derive next another criterion which is due to H. Cramér.

Theorem 4.2.3 (Cramér's criterion). *A bounded and continuous function $f(t)$ is a characteristic function if, and only if,*

(i) $f(0) = 1$

(ii) $\psi(x, A) = \int_0^A \int_0^A f(t - u) \exp\,[ix(t - u)]\, dt\, du$

is real and non-negative for all real x and for all $A > 0$.

We first prove the necessity of the condition by substituting

$$f(t-u) = \int_{-\infty}^{\infty} \exp\left[i(t-u)y\right] dF(y)$$

into (ii). Since the inversion of the order of integration is permissible we obtain easily

$$\psi(x, A) = 2 \int_{-\infty}^{\infty} \frac{[1 - \cos A(x+y)]}{(x+y)^2} dF(y).$$

This shows that $\psi(x, A)$ is always real and non-negative. To prove the sufficiency of the condition we assume (i) and (ii), so that

(4.2.10) $$p(x, A) = \frac{1}{A}\psi(x, A) = \frac{1}{A}\int_0^A \int_0^A f(u-v) e^{i(u-v)x} \, du \, dv \geqslant 0.$$

In the last integral we introduce new variables

$$t = u - v$$

$$z = v.$$

This change of variables transforms the original region of integration into a parallelogram. One diagonal of this parallelogram is located on the z-axis and decomposes it into two triangles. The function $p(x, A)$ is then computed by adding the two integrals taken over these triangular regions. Thus

$$p(x, A) = \frac{1}{A}\int_{-A}^0 f(t) e^{itx} \left[\int_{-t}^A dz\right] dt + \frac{1}{A}\int_0^A f(t) e^{itx} \left[\int_0^{A-t} dz\right] dt.$$

We introduce the function

(4.2.11) $$f_A(t) = \begin{cases} \left(1 - \dfrac{|t|}{A}\right) f(t) & \text{if } |t| < A \\ 0 & \text{otherwise} \end{cases}$$

and can write (4.2.10) in the form

$$p(x, A) = \int_{-\infty}^{\infty} e^{itx} f_A(t) \, dt \geqslant 0.$$

Let

$$J_B(u, A) = \frac{1}{2\pi}\int_{-B}^B \left(1 - \frac{|x|}{B}\right) p(x, A) e^{iux} \, dx,$$

then

$$J_B(u, A) = \frac{1}{2\pi}\int_{-B}^B \left(1 - \frac{|x|}{B}\right) \left[\int_{-\infty}^{\infty} e^{i(t+u)x} f_A(t) \, dt\right] dx.$$

The order of the integrations may be inverted; moreover a simple computation shows that

$$\int_{-B}^B e^{i(t+u)x} \left(1 - \frac{|x|}{B}\right) dx = 2 \frac{1 - \cos[(u+t)B]}{B(u+t)^2}.$$

Therefore

$$J_B\,(u,\,A) \;=\; \frac{1}{\pi} \int_{-\infty}^{\infty} \frac{1 - \cos\,[(u+t)B]}{B(u+t)^2}\, f_A\,(t)\,dt.$$

Here we introduce a new variable v by $t = (v/B) - u$ and obtain

(4.2.12) $\qquad J_B(u,\,A) \;=\; \frac{1}{\pi} \int_{-\infty}^{\infty} \frac{1 - \cos v}{v^2}\, f_A\!\left(\frac{v}{B} - u\right) dv.$

From the well-known relation[*]

$$\int_0^\infty \frac{1 - \cos v}{v^2}\, dv \;=\; \frac{\pi}{2}$$

and (4.2.12) it follows that

$$\lim_{B \to \infty} J_B\,(u,\,A) = f_A\,(-u).$$

The function which is defined as

$$\frac{1}{2\pi}\left(1 - \frac{|x|}{B}\right) p(x,\,A) \quad \text{for } |x| \leqslant B$$

and 0 outside the interval $(-B,\,B)$ is non-negative and bounded. If it is multiplied by a suitable normalizing constant C_B it becomes a frequency function. Therefore $C_B J_B\,(u,\,A)$ is a characteristic function for any B and A. We then conclude from corollary 2 to the continuity theorem that

$$\lim_{B \to \infty} C_B J_B\,(u,\,A) \;=\; C f_A\,(-u)$$

is a characteristic function. Since $f_A\,(0) = 1$, we see that $C = 1$ and that $f_A\,(u)$ is a characteristic function for any A. We apply once more the continuity theorem and see finally that

$$f(t) \;=\; \lim_{A \to \infty} f_A\,(t)$$

is a characteristic function. Thus the sufficiency of the condition is established.

Theorem 4.2.3 is a particular case of more general results derived by Cramér (1939). In this paper he also gave conditions for the possibility of representing more general classes of functions by Fourier integrals.

We derive next a condition for absolutely continuous distributions which will later be extended and will yield a general criterion.

Theorem 4.2.4.   The complex-valued function $f(t)$ of the real variable t is the characteristic function of an absolutely continuous distribution if, and only if, it admits the representation

(i) $f(t) \;=\; \displaystyle\int_{-\infty}^{\infty} g(t+\theta)\overline{g(\theta)}\, d\theta$

---

[*] See footnote on page 49.

where g(θ) is a complex-valued function of the real variable θ such that

$$\text{(ii)} \quad \int_{-\infty}^{\infty} |g(\theta)|^2 \, d\theta = 1$$

is satisfied.

Before proving this theorem we summarize some known results concerning quadratically integrable functions. For the definitions used in this summary as well as for the statements of the theorems quoted we refer the reader to R. E. A. C. Paley–N. Wiener (1934).

Let $\phi(x)$ be a function which is quadratically integrable over $(-\infty, +\infty)$; according to Plancherel's theorem $\phi(x)$ has a Fourier transform $\Phi(u)$ which is also quadratically integrable over $(-\infty, +\infty)$ and which can be written as

$$\text{(4.2.13)} \qquad \Phi(u) = \underset{A \to \infty}{\text{l.i.m.}} \frac{1}{\sqrt{2\pi}} \int_{-A}^{A} e^{iux} \phi(x) \, dx.$$

Here the symbol

$$\underset{A \to \infty}{\text{l.i.m.}}$$

denotes the limit in the mean as A tends to infinity. It is known that

$$\phi(x) = \underset{A \to \infty}{\text{l.i.m.}} \frac{1}{\sqrt{2\pi}} \int_{-A}^{A} e^{-iux} \Phi(u) \, du$$

or

$$\phi(x) = \underset{A \to \infty}{\text{l.i.m.}} \frac{1}{\sqrt{2\pi}} \int_{-A}^{A} e^{ivx} \Phi(-v) \, dv.$$

Hence $\phi(x)$ is the Fourier transform of $h(v) = \Phi(-v)$. It is easily seen also from (4.2.13) that $\overline{\Phi(u)}$ is the Fourier transform of $\overline{\phi(-y)}$. According to Plancherel's theorem we have the equation

$$\text{(4.2.14)} \qquad \int_{-\infty}^{\infty} |\phi(x)|^2 \, dx = \int_{-\infty}^{\infty} |\Phi(u)|^2 \, du.$$

From Parseval's theorem we get the following relations

$$\text{(4.2.15)} \quad \begin{cases} \displaystyle\int_{-\infty}^{\infty} [\phi(u)]^2 \, e^{-iux} \, du = \int_{-\infty}^{\infty} h(y) \, h(x-y) \, dy \\[2mm] \displaystyle\qquad\qquad\qquad = \int_{-\infty}^{\infty} \Phi(-y) \, \Phi(-x+y) \, dy \\[2mm] \displaystyle\int_{-\infty}^{\infty} \Phi(u) \, \overline{\Phi(u)} \, e^{-iux} \, du = \int_{-\infty}^{\infty} \phi(y) \, \overline{\phi(-x+y)} \, dy. \end{cases}$$

To prove the necessity of the conditions of theorem 4.2.4 we consider an arbitrary frequency function $p(x)$. Then $\phi(x) = \sqrt{p(x)}$ is quadratically integrable over $(-\infty, \infty)$ and we write $g(u)$ for its Fourier transform. From the first of the equations (4.2.15) we obtain

$$\int_{-\infty}^{\infty} e^{-iux} p(u)\, du = \int_{-\infty}^{\infty} g(-y)g(-x+y)\, dy.$$

Letting $x = -t$ we get

(4.2.16) $$\int_{-\infty}^{\infty} e^{itu} p(u)\, du = \int_{-\infty}^{\infty} g(t+y)g(-y)\, dy.$$

The function $\phi(x) = \sqrt{p(x)}$ is real valued; we see therefore from (4.2.13) that its Fourier transform $g(u)$ is Hermitian. Since the integral on the left of (4.2.16) is the characteristic function of the distribution whose frequency function is $p(x)$ we see that (i) is satisfied while (ii) follows then from $f(0) = 1$. This completes the proof of the necessity of the conditions (i) and (ii).

To prove their sufficiency we suppose that the function $f(t)$ admits the representation (i) by means of a function $g(\theta)$ which satisfies (ii). Then $g(\theta)$ is quadratically integrable over $(-\infty, +\infty)$ and has a Fourier transform which we denote by $G(u)$. We see from (ii) and (4.2.14) that

$$\int_{-\infty}^{\infty} |G(u)|^2\, du = 1$$

so that $|G(x)|^2$ is the frequency function of some absolutely continuous distribution. It follows then from the second equation (4.2.15) that

$$\int_{-\infty}^{\infty} |G(u)|^2 e^{iux}\, du = \int_{-\infty}^{\infty} g(y)\overline{g(x+y)}\, dy,$$

hence the integral on the right is the characteristic function of an absolutely continuous distribution. Applying theorem 2.1.3 we see that its complex conjugate

$$f(t) = \int_{-\infty}^{\infty} g(x+y)\overline{g(y)}\, dy$$

is also a characteristic function. This completes the proof of the theorem.

We next derive a condition which is not restricted to absolutely continuous distributions.

Theorem 4.2.5 (*Khinchine's criterion*).   *The complex-valued function $f(t)$ of the real variable t is a characteristic function if, and only if, there exists a sequence $\{g_n(\theta)\}$ of complex-valued functions of the real variable θ satisfying*

(i) $$\int_{-\infty}^{\infty} |g_n(\theta)|^2\, d\theta = 1$$

such that the relation

(ii) $$f(t) = \lim_{n\to\infty} \int_{-\infty}^{\infty} g_n(t+\theta)\,\overline{g_n(\theta)}\, d\theta$$

holds uniformly in every finite t-interval.

To prove the necessity of these conditions we must only note that every distribution function is the limit of a sequence of absolutely continuous distributions. We apply the preceding theorem to the characteristic functions of these approximating distributions and see that our conditions are satisfied.

To prove the sufficiency of the conditions we assume that the sequence $\{g_n(\theta)\}$ is given and that these functions satisfy (i). According to theorem 4.2.4 the functions

$$f_n(t) = \int_{-\infty}^{\infty} g_n(t+\theta)\,\overline{g_n(\theta)}\,d\theta$$

are characteristic functions and condition (ii) states that

$$f(t) = \lim_{n \to \infty} f_n(t)$$

is the uniform limit of a sequence of characteristic functions in every finite t-interval.

The sufficiency of the condition follows immediately from the second version of the continuity theorem.

We conclude this section by giving a necessary and sufficient condition which an even function must satisfy in order to be a characteristic function. This condition involves the Hermite polynomials which are defined by the relation

$$(4.2.17) \qquad H_n(x) = e^{x^2/2}\,\frac{d^n}{dx^n}\,e^{-x^2/2}.$$

It is easy to see that $H_n(x)$ is a polynomial of degree n in x.

We first derive an estimate for the polynomials $H_n(x)$.

Lemma 4.2.1. *Let $H_n(x)$ be the Hermite polynomial of degree n, then*

$$|H_n(x)| \leqslant e^{x^2/2}\,2^{n/2}\,\pi^{-1/2}\,\Gamma\!\left(\frac{n+1}{2}\right).$$

We differentiate the relation

$$\frac{1}{\sqrt{2\pi}}\int_{-\infty}^{\infty} \exp\{-y^2/2 + iyx\}\,dy = e^{-x^2/2}$$

n times and obtain, in view of (4.2.17),

$$(4.2.18) \qquad H_n(x) = e^{x^2/2}\,\frac{1}{\sqrt{2\pi}}\int_{-\infty}^{\infty} (iy)^n \exp[-y^2/2 + iyx]\,dy.$$

Therefore

$$|H_n(x)| \leqslant e^{x^2/2}\,\frac{1}{\sqrt{2\pi}}\int_{-\infty}^{\infty} |y|^n\,e^{-y^2/2}\,dy = \frac{2\,e^{x^2/2}}{\sqrt{2\pi}}\int_{0}^{\infty} t^n\,e^{-t^2/2}\,dt$$

$$= \frac{2^{n/2} e^{x^2/2}}{\sqrt{\pi}} \int_0^\infty v^{(n-1)/2} e^{-v} dv = e^{x^2/2} 2^{n/2} (\pi)^{-1/2} \Gamma\left(\frac{n+1}{2}\right)$$

so that the lemma is proved.

Theorem 4.2.6 (theorem of M. Mathias). *Let $f(t)$ be a real, even, continuous function which is absolutely integrable over $(-\infty, +\infty)$. Write for $p > 0$ and $n = 0, 1, 2, \ldots$*

$$c_{2n}(p) = (-1)^n \int_{-\infty}^\infty f(px) e^{-x^2/2} H_{2n}(x) dx.$$

The function $f(t)$ is a characteristic function if, and only if,

    (i) $f(0) = 1$

    (ii) $c_{2n}(p) \geqslant 0$

for all $n = 0, 1, 2, \ldots$, and for all $p > 0$.

We prove first that the condition of theorem 4.2.6 is necessary and assume that $f(t)$ is non-negative definite. It follows from the definition of $c_{2n}(p)$ and from formula (4.2.18) that

$$c_{2n}(p) = \frac{1}{\sqrt{2\pi}} \int_{-\infty}^\infty f(px) \left[\int_{-\infty}^\infty y^{2n} \exp\left(ixy - y^2/2\right) dy\right] dx.$$

Since $f(px)$ is absolutely integrable, the order of integration may be reversed and we see that

$$c_{2n}(p) = \frac{1}{\sqrt{2\pi}} \int_{-\infty}^\infty y^{2n} e^{-y^2/2} \left\{\int_{-\infty}^\infty f(px) e^{ixy} dx\right\} dy.$$

Since $f(x)$ is non-negative definite, the integral in the braces is non-negative and therefore $c_{2n}(p) \geqslant 0$.

For the proof of the sufficiency of the condition we need two lemmas.

Lemma 4.2.2. *The function $(-1)^n e^{-x^2/2} H_{2n}(x)$ is non-negative definite.*

It follows from (4.2.18) that

(4.2.19) $(-1)^n e^{-x^2/2} H_{2n}(x) = \dfrac{1}{\sqrt{2\pi}} \int_{-\infty}^\infty y^{2n} \exp\left[-y^2/2 + iyx\right] dy.$

The right-hand side of (4.2.19) is the Fourier transform of the bounded, non-negative function $(2\pi)^{-1/2} y^{2n} e^{-y^2/2}$; this is integrable over $(-\infty, +\infty)$. It follows from Bochner's theorem that its Fourier transform is non-negative definite.

Lemma 4.2.3. *Suppose that $\phi(x)$ is a real-valued, continuous and bounded function which is absolutely integrable over $(-\infty, +\infty)$ and put*

$$a_n = \int_{-\infty}^\infty \phi(x) e^{-x^2/2} H_n(x) dx \quad (n = 0, 1, 2, \ldots).$$

Let r be a real number $0 < r < 1$, and write

$$G(r, y) = \sum_{n=0}^{\infty} \frac{a_n r^n H_n(y)}{n! \sqrt{2\pi}}.$$

Then

$$G(r, y) = \frac{1}{\sqrt{2\pi(1-r^2)}} \int_{-\infty}^{\infty} \phi(x) \exp\left[-\frac{(x-ry)^2}{2(1-r^2)}\right] dx$$

and

$$\phi(y) = \lim_{r \to 1} G(r, y) = \lim_{r \to 1} \sum_{n=0}^{\infty} \frac{a_n r^n H_n(y)}{n! \sqrt{2\pi}}.$$

To prove the lemma we use first (4.2.18) and rewrite a_n as

$$(4.2.20) \quad a_n = \int_{-\infty}^{\infty} \Phi(x) \left[\frac{1}{\sqrt{2\pi}} \int_{-\infty}^{\infty} (it)^n \exp\left(itx - t^2/2\right) dt\right] dx$$

so that

$$(4.2.21) \quad G(r, y)$$
$$= \frac{1}{\sqrt{2\pi}} \sum_{n=0}^{\infty} \frac{1}{n!} \int_{-\infty}^{\infty} \phi(x) \frac{1}{\sqrt{2\pi}} \int_{-\infty}^{\infty} (itr)^n H_n(y) \exp\left[itx - t^2/2\right] dt \, dx.$$

For the sake of brevity, we write
(4.2.22)

$$f_n(x, y, r) = f_n(x) = \frac{\phi(x)}{n! \sqrt{2\pi}} \int_{-\infty}^{\infty} (itr)^n H_n(y) \exp\left[itx - t^2/2\right] dt,$$

then

$$(4.2.23) \quad G(r, y) = \frac{1}{\sqrt{2\pi}} \sum_{n=0}^{\infty} \int_{-\infty}^{\infty} f_n(x) \, dx.$$

We use lemma 4.2.1 to estimate the integral on the right-hand side of (4.2.22):

$$\left|\frac{1}{n! \sqrt{2\pi}} \int_{-\infty}^{\infty} (itr)^n H_n(y) \exp\left[itx - t^2/2\right] dt\right|$$

$$\leq \frac{r^n e^{y^2/2} 2^{n/2} \Gamma\left(\frac{n+1}{2}\right)}{n! \sqrt{2\pi} \sqrt{\pi}} \int_{-\infty}^{\infty} |t|^n e^{-t^2/2} dt = \frac{r^n e^{y^2/2} 2^n \left[\Gamma\left(\frac{n+1}{2}\right)\right]^2}{\pi \Gamma(n+1)}$$

We apply Stirling's formula and get

$$\left|\frac{1}{n! \sqrt{2\pi}} \int_{-\infty}^{\infty} (itr)^n H_n(y) \exp\left[itx - t^2/2\right] dt\right| = o(r^n e^{y^2/2}) \quad \text{as } n \to \infty.$$

Combining this with (4.2.22), and noting that $\phi(x)$ is bounded, we see that

(4.2.24) $\qquad |f_n(x)| = |\phi(x)| \, o(r^n \, e^{y^2/2}) = o(r^n) \quad$ as $n \to \infty$.

Clearly, $\{f_n(x)\}$ is a sequence of absolutely integrable, continuous functions, and it follows from (4.2.24) that $\sum\limits_{n=0}^{\infty} f_n(x)$ is absolutely and uniformly convergent and that the summation and integration can be interchanged in (4.2.23), so that

$$G(r, y) = \frac{1}{\sqrt{2\pi}} \int_{-\infty}^{\infty} \left[\sum_{n=0}^{\infty} f_n(x) \right] dx$$

or, in view of (4.2.22),

$G(r, y)$
$$= \frac{1}{\sqrt{2\pi}} \int_{-\infty}^{\infty} \phi(x) \left\{ \frac{1}{\sqrt{2\pi}} \sum_{n=0}^{\infty} \frac{1}{n!} \int_{-\infty}^{\infty} (itr)^n \, H_n(y) \exp \, (itx - t^2/2) \, dt \right\} dx.$$

We write

(4.2.25) $\qquad g_n(t) = \frac{1}{n! \sqrt{2\pi}} (itr)^n \, H_n(y) \exp \, (itx - t^2/2)$

so that

(4.2.26) $\qquad G(r, y) = \frac{1}{\sqrt{2\pi}} \int_{-\infty}^{\infty} \phi(x) \left\{ \sum_{n=0}^{\infty} \int_{-\infty}^{\infty} g_n(t) \, dt \right\} dx.$

We see from (4.2.25) and from lemma 4.2.1 that

$$\left| \int_{-\infty}^{\infty} g_n(t) \, dt \right| \leqslant \int_{-\infty}^{\infty} |g_n(t)| \, dt \leqslant e^{y^2/2} \, r^n \, \pi^{-1} \frac{2^n \left[\Gamma\!\left(\dfrac{n+1}{2} \right) \right]^2}{\Gamma(n+1)}$$
$$= o(r^n \, e^{y^2/2}) \quad \text{as } n \to \infty.$$

It then follows easily that

$$\sum_{n=0}^{\infty} \int_{-\infty}^{\infty} g_n(t) \, dt = \int_{-\infty}^{\infty} \left[\sum_{n=0}^{\infty} g_n(t) \right] dt,$$

so that

(4.2.27) $\quad \sum\limits_{n=0}^{\infty} \int_{-\infty}^{\infty} g_n(t) \, dt = \dfrac{1}{\sqrt{2\pi}} \int_{-\infty}^{\infty} \exp \, (itx - t^2/2) \left[\sum\limits_{n=0}^{\infty} \dfrac{(itr)^n \, H_n(y)}{n!} \right] dt.$

We use (4.2.18) to compute the sum on the right of (4.2.27) and obtain

$$\sum_{n=0}^{\infty} \frac{(itr)^n \, H_n(y)}{n!} = \frac{1}{\sqrt{2\pi}} \sum_{n=0}^{\infty} \frac{(itr)^n}{n!} e^{v^2/2} \int_{-\infty}^{\infty} (iv)^n \exp \, [-v^2/2 + ivy] \, dv.$$

It can be shown that the summation and integration can be interchanged, and we obtain by an elementary computation

(4.2.28)

$$\sum_{n=0}^{\infty} \frac{(itr)^n H_n(y)}{n!} = \frac{1}{\sqrt{2\pi}} \int_{-\infty}^{\infty} \exp\left[-(v^2-y^2)/2 + ivy - trv\right] dv$$

$$= \exp\left[t^2 r^2/2 - iytr\right].$$

We combine (4.2.27) and (4.2.28) and get

$$\sum_{n=0}^{\infty} \int_{-\infty}^{\infty} g_n(t)\, dt = \frac{1}{\sqrt{2\pi}} \int_{-\infty}^{\infty} \exp\left[itx - t^2/2 + t^2 r^2/2 - iytr\right] dt.$$

We then see easily that

(4.2.29) $$\sum_{n=0}^{\infty} \int_{-\infty}^{\infty} g_n(t)\, dt = \frac{1}{\sqrt{1-r^2}} \exp\left[-\frac{(x-ry)^2}{2(1-r^2)}\right].$$

We conclude from (4.2.26) and (4.2.29) that

(4.2.30) $$G(r, y) = \frac{1}{\sqrt{2\pi(1-r^2)}} \int_{-\infty}^{\infty} \phi(x) \exp\left[-\frac{(x-ry)^2}{2(1-r^2)}\right] dx.$$

This is the first part of the statement; the relation

$$\phi(y) = \lim_{r \to 1} G(r, y)$$

follows immediately from (4.2.30) and the extension of Helly's second theorem, so that lemma 4.2.3 is proved.

To prove that the condition of theorem 4.2.6 is sufficient, we assume that

$$c_{2n}(p) \geqslant 0$$

for every $p > 0$ and apply lemma 4.2.3 to the function $\phi(x) = f(px)$. Since $f(x)$ is, by assumption, a real and even function, we have

$$a_{2n+1} = \int_{-\infty}^{\infty} f(px) e^{-x^2/2} H_{2n+1}(x)\, dx \quad (n = 0, 1, 2, \ldots)$$

while

$$a_{2n} = (-1)^n c_{2n}(p),$$

and we conclude from lemma 4.2.3 that

$$\lim_{r \to 1} \sum_{n=0}^{\infty} \frac{(-1)^n c_{2n}(p) r^{2n} H_{2n}(y)}{(2n)!\, \sqrt{2\pi}} = f(py).$$

Therefore

(4.2.31) $$\lim_{r \to 1} \sum_{n=0}^{\infty} \frac{c_{2n}(p) r^{2n}}{(2n)!\, \sqrt{2\pi}} (-1)^n e^{-y^2/2} H_{2n}(y) = f(py) e^{-y^2/2}.$$

Since the function $(-1)^n e^{-y^2/2} H_{2n}(y)$ is, according to lemma 4.2.2, non-negative definite, we conclude from (4.2.31) that $f(py) e^{-y^2/2}$ is also non-negative definite. But then the same is true for $f(y) \exp(-y^2/2p^2)$; moreover, we see from assumption (ii) of the theorem that this is a characteristic function. We let $p \to \infty$ and conclude from the continuity theorem that $f(y)$ is a characteristic function. The following corollary is an immediate consequence of the preceding reasoning.

Corollary to theorem 4.2.6. *If condition* (ii) *of the theorem is not satisfied for all $p > 0$ but if for some $p_0 > 0$ we have $c_{2n}(p_0) \geq 0$ for $n = 0, 1, 2, \ldots$ ad inf., then $f(y) \exp(-y^2/2p_0)$ is a characteristic function.*

4.3 Sufficient conditions

The necessary and sufficient conditions discussed in the preceding section are often not readily applicable. In the present section we will give a very convenient and useful sufficient condition.

Theorem 4.3.1 (*Pólya's condition*). *Let $f(t)$ be a real-valued and continuous function which is defined for all real t and which satisfies the following conditions:*

(i) $f(0) = 1$
(ii) $f(-t) = f(t)$
(iii) $f(t)$ convex[*] for $t > 0$
(iv) $\lim\limits_{t \to \infty} f(t) = 0$.

Then $f(t)$ is the characteristic function of an absolutely continuous distribution $F(x)$.

Since $f(t)$ is a convex function it has everywhere a right-hand derivative which we denote by $f'(t)$. The function $f'(t)$ is non-decreasing for $t > 0$. It follows from (iv) that $f'(t) \leqslant 0$ for $t > 0$ and that

$$\lim_{t \to \infty} f'(t) = 0.$$

It is easily seen that the integral $\int_{-\infty}^{\infty} e^{-itx} f(t)\, dt$ exists for all $x \neq 0$. We write

(4.3.1) $p(x) = \dfrac{1}{2\pi} \int_{-\infty}^{\infty} e^{-itx} f(t)\, dt.$

We see from (ii) and (4.3.1) that

(4.3.2) $p(x) = \dfrac{1}{\pi} \int_{0}^{\infty} f(t) \cos tx\, dt.$

---

[*] A function $f(t)$ is said to be convex for $t > 0$ if

$$f\left(\frac{t_1 + t_2}{2}\right) \leqslant \frac{f(t_1) + f(t_2)}{2}$$

for all $t_1 > 0$, $t_2 > 0$. For a survey of the properties of convex functions we refer the reader to G. H. Hardy–J. E. Littlewood–G. Pólya (1934), 70–72, 91–96.

The conditions of Fourier's inversion theorem[*] are satisfied and we obtain

$$f(t) = \int_{-\infty}^{\infty} e^{itx} p(x)\, dx.$$

It follows from (i) that $\int_{-\infty}^{\infty} p(x)\, dx = 1$ and the proof of theorem 4.3.1 is completed as soon as we show that $p(x)$ is non-negative.

Integrating by parts and writing $g(t) = -f'(t)$ we get

$$(4.3.3) \qquad p(x) = \frac{1}{\pi x} \int_0^{\infty} g(t) \sin xt\, dt$$

where $g(t)$ is a non-increasing, non-negative function for $t > 0$ while

$$\lim_{t \to \infty} g(t) = 0.$$

Then

$$p(x) = \frac{1}{\pi x} \int_0^{\pi/x} \left[\sum_{j=0}^{\infty} (-1)^j g\left(t + \frac{j\pi}{x}\right) \right] \sin tx\, dt.$$

Let $x > 0$; the series

$$\sum_{j=0}^{\infty} (-1)^j g\left(t + \frac{j\pi}{x}\right)$$

is an alternating series whose terms are non-increasing in absolute value; since the first term of the series is non-negative one sees that the integrand is non-negative. Thus $p(x) \geqslant 0$ for $x > 0$. Formula (4.3.2) indicates that $p(x)$ is an even function of x so that $p(x) \geqslant 0$ if $x \neq 0$. Therefore $p(x)$ is a frequency function and $f(t)$ is the characteristic function of the absolutely continuous distribution $F(x) = \int_{-\infty}^{x} p(y)\, dy.$

We will occasionally call functions which satisfy the conditions of theorem 4.3.1 Pólya-type characteristic functions.

From the preceding proof it is clear that the frequency function $p(x)$ of a Pólya-type characteristic function $f(t)$ can always be obtained by means of the Fourier inversion formula (4.3.1), even if the condition of theorem 3.2.2 that $f(t)$ should be absolutely integrable is not satisfied.

(*) We use here the following theorem due to Pringsheim [Titchmarsh, (1937), p. 16]: If the function $f(t)$ is non-increasing over $(0, \infty)$ and if it is integrable over every finite interval $(0, a)$ (where $a > 0$) and if $\lim_{t \to \infty} f(t) = 0$ then the inversion formula

$$\tfrac{1}{2}[f(t+0) + f(t-0)] = (2/\pi) \int_0^{\infty} \cos tu \left[\int_0^{\infty} f(y) \cos yu\, dy \right] du$$

holds for any positive t. A short proof of Pringsheim's theorem can be found in M. Riesz–A. E. Livingstone (1955).

We list next a few Pólya-type characteristic functions.

(4.3.4a) $f(t) = e^{-|t|}$

(4.3.4b) $f(t) = \dfrac{1}{1+|t|}$

(4.3.4c) $f(t) = \begin{cases} 1-|t| & \text{for } 0 \leqslant |t| \leqslant \frac{1}{2} \\ \dfrac{1}{4|t|} & \text{for } |t| \geqslant \frac{1}{2} \end{cases}$

(4.3.4d) $f(t) = \begin{cases} 1-|t| & \text{for } |t| \leqslant 1 \\ 0 & \text{for } |t| \geqslant 1. \end{cases}$

Using the inversion formula (4.3.1) we see easily that (4.3.4a) is the characteristic function of the Cauchy distribution. The characteristic functions (4.3.4a) and (4.3.4d) are absolutely integrable; however (4.3.4b) and (4.3.4c) are examples of characteristic functions of absolutely continuous distributions which are not absolutely integrable (see page 34). The corresponding frequency functions can nevertheless be computed by means of formula (4.3.1) but lead to higher transcendental functions. The frequency function of the characteristic function (4.3.4d) is the function

$$\frac{1}{2\pi} \left[\frac{\sin (x/2)}{x/2} \right]^2.$$

Pólya's condition permits us to construct examples which help us to get a better insight into the assumptions of the uniqueness theorem.[*]

Example 1. Let $f(t)$ be any Pólya-type characteristic function whose right-hand derivative $f'(t)$ is strictly increasing for $t > 0$. Replace an arbitrarily small arc of the right-hand side of $f(t)$ by a chord and change the left-hand side symmetrically. In this manner one obtains a new function $f_1(t)$ which also satisfies the conditions of theorem 4.3.1. Thus $f_1(t)$ is a Pólya-type characteristic function which agrees with $f(t)$ everywhere, except on two symmetrically located arbitrarily small intervals. As a consequence of the uniqueness theorem $f_1(t)$ and $f(t)$ belong to two different distributions.

Example 2. Let $f_1(t)$ be the characteristic function (4.3.4c) while $f_2(t)$ is the function (4.3.4d). These are examples of two characteristic functions which agree over a finite interval but belong to different distributions.

Pólya's condition can be used to derive another sufficient condition which is applicable to certain periodic functions.

---

[*] See page 29.

Theorem 4.3.2.   Let $f(t)$ be a real-valued function which satisfies the following conditions[*]:

   (i) $f(0) = 1$
   (ii) $f(-t) = f(t)$
   (iii) $f(t)$ is convex and continuous in the interval $(0, r)$
   (iv) $f(t)$ is periodic with period $2r$
   (v) $f(r) = 0, f(t) \geqslant 0$ in $[0, r]$.

Then $f(t)$ is the characteristic function of a lattice distribution.

We consider the function $f_1(t)$ defined by

$$(4.3.5) \qquad f_1(t) = \begin{cases} f(t) & \text{if } |t| \leqslant r \\ 0 & \text{if } |t| > r. \end{cases}$$

Clearly, $f_1(t)$ satisfies the conditions of Pólya's theorem and is therefore a characteristic function. Hence it follows from (4.3.1) that

$$\int_{-\infty}^{\infty} e^{-itx} f_1(t)\, dt \geqslant 0$$

for all x. Combining this with (4.3.5) we obtain

$$(4.3.6) \qquad \int_{-r}^{r} f(t) \cos tx\, dt \geqslant 0$$

while condition (ii) implies that

$$(4.3.7) \qquad \int_{-r}^{r} f(t) \sin tx\, dt = 0.$$

We substitute $x = \pi n/r$ (n integer) in (4.3.6) and (4.3.7) and see that

$$(4.3.8) \qquad \begin{cases} A_n = \dfrac{1}{r} \displaystyle\int_{-r}^{r} f(t) \cos \dfrac{n\pi}{r} t\, dt \geqslant 0 \\[2ex] B_n = \dfrac{1}{r} \displaystyle\int_{-r}^{r} f(t) \sin \dfrac{n\pi}{r} t\, dt = 0. \end{cases}$$

The quantities A_n and B_n are the Fourier coefficients of the function $f(t)$. It follows from Dirichlet's conditions [Titchmarsh (1939)] that $f(t)$ is equal(†) to its Fourier series in the interval $(-r, +r)$. On account of the periodicity of $f(t)$ one has then

$$(4.3.9) \qquad f(t) = \frac{A_0}{2} + \sum_{n=1}^{\infty} A_n \cos \frac{n\pi}{r} t$$

(*) P. Lévy (1961) showed that condition (iii) can be replaced by (iii'): the function$g(t)$, which equals $f(t)$ in some interval $(0, r)$ and is zero for $t > r$, is a characteristic function.
   (†) D. Dugué (1955), (1957b) investigated the Fourier series of a characteristic function and showed that a characteristic function is, in a certain interval, equal to the sum of its Fourier series. L. Schmetterer (1965) supplemented these results and showed that a similar statement is true if the trigonometric system is replaced by certain orthogonal systems.

for any real value of t. Formula (4.3.9) indicates that $f(t)$ is the characteristic function of a lattice distribution whose lattice points are the points $(n\pi/r)$ $(n = 0, \pm1, \pm2, \ldots)$.

The functions $f(t)$ and $f_1(t)$ discussed in this proof are also examples of characteristic functions which agree over a finite interval. The first example of this kind is due to Khinchine.

Extensions of Pólya's condition can be found in Girault (1954) and in Dugué (1957b). These authors also obtained some interesting results concerning Pólya-type characteristic functions [D. Dugué–M. Girault (1955)].

We discuss here only one of their theorems.

Theorem 4.3.3. A characteristic function is a Pólya-type characteristic function if, and only if, it can be represented in the form

$$(4.3.10) \qquad f(t) = \int_0^\infty k\left(\frac{t}{x}\right) dF(x)$$

for $t > 0$ and $f(t) = f(-t)$ for $t < 0$. Here

$$(4.3.11) \qquad k(t) = \begin{cases} 1-|t| & \text{if } |t| \leqslant 1 \\ 0 & \text{if } |t| \geqslant 1 \end{cases}$$

while $F(x)$ is a distribution function such that $F(0) = 0$.

We note that $k(t)$ is the characteristic function (4.3.4d) so that $k\left(\frac{t}{x}\right)$ is also a Pólya-type characteristic function, and we see easily that $f(t)$, as given by (4.3.10), satisfies the conditions of theorem 4.3.1 and is therefore a Pólya-type characteristic function. We prove next that every Pólya-type characteristic function admits a representation (4.3.10). Let $f(t)$ be a Pólya-type characteristic function; we mentioned above that $f(t)$ has everywhere a right-hand derivative $f'(t)$ which is non-decreasing for $t > 0$. We note that $f(x) - xf'(x)$ is the ordinate at the origin of the tangent of the curve $y = f(t)$ taken to the right of the point $t = x$. Therefore $f(x) - xf'(x)$ tends to zero as $x \to \infty$. We use integration by parts to show that

$$\int_t^\infty \left(1 - \frac{t}{x}\right) d[1 - f(x) + xf'(x)] = -t \int_t^\infty \frac{d}{dx}\left[\frac{f(x)}{x}\right] dx.$$

The symbol $\dfrac{d}{dx}$ stands here for the right-hand derivative. It follows immediately that

$$(4.3.12) \qquad \int_t^\infty \left(1 - \frac{t}{x}\right) d[1 - f(x) + xf'(x)] = f(t).$$

We see that

$$F(x) = 1 - f(x) + xf'(x)$$

D

is a distribution function and introduce $F(x)$ and the function $k\left(\dfrac{t}{x}\right)$ into formula (4.3.12) and obtain the desired result.

The decision whether a given function $f(t)$ is a characteristic function can sometimes be made by means of the results derived in earlier chapters. The continuity theorem is frequently useful in this connection; we consider next a simple example. Let

$$f(t) = \frac{1}{\cosh t} = \frac{1}{e^t + e^{-t}}.$$

The function $\cosh t$ is an entire function which has zeros at the points $i\pi(2j-1)/2$. Applying Weierstrass' theorem on the factorization of entire (integral) functions we get

$$\cosh t = \prod_{j=1}^{\infty}\left[1 + \frac{4t^2}{(2j-1)^2\pi^2}\right]$$

so that

$$f(t) = \prod_{j=1}^{\infty} g_j(t) \quad \text{where} \quad g_j(t) = \left[1 + \frac{4t^2}{(2j-1)^2\pi^2}\right]^{-1}.$$

Let $l(t) = 1/(1+t^2)$ be the characteristic function of the Laplace distribution, then

$$g_j(t) = l\left(\frac{2}{(2j-1)\pi} t\right)$$

is also a characteristic function. Then [corollary 1 to theorem 3.3.1]

$$h_n(t) = \prod_{j=1}^{n} g_j(t)$$

is also a characteristic function. Finally we conclude from the continuity theorem that

$$f(t) = \lim_{n\to\infty} h_n(t)$$

is also a characteristic function. In a similar way one can show that the reciprocal of an entire function of order 1 which has only purely imaginary zeros and which equals 1 at the origin is always a characteristic function.

4.4 Supplementary remarks concerning non-negative definite functions

In the preceding section we saw (Example 2 on page 85) that two different characteristic functions can agree over a finite interval. This observation motivates the introduction of a new concept, namely of functions which are non-negative definite on a finite interval.

A complex-valued function $f(t)$ of a real variable t is said to be non-negative definite over the interval $(-A, A)$ if

    (i) $f(t)$ is continuous in $(-A, A)$;

    (ii) for any positive integer N and any real numbers $t_1, t_2, \ldots, t_N$ such that $|t_j| < A$ $(j = 1, 2, \ldots, N)$ and any complex numbers $\xi_1, \xi_2, \ldots, \xi_N$ the sum

$$\sum_{j=1}^{N} \sum_{k=1}^{N} f(t_j - t_k)\xi_j \bar{\xi}_k$$

is real and non-negative.

We denote the set of functions which are non-negative definite over $(-A, A)$ by $\mathscr{P}_A$ and write $\mathscr{P}_\infty$ for the set of functions which are non-negative definite over $(-\infty, \infty)$.

Bochner's theorem and the example mentioned above suggest several problems. The first of these is a characterization of the class $\mathscr{P}_A$, the second deals with the possibility of extrapolating a function non-negative definite on $(-A, A)$ to the whole real line. Finally, one is interested in conditions for the uniqueness of this extension. A number of authors, M. Krein (1940), (1943), D. A. Raikov (1940), E. J. Akutowicz (1959), (1960), and P. Lévy (1961), have investigated these problems and obtained interesting solutions. The tools used in these investigations exceed the scope of the methods employed in this monograph. Therefore we only list here some of the results, without proofs. Omission of these proofs will not cause any difficulty in reading the book since the present section is only loosely connected with the rest of the monograph.

Theorem 4.4.1 (*Krein's theorem*). *A function $f(t)$, defined on a finite or infinite interval $(-A, A)$, belongs to $\mathscr{P}_A$ if, and only if, it admits the representation*

$$(4.4.1) \qquad f(t) = \int_{-\infty}^{\infty} e^{itx} \, dF(x) \quad (|t| < A)$$

where $F(x)$ is a non-decreasing function of bounded variation.

Theorem 4.4.1 is due to M. Krein (1940); an elementary proof was given by D. A. Raikov (1940). In the case where A is infinite, Krein's theorem reduces to Bochner's theorem. The integral representation (4.4.1) is unique if $A = \infty$; however, for a finite interval $F(x)$ is in general not uniquely determined by $f(t)$. This means that a function $f(t)$ which is non-negative definite over a finite interval may admit several different non-negative definite extensions to the full real line. Conditions for the uniqueness of the extension can also be found in Krein's paper. To formulate these we introduce the following terminology.

Let $f(t) \in \mathscr{P}_A$ and denote the set of non-decreasing functions of bounded variation which admit the representation (4.4.1) for $f(t)$ by V_f. We norm the functions of V_f so that $F(-\infty) = 0$ while

$$F(x) = [F(x-0)+F(x+0)]/2.$$

We say that the extension (extrapolation) of $f \in \mathscr{P}_A$ is unique if V_f contains only one element; otherwise we say that the extension of f is indeterminate.

Let $\mathfrak{B}_A$ be the set of all entire functions $g(z)$ of the complex variable $z = t+iy$ such that

(i) $\sup\limits_{-\infty<t<\infty} |g(t)| < \infty$

(ii) $\limsup\limits_{r\to\infty} r^{-1} \log M(r) \leqslant A,$

where $M(r) = \max\limits_{|z|\leqslant r} |g(z)|$. This means that $g(z)$ is an entire function of exponential type not exceeding A and is bounded on the real axis. Let $g \in \mathfrak{B}_A$, $f \in \mathscr{P}_A$ and $F \in V_f$. We define a functional Φ_f in the space $\mathfrak{B}_A$ by the formula

$$\Phi_f(g) = \int_{-\infty}^{\infty} g(t)\,dF(t).$$

It can be shown that Φ_f depends only on f and g but is independent of F. We are now in a position to formulate Krein's result.

Theorem 4.4.2.   The extension of the function $f \in \mathscr{P}_A$ is unique if there exists a non-negative function $g \in \mathfrak{B}_A$, $g \not\equiv 0$ such that $\Phi_f(g) = 0$.

Krein also gave a necessary and sufficient condition for the indeterminateness of the extension of a function which is non-negative definite in a finite interval.

Theorem 4.4.3.   The extension of the function $f \in \mathscr{P}_A$ is indeterminate if, and only if, the following two conditions are satisfied:

(i) *For every function $\tau(x)$ of bounded variation for which*

$$\tau(x) = \tfrac{1}{2}[\tau(x+0)+\tau(x-0)] \neq \text{const} \ (0 \leqslant x \leqslant A)$$

the inequality

$$\int_0^A \int_0^A f(x-y)\,d\tau(x)\,d\tau(y) > 0$$

holds.

(ii) *The series*

$$\sum_{n=1}^{\infty} \lambda_n \left| \int_0^A e^{ixt} \phi_n(x)\,dx \right|^2 < \infty$$

for all real t $(-\infty < t < \infty)$.

Here $\{\phi_n(x)\}$ is a complete orthonormal system of fundamental solutions of the integral equation

$$\phi(x) = \lambda \int_0^A f(x-y)\phi(y)\,dy$$

and $\{\lambda_n\}$ is the corresponding sequence of eigenvalues.

We conclude this section with a remark concerning a generalization of Bochner's theorem. A non-negative definite function is by definition continuous. F. Riesz (1933) replaced the assumption of continuity by measurability and showed that the representation of such a function by the Fourier–Stieltjes integral of a bounded non-decreasing function is valid almost everywhere. M. Crum (1956) carried out a detailed investigation and obtained the following result.

Theorem 4.4.4. Let $f(t)$ be a complex-valued function of the real variable t $(-\infty < t < \infty)$ which satisfies the following conditions:

(i) $f(t)$ is measurable;
(ii) for any positive integer N and any real t_1, t_2, ..., t_N and any complex ξ_1, ξ_2, ..., ξ_N the relation

$$\sum_{j=1}^{N} \sum_{k=1}^{N} f(t_j - t_k)\xi_j \bar{\xi}_k \geqslant 0$$

holds.

Then $f(t)$ admits the decomposition $f(t) = \phi(t) + \psi(t)$, where

$$\phi(t) = \int_{-\infty}^{\infty} e^{itx}\,dF(x),$$

while $\psi(t) = 0$ almost everywhere and satisfies condition (ii). Here $F(x)$ is a bounded and non-decreasing function.

Conditions generalizing Cramér's criterion in a similar way were given by G. Letta (1963).

4.5 Unimodal distributions

A distribution function $F(x)$ is said to be unimodal if there exists at least one value $x = a$ such that $F(x)$ is convex for $x < a$ and concave for $x > a$. The point $x = a$ is called a vertex of $F(x)$.

As examples of unimodal distributions we mention the normal distribution and the Cauchy distribution.

In this section we study properties of unimodal distributions and derive criteria which assure that a characteristic function belongs to a unimodal distribution. For the sake of simplicity we shall often assume that the vertex is the point $a = 0$.

Theorem 4.5.1.   A distribution function $F(x)$ is unimodal with vertex at $x = 0$ if, and only if, its characteristic function $f(t)$ can be represented as

$$f(t) = \frac{1}{t} \int_0^t g(u)\, du \quad (-\infty < t < \infty),$$

where $g(u)$ is a characteristic function.

Theorem 4.5.1 is due to A. Ya. Khinchine; for its proof we need two lemmas:

Lemma 4.5.1.   The relations

$$\text{(i)} \quad \lim_{x \to +\infty} x \int_x^{+\infty} \frac{dG(y)}{y} = 0, \quad \lim_{x \to -\infty} x \int_{-\infty}^x \frac{dG(y)}{y} = 0$$

$$\text{(ii)} \quad \lim_{x \to -0} x \int_{-\infty}^x \frac{dG(y)}{y} = 0, \quad \lim_{x \to +0} x \int_x^{+\infty} \frac{dG(y)}{y} = 0$$

hold for an arbitrary distribution function $G(x)$.

For $x > 0$ we have the inequalities

$$0 \leqslant x \int_x^{+\infty} \frac{dG(y)}{y} \leqslant \int_x^{+\infty} dG(y).$$

The last integral tends to zero as x tends to infinity, and we obtain the first equation in (i); the second equation in (i) is derived in the same way. Let $x \to +0$ and note that

$$0 \leqslant x \int_x^{+\infty} \frac{dG(y)}{y} = x \int_x^{\sqrt{x}} \frac{dG(y)}{y} + x \int_{\sqrt{x}}^{+\infty} \frac{dG(y)}{y}$$

$$\leqslant \int_x^{\sqrt{x}} dG(y) + \sqrt{x} \int_{\sqrt{x}}^{+\infty} dG(y)$$

$$= G(\sqrt{x}) - G(x) + \sqrt{x}(1 - G(\sqrt{x})).$$

The expression on the right-hand side tends to zero as $x \to +0$, so that the second equation in (ii) follows. The first equation in (ii) is proved in the same way.

Lemma 4.5.2.   If a distribution function $F(x)$ is convex in $(-\infty, 0)$ then there exists a function $p(u)$ which is non-decreasing and integrable on $(-\infty, 0)$ such that $F(x) = \int_{-\infty}^x p(u)\, du$. Similarly, if a distribution function $F(x)$ is concave in $(0, +\infty)$ then it admits a representation $F(x) = 1 - \int_x^\infty q(u)\, du$ where $q(u)$ is non-increasing and integrable on $(0, +\infty)$.

The first statement of the lemma follows from a well-known property of convex functions [see A. Zygmund (1952), 4.141]; the second statement is an immediate consequence of the first part of the lemma.

We now proceed to the proof of theorem 4.5.1 and show first that the condition is sufficient. Suppose therefore that a characteristic function $f(t)$ can be represented in the form

$$(4.5.1) \qquad f(t) = \frac{1}{t} \int_0^t g(u)\, du$$

where $g(u)$ is the characteristic function of some distribution $G(x)$. We introduce the function

$$(4.5.2) \qquad F(x) = \begin{cases} \int_{-\infty}^x \left[-\int_{-\infty}^y \frac{dG(u)}{u} \right] dy & \text{for } x < 0 \\ \int_{+0}^x \left[\int_y^\infty \frac{dG(u)}{u} \right] dy + G(+0) & \text{for } x > 0. \end{cases}$$

We rewrite (4.5.2), using integration by parts and lemma 4.5.1, and obtain

$$(4.5.3) \qquad F(x) = \begin{cases} G(x) - x \int_{-\infty}^x \frac{dG(y)}{y} & \text{for } x < 0 \\ G(x) + x \int_x^\infty \frac{dG(y)}{y} & \text{for } x > 0. \end{cases}$$

It follows immediately from (4.5.2) that $F(x)$ is non-decreasing for $x < 0$ and also for $x > 0$. We also conclude from (4.5.3) and lemma 4.5.1 that $F(+\infty) = 1$ while $F(-\infty) = 0$; moreover we see in the same way that $F(+0) = G(+0)$ and $F(-0) = G(-0)$. The function $F(x)$ is therefore a distribution function. Since $F(x)$ is the integral of a non-decreasing function in $(-\infty, 0)$ and is the integral of a non-increasing function in $(0, \infty)$ it is easily seen that $F(x)$ is unimodal with vertex at $x = 0$.

In order to complete the proof of the sufficiency of the condition of theorem 4.5.1 we must show that $f(t)$, as given by (4.5.1), is the characteristic function of the distribution function $F(x)$. According to (4.5.2) we have

$$\int_{-\infty}^\infty e^{itx}\, dF(x) = -\int_{-\infty}^{-0} e^{itx} \left[\int_{-\infty}^x \frac{dG(u)}{u} \right] dx + F(+0) - F(-0)$$
$$+ \int_{+0}^\infty e^{itx} \left[\int_x^\infty \frac{dG(u)}{u} \right] dx.$$

We note that $F(+0) - F(-0) = G(+0) - G(-0)$ and using integration by parts and lemma 4.5.1, we see after some elementary computations that

$$(4.5.4) \qquad \int_{-\infty}^\infty e^{itx}\, dF(x) = \int_{-\infty}^\infty \frac{e^{itx} - 1}{itx}\, dG(x).$$

We note that

$$\frac{e^{itx} - 1}{itx} = \frac{1}{t} \int_0^t e^{ixu}\, du;$$

we substitute this into (4.5.4) and obtain

$$\int_{-\infty}^{\infty} e^{itx}\, dF(x) = \frac{1}{t} \int_{0}^{t} g(u)\, du = f(t),$$

so that the condition of the theorem is sufficient. We still have to show that (4.5.1) is necessary and assume therefore that $F(x)$ is a unimodal distribution. We see then from lemma 4.5.2 that there exists a non-decreasing function $p(u)$, defined for $u < 0$, and a non-increasing function $q(u)$, defined for $u > 0$, such that

$$(4.5.5) \qquad F(x) = \begin{cases} \displaystyle\int_{-\infty}^{x} p(u)\, du & \text{for } x < 0 \\[2ex] 1 - \displaystyle\int_{x}^{\infty} q(u)\, du & \text{for } x > 0. \end{cases}$$

Let

$$(4.5.6) \qquad G(x) = \begin{cases} \displaystyle -\int_{-\infty}^{x} u\, dp(u) & \text{for } x < 0 \\[2ex] 1 + \displaystyle\int_{x}^{\infty} u\, dq(u) & \text{for } x > 0. \end{cases}$$

Since $p(x)$ is non-negative and non-decreasing in $(-\infty, 0)$ we see that $\int_{x}^{2x} p(u)\, du \leqslant xp(x) \leqslant 0$ for $x < 0$, so that

$$(4.5.7) \qquad \lim_{x \to -0} xp(x) = 0.$$

Moreover it follows from (4.5.6) that

$$G(x) = -xp(x) + F(x)$$

for $x < 0$; we conclude from (4.5.7) that

$$(4.5.8a) \qquad G(-0) = F(-0).$$

Similarly we show that

$$(4.5.8b) \qquad G(+0) = F(+0)$$

so that $G(+0) \geqslant G(-0)$. We see from (4.5.6) that $G(x)$ is non-decreasing in $(-\infty, -0)$ and $(+0, +\infty)$, so that $G(x)$ is a distribution function.[*]
Let

$$g(t) = \int_{-\infty}^{\infty} e^{itx}\, dG(x)$$

be the characteristic function of $G(x)$; then

$$\frac{1}{t} \int_{0}^{t} g(u)\, du = \int_{-\infty}^{\infty} \frac{e^{itx} - 1}{itx}\, dG(x).$$

---

[*] It might be necessary to modify $G(x)$ at its discontinuity points to make it right continuous.

We substitute for $G(x)$ the expression from (4.5.6) and integrate by parts and obtain, using (4.5.8a) and (4.5.8b),

$$\frac{1}{t}\int_0^t g(u)\,du = \int_{-\infty}^{-0} e^{itx} p(x)\,dx + F(+0) - F(-0) - \int_{+0}^{\infty} e^{itx} q(x)\,dx,$$

or, in view of (4.5.5)

$$\frac{1}{t}\int_0^t g(u)\,du = \int_{-\infty}^{\infty} e^{itx}\,dF(x) = f(t),$$

so that the theorem is proved.

It is worthwhile to remark that P. Medgyessy (1963) has shown that it is possible to derive theorem 4.5.1 from theorem 4.3.3 and also theorem 4.3.3 from theorem 4.5.1, so that these two theorems are equivalent. Paul Lévy (1962) gave some interesting extensions of theorems 4.3.3 and 4.5.1.

The next theorem gives a sufficient condition which assures that a characteristic function belongs to a unimodal distribution.

Theorem 4.5.2.   Let $f(t)$ be a continuous, real-valued and even function of the real variable t such that $f(0) = 1$ and let $A(z)$ be a function of the complex variable z ($z = t+iy = r e^{i\theta}$; t, y, and θ real) which satisfies the following conditions:

(i) *$A(z)$ is regular in the region* $\mathfrak{D} = \left\{ z : r > 0,\ -\varepsilon_1 < \theta < \dfrac{\pi}{2}+\varepsilon_2 \right\}$

   where ε_1 and ε_2 can be arbitrarily small;

(ii) *$|A(z)| = O(1)$ as $|z| \to 0$;*

(iii) *$|A(z)| = O(|z|^{-\delta})$ as $|z| \to \infty$ ($\delta > 1$);*

(iv) *$\operatorname{Im} A(iy) \leqslant 0$ for $y > 0$;*

(v) *$f(t) = A(t)$ for $t > 0$.*

Then $f(t)$ is the characteristic function of a symmetrical unimodal and absolutely continuous distribution function.

It follows from our assumptions that $f(t)$ is absolutely integrable over $(-\infty, +\infty)$. Therefore

$$p(x) = \frac{1}{2\pi}\int_{-\infty}^{\infty} e^{-itx} f(t)\,dt = \frac{1}{\pi}\int_0^{\infty} \cos tx\, f(t)\,dt$$

is a continuous, real-valued and even function of x. It follows from the preceding equation that

(4.5.9) $p(x) = \dfrac{1}{\pi}\operatorname{Re}\displaystyle\int_0^{\infty} e^{itx} f(t)\,dt = \dfrac{1}{\pi}\operatorname{Re}\displaystyle\int_0^{\infty} e^{itx} A(t)\,dt.$

In order to compute the last integral in (4.5.9) we consider the function $\psi(z) = e^{izx} A(z)$ (z complex, $x \geqslant 0$) along the contour Γ which consists of the segment $[r, R]$ of the positive real axis, the circular arc

$$C_R = \left\{ z : z = R\, e^{i\phi}, 0 \leqslant \phi \leqslant \frac{\pi}{2} \right\},$$

the segment $[iR, ir]$ of the positive imaginary axis, and the circular arc

$$C_r = \left\{ z : z = r\, e^{i\phi}, \frac{\pi}{2} \geqslant \phi \geqslant 0 \right\}.$$

Since $\psi(z)$ is regular in $\mathfrak{D}$, we can apply Cauchy's theorem and see that

$$\int_\Gamma \psi(z)\, dz = \int_\Gamma e^{izx} A(z)\, dz = 0$$

or

(4.5.10)

$$\int_r^R e^{itx} A(t)\, dt + \int_{C_R} \psi(z)\, dz + i \int_R^r e^{-yx} A(iy)\, dy + \int_{C_R} \psi(z)\, dz = 0.$$

It is easily seen that

$$\lim_{r \to 0} \int_{C_r} \psi(z)\, dz = \lim_{R \to \infty} \int_{C_R} \psi(z)\, dz = 0,$$

so that one obtains from (4.5.10)

$$\int_0^\infty e^{itx} A(t)\, dt = i \int_0^\infty e^{-yx} A(iy)\, dy.$$

We conclude from the last equation and (4.5.9) that

(4.5.11) $$p(x) = -\frac{1}{\pi} \int_0^\infty e^{-yx} [\operatorname{Im} A(iy)]\, dy.$$

It follows from condition (iv) and the assumption that $f(t)$ is an even function, that $p(x) \geqslant 0$ for all real x. Since $f(0) = 1$ we conclude that $p(x)$ is a frequency function whose characteristic function is $f(t)$. To complete the proof we must show that the corresponding distribution is unimodal. Let $x_1 > x_2 > 0$; it follows immediately from (4.5.11) that

$$p(x_1) < p(x_2) < p(0),$$

so that $p(x)$ is a decreasing function for $x \geqslant 0$. Since $p(x)$ is symmetric we see that it has a unique maximum at $x = 0$.

We give next an application of theorems 4.5.1 and 4.5.2 and show that certain functions are characteristic functions of unimodal distributions. This result will be used in the next chapter.

Theorem 4.5.3. Let α be a real number such that $0 < \alpha \leqslant 2$; then the function $f(t) = \dfrac{1}{1 + |t|^\alpha}$ is the characteristic function of a unimodal distribution.

In proving the theorem we must distinguish three cases.

(a) $0 < \alpha \leqslant 1$. In this case we introduce the function

$$(4.5.12) \qquad g(t) = \frac{1 + (1 - \alpha)|t|^\alpha}{(1 + |t|^\alpha)^2}.$$

It is easily seen that for $t > 0$

$$g''(t) = \frac{\alpha t^{\alpha - 2}}{(1 + t^\alpha)^4}[(1 - \alpha^2) + 2(1 + 2\alpha^2)t^\alpha + (1 - \alpha^2)t^{2\alpha}] > 0.$$

The function $g(t)$ therefore satisfies Pólya's condition (theorem 4.3.1) and is thus a characteristic function. It follows also from (4.5.12) that

$$g(t) = f(t) + tf'(t) \text{ for } t > 0; \text{ therefore } f(t) = \frac{1}{t}\int_0^t g(u)\, du \text{ and we con-}$$

clude from theorem 4.5.1 that $f(t)$ is the characteristic function of a unimodal distribution.

(b) $1 < \alpha < 2$. In this case we introduce the function $A(z) = \dfrac{1}{1 + z^\alpha}$

of the complex variable z and see that $A(z)$ satisfies the conditions of theorem 4.5.2, and we conclude from theorem 4.5.2 that $f(t)$ is the characteristic function of a unimodal distribution.

(c) $\alpha = 2$. In this case the frequency function of $f(t)$ is $p(x) = \frac{1}{2}e^{-|x|}$ which has a unique maximum at $x = 0$.

The fact that $f(t) = \dfrac{1}{1 + |t|^\alpha}$ is a characteristic function was established by Yu. V. Linnik (1953), and the unimodality of the corresponding distribution was shown by R. G. Laha.

Theorem 4.5.4.   Let $\{F_n(x)\}$ be a sequence of unimodal distribution functions and suppose that the distributions $F_n(x)$ converge weakly to a distribution function $F(x)$; then $F(x)$ is also unimodal.

Let a_n be a vertex of $F_n(x)$ and $a = \varlimsup_{n \to \infty} a_n$. We consider first the case where $|a| < \infty$ and select a subsequence n_k such that $\lim_{k \to \infty} a_{n_k} = a$. Let x_1, x_2 and $(x_1 + x_2)/2$ be continuity points of $F(x)$ such that $x_1 < a$ and $x_2 < a$. For k sufficiently large one has $x_1 < a_{n_k}$, $x_2 < a_{n_k}$. Since $F_{n_k}(x)$ is assumed to be unimodal we see that

$$F_{n_k}(x_1) + F_{n_k}(x_2) \geqslant 2F_{n_k}\left(\frac{x_1 + x_2}{2}\right).$$

We go with k to the limit and obtain

$$(4.5.13a) \qquad F(x_1) + F(x_2) \geqslant 2F\left(\frac{x_1 + x_2}{2}\right).$$

We assumed that x_1 and x_2 are continuity points of $F(x)$; however, inequality (4.5.13a) is also true for arbitrary points. This follows from the right-continuity of $F(x)$ and the fact that an arbitrary point can be approximated by a sequence of continuity points. In a similar way we obtain for points x_3 and x_4, such that $x_3 > a$, $x_4 > a$, the inequality

$$(4.5.13b) \qquad F(x_3) + F(x_4) \leqslant 2F\left(\frac{x_3 + x_4}{2}\right).$$

It follows from equations (4.5.13a) and (4.5.13b) that $F(x)$ is unimodal. Finally we note that $|a|$ is necessarily finite, otherwise $F(x)$ would be either convex or concave for all x. This is not possible, since a distribution function is monotone and bounded.

Theorem 4.5.5.   The convolution of two symmetric and unimodal distributions is symmetric and unimodal.

For the proof of the theorem we need the following lemma.

Lemma 4.5.3.   Let $F(x)$ be a unimodal distribution function. Then there exists a sequence $\{F_n(x)\}$ of absolutely continuous unimodal distribution functions such that $\mathrm{Lim}_{n \to \infty} F_n(x) = F(x)$ and $F_n(x)$ is absolutely continuous.

We first note that if $\mathrm{Lim}_{n \to \infty} F_n(x) = F(x)$ and $\mathrm{Lim}_{m \to \infty} F_{m,n}(x) = F_n(x)$, there exists a sequence such that $\mathrm{Lim}_{k \to \infty} F_{m_k, n_k}(x) = F(x)$. It is therefore sufficient to consider distribution functions $F(x)$ whose derivative is a step function. In this case there exist absolutely continuous functions $p_n(x)$ which do not decrease on $(-\infty, 0)$ and do not increase on $(0, \infty)$, such that

$$\lim_{k \to \infty} \int_{-\infty}^{x} p_k(y)\, dy = \int_{-\infty}^{x} F'(y)\, dy.$$

We write

$$F_n(x) = \frac{1}{\int_{-\infty}^{\infty} p_n(y)\, dy} \int_{-\infty}^{x} p_n(y)\, dy$$

and see that $\mathrm{Lim}_{n \to \infty} F_n(x) = F(x)$, so that the lemma is proved.

We proceed to prove the theorem. Let $F_1(x)$ and $F_2(x)$ be two symmetric unimodal distributions and denote their convolution by $F(x)$, $F(x) = F_1(x) * F_2(x)$. Clearly $F(x)$ is also symmetric, so that we have only to show that it is unimodal. It is no restriction to assume that $F_1(x)$ and $F_2(x)$ are twice differentiable; this follows from theorem 4.5.4 and the fact that—according to lemma 4.5.3—we can approximate $F_1(x)$ and $F_2(x)$ by two sequences $\{F_{1,n}(x)\}$ and $\{F_{2,n}(x)\}$ respectively of twice differentiable, symmetric, and unimodal distribution functions.

If $F_1(x)$ and $F_2(x)$ are twice differentiable, we see that

$$F''(x) = \int_{-\infty}^{\infty} F_2''(x-t)F_1'(t)\,dt = \int_{-\infty}^{\infty} F_1'(x-t)F_2''(t)\,dt$$

or

(4.5.14) $$F''(x) = \int_0^{\infty} [F_1'(x-t) - F_1'(x+t)] F_2''(t)\,dt.$$

Since $F_1(t)$ and $F_2(t)$ are both unimodal we conclude that

(4.5.15) $F_2''(t) \leqslant 0$ for $t > 0$.

(4.5.16) $$\begin{cases} F_1'(x-t) - F_1'(x+t) \leqslant 0 & \text{for } x < 0 \\ F_1'(x-t) - F_1'(x+t) \geqslant 0 & \text{if } x > 0. \end{cases}$$

It follows from (4.5.14), (4.5.15) and (4.5.16) that $F''(x) \geqslant 0$ if $x < 0$ but $F''(x) \leqslant 0$ if $x > 0$. This completes the proof of the theorem.

Remark. The assumption of theorem 4.5.5 that $F_1(x)$ and $F_2(x)$ are symmetric is essential. The convolution of two unimodal distribution functions is in general not unimodal. K. L. Chung (1953) gave an example of an absolutely continuous distribution function $F(x)$ which has its vertex at $x = 0$ and which has the property that the density function of $F * F$ has two maxima so that $F * F$ is not unimodal.

I. A. Ibragimov (1956a) calls a distribution function strongly unimodal if its convolution with any unimodal distribution is unimodal. He obtained the following result:

Theorem 4.5.6.   A (non-degenerate) unimodal distribution function $F(x)$ is strongly unimodal if, and only if, $F(x)$ is continuous and if $\log F'(x)$ is concave on the set of points at which neither the right-hand nor the left-hand derivative of $F(x)$ vanishes.

4.6   An essential property of characteristic functions

We have already mentioned that every distribution function has a characteristic function and have discussed in Chapter 3 some other very important theorems concerning characteristic functions, such as the uniqueness theorem, the convolution theorem, and the continuity theorem. The great usefulness and importance of characteristic functions in probability theory is largely explained by the fact that these properties make them a very convenient tool for the solution of many problems. The present section deals with the question whether there are any other integral transforms of distribution functions which have these properties.

Let $G(x)$ be a distribution function and consider its integral transform by means of the kernel $K(s, x)$, that is

(4.6.1) $$g(s) = \int_{-\infty}^{\infty} K(s, x)\,dG(x).$$

In the following we denote by $G_1(x)$, $G_2(x)$ distribution functions and by $g_1(s)$, $g_2(s)$ their respective transforms (4.6.1).

In this section we show that the uniqueness and convolution properties essentially determine the kernel. The following theorem gives a precise formulation of this statement.

Theorem 4.6.1. *Suppose that a kernel $K(s, x)$ satisfies the following conditions:*

    (I) *$K(s, x)$ is a complex-valued function defined for all values of the real variables s and x and is bounded and measurable in x.*

  (II) *(Uniqueness property): $g_1(s) \equiv g_2(s)$ if, and only if, $G_1(x) \equiv G_2(x)$.*

 (III) *(Convolution property): If*

$$G(x) = G_1 * G_2 = \int_{-\infty}^{\infty} G_1(x-t)\, dG_2(t)$$

    then $g(s) = g_1(s)\, g_2(s)$.

Then $K(s, x)$ has the form

$$K(s, x) = e^{ixA(s}$$

where $A(s)$ is a real-valued function of s such that the values assumed by $|A(s)|$ form a set which is dense on $(0, +\infty)$. The converse statement is also true.

We see from assumption (I) that every distribution function $G(x)$ has a transform given by (4.6.1). We write assumption (III) in terms of the kernel and obtain

$$\int_{-\infty}^{\infty} K(s, x)\, d_x \int_{-\infty}^{\infty} G_1(x-u)\, dG_2(u)$$

$$= \int_{-\infty}^{\infty} K(s, t)\, dG_1(t) \int_{-\infty}^{\infty} K(s, u)\, dG_2(u)$$

$$= \int_{-\infty}^{\infty} \int_{-\infty}^{\infty} K(s, t)\, K(s, u)\, dG_1(t)\, dG_2(u).$$

On the other hand

$$\int_{-\infty}^{\infty} K(s, x)\, d_x \int_{-\infty}^{\infty} G_1(x-u)\, dG_2(u)$$

$$= \int_{-\infty}^{\infty} \int_{-\infty}^{\infty} K(s, t+u)\, dG_1(t)\, dG_2(u)$$

so that

(4.6.2) $$\int_{-\infty}^{\infty} \int_{-\infty}^{\infty} K(s, t+u)\, dG_1(t)\, dG_2(u)$$

$$= \int_{-\infty}^{\infty} \int_{-\infty}^{\infty} K(s, t)\, K(s, u)\, dG_1(t)\, dG_2(u)$$

holds for every pair of distributions $G_1(x)$ and $G_2(x)$. Let ξ and η be arbitrary real numbers and put

(4.6.3) $\begin{cases} G_1(x) = \varepsilon(x-\eta) \\ G_2(x) = \frac{1}{2}[\varepsilon(x)+\varepsilon(x-\xi)]. \end{cases}$

Substituting (4.6.3) into (4.6.2) we get

(4.6.4) $K(s,\eta)+K(s,\eta+\xi) = K(s,\eta)[K(s,0)+K(s,\xi)]$

for any real ξ and η. We obtain in particular for $\xi = 0$

$$2K(s,\eta) = 2K(s,0)K(s,\eta).$$

Therefore (4.6.4) reduces to

(4.6.5) $K(s,\eta+\xi) = K(s,\eta)K(s,\xi).$

It is known [see for instance Hahn–Rosenthal (1948), pages 116–118] that every measurable solution of the functional equation

$$\psi(\eta+\xi) = \psi(\eta)\psi(\xi)$$

has the form $\psi(\xi) = e^{C\xi}$ where C is a constant. Since $K(s,x)$ is by assumption (I) measurable in x, every solution of (4.6.5) is of the form

(4.6.6) $K(s,x) = e^{x\rho(s)}.$

Let $\rho(s) = B(s)+iA(s)$; then $|K(s,x)| = e^{xB(s)}$. Since $K(s,x)$ is bounded we have $B(s) \equiv 0$. The kernel therefore has the form

(4.6.7) $K(s,x) = e^{ixA(s)}.$

The transform (4.6.1) of a distribution $G(x)$ is therefore

(4.6.8) $\mathfrak{g}(s) = \int_{-\infty}^{\infty} e^{ixA(s)}\,dG(x)$

while the characteristic function $g(t)$ of $G(x)$ is

(4.6.9) $g(t) = \int_{-\infty}^{\infty} e^{itx}\,dG(x).$

It follows from (4.6.8) and (4.6.9) that

(4.6.10) $g[A(s)] = \mathfrak{g}(s).$

We show next by an indirect proof that $|A(s)|$ must assume all values of a set dense in $(0,+\infty)$. Suppose tentatively that $|A(s)|$ omits an arbitrary interval $I = (a,a+h)$ on $(0,+\infty)$ and denote by $I' = (-a,-a-h)$ the interval which is symmetric to I with respect to the origin. It is then possible to construct two Pólya-type characteristic functions $g_1(t)$ and $g_2(t)$ which agree everywhere except on I and I'. The two corresponding transforms (4.6.1) are $\mathfrak{g}_j(s) = g_j[A(s)]$ $(j = 1, 2)$. Since $|A(s)|$ does not assume values of I we see that $\mathfrak{g}_1(s)$ and $\mathfrak{g}_2(s)$ agree for all values s but belong to different distribution functions in contradiction to the uniqueness assumption (II).

We still have to prove the converse statement. Suppose that the kernel is given by (4.6.7), then it is immediately seen that (I) holds. The proof of (II) can be carried out in the customary manner with the aid of Weierstrass' approximation theorem. Finally it is easy to show that (III) is also satisfied.

We see therefore that an integral transform (4.6.1) which is defined for every distribution function and for which the uniqueness and the convolution theorems hold, is obtained from the characteristic function by a simple change of the variable. We note that we have arrived at this conclusion without using the continuity theorem.

This fact can be used [see E. Lukacs (1964)] to obtain a more general characterization of the transform (4.6.8) which also uses the continuity theorem but considers a linear mapping of the space of distribution functions onto a set of bounded continuous functions instead of the integral transform (4.6.1).

5 FACTORIZATION PROBLEMS—INFINITELY DIVISIBLE CHARACTERISTIC FUNCTIONS

5.1 Preliminary remarks on factorizations

We showed in Chapter 3 that the product of two characteristic functions is always a characteristic function. It is therefore obvious that some characteristic functions can be written as products of two or more characteristic functions.

Every characteristic function $f(t)$ can be written as the product of the two characteristic functions $f_1(t) = e^{imt}$ (m real) and $f_2(t) = f(t) e^{-imt}$. We say that the representation of a characteristic function as the product of two characteristic functions is trivial if one of the factors has the form e^{imt}. In order to avoid trivial product representations, we introduce the following definition.

A characteristic function $f(t)$ is said to be decomposable if it can be written in the form

$$(5.1.1) \qquad f(t) = f_1(t) f_2(t)$$

where $f_1(t)$ and $f_2(t)$ are both characteristic functions of non-degenerate distributions. We then say that $f_1(t)$ and $f_2(t)$ are factors of $f(t)$.

A characteristic function which admits only trivial product representations is called indecomposable.

We show next that there exist indecomposable characteristic functions.

Theorem 5.1.1. Let $F(x)$ be a purely discrete distribution function which has only two discontinuity points. Then its characteristic function is indecomposable.

We see from the corollary to theorem 3.3.3 that the components of $F(x)$ are necessarily purely discrete distributions with a finite number of discontinuity points. The inequality, given in this corollary, indicates that at least one of the components must be a degenerate distribution. This proves our assertion.

The factorization of a characteristic function into indecomposable factors is somewhat similar to the factorization of integers into prime factors. This is the reason why the theory of the decomposition of characteristic functions is often called the arithmetic of distribution functions. However, this analogy does not go very far; as an illustration we give an example which shows that the factorization of a characteristic function into indecomposable factors is not always unique.

Example.   Let $f(t) = \frac{1}{6}\sum\limits_{j=0}^{5} e^{itj}$ and write $f_1(t) = \frac{1}{3}(1+e^{2it}+e^{4it})$,

$$f_2(t) = \frac{1}{2}(1+e^{it}), \quad g_1(t) = \frac{1}{3}(1+e^{it}+e^{2it}), \quad g_2(t) = \frac{1}{2}(1+e^{3it}).$$

It follows from theorem 2.1.3 that the functions $f_1(t)$, $f_2(t)$, $g_1(t)$, $g_2(t)$ and $f(t)$ are characteristic functions. Moreover it is easily seen that $f(t) = f_1(t) f_2(t) = g_1(t) g_2(t)$. We conclude from theorem 5.1.1 that $f_2(t)$ and $g_2(t)$ are indecomposable. It follows from theorem 3.3.3 that a factorization of $g_1(t)$ must necessarily have the form

(5.1.2) $g_1(t) = [p\, e^{it\xi_1} + (1-p)\, e^{it\xi_2}]\, [q\, e^{it\eta_1} + (1-q)\, e^{it\eta_2}]$

where

(5.1.3) $0 < p < 1, \quad 0 < q < 1.$

As a consequence of (5.1.2) p and q must satisfy the relations

$$pq = (1-p)(1-q) = p(1-q)+q(1-p) = \tfrac{1}{3}$$

which are incompatible with (5.1.3). Thus $g_1(t)$ is indecomposable, and since $f_1(t) = g_1(2t)$ we see that $f_1(t)$ is also indecomposable.

We give a second example which emphasizes another difference between the arithmetic of distribution functions and the factorization of integers. This example is due to B. V. Gnedenko.

Let $f_1(t)$ be a real-valued periodic function with period 2 which is defined by $f_1(t) = 1-|t|$ in the interval $|t| \leqslant 1$. According to theorem 4.3.2 the function $f_1(t)$ is the characteristic function of a lattice distribution. Let further

$$f_2(t) = \begin{cases} 1-|t| & \text{for } |t| \leqslant 1 \\ 0 & \text{for } |t| > 1. \end{cases}$$

Clearly $f_2(t)$ is the Pólya-type characteristic function $k(t)$ defined by (4.3.11), and $f_2(t)$ agrees with $f_1(t)$ in the interval $|t| \leqslant 1$. According to a remark of A. Ya. Khinchine, this example shows that it is possible to find two different characteristic functions $f_1(t)$ and $f_2(t)$:

(5.1.4) $f(t) = f_1(t) f_2(t) = f_2(t) f_2(t).$

This fact—sometimes called the Khinchine phenomenon—shows that the cancellation law is not valid in the arithmetic of distribution functions.

It is known that the quotient of two characteristic functions is in general not a characteristic function (an example is given on p. 194).

We see from (5.1.4) that the quotient of two characteristic functions [in our example: $f(t)/f_2(t)$] need not be uniquely defined even in cases when it is a characteristic function. Formula (5.1.4) indicates that there might be a connection between the possibility of a factorization of type (5.1.4) and the fact that one of the factors vanishes outside an interval. The possibility of constructing characteristic functions which admit factorizations of the form (5.1.4) was investigated by T. Kawata (1940), and we now give some of his results.

Pólya's theorem shows that it is possible to construct characteristic functions vanishing outside a finite interval. In the following we present a different method for the construction of such functions.

Theorem 5.1.2.   Let $\theta(u)$ be a positive, non-decreasing function defined on $(0, \infty)$ such that

(5.1.5) $\displaystyle\int_1^\infty \frac{\theta(u)}{u^2}\, du < \infty$

and let b be an arbitrary (but fixed) positive number. Then there exists a distribution function $F(x)$ which satisfies for every a the relation

(5.1.6) $F(-x+a) - F(-x-a) = O\{\exp[-\theta(x)]\}$ *(as $x \to \infty$)*

and whose characteristic function $f(t)$ vanishes for $|t| > b$.

For the proof of this theorem we need the following lemma which is due to A. Ingham (1936) and N. Levinson (1936), (1938), and which we state here without proof.

Lemma 5.1.1.   Let $\theta(u)$ be a positive, non-decreasing function which satisfies (5.1.5) and let b be an arbitrary, fixed positive number. Then there exists a non-null function $G(x)$ such that

(5.1.7) $G(x) = O\{\exp[-\theta(|x|)]\}$ *(as $|x| \to \infty$)*

which has the property that its Fourier transform

$$g(u) = \frac{1}{\sqrt{2\pi}} \int_{-\infty}^\infty G(x) e^{-iux}\, dx$$

vanishes for $|u| > b$.

To prove theorem 5.1.2 we consider $\theta(2u)$ instead of $\theta(u)$. The function $\theta(2u)$ has the same properties as $\theta(u)$, so that we can apply lemma 5.1.1, replacing b by $b/2$. We put

$$f(t) = \frac{1}{A} \int_{-\infty}^\infty g(x)\overline{g(x+t)}\, dx,$$

where

$$A = \int_{-\infty}^\infty |g(x)|^2\, dx.$$

According to theorem 4.2.4 $f(t)$ is a characteristic function, and it follows from lemma 5.1.1 that $f(t) = 0$ for $|t| > b$. Using the inversion formula, Parseval's theorem, and relation (5.1.7), one sees by means of a simple computation that (5.1.6) is satisfied.

Theorem 5.1.3.   Let $\theta(u)$ be a positive non-decreasing function which satisfies (5.1.5). Then there exists a distribution function $F(x)$ whose characteristic *function $f(t)$ admits a factorization of the form (5.1.4). Moreover $F(x)$ satisfies the condition (5.1.6) for $a > 0$.*

We consider again $\theta(2u)$ instead of $\theta(u)$ and put $b = \dfrac{\pi}{2}$ in theorem 5.1.2. Then there exists a distribution function $F_1(x)$ whose characteristic function $f_1(t)$ vanishes for $|t| > \pi$. The function $f_1(t)$ is constructed using the function $g(x)$ of lemma 5.1.1 and is given by

$$(5.1.8) \qquad f_1(t) = \frac{1}{A}\int_{-\infty}^{\infty} g(x)\overline{g(x+t)}\,dx \quad \left(A = \int_{-\infty}^{\infty} |g(x)|^2\,dx\right).$$

We see also that

$$(5.1.9) \qquad g(x) = 0 \quad \text{for } |x| > \frac{\pi}{2}$$

and that

$$F_1(-x+a) - F_1(-x-a) = O\{\exp[-\theta(|2x|)]\} \quad \text{as } |x| \to \infty.$$

It follows from (5.1.8) and (5.1.9) that

$$(5.1.10) \qquad f_1(t) = \frac{1}{A}\int_{-\pi/2}^{\pi/2} g(x)\overline{g(x+t)}\,dx.$$

We see from (5.1.9) and (5.1.10) that

$$(5.1.11) \qquad f_1(\pi) = f_1(-\pi) = 0.$$

We define a function $f_2(t)$ by requiring that $f_2(t)$ is periodic with period 2π and coincides with $f_1(t)$ for $|t| \leqslant \pi$. It follows from (5.1.11) that $f_2(t)$ is a continuous function of t.

Let $\{c_n\}$ be the sequence of Fourier coefficients of $f_2(t)$; then

$$c_n = \frac{1}{2\pi}\int_{-\pi}^{\pi} f_2(t)e^{-int}\,dt = \frac{1}{2\pi}\int_{-\pi}^{\pi} e^{-int}\left[\frac{1}{A}\int_{-\pi/2}^{\pi/2} g(x)\overline{g(x+t)}\,dx\right]dt$$

$$= \frac{1}{2\pi A}\int_{-\pi/2}^{\pi/2} g(x)e^{inx}\left[\int_{-\pi+x}^{\pi+x} \overline{g(y)}\,e^{-iny}\,dy\right]dx.$$

It follows from (5.1.9) that

$$c_n = \frac{1}{2\pi A}\int_{-\pi/2}^{\pi/2} g(x)e^{inx}\,dx \int_{-\pi/2}^{\pi/2} \overline{g(y)}e^{-iny}\,dy$$

so that

$$c_n = \frac{1}{2\pi A}\left|\int_{-\pi/2}^{\pi/2} g(x)e^{inx}\,dx\right|^2.$$

Therefore

$$(5.1.12) \qquad c_n \geqslant 0$$

and

$$f_2(t) = \sum_{n=-\infty}^{\infty} c_n e^{int}.$$

Since $f_1(0) = f_2(0) = \sum_{n=-\infty}^{\infty} c_n = 1$, we see that $f_2(t)$ is the characteristic function of a lattice distribution whose discontinuity points are contained in a set of integers. The saltus of $F_2(x)$ at the point $x = n$ equals c_n ($n = 0$, $\pm 1, \pm 2, \ldots$). Clearly $f_2(t)$ is not identical with $f_1(t)$, and

$$f(t) = [f_1(t)]^2 = f_1(t) f_2(t),$$

so that the first part of the statement is proved. Let $F(x)$ be the distribution function corresponding to $f(t)$; the statement that $F(x)$ satisfies condition (5.1.6) is obtained by a somewhat lengthy but straightforward computation.

T. Kawata also obtained a condition which assures that a factorization of the form (5.1.4) is not possible.

Theorem 5.1.4. *Let $F(x)$ be a distribution function and let $\theta(u)$ be a positive, non-decreasing function defined in $(0, \infty)$ such that*

$$\int_1^\infty \frac{\theta(u)}{u^2}\, du = \infty.$$

Suppose that for some $a > 0$ the relation (5.1.6) holds and that the characteristic function $f(t)$ of $F(x)$ admits the factorization

$$f(t) = f_1(t) f_2(t).$$

Then $f_2(t)$ is uniquely determined by $f(t)$ and $f_1(t)$.

For the proof we refer to Kawata (1940).

5.2 Definition of infinitely divisible characteristic functions

In this section we define infinitely divisible characteristic functions and distribution functions and also give some simple examples. The concept of infinite divisibility is very important in probability theory, particularly in the study of limit theorems. Since the discussion of limit theorems is beyond the scope of this monograph, we will not be able to reveal here the full significance of infinitely divisible characteristic functions. However, the analytic properties of this class of characteristic functions are of independent interest and will be studied in this chapter.

A characteristic function $f(t)$ is said to be infinitely divisible, if for every positive integer n, it is the nth power of some characteristic function.

This means that there exists for every positive integer n a characteristic function $f_n(t)$, such that

(5.2.1) $f(t) = [f_n(t)]^n$.

The function $f_n(t)$ is uniquely determined by $f(t)$, $f_n(t) = [f(t)]^{1/n}$, provided that one selects for the nth root the principal branch.[*] The

---

[*] For this determination $f_n(t)$ is continuous and $f_n(0) = 1$. It is defined in a neighbourhood of the origin in which $f(t)$ does not vanish. We shall see that $f(t) \neq 0$ for all t.

distribution functions which correspond to infinitely divisible characteristic functions are called infinitely divisible distributions.

Alternatively one could start by defining infinitely divisible distributions as distributions which can be written—for every positive integer n—as the n-fold convolution of some distribution function. It is obvious that this approach is equivalent to the one we used; we mention it here because it is sometimes convenient to express infinite divisibility in terms of distribution functions.

We give next a few examples of infinitely divisible distributions. In all these examples $f_n(t)$ has the same functional form as $f(t)$ but contains different parameters. In these cases we see immediately that $f(t)$ is infinitely divisible.

Examples of infinitely divisible characteristic functions

(a) The Degenerate distribution
$$f(t) = e^{i\xi t}, \qquad\qquad f_n(t) = e^{i(\xi/n)t}.$$

(b) The Poisson distribution
$$f(t) = \exp\{\lambda(e^{it} - 1)\}, \qquad f_n(t) = \exp\left\{\frac{\lambda}{n}(e^{it} - 1)\right\}.$$

(c) The Negative Binomial distribution
$$f(t) = \{p[1 - q\,e^{it}]^{-1}\}^r, \qquad f_n(t) = \{p[1 - q\,e^{it}]^{-1}\}^{r/n}.$$

(d) The Normal distribution
$$f(t) = \exp\left\{i\mu t - \frac{\sigma^2 t^2}{2}\right\}, \qquad f_n(t) = \exp\left\{i\frac{\mu}{n}t - \frac{\sigma^2 t^2}{2n}\right\}.$$

(e) The Cauchy distribution
$$f(t) = \exp\{i\mu t - \theta\,|t|\}, \qquad f_n(t) = \exp\left\{i\frac{\mu}{n}t - \frac{\theta}{n}|t|\right\}.$$

(f) The Gamma distribution
$$f(t) = [1 - (it/\theta)]^{-\lambda}, \qquad f_n(t) = [1 - (it/\theta)]^{-\lambda/n}.$$

5.3 Elementary properties of infinitely divisible characteristic functions

We establish first a simple but rather important property of infinitely divisible characteristic functions.

Theorem 5.3.1.   *An infinitely divisible characteristic function has no real zeros.*

Let $f(t)$ be an infinitely divisible characteristic function; then $|f_n(t)|^2 = |f(t)|^{2/n}$ is a characteristic function for any positive integer n. We consider
$$g(t) = \lim_{n\to\infty} |f_n(t)|^2 = \lim_{n\to\infty} |f(t)|^{2/n}.$$

The function $g(t)$ can assume only the two values 0 or 1 since $g(t) = 1$ whenever $f(t) \neq 0$, while $g(t) = 0$ for all t for which $f(t) = 0$. The function $f(t)$ is continuous and $f(0) = 1$, therefore $f(t) \neq 0$ in a certain neighbourhood of the origin. In the same neighbourhood $g(t) = 1$, thus $g(t)$ is continuous at $t = 0$ and is, as a limit of characteristic functions, also a characteristic function. But then it must be continuous everywhere and we see that $g(t) \equiv 1$. This means that $f(t) \neq 0$ for all real t.

The characteristic function of a purely discrete distribution with two discontinuity points (theorem 5.1.1) is indecomposable and therefore *a fortiori* not infinitely divisible. But such a function, for instance $f(t) = \frac{1}{3}(2 + e^{it})$, need not have real zeros. This example indicates that the converse of theorem 5.3.1 is not true; a characteristic function which has no real zeros is not necessarily infinitely divisible.

Theorem 5.3.1 can be used to show that a given distribution is not infinitely divisible. Consider for example the rectangular distribution; its characteristic function is

$$f(t) = e^{ita} \frac{\sin tr}{tr}.$$

Since $f(t)$ has real zeros it cannot be infinitely divisible.

We next discuss two theorems which permit us to assert that a given characteristic function is infinitely divisible.

Theorem 5.3.2.[*] *The product of a finite number of infinitely divisible characteristic functions is infinitely divisible.*

It is sufficient to prove the theorem for the case of two factors. Suppose therefore that $f(t)$ and $g(t)$ are infinitely divisible characteristic functions. Then there exist for any positive integer n two characteristic functions $f_n(t)$ and $g_n(t)$ such that $f(t) = [f_n(t)]^n$ and $g(t) = [g_n(t)]^n$. Then $h(t) = g(t) f(t) = [g_n(t) f_n(t)]^n$ so that $h(t)$ is also infinitely divisible.

As an example we consider the Laplace distribution which has the characteristic function $f(t) = 1/(1 + t^2)$. We can write

$$f(t) = \frac{1}{1 + it} \frac{1}{1 - it}$$

as the product of characteristic functions of two Gamma distributions with parameters $\theta = -1$, $\lambda = 1$ and $\theta = +1$, $\lambda = 1$ respectively. We know already that the Gamma distribution is infinitely divisible and conclude therefore that the Laplace distribution is also infinitely divisible.

---

[*] We give later [formula (5.5.12)] an example which shows that the converse statement is not true.

Corollary to theorem 5.3.2.   Let $f(t)$ be an infinitely divisible characteristic function, then $|f(t)|$ is also an infinitely divisible characteristic function.

It is immediately seen that $f(-t)$ is an infinitely divisible characteristic function whenever $f(t)$ is infinitely divisible. It follows then from theorem 5.3.2 that $|f(t)|^2$ is also infinitely divisible. This means that

$$(|f(t)|^2)^{1/2n} = |f(t)|^{1/n}$$

is a characteristic function for any positive integer n. But this implies the statement of the corollary.

We note that the result of this corollary cannot be improved since it is not possible to assert that $|f(t)|$ is a characteristic function whenever $f(t)$ is a characteristic function. Let for example $f(t) = \frac{1}{8}(1+7e^{it})$; then $|f(t)|^2 = \frac{1}{64}(50+7e^{-it}+7e^{it})$. We show by means of an indirect proof that $|f(t)|$ is not a characteristic function. According to the corollary to theorem 3.3.3 it must have the form $|f(t)| = a\,e^{it\xi}+(1-a)\,e^{it\eta}$. Therefore a should satisfy the relations $a^2 = (1-a)^2 = \frac{7}{64}$, $2a(1-a) = \frac{50}{64}$. Since these relations are inconsistent we conclude that $|f(t)|$ cannot be a characteristic function.

Theorem 5.3.3.   A characteristic function which is the limit of a sequence of infinitely divisible characteristic functions is infinitely divisible.

Let $f^{(k)}(t)$ be a sequence of infinitely divisible characteristic functions and suppose that this sequence converges to a characteristic function $f(t)$, so that

(5.3.1) $f(t) = \lim_{k\to\infty} f^{(k)}(t)$

is continuous.

Let n be an arbitrary positive integer. Then $|f^{(k)}(t)|^2$ and $|f(t)|^2$ are real characteristic functions and

$$\lim_{k\to\infty} |f^{(k)}(t)|^{2/n} = |f(t)|^{2/n}.$$

It follows from the continuity theorem that $|f(t)|^{2/n}$ is a characteristic function; hence $|f(t)|^2$ is infinitely divisible and therefore has (theorem 5.3.1) no real zero, so that it is possible to define its nth root

(5.3.2a) $f_n(t) = [f(t)]^{1/n} = \exp\left\{\frac{1}{n}\log f(t)\right\}.$

We write also

(5.3.2b) $f_n^{(k)}(t) = [f^{(k)}(t)]^{1/n} = \exp\left\{\frac{1}{n}\log f^{(k)}(t)\right\}.$

It follows from (5.3.1), (5.3.2a) and (5.3.2b) that

(5.3.3) $\lim_{k\to\infty} f_n^{(k)}(t) = f_n(t)$

where $f_n(t)$ is continuous at $t = 0$.

The characteristic functions $f^{(k)}(t)$ are by assumption infinitely divisible, so that the $f_n^{(k)}(t)$ are also characteristic functions. We conclude from (5.3.3) and the continuity theorem that $f_n(t)$ is also a characteristic function. Equation (5.3.2a) then indicates that $f(t)$ is infinitely divisible.

Corollary to theorem 5.3.3. *Let $f(t)$ be an infinitely divisible characteristic function; then $[f(t)]^\alpha$ is also a characteristic function for any real, positive α. The converse is also true.*

If $f(t)$ is infinitely divisible then the statement follows from the defining property for rational α and is obtained from the continuity theorem for arbitrary positive α. The converse is trivial.

Remark. A similar argument can be used to show that infinitely divisible characteristic functions could have been defined in a slightly different manner. A characteristic function is infinitely divisible if, and only if, there exists a sequence of positive integers n_k which tends to infinity and is such that for any k the function $f(t)$ is the (n_k)th power of some characteristic function $f_k(t)$.

Theorems 5.3.2 and 5.3.3 are closure theorems since they indicate that the family of infinitely divisible characteristic functions is closed under certain operations.

5.4 Construction of infinitely divisible characteristic functions

In this section we discuss two methods for the construction of infinitely divisible characteristic functions. These methods give some interesting information concerning the structure of infinitely divisible distributions.

We first prove a lemma which is of some independent interest.

Lemma 5.4.1. *Let $g(t)$ be an arbitrary characteristic function and suppose that p is a positive real number. Then $f(t) = \exp\{p[g(t)-1]\}$ is an infinitely divisible characteristic function.*

Let n be a positive integer such that $n > p$. Then

$$f_n(t) = \{[1-(p/n)]+(p/n)g(t)\}^n = \left\{1+\frac{p[g(t)-1]}{n}\right\}^n$$

is also a characteristic function. We see then from the continuity theorem that

$$f(t) = \lim_{n\to\infty} f_n(t) = \exp\{p[g(t)-1]\}$$

is also a characteristic function. The function $[f(t)]^\alpha$ $(\alpha > 0)$ satisfies the conditions of the lemma and is also a characteristic function. We conclude from the corollary to theorem 5.3.3 that $f(t)$ is infinitely divisible.

We use this lemma to prove the following theorem:

Theorem 5.4.1 (De Finetti's theorem).   A characteristic function is infinitely divisible if, and only if, it has the form

$$f(t) = \lim_{m \to \infty} \exp \{p_m[g_m(t)-1]\}$$

where the p_m are positive real numbers while the $g_m(t)$ are characteristic functions.

The sufficiency of the condition of the theorem follows immediately from lemma 5.4.1 and from the continuity theorem. We show next that the condition is necessary and assume that $f(t)$ is infinitely divisible. It follows from the corollary to theorem 5.3.3 and from lemma 5.4.1 that

$$f_\alpha(t) = \exp \left\{\frac{1}{\alpha}[(f(t))^\alpha - 1]\right\} \text{ is, for any real positive } \alpha, \text{ a characteristic}$$

function. Since

$$f(t) = \lim_{\alpha \to 0} f_\alpha(t)$$

we see that $f(t)$ can be represented in the above form with

$$p_m = m \quad \text{and} \quad g_m(t) = [f(t)]^{1/m}.$$

Theorem 5.4.2.   The limit of a sequence of finite products of Poisson-type characteristic functions is infinitely divisible. The converse is also true. Every infinitely divisible characteristic function can be written as the limit of a sequence of finite products of Poisson-type characteristic functions.

The first part of the theorem is a consequence of the closure theorems. To prove the second part we assume that $f(t)$ is infinitely divisible; according to De Finetti's theorem it can be represented as

$$(5.4.1) \qquad f(t) = \lim_{n \to \infty} \exp \{p_n [g_n(t)-1]\}$$

where the $g_n(t)$ are the characteristic functions of some distributions $G_n(x)$, so that

$$g_n(t) = \int_{-\infty}^{\infty} e^{itx} dG_n(x).$$

Then we see that

$$(5.4.2) \qquad p_n[g_n(t)-1] = \lim_{A \to \infty} p_n \int_{-A}^{A} (e^{itx}-1) dG_n(x).$$

We wish to approximate the integral by Darboux sums and therefore introduce the subdivision

$$-A = a_0 < a_1 < \ldots < a_{N-1} < a_N = +A$$

and write $c_k = p_n[G_n(a_k) - G_n(a_{k-1})]$. Then

$$p_n \int_{-A}^{A} (e^{itx} - 1)\, dG_n(x) = \lim_{N \to \infty} \sum_{k=1}^{N} c_k(e^{ita_k} - 1)$$

so that

$$(5.4.3) \qquad \exp\left[p_n \int_{-A}^{A} (e^{itx} - 1)\, dG_n(x) \right] = \lim_{N \to \infty} \prod_{k=1}^{N} \exp\left[c_k(e^{ita_k} - 1) \right].$$

The function (5.4.3) is the limit of a finite product of Poisson-type characteristic functions and we see from (5.4.1) and (5.4.2) that $f(t)$ also has this property.

The theorem can be used to show that a given characteristic function is infinitely divisible. As an example we consider the characteristic function

$$f(t) = \frac{p-1}{p - e^{it}} \quad (p > 1).$$

It is easily seen that

$$f(t) = \sum_{k=0}^{\infty} [1 - (1/p)](1/p)^k\, e^{itk},$$

and we note that this is the characteristic function of the geometric distribution listed in Table 1. We expand

$$\log f(t) = \log\left(1 - \frac{1}{p}\right) - \log\left(1 - \frac{e^{it}}{p}\right)$$

into a series and see that

$$f(t) = \prod_{k=1}^{\infty} \exp\left\{ \frac{1}{kp^k} (e^{itk} - 1) \right\}.$$

We can apply theorem 5.4.2 and see that $f(t)$ is infinitely divisible.

5.5 Canonical representations

The results of the preceding section can be used to deduce explicit formulae for infinitely divisible characteristic functions. For their derivation we need several auxiliary theorems.

Lemma 5.5.1. Let a be a real constant and let $\theta(x)$ be a real-valued, bounded and non-decreasing function of the real variable x such that $\theta(-\infty) = 0$. Suppose that a function $f(t)$ of the real variable t admits the representation

$$(5.5.1) \qquad \log f(t) = ita + \int_{-\infty}^{\infty} \left(e^{itx} - 1 - \frac{itx}{1+x^2} \right) \frac{1+x^2}{x^2}\, d\theta(x).$$

The integrand is defined for $x = 0$ by continuity, and is therefore equal to $-t^2/2$ if $x = 0$. Then $f(t)$ is an infinitely divisible characteristic function. Moreover, the constant a and the function $\theta(x)$ are uniquely determined by $f(t)$.

Let t belong to an arbitrary fixed interval; then it is seen that the integrand of (5.5.1) is bounded and continuous in x, so that the integral exists for all values of t. We first prove by repeated applications of the continuity theorem and of the closure theorems that $f(t)$ is an infinitely divisible characteristic function. Let $0 < \varepsilon < 1$ and define

$$(5.5.2) \qquad I_\varepsilon(t) = \int_{\varepsilon < |x| < (1/\varepsilon)} \left(e^{itx} - 1 - \frac{itx}{1+x^2} \right) \frac{1+x^2}{x^2} \, d\theta(x).$$

The function $I_\varepsilon(t)$ is continuous at $t = 0$; we can write it as a limit of Darboux sums $S_m(t)$ where

$$S_m(t) = \sum_{k=1}^{m} [\lambda_k (e^{itx_k} - 1) - i\mu_k t] \text{ with } \lambda_k = \frac{1+x_k^2}{x_k^2} [\theta(x_k) - \theta(x_{k-1})],$$

$$\mu_k = \frac{1}{x_k} [\theta(x_k) - \theta(x_{k-1})].$$

$S_m(t)$ is the second characteristic of a product of Poisson type characteristic functions. $I_\varepsilon(t)$ is the limit of these functions and therefore the logarithm of an infinitely divisible characteristic function. Let now

$$(5.5.3) \qquad I_0(t) = \lim_{\varepsilon \to 0} I_\varepsilon(t)$$

$$= \int_{|x| > 0} \left(e^{itx} - 1 - \frac{itx}{1+x^2} \right) \frac{1+x^2}{x^2} \, d\theta(x).$$

Clearly $I_0(t)$ is continuous at $t = 0$; we conclude again from the continuity theorem that $\exp[I_0(t)]$ is a characteristic function and then from theorem 5.3.3 that it is infinitely divisible. Finally it follows from (5.5.1) that

$$\log f(t) = I_0(t) + ita - \frac{t^2}{2} [\theta(+0) - \theta(-0)].$$

The last equation shows that $f(t)$ is the product of the infinitely divisible characteristic function $\exp[I_0(t)]$ and the characteristic function of a normal distribution, so that $f(t)$ is also infinitely divisible.

We show next that the constant a and the function $\theta(x)$ are uniquely determined by (5.5.1). We write $\phi(t) = \log f(t)$ for the second characteristic and see easily that

$$(5.5.4) \qquad \phi(t) - \tfrac{1}{2}[\phi(t+h) + \phi(t-h)]$$

$$= \int_{-\infty}^{\infty} e^{itx} (1 - \cos xh) \frac{1+x^2}{x^2} \, d\theta(x).$$

We now introduce the function

$$\lambda(t) = \int_0^1 \left[\phi(t) - \frac{\phi(t+h) + \phi(t-h)}{2} \right] dh.$$

Since the integrand in (5.5.4) is bounded, we can integrate with respect to h under the integral sign and obtain

$$\lambda(t) = \int_{-\infty}^{\infty} e^{itx} \left(1 - \frac{\sin x}{x}\right) \frac{1+x^2}{x^2}\, d\theta(x).$$

We next introduce the function

$$\Lambda(x) = \int_{-\infty}^{x} \left(1 - \frac{\sin y}{y}\right) \frac{1+y^2}{y^2}\, d\theta(y).$$

Then

$$\theta(x) = \int_{-\infty}^{x} \frac{y^2}{1+y^2} \left(1 - \frac{\sin y}{y}\right)^{-1} d\Lambda(y)$$

while

$$\lambda(t) = \int_{-\infty}^{\infty} e^{itx}\, d\Lambda(x).$$

It is easily seen that there exist two positive constants c_1 and c_2 such that

$$0 < c_1 \leqslant \left(1 - \frac{\sin y}{y}\right) \frac{1+y^2}{y^2} \leqslant c_2.$$

The function $\Lambda(x)$ is therefore non-decreasing and bounded; moreover $\Lambda(-\infty) = 0$. We conclude then that $\Lambda(x)/\Lambda(\infty)$ agrees with a distribution function at all continuity points of $\Lambda(x)$. Hence $\Lambda(x)$ is uniquely determined by its Fourier transform $\lambda(t)$. Since $\lambda(t)$ is defined in terms of $f(t)$, we see that $\Lambda(x)$ is uniquely determined by $f(t)$. The fact that the constant a is also determined by $f(t)$ is a consequence of (5.5.1).

Lemma 5.5.2. *Let* $\{\phi_n(t)\}$ *be a sequence of functions and suppose that* $f_n(t) = \exp[\phi_n(t)]$ *is determined by some constant* a_n *and some function* $\theta_n(x)$ *according to* (5.5.1). *Assume that the sequence* $\phi_n(t)$ *converges to some function* $\phi(t)$ *which is continuous at* $t = 0$. *Then there exists a constant* a *and a bounded and non-decreasing function* $\theta(x)$ *such that*

(i) $\lim_{n \to \infty} a_n = a$

(ii) $\operatorname{Lim}_{n \to \infty} \theta_n(x) = \theta(x)$

(iii) $\lim_{n \to \infty} \int_{-\infty}^{\infty} d\theta_n(x) = \int_{-\infty}^{\infty} d\theta(x).$

The function $\theta(x)$, *together with* a, *determines* $f(t) = \exp[\phi(t)]$ *according to* (5.5.1).

The functions $f_n(t)$ are characteristic functions. Therefore $f(t) = e^{\phi(t)}$ is also a characteristic function (by the continuity theorem) and $\phi(t)$ is everywhere continuous.

We use the same notation as before and write

$$\lambda_n(t) = \int_0^1 \left[\phi_n(t) - \frac{\phi_n(t+h) + \phi_n(t-h)}{2} \right] dh$$

$$\Lambda_n(x) = \int_{-\infty}^x \left(1 - \frac{\sin y}{y} \right) \frac{1+y^2}{y^2} \, d\theta_n(y)$$

so that

$$\lambda_n(t) = \int_{-\infty}^{\infty} e^{itx} \, d\Lambda_n(x).$$

From the continuity of $\phi(t)$ we conclude that the sequence $\lambda_n(t)$ converges to a continuous function. We apply corollary 3 to the continuity theorem (see page 52) to show that the sequence $\Lambda_n(x)$ converges weakly to a bounded non-decreasing function $\Lambda(x)$ and that

$$\lim_{n \to \infty} \int_{-\infty}^{\infty} d\Lambda_n(x) = \int_{-\infty}^{\infty} d\Lambda(x).$$

We have

$$\theta_n(x) = \int_{-\infty}^x \left(1 - \frac{\sin y}{y} \right)^{-1} \frac{y^2}{1+y^2} \, d\Lambda_n(y)$$

and conclude from Helly's second theorem that

$$\operatorname*{Lim}_{n \to \infty} \theta_n(x) = \int_{-\infty}^x \left(1 - \frac{\sin y}{y} \right)^{-1} \frac{y^2}{1+y^2} \, d\Lambda(y) = \theta(x) \text{ (say)}.$$

We write

$$I_n(t) = \int_{-\infty}^{\infty} \left(e^{itx} - 1 - \frac{itx}{1+x^2} \right) \frac{1+x^2}{x^2} \, d\theta_n(x)$$

and once more use Helly's second theorem to show that

$$\lim_{n \to \infty} I_n(t) = I(t)$$

where

$$I(t) = \int_{-\infty}^{\infty} \left(e^{itx} - 1 - \frac{itx}{1+x^2} \right) \frac{1+x^2}{x^2} \, d\theta(x).$$

From the convergence of the $\phi_n(t)$ and the $I_n(t)$ it follows that the sequence $\{a_n\}$ must also converge and that $\phi(t)$ is determined by

$$a = \lim_{n \to \infty} a_n$$

and $\theta(x)$ according to formula (5.5.1).

Lemma 5.5.3. Let $f(t)$ be an infinitely divisible characteristic function. Then there exists a sequence of functions $\phi_n(t)$ which have the form (5.5.1) such that

$$\lim_{n \to \infty} \phi_n(t) = \phi(t) = \log f(t).$$

We have, as $n \to \infty$,

$$n\{[f(t)]^{(1/n)} - 1\} = n\{e^{(1/n)\phi(t)} - 1\} = n\{(1/n)\,\phi(t) + o(1/n)\} = \phi(t) + o(1)$$

so that

(5.5.5) $\qquad \phi(t) = \lim_{n \to \infty} n\{[f(t)]^{1/n} - 1\}.$

Since, by assumption, $f(t)$ is infinitely divisible, $[f(t)]^{1/n}$ is a characteristic function. Denote the corresponding distribution function by $F_n(x)$; then

(5.5.6) $\qquad n\{[f(t)]^{1/n} - 1\} = n \int_{-\infty}^{\infty} (e^{itx} - 1)\, dF_n(x)$

$$= nit \int_{-\infty}^{\infty} \frac{x}{1+x^2}\, dF_n(x) + n \int_{-\infty}^{\infty} \left(e^{itx} - 1 - \frac{itx}{1+x^2}\right) dF_n(x).$$

If we write

$$a_n = n \int_{-\infty}^{\infty} \frac{x}{1+x^2}\, dF_n(x)$$

(5.5.7) $\qquad \theta_n(x) = n \int_{-\infty}^{x} \frac{y^2}{1+y^2}\, dF_n(y)$

$$\phi_n(t) = a_n it + \int_{-\infty}^{\infty} \left(e^{itx} - 1 - \frac{itx}{1+x^2}\right) \frac{1+x^2}{x^2}\, d\theta_n(x)$$

then we see from (5.5.5) and (5.5.6) that $\phi_n(t)$ has the form (5.5.1) and that

$$\lim_{n \to \infty} \phi_n(t) = \phi(t).$$

The three lemmas permit the derivation of the desired canonical representations for infinitely divisible characteristic functions.

Let now $f(t)$ be an infinitely divisible characteristic function. Since $f(t)$ cannot vanish, the function $\phi(t) = \log f(t)$ is defined for all values of t. According to lemma 5.5.3 there exists a sequence of functions $\phi_n(t)$ which has the following property: each $\phi_n(t)$ has the form (5.5.1) and the sequence $\phi_n(t)$ converges to $\phi(t)$ as n tends to infinity. It follows from lemma 5.5.2 that $\phi(t)$ also has the form (5.5.1). If we combine this with the result of lemma 5.5.1 we obtain the following theorem.

Theorem 5.5.1 (the Lévy–Khinchine canonical representation). The function $f(t)$ is an infinitely divisible characteristic function if, and only if, it can be written in the canonical form

(5.5.1) $\qquad \log f(t) = ita + \int_{-\infty}^{\infty} \left(e^{itx} - 1 - \frac{itx}{1+x^2}\right) \frac{1+x^2}{x^2}\, d\theta(x)$

where a is real and where $\theta(x)$ is a non-decreasing and bounded function such that $\theta(-\infty) = 0$. The integrand is defined for $x = 0$ by continuity to be equal to $-(t^2/2)$. The representation (5.5.1) is unique.

Remark 1.   It can happen that a characteristic function $f(t)$ admits a representation of the form (5.5.1) with a function $\theta(x)$ which is not a bounded non-decreasing function, but a function of bounded variation. Such a characteristic function $f(t)$ cannot be infinitely divisible.

Remark 2.   A proof of the Lévy–Khinchine representation by means of Choquet's theorem was given by S. Johansen (1966). The same paper contains also a characterization of the logarithm of an infinitely divisible characteristic function which is similar to Bochner's theorem.

The canonical representation given by the last theorem can be somewhat modified. We define two functions, $M(u)$ and $N(u)$ and a constant σ^2 by writing

$$M(u) = \int_{-\infty}^{u} \frac{1+x^2}{x^2}\, d\theta(x) \quad \text{for } u < 0$$

$$(5.5.8) \quad N(u) = -\int_{u}^{\infty} \frac{1+x^2}{x^2}\, d\theta(x) \quad \text{for } u > 0$$

$$\sigma^2 = \theta(+0) - \theta(-0).$$

The functions $M(u)$ and $N(u)$ are non-decreasing in the intervals $(-\infty, 0)$ and $(0, +\infty)$ respectively and $M(-\infty) = N(+\infty) = 0$. For every finite $\varepsilon > 0$, the integrals $\int_{-\varepsilon}^{0} u^2\, dM(u)$ and $\int_{0}^{\varepsilon} u^2\, dN(u)$ are finite. Conversely, any two functions $M(u)$ and $N(u)$ and any constant σ^2 satisfying these conditions determine, by (5.5.8) and (5.5.1), an infinitely divisible characteristic function. We have therefore obtained a second canonical form.

Theorem 5.5.2 (*the Lévy canonical representation*).   *The function $f(t)$ is an infinitely divisible characteristic function if, and only if, it can be written in the form*

$$(5.5.9) \quad \log f(t) = ita - \frac{\sigma^2}{2}t^2 + \int_{-\infty}^{-0} \left(e^{itu} - 1 - \frac{itu}{1+u^2}\right) dM(u)$$

$$+ \int_{+0}^{\infty} \left(e^{itu} - 1 - \frac{itu}{1+u^2}\right) dN(u)$$

where $M(u)$, $N(u)$ and σ^2 satisfy the following conditions:

   (i) *$M(u)$ and $N(u)$ are non-decreasing in the intervals $(-\infty, 0)$ and $(0, +\infty)$ respectively.*

   (ii) *$M(-\infty) = N(+\infty) = 0$.*

   (iii) *The integrals $\int_{-\varepsilon}^{0} u^2\, dM(u)$ and $\int_{0}^{\varepsilon} u^2\, dN(u)$ are finite for every $\varepsilon > 0$.*

   (iv) *The constant σ^2 is real and non-negative.*

The representation (5.5.9) is unique.

The canonical representations (5.5.1) and (5.5.9) are generalizations of a representation, due to Kolmogorov, which is valid only for the characteristic functions of infinitely divisible distributions with finite variance.

Theorem 5.5.3 (*the Kolmogorov canonical representation*). *The function $f(t)$ is the characteristic function of an infinitely divisible distribution with finite second moment if, and only if, it can be written in the form*

$$(5.5.10) \qquad \log f(t) = ict + \int_{-\infty}^{\infty} (e^{itx} - 1 - itx) \frac{dK(x)}{x^2}$$

where c is a real constant while $K(u)$ is a non-decreasing and bounded function such that $K(-\infty) = 0$. The representation is unique.

The integrand $(e^{itx} - 1 - itx)/x^2$ is defined for $x = 0$ to be equal to $-(t^2/2)$.

Let $f(t)$ be an infinitely divisible characteristic function and suppose that the second moment of its distribution function exists and is finite. Then $f(t)$, and therefore also $\phi(t) = \log f(t)$, can be differentiated twice. We form the second central difference quotient

$$\frac{\Delta_2^h \phi(0)}{(2h)^2}$$

and conclude that

$$(5.5.11) \qquad \liminf_{h \to 0} \left| \frac{\Delta_2^h \phi(0)}{(2h)^2} \right| < \infty.$$

We note that $f(t)$ admits a representation (5.5.1) and use (5.5.11) to show

that the integral $\int_{-\infty}^{\infty} (1+x^2) \, d\theta(x)$ is finite. Then $\int_{-\infty}^{\infty} x \, d\theta(x)$ is also finite.

We write $K(x) = \int_{-\infty}^{x} (1+y^2) \, d\theta(y)$ and $c = a + \int_{-\infty}^{\infty} y \, d\theta(y)$ and ob-

tain (5.5.10).

Conversely, suppose that the function $\phi(t) = \log f(t)$ admits a representation (5.5.10). Then

$$\theta(x) = \int_{-\infty}^{x} \frac{dK(y)}{1+y^2}$$

satisfies the conditions of theorem 5.5.1, so that $f(t)$ is an infinitely divisible characteristic function. Moreover, it is easily seen that (5.5.10) may be differentiated twice under the integral sign, so that the second moment of the distribution function corresponding to $f(t)$ exists. The uniqueness of the representation is an immediate consequence of the uniqueness of the representation (5.5.1).

R

As an illustration we determine the canonical representation for a given infinitely divisible characteristic function. The procedure repeats the steps of the proofs of lemmas 5.5.3 and 5.5.2. We consider as an example the Gamma distribution

$$F(x) = \begin{cases} \dfrac{\theta^\lambda}{\Gamma(\lambda)} \displaystyle\int_0^x y^{\lambda-1} e^{-\theta y}\, dy & \text{for } x > 0, \\ 0 & \text{for } x < 0. \end{cases}$$

The corresponding characteristic function is

$$f(t) = \left(1 - \frac{it}{\theta}\right)^{-\lambda}$$

where θ and λ are two positive parameters. It follows from the form of $f(t)$ that it is an infinitely divisible characteristic function, so that $[f(t)]^{1/n}$ is also a characteristic function. We denote the corresponding distribution function by $F_n(x)$; clearly $F_n(x)$ is also a Gamma distribution and

$$F_n(x) = \begin{cases} \dfrac{\theta^{(\lambda/n)}}{\Gamma(\lambda/n)} \displaystyle\int_0^x y^{(\lambda/n)-1} e^{-\theta y}\, dy & \text{for } x > 0 \\ 0 & \text{for } x < 0. \end{cases}$$

Substituting this into (5.5.7) we get

$$\theta_n(x) = \begin{cases} \dfrac{n\theta^{\lambda/n}}{\Gamma(\lambda/n)} \displaystyle\int_0^x \dfrac{y}{1+y^2}\, y^{\lambda/n} e^{-\theta y}\, dy & \text{for } x > 0 \\ 0 & \text{for } x < 0 \end{cases}$$

and

$$a_n = \frac{n\theta^{\lambda/n}}{\Gamma(\lambda/n)} \int_0^\infty \frac{1}{1+y^2}\, y^{\lambda/n} e^{-\theta y}\, dy.$$

We note that

$$\lim_{n\to\infty} \frac{n}{\Gamma(\lambda/n)} = \lim_{n\to\infty} \frac{\lambda}{(\lambda/n)\,\Gamma(\lambda/n)} = \lim_{n\to\infty} \frac{\lambda}{\Gamma[(\lambda/n)+1]} = \lambda$$

and obtain from lemma 5.5.2

$$\theta(x) = \operatorname*{Lim}_{n\to\infty} \theta_n(x) = \begin{cases} \lambda \displaystyle\int_0^x \dfrac{y}{1+y^2}\, e^{-\theta y}\, dy & \text{for } x > 0 \\ 0 & \text{for } x < 0 \end{cases}$$

while

$$a = \lim_{n\to\infty} a_n = \lambda \int_0^\infty \frac{e^{-\theta y}}{1+y^2}\, dy.$$

It is then easy to compute the other canonical representations.

Table 5 lists the canonical representations of some of the more common infinitely divisible characteristic functions.

Table 5
Canonical representations of infinitely divisible characteristic functions

Name of distribution	Characteristic function	Lévy-Khinchine representation		Lévy representation				Kolmogorov representation	
		a	$\theta(x)$	a	σ	$M(u)$ $u<0$	$N(u)$ $u>0$	c	$K(x)$
Normal	$\exp\left[it\mu-\tfrac{1}{2}\sigma^2 t^2\right]$ μ real, $\sigma^2\geq 0$	μ	$\sigma^2\epsilon(x)$	μ	σ	0	0	μ	$\sigma^2\epsilon(x)$
Gamma	$(1-it/\theta)^{-\lambda}$ $\theta>0,\ \lambda>0$	$\lambda\displaystyle\int_0^\infty \frac{e^{-\theta y}}{1+y^2}\,dy$	0 for $x<0$ $\lambda\displaystyle\int_0^x \frac{y\,e^{-\theta y}}{1+y^2}\,dy$ for $x>0$	$\lambda\displaystyle\int_0^\infty \frac{e^{-\theta y}}{1+y^2}\,dy$	0	0	$-\lambda\displaystyle\int_u^\infty \frac{e^{-\theta x}}{x}\,dx$	λ/θ	0 for $x<0$ $\lambda\displaystyle\int_0^x y\,e^{-\theta y}\,dy$ for $x>0$
Cauchy	$e^{-\theta|t|}$ $\theta>0$	0	$(\theta/\pi)\ \text{arc tan } x+\theta/2$		0	$-\dfrac{\theta}{\pi u}$	$\dfrac{\theta}{\pi u}$	No representation possible	
Degenerate	$e^{it\xi}$ ξ real	ξ	0	ξ	0	0	0	ξ	0
Poisson	$\exp[\lambda(e^{it}-1)]$ $\lambda>0$	$\lambda/2$	$(\lambda/2)\epsilon(x-1)$	$\lambda/2$	0	0	$\lambda\epsilon(u-1)$	λ	$\lambda\epsilon(x-1)$
Negative Binomial	$\left(\dfrac{p}{1-qe^{it}}\right)^r$ $p>0$ $q=1-p>0$ $r>0$	$r\displaystyle\sum_{k=1}^\infty \frac{q^k}{1+k^2}$	0 for $x<0$ $r\displaystyle\sum_{k=0}^\infty \frac{k}{1+k^2}q^k\epsilon(x-k)$ for $x>0$	$r\displaystyle\sum_{k=1}^\infty \frac{q^k}{1+k^2}$	0	0	$r\displaystyle\sum_{k=1}^\infty \frac{q^k}{k}\epsilon(u-k)$ $+r\log p$	$\dfrac{rq}{p}$	0 for $x<0$ $r\displaystyle\sum_{k=0}^\infty kq^k\epsilon(x-k)$ for $x>0$

We conclude this section with a few remarks concerning the factorization of infinitely divisible characteristic functions.

Theorem 5.5.4. Let $f(t)$ be an infinitely divisible characteristic function and suppose that it can be decomposed into two infinitely divisible factors, $f(t) = f_1(t)f_2(t)$. Then $f(t)$ and $f_1(t)$ determine $f_2(t)$ uniquely.

The theorem follows immediately from the uniqueness of the canonical representation; it shows that the cancellation law holds if we restrict the decompositions to infinitely divisible factors.

However, these are not the only possible decompositions; infinitely divisible characteristic functions can have factors which are not themselves infinitely divisible. We give the following example.

Let a and b be two positive real numbers and write $v = a+ib$. It can be shown that the function

$$(5.5.12) \qquad f(t) = \frac{[1+(it/v)][1+(it/\bar{v})]}{[1-(it/a)][1-(it/v)][1-(it/\bar{v})]}$$

is a characteristic function [*] if

$$(5.5.13) \qquad b \geqslant 2a\sqrt{2}.$$

Then $f(-t)$ is also a characteristic function, as is

$$g(t) = f(t)f(-t) = |f(t)|^2 = \frac{1}{1+(t^2/a^2)}.$$

We will show later (theorem 8.4.1) that $f(t)$ and therefore also $f(-t)$ are not infinitely divisible. The product $g(t) = f(t)f(-t)$ is the characteristic function of the Laplace distribution which is known to be infinitely divisible (see page 109). The function $f(t)$, determined by (5.5.12) and (5.5.13), has the following interesting property: $f(t)$ is a characteristic function but is not infinitely divisible, however $|f(t)|^2$ and therefore also $|f(t)|$ are infinitely divisible characteristic functions. Thus, the infinitely divisible characteristic function $|f(t)|^2$ admits two decompositions,

$$|f(t)|^2 = |f(t)| \cdot |f(t)| = f(t)f(-t).$$

The first decomposition has two infinitely divisible factors while the factors of the second decomposition are not infinitely divisible. This example shows that two different characteristic functions, namely $f(t)$ and $|f(t)|$, can have the same absolute value.

The next example [†] presents an even more surprising phenomenon by

---

[*] To show this, one expands $f(t)$ into partial fractions and computes

$$\frac{1}{2\pi} \int_{-\infty}^{\infty} e^{-itx} f(t)\, dt$$

by integrating the expansion term by term. It is not difficult to show that the resulting expression is non-negative if (5.5.13) is satisfied.

[†] Due to W. Feller.

showing that two different real characteristic functions may have the same square.

Let $f(t)$ be a real periodic function with period 2 which is defined by putting $f(t) = 1 - |t|$ for $|t| \leqslant 1$. The function $f(t)$ satisfies the conditions of theorem 4.3.2 and is therefore a characteristic function. We consider also the Pólya-type characteristic function (4.3.11), that is,

$$k(t) = \begin{cases} 1 - |t| & \text{for } |t| \leqslant 1 \\ 0 & \text{for } |t| \geqslant 1. \end{cases}$$

It follows from (4.3.9) that

$$(5.5.14) \qquad f(t) = \frac{A_0}{2} + \sum_{n=1}^{\infty} A_n \cos n\pi t$$

where $\quad A_n = \int_{-1}^{+1} f(t) \cos n\pi t \, dt = 2 \int_{0}^{1} (1-t) \cos n\pi t \, dt \geqslant 0$

so that $\qquad A_0 = 1 \quad$ while $\quad \sum_{n=1}^{\infty} A_n = \frac{1}{2}.$

Clearly $f(t)$ is the characteristic function of a lattice distribution $F(x)$ which has a jump of magnitude $\frac{1}{2}$ at $x = 0$ and jumps $A_n/2$ at the points $n = k\pi$ $(k = \pm 1, \pm 2, \ldots)$. We introduce now a second lattice distribution $H(x)$ which has saltus 0 at $x = 0$ and saltus A_n at the points $n = k\pi$ $(k = \pm 1, \pm 2, \ldots)$. The corresponding characteristic function is

$$h(t) = 2 \sum_{n=1}^{\infty} A_n \cos n\pi t.$$

It is easily seen that

$$h(t) = 2[f(t) - \tfrac{1}{2}]$$

so that

$$(5.5.15) \qquad g(t) = h\left(\frac{t}{2}\right) = 2\left[f\left(\frac{t}{2}\right) - \tfrac{1}{2}\right]$$

is also a characteristic function. It follows from (5.5.15) that $g(t)$ is periodic with period 4 and that $g(t) = 1 - |t|$ for $|t| \leqslant 2$. It is easily seen [for instance by considering the graphs of $f(t)$ and $g(t)$] that $|f(t)| = |g(t)|$. Since $f(t)$ and $g(t)$ are both real-valued functions this means that $[f(t)]^2 = [g(t)]^2$.

We next give another example which shows that an infinitely divisible characteristic function may have an indecomposable factor.

Let p and q be two positive real numbers such that

$$p > q > 0 \quad \text{and} \quad p + q = 1.$$

The function

$$g_1(t) = p + q e^{it}$$

is then—according to theorem 5.1.1—an indecomposable characteristic function. We write

$$\gamma_1(t) = \log g_1(t) = \log p + \log [1 + (q/p) e^{it}]$$

$$= \log p + \sum_{j=1}^{\infty} \frac{(-1)^{j-1}}{j} \left(\frac{q}{p}\right)^j e^{ijt}.$$

It is then easily seen that

$$\gamma_1(t) = \sum_{j=1}^{\infty} \frac{(-1)^{j-1}}{j} \left(\frac{q}{p}\right)^j (e^{itj} - 1).$$

Let

$$\phi(t) = \sum_{n=1}^{\infty} \frac{1}{2n-1} \left(\frac{q}{p}\right)^{2n-1} [e^{it(2n-1)} - 1]$$

$$\gamma_2(t) = \sum_{n=1}^{\infty} \frac{1}{2n} \left(\frac{q}{p}\right)^{2n} [e^{2nit} - 1],$$

then

$$\gamma_1(t) = \phi(t) - \gamma_2(t).$$

The functions $f(t) = e^{\phi}$ and $g_2(t) = e^{\gamma_2(t)}$ are infinitely divisible characteristic functions; moreover,

$$f(t) = g_1(t) g_2(t).$$

The infinitely divisible characteristic function $f(t)$ therefore has an indecomposable factor $g_1(t)$.

We conclude this section by mentioning certain investigations concerning the "Lebesgue properties" (absolute continuity, singularity, discreteness) of infinitely divisible distributions. P. Hartman and A. Wintner (1942) proved that an infinitely divisible characteristic function belongs to a pure distribution if the function $\theta(x)$ in its Lévy–Khinchine canonical representation is discrete. These authors also gave examples of the three possible pure types of infinitely divisible characteristic functions. The existence of infinitely divisible distribution functions of all these types suggests the problem of finding conditions on the function $\theta(x)$ of the Lévy–Khinchine canonical representation [respectively on σ^2, $M(u)$, $N(u)$ of the Lévy canonical representation] which assure that the corresponding distribution function belongs to a specified type.

J. R. Blum and M. Rosenblatt (1959) obtained the following result in this direction.

Theorem 5.5.5.   *Let $F(x)$ be an infinitely divisible distribution with characteristic function $f(t)$ and let $\theta(x)$ be the function in its Lévy–Khinchine canonical representation. Then*

(i) *$F(x)$ is discrete if, and only if,*

$$\int_{-\infty}^{\infty} \frac{1}{x^2} d\theta(x) < \infty \text{ and if } \theta(x) \text{ is purely discrete.}$$

(ii) $F(x)$ *is a mixture if, and only if,*

$$\int_{-\infty}^{\infty} \frac{1}{x^2} d\theta(x) < \infty \text{ while } \theta(x) \text{ is not purely discrete.}$$

(iii) $F(x)$ *is continuous*[*] *if, and only if,*

$$\int_{-\infty}^{\infty} \frac{1}{x^2} d\theta(x) = \infty.$$

Theorem 5.5.5 gives a satisfactory criterion for the discreteness of an infinitely divisible distribution but does not permit us to distinguish between purely singular and purely absolutely continuous distributions.

H. G. Tucker (1962) supplemented this result by giving a sufficient condition which assures that an infinitely divisible distribution is absolutely continuous.

Theorem 5.5.6. *Let $F(x)$ be an infinitely divisible distribution with characteristic function $f(t)$ and let $\theta(x)$ be the function in its Lévy–Khinchine canonical representation. Then $F(x)$ is absolutely continuous if at least one of the following two conditions is satisfied:*

(i) $\theta(x)$ *is not continuous at $x = 0$, or*

(ii) $\displaystyle\int_{-\infty}^{\infty} \frac{1}{x^2} d\theta_{ac}(x) = 0.$

The function $\theta_{ac}(x)$ is the absolutely continuous component of $\theta(x)$. We write here and in the following $\displaystyle\int_{-\infty}^{\infty} = \int_{-\infty}^{-0} + \int_{+0}^{\infty}.$

A similar sufficient condition was given by M. Fisz and V. S. Varadarajan (1963) who used the Lévy canonical representation.

In a subsequent paper H. G. Tucker (1964) gave sufficient conditions which assure that a discrete $\theta(x)$ such that $\theta(+0) - \theta(-0) = 0$ [or alternatively the discrete functions $M(u)$ and $N(u)$ defined by (5.5.8) for the Lévy canonical representation] produce the characteristic function of a purely singular infinitely divisible distribution function. These sufficient conditions are not satisfied for an example given by P. Hartman–A. Wintner (1942) of discrete functions $M(u)$ and $N(u)$ which produce a purely singular distribution function.

A necessary and sufficient condition for the absolute continuity of an infinitely divisible distribution was also given by H. G. Tucker (1965), and this we now state. For the formulation of this condition it is convenient to

---

[*] i.e. absolutely continuous, or continuous singular, or a mixture of an absolutely continuous and a singular component.

write (5.5.8) in a slightly different form. We put

$$G(u) = \begin{cases} M(u) = \displaystyle\int_{-\infty}^{u} \frac{1+x^2}{x^2}\,d\theta(x) & \text{for } u < 0 \\[3mm] N(u) = -\displaystyle\int_{u}^{\infty} \frac{1+x^2}{x^2}\,d\theta(x) & \text{for } u > 0. \end{cases}$$

The Lévy canonical representation is then given by

$$(5.5.16) \qquad \log f(t) = ita - \sigma^2 t^2/2 + \int_{-\infty}^{\infty} \left(e^{itu} - 1 - \frac{itu}{1+u^2} \right) dG(u).$$

We also introduce the following notation. Let $G_{ac}(u)$, $G_s(u)$ and $G_d(u)$ be the absolutely continuous, the singular, and the discrete component of $G(u)$, respectively, and write $F^i(x)$ for the infinitely divisible distribution function which is obtained if $G(u)$ is replaced by $G_i(u)$ ($i = ac, s, d$) in (5.5.16).

We can now formulate Tucker's necessary and sufficient condition:

Theorem 5.5.7.   Let $F(x)$ be an infinitely divisible distribution function with characteristic function given by (5.5.16). A necessary and sufficient condition that $F(x)$ be absolutely continuous is that at least one of the following five conditions holds:

(i) $\displaystyle\int_{-\infty}^{\infty} dG_{ac}(u) = \infty$;

(ii) $\sigma^2 > 0$ [*i.e. $\theta(u)$ not continuous at $u = 0$*];
(iii) $F^d(x)$ *is absolutely continuous*;
(iv) $F^s(x)$ *is absolutely continuous*;
(v) $F^d(x)$ *is singular, $F^s(x)$ is continuous but not absolutely continuous, while $F^d * F^s$ is absolutely continuous.*

Remark.   The theorem does not state that each of the conditions (i) to (v) is necessary, but it states that at least one of them is necessary. Each of these conditions is sufficient for the absolute continuity of $F(x)$.

5.6   A limit theorem

We have shown (theorem 5.3.3) that a characteristic function which is the limit of a sequence of infinitely divisible characteristic functions is also infinitely divisible. In the present section we show that under certain conditions the limit of a sequence of characteristic functions is infinitely divisible, even if the elements of the sequence are not infinitely divisible characteristic functions.

We consider in the following an infinite sequence of finite sets of characteristic functions. Such a system $\{f_{nj}(t)\}$ ($j = 1, 2, \ldots, k_n$;

$n = 1, 2, \ldots,$ *ad. inf.*) can be arranged in a two-dimensional array:

$$(5.6.1) \quad \begin{cases} f_{11}(t),\ f_{12}(t),\ \ldots,\ f_{1k_1}(t); \\ f_{21}(t),\ f_{22}(t),\ \ldots,\ f_{2k_2}(t); \\ \cdots\cdots\cdots\cdots\cdots\cdots; \\ \cdots\cdots\cdots\cdots\cdots\cdots; \\ f_{n1}(t),\ f_{n2}(t),\ \ldots,\ f_{nk_n}(t); \\ \cdots\cdots\cdots\cdots\cdots\cdots \end{cases}$$

We form the (finite) products

$$f_n(t) = \prod_{j=1}^{k_n} f_{nj}(t)$$

of the functions in each row of the scheme (5.6.1) and wish to investigate their limits. As usual, we denote by $F_{nj}(x)$ the distribution function which corresponds to $f_{nj}(t)$. The following theorem contains a very important result.

Theorem 5.6.1. Let $\{f_{nj}(t)\}$ $(j = 1, 2, \ldots, k_n; n = 1, 2, \ldots,$ ad. inf.) be a system of characteristic functions and suppose that, for all t,

$$(5.6.2) \quad \lim_{n \to \infty} [\ \sup_{1 < j < k_n}\ |f_{nj}(t) - 1|\ ] = 0.$$

Denote by $g_n(t)$ the characteristic function determined by

$$(5.6.3) \quad \log g_n(t) = \sum_{j=1}^{k_n} \left\{ it\alpha_{nj} + \int_{-\infty}^{\infty} (e^{itx} - 1)\, dF_{nj}(x + \alpha_{nj}) \right\}$$

where

$$\alpha_{nj} = \int_{|x| < \tau} x\, dF_{nj}(x)$$

and where $\tau > 0$ is a constant. The necessary and sufficient condition for the convergence of the sequence of characteristic functions

$$(5.6.4) \quad f_n(t) = \prod_{j=1}^{k_n} f_{nj}(t)$$

to a characteristic function $f(t)$ is that the sequence $g_n(t)$ converge to a limit. Then the limits of the sequences $f_n(t)$ and $g_n(t)$ coincide.

The characteristic functions $g_n(t)$ are infinitely divisible. This can be seen by writing them in the canonical form (5.5.1) with

$$\theta(x) = \sum_{j=1}^{k_n} \int_{-\infty}^{x} \frac{y^2}{1+y^2}\, dF_{nj}(y + \alpha_{nj})$$

and

$$a = \sum_{j=1}^{k_n} \left[\alpha_{nj} + \int_{-\infty}^{\infty} \frac{x}{1+x^2}\, dF_{nj}(x + \alpha_{nj}) \right]$$

or by noting that the $g_n(t)$ are finite products of limits of Poisson-type characteristic functions. Theorem 5.6.1 indicates that it is possible to replace the investigation of the limit of a system of arbitrary characteristic functions [subject to the restriction (5.6.2)] by the investigation of the limit of a sequence of infinitely divisible characteristic functions. This circumstance explains the great importance of theorem 5.6.1 in connection with the study of limit distributions for sums of independent random variables.

We do not intend to discuss limit theorems in this monograph and will therefore not be in a position to appreciate the full significance of this theorem. For its proof we refer the reader to B. V. Gnedenko–A. N. Kolmogorov (1954), p. 112, where this result can be found in its proper context.

In connection with our investigation of factorization problems we will use a corollary to theorem 5.6.1.

Corollary to theorem 5.6.1. *Let $f(t)$ be a characteristic function and suppose that $f(t)$ admits a sequence of decompositions*

$$f(t) = \prod_{j=1}^{k_n} f_{nj}(t) \qquad (n = 1, 2, \ldots)$$

where the $f_{nj}(t)$ $(j = 1, 2, \ldots, k_n; n = 1, 2, \ldots)$ form a system of characteristic functions which satisfy (5.6.2). Then $f(t)$ is infinitely divisible.

The corollary follows immediately from theorem 5.6.1 if we observe that $f_n(t) = f(t)$.

5.7 Characteristic functions of stable distributions

In this section we discuss a class of infinitely divisible distribution functions, the so-called stable distributions. Stable distributions and their characteristic functions are important in connection with certain limit theorems and were originally introduced in this context. Our study of these distributions is motivated by the fact that the class of stable characteristic functions is of independent interest and occurs also in some problems not related to limit theorems.

A distribution function $F(x)$ is said to be stable if to every $b_1 > 0$, $b_2 > 0$, and real c_1, c_2 there corresponds a positive number b and a real number c such that the relation

$$(5.7.1) \qquad F\left(\frac{x-c_1}{b_1}\right) * F\left(\frac{x-c_2}{b_2}\right) = F\left(\frac{x-c}{b}\right)$$

holds.

The characteristic function of a stable distribution is called a stable characteristic function.

Equation (5.7.1) is not so much a property of an individual distribution function $F(x)$ but is rather a characteristic of the type to which $F(x)$

belongs. It would therefore be more appropriate to say that a distribution belongs to a stable type if its type is closed with respect to convolutions.

The defining relation (5.7.1) can be expressed in terms of characteristic functions as

$$(5.7.2) \qquad f(b_1 t) f(b_2 t) = f(bt) e^{i\gamma t}$$

where $\gamma = c - c_1 - c_2$.

Let $b_1', b_2', \ldots, b_n'$ be n positive real numbers; it follows then from (5.7.2) that

$$f(b_1' t) f(b_2' t) \ldots f(b_n' t) = f(b' t) e^{i\gamma' t}$$

where γ' is some real number, while b' is a positive number. If we put $b_j' = 1 \ (j = 1, \ldots, n)$ and write b_n for the corresponding value of b', then we get

$$[f(t)]^n = f(b_n t) e^{i\gamma' t}$$

or

$$f(t) = \left\{ f\left(\frac{t}{b_n}\right) \exp\left[-\frac{i\gamma' t}{n b_n}\right] \right\}^n.$$

The last formula implies the following result:

Theorem 5.7.1. *A stable characteristic function is always infinitely divisible.*

We see therefore that a stable characteristic function has no real zeros. We can take logarithms in (5.7.2) and express this equation in terms of the second characteristic $\phi(t)$. We obtain

$$(5.7.3) \qquad \phi(b_1 t) + \phi(b_2 t) = \phi(bt) + i\gamma t.$$

Since $\phi(t)$ is the logarithm of an infinitely divisible characteristic function, we can write it in the canonical form (5.5.1) as

$$\phi(t) = ita + \int_{-\infty}^{\infty} \left(e^{itx} - 1 - \frac{itx}{1+x^2} \right) \frac{1+x^2}{x^2} \, d\theta(x).$$

It follows that

$$\phi(bt) = iatb + \int_{-\infty}^{\infty} \left(e^{ity} - 1 - \frac{ity}{1+b^{-2}y^2} \right) \frac{1+b^{-2}y^2}{b^{-2}y^2} \, d\theta(b^{-1}y).$$

Since the function $z/(1+b^2 z^2)$ is bounded, we see that the integral

$$b \int_{-\infty}^{\infty} \frac{z}{1+b^2 z^2} \, d\theta(z) = \int_{-\infty}^{\infty} \frac{y}{1+y^2} \, d\theta(b^{-1}y)$$

exists. We write

$$a_b = ba + (1 - b^2) \int_{-\infty}^{\infty} \frac{y}{1+y^2} \, d\theta(b^{-1}y)$$

and obtain, by means of an elementary computation,

$$(5.7.4) \qquad \phi(bt) = ita_b + \int_{-\infty}^{\infty} \left(e^{ity} - 1 - \frac{ity}{1+y^2} \right) \frac{1+b^{-2}y^2}{b^{-2}y^2} \, d\theta(b^{-1}y).$$

We introduce again the functions

$$M(u) = \int_{-\infty}^{u} \frac{1+y^2}{y^2} d\theta(y) \quad \text{where } u < 0$$

$$N(u) = -\int_{u}^{\infty} \frac{1+y^2}{y^2} d\theta(y) \quad \text{where } u > 0$$

and write $\sigma^2 = \theta(+0) - \theta(-0)$. With this notation we obtain from (5.7.3) and (5.7.4) the relation

$$ita_{b_1} - \frac{b_1^2 \sigma^2}{2} t^2 + \int_{-\infty}^{-0} \left(e^{ity} - 1 - \frac{ity}{1+y^2} \right) dM(b_1^{-1}y)$$

$$+ \int_{+0}^{\infty} \left(e^{ity} - 1 - \frac{ity}{1+y^2} \right) dN(b_1^{-1}y) + ita_{b_2} - \frac{b_2^2 \sigma^2}{2} t^2$$

$$+ \int_{-\infty}^{-0} \left(e^{ity} - 1 - \frac{ity}{1+y^2} \right) dM(b_2^{-1}y) + \int_{+0}^{\infty} \left(e^{ity} - 1 - \frac{ity}{1+y^2} \right) dN(b_2^{-1}y)$$

$$= ita_b - \frac{b^2 \sigma^2}{2} t^2 + \int_{-\infty}^{-0} \left(e^{ity} - 1 - \frac{ity}{1+y^2} \right) dM(b^{-1}y)$$

$$+ \int_{+0}^{\infty} \left(e^{ity} - 1 - \frac{ity}{1+y^2} \right) dN(b^{-1}y) + i\gamma t.$$

From the uniqueness of the canonical representation we see that

(5.7.5a) $\sigma^2(b^2 - b_1^2 - b_2^2) = 0$

(5.7.5b) $M(b^{-1}y) = M(b_1^{-1}y) + M(b_2^{-1}y) \quad \text{if } y < 0$

(5.7.5c) $N(b^{-1}y) = N(b_1^{-1}y) + N(b_2^{-1}y) \quad \text{if } y > 0.$

We first determine the function $M(u)$ $(u < 0)$. Let $\beta_1, \beta_2, \ldots, \beta_n$ be n positive real numbers; it follows from (5.7.5b) that there exists a positive number $\beta = \beta(\beta_1, \beta_2, \ldots, \beta_n)$ such that

$$M(\beta_1 y) + M(\beta_2 y) + \ldots + M(\beta_n y) = M(\beta y).$$

We substitute here $\beta_j = 1$ $(j = 1, \ldots, n)$ and write $\beta(1, 1, \ldots, 1) = A_n$ and see that

$$nM(y) = M(yA_n)$$

or

$$(1/n)M(y) = M(y/A_n).$$

Here $y < 0$ and $A_n > 0$. Using this reasoning we see that to every positive rational number $r = m/n$ (m, n positive integers) there corresponds a positive real number $A = A(r) = A_m/A_n$ such that

(5.7.6) $rM(y) = M(Ay)$ $(y < 0).$

The function $A = A(r)$ is defined for all rational $r > 0$; we show next that $A(r)$ is non-increasing for rational values of the argument. Let r_1 and r_2 be two rational numbers and suppose that $r_1 < r_2$. Since

$M(u) \geqslant 0$ we see that $r_1 M(u) \leqslant r_2 M(u)$ or, according to (5.7.6), $M[A(r_1)u] \leqslant M[A(r_2)u]$. Since $M(u)$ is non-decreasing and $u < 0$ we conclude that $A(r_1) \geqslant A(r_2)$. By the same reasoning we can show that $A(r)$ is strictly decreasing, provided that $M(u) \not\equiv 0$. Let us suppose from now on that $M(u) \not\equiv 0$.

We now define a function for all positive real values of x by means of

$$(5.7.7) \qquad B(x) = \begin{cases} A(x) & \text{if } x \text{ is a positive rational number} \\ \operatorname*{l.u.b.}_{r>x} A(r) & \text{if } x > 0 \text{ is irrational.} \end{cases}$$

It follows from this definition that $B(x)$ is non-increasing and it is easy to show that $B(x)$ is strictly decreasing. Let now x be an arbitrary positive real number; then there exist two sequences $\{r_v\}$ and $\{r'_v\}$ of rational numbers such that the r_v approach x from below while the r'_v tend to x from above. Since $r_v < x < r'_v$ we have $B(r_v) > B(x) > B(r'_v)$ and hence $yB(r_v) < yB(x) < yB(r'_v)$ for any $y < 0$. Since $M(u)$ is non-decreasing we see that

$$M[yB(r_v)] \leqslant M[yB(x)] \leqslant M[yB(r'_v)].$$

It follows from (5.7.7) and (5.7.6) that

$$r_v M(y) \leqslant M[yB(x)] \leqslant r'_v M(y).$$

We let v tend to infinity and see that for every real positive x there exists a $B(x) > 0$ such that

$$(5.7.8) \qquad xM(y) = M[yB(x)] \qquad (y < 0).$$

Since the function $M(u)$ is non-decreasing and has the property that $M(-\infty) = 0$, we see that

$$B(0) = \infty, \qquad B(1) = 1, \qquad B(\infty) = 0.$$

The strictly decreasing function $z = B(x)$ has an inverse function $x = \beta(z)$. This function is defined for $z \geqslant 0$ and is single-valued and non-negative. We rewrite (5.7.8) in terms of $\beta(z)$ and see that to every real $z > 0$ there corresponds a $\beta(z) > 0$ such that

$$(5.7.9) \quad \beta(z)M(y) = M(yz)$$

is satisfied. Let $m_1(y)$ and $m_2(y)$ be two solutions of (5.7.9) and suppose that $m_1(y) \neq 0$. We put

$$m(y) = \frac{m_2(y)}{m_1(y)}$$

and see that

$$m(zy) = \frac{m_2(zy)}{m_1(zy)} = \frac{\beta(z)m_2(y)}{\beta(z)m_1(y)} = \frac{m_2(y)}{m_1(y)} = m(y).$$

This indicates that the quotient of two solutions of (5.7.9) is a constant. Moreover $m_1(y) = |y|^{-\alpha}$ is a solution and $\beta(z) = |z|^{-\alpha}$. Therefore the general solution of (5.7.9) has the form

$$M(y) = C_1 |y|^{-\alpha_1}.$$

Since $M(-\infty) = 0$ we must have $\alpha_1 > 0$ and since $M(y)$ is non-decreasing we see that $C_1 \geqslant 0$. We know (theorem 5.5.2) that the integral $\int_{-1}^{0} u^2 \, dM(u)$ is finite; this permits the conclusion $\alpha_1 < 2$. We have therefore found that

(5.7.10) $M(u) = C_1 |u|^{-\alpha_1}$ $(C_1 \geqslant 0, \quad 0 < \alpha_1 < 2, \quad u < 0).$

The solution (5.7.10) includes the case $M(y) \equiv 0$, since we admitted the possibility that $C_1 = 0$. We substitute (5.7.10) into (5.7.5b) and see that

(5.7.11a) $C_1 [b^{\alpha_1} - b_1^{\alpha_1} - b_2^{\alpha_1}] = 0.$

The function $N(u)$ can be determined from relation (5.7.5c) in the same way in which $M(u)$ was found. One obtains

(5.7.12) $N(u) = -C_2 u^{\alpha_2}$ $(C_2 \geqslant 0, \quad 0 < \alpha_2 < 2, \quad u > 0)$

and notes that

(5.7.11b) $C_2 [b^{\alpha_2} - b_1^{\alpha_2} - b_2^{\alpha_2}] = 0.$

We show next that $\sigma^2 \neq 0$ implies $C_1 = C_2 = 0$ so that $M(u) \equiv 0$ and $N(u) \equiv 0$. We conclude from (5.7.5a) that $\sigma^2 \neq 0$ implies $b^2 - b_1^2 - b_2^2 = 0$. Since $\alpha_1 < 2$, $\alpha_2 < 2$, we infer from (5.7.11a) and (5.7.11b) that $C_1 = C_2 = 0$. If, on the other hand, $M(u)$ [or $N(u)$] is not identically zero, then $C_1 > 0$ [or $C_2 > 0$]. We put $b_1 = b_2 = 1$ and conclude from (5.7.11a) [or (5.7.11b)] that b^{α_1} (or b^{α_2}) $= 2$. Then necessarily $b^2 \neq 2$ so that it follows from (5.7.5a) that $\sigma^2 = 0$.

We finally show that $\alpha_1 = \alpha_2$. Suppose that $C_1 > 0$, $C_2 > 0$, and put again $b_1 = b_2 = 1$; it follows from (5.7.11a) and (5.7.11b) that $b^{\alpha_1} = 2 = b^{\alpha_2}$ so that $\alpha_1 = \alpha_2$.

We have therefore determined the canonical representation (in Lévy's form) of stable distributions and summarize our result.

Theorem 5.7.2.   The characteristic function of a stable distribution has the canonical representation

(5.7.13) $\log f(t) = ita - \dfrac{\sigma^2}{2} t^2 + \displaystyle\int_{-\infty}^{0} \left(e^{itu} - 1 - \dfrac{itu}{1+u^2} \right) dM(u)$

$$+ \int_{0}^{\infty} \left(e^{itu} - 1 - \dfrac{itu}{1+u^2} \right) dN(u)$$

where either

$$\sigma^2 \neq 0 \quad and \quad M(u) \equiv 0, \quad N(u) \equiv 0$$

or

$$\sigma^2 = 0, \quad M(u) = C_1 |u|^{-\alpha} \quad (u < 0), \quad N(u) = -C_2 u^{-\alpha} \quad (u > 0).$$

The parameters are here subject to the restrictions

$$0 < \alpha < 2, \quad C_1 \geqslant 0, \quad C_2 \geqslant 0, \quad C_1 + C_2 > 0.$$

Conversely, any characteristic function of the form (5.7.13) is stable.

The last statement of the theorem is easily verified by elementary computations. The parameter α is called the exponent of the stable distribution.

It is possible to obtain an explicit formula for the second characteristic of stable distributions by evaluating the integrals

$$(5.7.14a) \qquad \int_{-\infty}^{0} \left(e^{itu} - 1 - \frac{itu}{1+u^2} \right) \frac{du}{|u|^{\alpha+1}}$$

and

$$(5.7.14b) \qquad \int_{0}^{\infty} \left(e^{itu} - 1 - \frac{itu}{1+u^2} \right) \frac{du}{u^{\alpha+1}}$$

which occur in their canonical representation. The computations are carried out separately for the three cases $0 < \alpha < 1, \alpha = 1$ and $1 < \alpha < 2$.

We first consider the case **$0 < \alpha < 1$**. It is then easily seen that the integrals

$$\int_{-\infty}^{0} \frac{u}{1+u^2} \frac{du}{|u|^{1+\alpha}} \quad \text{and} \quad \int_{0}^{\infty} \frac{u}{1+u^2} \frac{du}{u^{1+\alpha}}$$

are finite. Therefore one can rewrite (5.7.13) in the form

$$(5.7.15) \qquad \log f(t) = ita' + \alpha C_1 \int_{-\infty}^{0} (e^{itu} - 1) \frac{du}{|u|^{\alpha+1}}$$

$$+ \alpha C_2 \int_{0}^{\infty} (e^{itu} - 1) \frac{du}{u^{\alpha+1}}.$$

We suppose first that $t > 0$; changing the variables of integration in (5.7.15), we get

$$(5.7.16) \qquad \log f(t) =$$

$$ita' + \alpha t^{\alpha} \left[C_1 \int_{0}^{\infty} (e^{-iv} - 1) \frac{dv}{v^{1+\alpha}} + C_2 \int_{0}^{\infty} (e^{iv} - 1) \frac{dv}{v^{\alpha+1}} \right]$$

Let Γ be the contour consisting of the segment $[r, R]$ of the real axis, the arc $z = Re^{i\phi} \left(0 \leqslant \phi \leqslant \frac{\pi}{2} \right)$ of the circle with radius R around the origin, the segment $[iR, ir]$ of the imaginary axis, and the arc $z = re^{i\phi} \left(\frac{\pi}{2} \geqslant \phi \geqslant 0 \right)$ of the circle with radius r around the origin. It follows from Cauchy's theorem that

$$\int_{\Gamma} (e^{iz} - 1) \frac{dz}{z^{1+\alpha}} = 0.$$

Moreover it is easily seen that the integrals over the circular arcs tend to zero as $r \to 0$, or as $R \to 0$. Therefore

$$\int_0^\infty (e^{iv} - 1) \frac{dv}{v^{1+\alpha}} = e^{-i\pi\alpha/2} L_1(\alpha)$$

where

$$L_1(\alpha) = \int_0^\infty (e^{-y} - 1) \frac{dy}{y^{1+\alpha}} < 0.$$

Similarly

$$\int_0^\infty (e^{-iv} - 1) \frac{dv}{v^{1+\alpha}} = e^{i\pi\alpha/2} L_1(\alpha).$$

It follows from (5.7.16) that

$$\log f(t) = ita' + t^\alpha \alpha L_1(\alpha)(C_1 + C_2) \cos \frac{\pi\alpha}{2} \left[1 - i \frac{C_1 - C_2}{C_1 + C_2} \tan \frac{\pi\alpha}{2} \right].$$

Considering the Hermitian property of characteristic functions and writing

$$c = -\alpha L_1(\alpha)(C_1 + C_2) \cos \frac{\pi\alpha}{2} > 0$$

$$\beta = -\frac{C_1 - C_2}{C_1 + C_2},$$

we see that for $0 < \alpha < 1$ and every t,

(5.7.17a) $\quad \log f(t) = ita' - c|t|^\alpha \left(1 + i\beta \frac{t}{|t|} \tan \frac{\pi\alpha}{2} \right),$

where $c > 0$ and $|\beta| < 1$.

We next consider the case $1 < \alpha < 2$. It is easily seen that

$$\int_0^\infty \frac{u^2}{1+u^2} \frac{du}{u^\alpha} = \int_{-\infty}^0 \frac{u^2}{1+u^2} \frac{du}{|u|^\alpha} < \infty.$$

By changing the constant a, we can rewrite (5.7.13) in the form
$\log f(t) =$

$$ita'' + C_1 \alpha \int_{-\infty}^0 (e^{itu} - 1 - itu) \frac{du}{|u|^{\alpha+1}} + C_2 \alpha \int_0^\infty (e^{itu} - 1 - itu) \frac{du}{u^{\alpha+1}},$$

or for $t > 0$,

(5.7.18) $\quad \log f(t) =$

$$ita'' + t^\alpha \left\{ C_1 \alpha \int_0^\infty (e^{-iv} - 1 + iv) \frac{dv}{v^{\alpha+1}} + C_2 \alpha \int_0^\infty (e^{iv} - 1 - iv) \frac{dv}{v^{\alpha+1}} \right\}.$$

We integrate the function $(e^{-iz} - 1 + iz)\,\dfrac{1}{z^{\alpha+1}}$ along the contour Γ and, repeating the argument used above, we see that

$$\int_0^\infty (e^{-iv} - 1 + iv)\,\frac{dv}{v^{\alpha+1}} = e^{i\pi\alpha/2} L_2(\alpha)$$

while

$$\int_0^\infty (e^{iv} - 1 - iv)\,\frac{dv}{v^{\alpha+1}} = e^{-i\pi\alpha/2} L_2(\alpha)$$

where

$$L_2(\alpha) = \int_0^\infty (e^{-v} - 1 + v)\,\frac{dv}{v^{1+\alpha}} > 0.$$

We then see from (5.7.18) that for $t > 0$

$$\log f(t) = ita'' - ct^\alpha \left(1 + i\beta\ \text{tg}\ \frac{\pi\alpha}{2}\right)$$

where $c = -\alpha(C_1 + C_2) L_2(\alpha) \cos \dfrac{\pi\alpha}{2} > 0$ while $\beta = \dfrac{C_1 - C_2}{C_1 + C_2}$. For $t < 0$, $f(t)$ can be determined by means of the Hermitian property of characteristic functions and we have for $1 < \alpha < 2$

(5.7.17b) $\quad \log f(t) = ita'' - c|t|^\alpha \left(1 + i\beta\,\dfrac{t}{|t|}\ \text{tg}\ \dfrac{\pi\alpha}{2}\right)$

with $c > 0$, $|\beta| \leqslant 1$.

We still have to discuss the case $\alpha = 1$. We note that (see page 49)

$$\int_0^\infty \frac{1 - \cos y}{y^2}\,dy = \frac{\pi}{2}$$

and use this to compute the integrals in (5.7.13). We see that for $t > 0$

$$\int_0^\infty \left(e^{itu} - 1 - \frac{itu}{1+u^2}\right)\frac{du}{u^2} = \int_0^\infty \frac{\cos tu - 1}{u^2}\,du + i\int_0^\infty \left(\sin tu - \frac{tu}{1+u^2}\right)\frac{du}{u^2}$$

$$= -\frac{\pi}{2}t + i \lim_{\varepsilon \to 0}\left[\int_\varepsilon^\infty \frac{\sin tu}{u^2}\,du - t\int_\varepsilon^\infty \frac{du}{u(1+u^2)}\right]$$

$$= -\frac{\pi}{2}t + i \lim_{\varepsilon \to 0}\left\{-t\int_\varepsilon^{\varepsilon t} \frac{\sin v}{v^2}\,dv \right.$$

$$\left. + t\left[\int_\varepsilon^\infty \left(\frac{\sin v}{v^2} - \frac{1}{v(1+v^2)}\right)dv\right]\right\}.$$

It is easily seen that

$$A = \int_0^\infty \left(\frac{\sin x}{x^2} - \frac{1}{x(1+x^2)}\right)dx = \lim_{\varepsilon \to 0}\int_\varepsilon^\infty \left(\frac{\sin x}{x^2} - \frac{1}{x(1+x^2)}\right)dx < \infty;$$

moreover,

$$\lim_{\varepsilon \to 0} \int_{\varepsilon}^{\varepsilon t} \frac{\sin v}{v^2} \, dv = \lim_{\varepsilon \to 0} \int_{\varepsilon}^{\varepsilon t} \frac{dv}{v} = \log t$$

so that

$$\int_0^\infty \left(e^{itu} - 1 - \frac{itu}{1+u^2} \right) \frac{du}{u^2} = -\frac{\pi}{2} t - it \log t + Ait.$$

Since the two integrals in (5.7.14) are complex conjugates, we see that

$$\int_{-\infty}^0 \left(e^{itu} - 1 - \frac{itu}{1+u^2} \right) \frac{du}{u^2} = \int_0^\infty \left(e^{-itu} - 1 + \frac{itu}{1+u^2} \right) \frac{du}{u^2}$$

$$= -\frac{\pi}{2} t + it \log t - Ait$$

so that for $t > 0$

$$\log f(t) = ita'' - (C_1 + C_2) \frac{\pi}{2} t + (C_1 - C_2) it \log t.$$

It follows from the Hermitian property that for $\alpha = 1$ and all real t

(5.7.17c) $$\log f(t) = ita'' - c|t| \left\{ 1 + i\beta \frac{t}{|t|} \frac{2}{\pi} \log |t| \right\}.$$

Here $c = (C_1 + C_2) \dfrac{\pi}{2}$ and $\beta = \dfrac{C_1 - C_2}{C_1 + C_2}$.

We have therefore obtained the following result:

Theorem 5.7.3. *A characteristic function $f(t)$ is stable if, and only if, its second characteristic has the form*[*]

(5.7.19) $$\phi(t) = \log f(t) = iat - c|t|^\alpha \left\{ 1 + i\beta \frac{t}{|t|} \omega(|t|, \alpha) \right\}$$

where the constants c, β, α satisfy the conditions $c \geqslant 0, |\beta| \leqslant 1, 0 < \alpha \leqslant 2$, while a is a real number. The function $\omega(|t|, \alpha)$ is given by

$$\omega(|t|, \alpha) = \begin{cases} \tan(\pi\alpha/2) & \text{if } \alpha \neq 1 \\ (2/\pi) \log |t| & \text{if } \alpha = 1. \end{cases}$$

We note that $\omega(|t|, 2) \equiv 0$, so that one obtains the normal distribution for $\alpha = 2$.

We remark that P. Lévy (1937a) used the term stable distribution to describe a somewhat narrower class. He used instead of (5.7.1) the equation

(5.7.20) $$F\left(\frac{x}{b_1}\right) * F\left(\frac{x}{b_2}\right) = F\left(\frac{x}{b}\right)$$

---

[*] We follow in our notation B. V. Gnedenko–A. N. Kolmogorov (1954) and Loève (1963). This differs from the notation used by other authors who follow Lévy (1937a) and assign the opposite sign to β in the canonical form (5.7.19).

as the defining relation. P. Lévy [(1937a), p. 208] called the distributions defined by (5.7.1) quasi-stable distributions. We adopt here the terminology used by B. V. Gnedenko–A. N. Kolmogorov (1954) and we will call the sub-class defined by (5.7.20) the stable distributions in the restricted sense. The characteristic functions of these distributions can be determined by an argument similar to the one which we used in deriving the representation (5.7.19). The only essential difference between the two classes occurs if $\alpha = 1$. In this case (5.7.20) yields only the characteristic function of the Cauchy distribution, $\log f(t) = -c|t| + iat$, which corresponds to the case $\alpha = 1$, $\beta = 0$ in (5.7.19). If $\alpha \neq 1$ then the characteristic function of the class defined by (5.7.20) is obtained by putting $a = 0$ in (5.7.19).

It is sometimes convenient to modify the representation (5.7.19) and to write the characteristic function of stable distributions with exponent $\alpha \neq 1$ in a different form. We show that the second characteristic of a stable distribution with exponent $\alpha \neq 1$ is also given by the formula[*]

$$(5.7.21) \qquad \phi(t) = iat - \lambda|t|^{\alpha} \exp\left\{-i\frac{t}{|t|}\frac{\pi\gamma}{2}\right\}.$$

Here α is the exponent of the stable distribution, while $\lambda > 0$ and γ are the parameters to be determined. Comparing (5.7.19) and (5.7.21), we obtain the relations

$$(5.7.22a) \qquad \begin{cases} c = \lambda \cos\dfrac{\pi\gamma}{2} \\[2mm] \beta = -\cot\dfrac{\pi\alpha}{2}\tan\dfrac{\pi\gamma}{2}. \end{cases}$$

Formula (5.7.22a) gives the parameters c and β in terms of α, λ and γ. We can also obtain expressions for λ and γ as functions of α, c and β. For this we introduce a quantity Δ, defined by the equation

$$\Delta^2 = \cos^2\frac{\pi\alpha}{2} + \beta^2 \sin^2\frac{\pi\alpha}{2} = \frac{\cos^2\dfrac{\pi\alpha}{2}}{\cos^2\dfrac{\pi\gamma}{2}}.$$

Then

$$(5.7.22b) \qquad \begin{cases} \cos\dfrac{\pi\gamma}{2} = \Delta^{-1}\cos\dfrac{\pi\alpha}{2} \\[2mm] \lambda = c\Delta\left(\cos\dfrac{\pi\alpha}{2}\right)^{-1} \\[2mm] \operatorname{sgn}\Delta = \operatorname{sgn}(1-\alpha). \end{cases}$$

[*] If $\alpha = 2$, we put $\gamma = 0$ so that formula (5.7.21) is also valid in this case.

The last relation in (5.7.22b) follows from the inequalities $c \geqslant 0$, $\lambda \geqslant 0$. Using the relation $|\beta| \leqslant 1$ one can conclude that $|\gamma| \leqslant \alpha$ if $0 < \alpha < 1$, while $|\gamma| \leqslant 2 - \alpha$ if $1 < \alpha \leqslant 2$. We write

$$K(\alpha) = 1 - |1 - \alpha|$$

and see that

$$|\gamma| \leqslant K(\alpha).$$

We note that $K(\alpha) = \alpha$ if $0 < \alpha < 1$, while $K(\alpha) < \alpha$ if $1 < \alpha < 2$. If we put $\gamma = K(\alpha)\delta$ we obtain the representation

$$(5.7.23) \qquad \phi(t) = iat - \gamma |t|^\alpha \exp\left\{-i \frac{t}{|t|} \frac{\pi K(\alpha)}{2}\delta\right\}$$

where $\lambda \geqslant 0$, $0 < \alpha \leqslant 2$, $\alpha \neq 1$, $|\delta| \leqslant 1$. The constants λ and c are scale factors, and by a suitable choice of the variable they can be made equal to 1.

5.8   Frequency functions of stable distributions

Let $f(t)$ be the characteristic function of a stable distribution. It follows from (5.7.19) that $|f(t)| = \exp\left[-c|t|^\alpha\right]$. It is easily seen that $f(t)$ is absolutely integrable over $(-\infty, \infty)$ and we then obtain from theorem 3.2.2 the following result:

Theorem 5.8.1.   All stable distributions are absolutely continuous.

In this section we study the analytical properties of the frequency functions of stable distributions and shall refer to these as stable frequency functions or stable densities. We assume first that $\alpha \neq 1$ (α is the exponent of the stable distribution) and defer the investigation of the case $\alpha = 1$. We denote the frequency function of the stable distribution with parameters a, α, γ, λ by $p_a(x; \alpha, \gamma, \lambda)$ and write $p(x; \alpha, \gamma, \lambda)$ for $p_0(x; \alpha, \gamma, \lambda)$. These functions can be determined by means of the inversion formula (theorem 3.2.2), and we obtain from (5.7.21)

$$(5.8.1a) \qquad p_a(x; \alpha, \gamma, \lambda) = \frac{1}{2\pi} \int_0^\infty \exp\left[-itx + ita - \lambda t^\alpha e^{-i\pi\gamma/2}\right] dt$$

$$+ \frac{1}{2\pi} \int_0^\infty \exp\left[itx - ita - \lambda t^\alpha e^{i\pi\gamma/2}\right] dt$$

$$(\alpha \neq 1)$$

or

$$(5.8.1b) \qquad p_a(x; \alpha, \gamma, \lambda) = \frac{1}{\pi} \operatorname{Re} \int_0^\infty \exp\left[-itx + ita - \lambda t^\alpha e^{-i\pi\gamma/2}\right] dt.$$

The following relations follow immediately from (5.8.1a):

$$(5.8.2a) \qquad p_a(x; \alpha, \gamma, \lambda) = p(x - a; \alpha, \gamma, \lambda)$$

$$(5.8.2b) \qquad p(x; \alpha, \gamma, \lambda) = \lambda^{-1/\alpha} p(\lambda^{-1/\alpha} x; \alpha, \gamma, 1)$$

$$(5.8.2c) \qquad p(x; \alpha, \gamma, \lambda) = p(-x; \alpha, -\gamma, \lambda)$$

Equations (5.8.2a) and (5.8.2b) indicate that it is sufficient to study the frequency function only for the values $a = 0$, $\lambda = 1$ of the parameters. For the sake of brevity we shall write $p_{\alpha\gamma}(x)$ for $p(x; \alpha, \gamma, 1)$. We say that $p_{\alpha\gamma}(x)$ is the standardized density and refer to γ as its second parameter.

Explicit expressions for stable frequency functions in terms of elementary functions are known only in a few isolated cases. We obtain from (5.7.21) for $\alpha = 2$, $\gamma = 0$ the characteristic function of the normal distribution, while (5.7.19) yields for $\alpha = 1$, $\beta = 0$ the characteristic function of the Cauchy distribution. In addition to these distributions, only the stable frequency corresponding to $\alpha = \frac{1}{2}$, $\gamma = \frac{1}{2}$ is known to admit representation by a simple formula involving elementary functions (see p. 143). In view of this situation it is of interest to obtain series expansions for stable densities.

We first consider the case where $0 < \alpha < 1$ and assume also that $x > 0$ (in view of (5.8.2c) the condition $x > 0$ is not a serious restriction). We see from (5.8.1b) that

(5.8.3) $\qquad p_{\alpha\gamma}(x) = \frac{1}{\pi} \operatorname{Re} \int_0^\infty \exp\left[-itx - t^\alpha e^{-i\pi\gamma/2}\right] dt.$

Let

(5.8.4) $\qquad g(z) = \exp\left[-ixz - z^\alpha \exp\left(-i\pi\gamma/2\right)\right],$

where z is a complex variable. Denote the arc of the circle with centre at $z = 0$ and radius ρ which is located in the fourth quadrant by

$$C_\rho = \left\{\rho e^{i\phi}: -\frac{\pi}{2} \leqslant \phi \leqslant 0\right\}$$

and consider a closed contour Γ consisting of the segment $[-ir, -iR]$ of the imaginary axis $(r < R)$, the arc C_R, the segment $[R, r]$ of the real axis, and the arc C_r. According to Cauchy's theorem we have

(5.8.5a) $\qquad \int_\Gamma g(z)\, dz = 0.$

We next consider the integral along the arc C_r,

$$I(C_r) = \int_{C_r} g(z)\, dz = ir \int_{-\pi/2}^0 \exp\left[-ixr\, e^{i\phi} - r^\alpha e^{i\phi\alpha} e^{-i\pi\gamma/2} + i\phi\right] d\phi.$$

Then

$$|I(C_r)| \leqslant r \int_0^{\pi/2} \exp\left[-xr \sin\phi - r^\alpha \cos\left(\phi\alpha + \frac{\pi\gamma}{2}\right)\right] d\phi.$$

It is then easily seen that

(5.8.5b) $\qquad \lim_{r\to 0} I(C_r) = 0.$

We next show that also

(5.8.5c) $\qquad \lim_{R\to\infty} I(C_R) = 0.$

Since $|\gamma| \leqslant \alpha < 1$ it is always possible to find an $\varepsilon > 0$ and a ϕ_0 such that

$$\frac{\pi}{2} > \left| \phi_0 \alpha + \frac{\pi\gamma}{2} \right| > \left| \phi\alpha + \frac{\pi\gamma}{2} \right|$$

holds for $0 \leqslant \phi \leqslant \varepsilon$. We have

$$|I(C_R)| \leqslant R \int_0^\varepsilon \exp\left[-xR\sin\phi - R^\alpha \cos\left(\phi\alpha + \frac{\pi\gamma}{2} \right) \right] d\phi$$

$$+ R \int_\varepsilon^{\pi/2} \exp\left[-xR\sin\phi - R^\alpha \cos\left(\phi\alpha + \frac{\pi\gamma}{2} \right) \right] d\phi,$$

and it is easily seen that each term in this inequality tends to zero as R goes to infinity, so that (5.8.5c) holds.

We see therefore from (5.8.5a), (5.8.5b) and (5.8.5c) that

$$\int_0^\infty \exp\left[-ixt - t^\alpha e^{-i\pi\gamma/2} \right] dt = -i \int_0^\infty \exp\left\{ -xy - y^\alpha \exp\left[-\frac{i\pi}{2}(\gamma + \alpha) \right] \right\} dy.$$

It follows from (5.8.3) that

$$p_{\alpha\gamma}(x) = \frac{1}{\pi} \mathrm{Re}\left\{ -i \int_0^\infty \exp\left\{ -xy - y^\alpha \exp\left[-\frac{i\pi}{2}(\gamma + \alpha) \right] \right\} dy \right\}$$

$$= \frac{1}{\pi x} \mathrm{Re}\left\{ -i \int_0^\infty e^{-t} \exp\left[-\frac{t^\alpha}{x^\alpha} e^{-i\pi(\gamma + \alpha)/2} \right] dt \right\}.$$

We expand $\exp[-t^\alpha x^{-\alpha} e^{-i\pi(\gamma + \alpha)/2}]$ into a series and note that it is possible[*] to exchange the integration and the summation and get

$$p_{\alpha\gamma}(x) = \frac{1}{\pi x} \sum_{k=1}^\infty \frac{(-1)^{k-1}(x^{-\alpha})^k}{k!} \Gamma(\alpha k + 1) \sin[k\pi(\gamma + \alpha)/2],$$

provided that $x > 0$ and $0 < \alpha < 1$.

Using formula (5.8.2c) we obtain an expansion for $x < 0$, and it is then possible to obtain a formula which is valid for $x > 0$ and $x < 0$, namely (5.8.6)

$$p_{\alpha\gamma}(x) = \frac{1}{\pi x} \sum_{k=1}^\infty \frac{(-1)^{k-1}\Gamma(\alpha k + 1)}{k!} \left[\sin\frac{k\pi}{2}\left(\gamma + \alpha - \frac{2\alpha}{\pi} \arg x \right) \right] (|x|^{-\alpha})^k.$$

Here $\arg x = \pi$ for $x < 0$ and $\arg x = 0$ for $x > 0$.

We consider next the case where $1 < \alpha < 2$ and assume again that $x > 0$. We choose the following contour for integrating the function $g(z)$ defined by equation (5.8.4). In the case when $\gamma < 0$ the contour consists of the straight-line segment $\left[r \exp\left(-\frac{i\pi|\gamma|}{2\alpha} \right), R \exp\left(-\frac{i\pi|\gamma|}{2\alpha} \right) \right]$, the cir-

---

[*] See E. W. Hobson (1927) vol. 2, p. 306.

cular arc $z = Re^{i\phi}$ with $-\dfrac{\pi|\gamma|}{2\alpha} \leqslant \phi \leqslant 0$, the segment $[R, r]$ of the real

axis, and the circular arc $z = re^{i\phi}$ with $0 \geqslant \phi \geqslant -\dfrac{\pi|\gamma|}{2\alpha}$. If $\gamma > 0$ we use

the contour which consists of the line segment $[r, R]$ of the real axis, the

circular arc $z = Re^{i\phi}$ with $0 \leqslant \phi \leqslant \dfrac{\pi\gamma}{2\alpha}$, the line segment

$$\left[R \exp\left(\frac{i\pi\gamma}{2\alpha}\right), r \exp\left(\frac{i\pi\gamma}{2\alpha}\right) \right],$$

and the circular arc $z = re^{i\phi}$ with $\dfrac{\pi\gamma}{2\alpha} \geqslant \phi \geqslant 0$. It is easily seen that in both

cases the integrals taken over the circular arcs tend to zero as $r \to 0$, or as $R \to \infty$. It follows from Cauchy's theorem that

(5.8.7)

$$\int_0^\infty \exp\left[-ixt - t^\alpha e^{-\frac{i\pi\gamma}{2}} \right] dt = e^{\frac{i\pi\gamma}{2\alpha}} \int_0^\infty \exp\left[-ixu\, e^{\frac{i\pi\gamma}{2\alpha}} - u^\alpha \right] du$$

or

$$\int_0^\infty \exp\left[-ixt - t^\alpha e^{-\frac{i\pi\gamma}{2}} \right] dt = \alpha^{-1} e^{\frac{i\pi\gamma}{2\alpha}} \int_0^\infty \exp\left[-ixs^{\frac{1}{\alpha}} e^{\frac{i\pi\gamma}{2\alpha}} \right] e^{-s}\, s^{\frac{1}{\alpha}-1}\, ds$$

(the last expression is obtained from (5.8.7) by introducing a new variable

$s = u^\alpha$ in the integral on the right-hand side). We expand $\exp\left[-ixs^{\frac{1}{\alpha}} e^{\frac{i\pi\gamma}{2\alpha}} \right]$

into a series and see, as before, that the order of integration and summation may be exchanged. In this way we obtain

$$\int_0^\infty \exp\left[-ixt - t^\alpha e^{-\frac{i\pi\gamma}{2}} \right] dt = \frac{i}{x} \sum_{k=1}^\infty \frac{\Gamma\left(\frac{k}{\alpha}+1\right)}{k!} \exp\left[\frac{\pi i(\gamma+\alpha)k}{2\alpha} \right] (-x)^k.$$

We see then from (5.8.3) that for $x > 0$

$$p_{\alpha\gamma}(x) = -\frac{1}{\pi x} \sum_{k=1}^\infty \frac{\Gamma\left(\frac{k}{\alpha}+1\right)}{k!} \sin\left[k\frac{\pi(\gamma+\alpha)}{2\alpha} \right] (-x)^k.$$

Using relation (5.8.2c) one obtains a similar formula for $x < 0$. We summarize these results in the following statement:

Theorem 5.8.2. The stable frequencies admit the following representation by convergent series.

If $0 < \alpha < 1$,

(5.8.8a)

$$p_{\alpha\gamma}(x) = \frac{1}{\pi x} \sum_{k=1}^{\infty} \frac{(-1)^{k-1}\Gamma(\alpha k+1)}{k!} \sin\left[\frac{k\pi}{2}\left(\gamma+\alpha-\frac{2\alpha}{\pi}\arg x\right)\right](|x|^{-\alpha})^k,$$

while for $1 < \alpha \leqslant 2$,

(5.8.8b)

$$p_{\alpha\gamma}(x) = \frac{1}{\pi x} \sum_{k=1}^{\infty} \frac{(-1)^{k-1}\Gamma\left(\dfrac{k}{\alpha}+1\right)}{k!} \sin\left[\frac{k\pi}{2\alpha}\left(\gamma+\alpha-\frac{2\alpha}{\pi}\arg x\right)\right]|x|^{k}$$

holds.

The expansions of stable frequency functions into convergent series were obtained independently by H. Bergström (1952) and W. Feller (1952).

Several interesting properties of stable frequency functions follow from theorem 5.8.2.

We assume that $\alpha \neq 1$ and select $|\gamma| = \alpha$ in the representation (5.7.21) [this corresponds to the choice of $|\beta| = 1$ in formula (5.7.20)]. It follows from (5.8.8a) that

$$p_{\alpha\gamma}(x) = 0 \quad \text{if } x > 0, \gamma = -\alpha, 0 < \alpha < 1$$

and also

$$p_{\alpha\gamma}(x) = 0 \quad \text{if } x < 0, \gamma = \alpha, 0 < \alpha < 1.$$

To formulate this result we introduce the following terminology which will also be useful later. We say that a distribution function $F(x)$ is bounded to the left and that a is its left extremity; in symbols, $a = \text{lext}\,[F]$, if for any $\varepsilon > 0$ we have $F(a-\varepsilon) = 0$ while $F(a+\varepsilon) > 0$. Similarly we say that $F(x)$ is bounded to the right, and that b is its right extremity; in symbols, $b = \text{rext}\,[F]$, if $F(b-\varepsilon) < 1$ for any positive ε while $F(b) = 1$. Distributions which are bounded either to the right or to the left are called one-sided distributions, distributions which are bounded both to the right and to the left are called finite distributions. Our preceding result can now be formulated in the following manner.

Theorem 5.8.3. *The stable distribution functions with exponent* $0 < \alpha < 1$ *and parameter* $|\gamma| = \alpha$ *are one-sided distributions. They are bounded to the right (with* $\text{rext}\,[F] = 0$*) if* $\gamma = -\alpha$ *and bounded to the left (with* $\text{lext}\,[F] = 0$*) if* $\gamma = +\alpha$.

Remark. It is not possible to apply a similar reasoning to formula (5.8.8b) since we have always $|\gamma| \leqslant 2-\alpha < \alpha$ in the case when $1 < \alpha \leqslant 2$.

V. M. Zolotarev (1954) as well as P. Medgyessy (1956) obtained differential equations for stable frequency functions with rational exponents. V. M. Zolotarev (1956) also derived a number of relations between stable distribution functions (density functions). A simple relation of this type is equation (5.8.2c).

Theorem 5.8.2 can also be used to express a stable density with exponent α greater than 1 in terms of a density with exponent $1/\alpha$.

Let α be the exponent of a standardized stable density with second parameter γ and suppose that $2 \geqslant \alpha > 1$. Using formulae (5.8.8a) and (5.8.8b), we derive easily the following result:

Theorem 5.8.4. *Let $\alpha^* = 1/\alpha$ and $\gamma^* = \dfrac{\gamma - 1}{\alpha} + 1$;*

then $$p_{\alpha^* \gamma^*}(x) = x^{-(\alpha^* + 1)} p_{\alpha \gamma}(x^{-\alpha^*})$$

for $x > 0$ and $1 < \alpha \leqslant 2$.

It is easily seen that $|\gamma^*| \leqslant \alpha^*$ so that $p_{\alpha^* \gamma^*}(x)$ is indeed a stable frequency function.

Theorem 5.8.4 is due to V. M. Zolotarev (1954) who gave a different proof which did not use the series expansions of theorem 5.8.2. He also obtained a similar relation for stable distribution functions [V. M. Zolotarev (1956)].

A particular case is of some interest. Let $\alpha = 2, \gamma = 0$; then $\alpha^* = \gamma^* = \frac{1}{2}$ and the corresponding density is, according to theorem 5.8.3, bounded to the left. Since $p_{20}(x) = \dfrac{1}{2\sqrt{\pi}} e^{-x^2/4}$ we obtain from theorem 5.8.4 the stable density with parameters $\alpha = \frac{1}{2}, \gamma = \frac{1}{2}$, namely:

$$(5.8.9) \quad p_{\frac{1}{2}, \frac{1}{2}}(x) = \begin{cases} 0 & \text{if } x < 0 \\ \dfrac{1}{2\sqrt{\pi}} x^{-3/2} e^{-1/(4x)} & \text{if } x > 0. \end{cases}$$

The frequency function (5.8.9) can also be obtained directly from the series expansion (5.8.8a); it was derived by P. Lévy (1939) by a different method.(†)

Apart from the normal distribution, the Cauchy distribution and the distribution given by (5.8.9), no stable distributions are known whose frequency functions are elementary functions. However, V. M. Zolotarev (1954) expressed the standardized(§) frequency function of stable laws for certain combinations of the parameters α and β in terms of higher transcendental functions. These combinations of the parameters are $(\alpha = \frac{2}{3}, \beta = 1)$, $(\alpha = \frac{3}{2}, \beta = 1)$, $(\alpha = \frac{2}{3}, \beta = 0)$, $(\alpha = \frac{1}{3}, \beta = 1)$, $(\alpha = \frac{1}{2}, \beta$ arbitrary).

(†) B. V. Gnedenko–A. N. Kolmogorov (1954) mention that this frequency function was also found by N. V. Smirnov.

(§) i.e. those obtained by putting $a = 0, c = 1$ in (5.7.14).

We study next the analytical properties of stable densities and see from (5.8.8a) and (5.8.8b) that they have the form

$$(5.8.10) \qquad p_{\alpha\gamma}(x) = \begin{cases} \dfrac{1}{\pi x}\Phi_1(x^{-\alpha}) & \text{for } x > 0 \\[2mm] \dfrac{1}{\pi x}\Phi_2(|x|^{-\alpha}) & \text{for } x < 0 \end{cases} \qquad (0 < \alpha < 1)$$

and

$$(5.8.11) \qquad p_{\alpha\gamma}(x) = \begin{cases} \dfrac{1}{\pi x}\Psi_1(x) & \text{for } x > 0 \\[2mm] \dfrac{1}{\pi x}\Psi_2(|x|) & \text{for } x < 0, \end{cases} \qquad (1 < \alpha \leqslant 2)$$

where $\Phi_j(z) = \sum\limits_{k=1}^{\infty} a_k^{(j)} z^k$, $\Psi_j(z) = \sum\limits_{k=1}^{\infty} b_k^{(j)} z^k$, $(j = 1, 2)$ with

$$a_k^{(j)} = \frac{(-1)^{k-1}}{k!}\,\Gamma(\alpha k + 1) \sin\left\{\frac{k\pi}{2}\left[\gamma + (-1)^{j-1}\alpha\right]\right\}$$

$$b_k^{(j)} = \frac{(-1)^{k-1}}{k!}\,\Gamma\!\left(\frac{k}{\alpha}+1\right) \sin\left\{\frac{k\pi}{2\alpha}\left[\gamma + (-1)^{j-1}\alpha\right]\right\}.$$

Since $b_k^{(2)} = (-1)^k b_k^{(1)}$, we see that $\Psi_2(|x|) = \Psi_1(x)$ and can rewrite (5.8.11) in the form

$$(5.8.11a) \qquad p_{\alpha\gamma}(x) = \frac{1}{\pi}\Psi(x) \quad (1 < \alpha \leqslant 2),$$

where $\Psi(x) = x^{-1}\Psi_1(x)$.

Using Stirling's formula, one sees easily that

$$\limsup_{k\to\infty} |a_k^{(j)}|^{1/k} = \limsup_{k\to\infty} |b_k^{(j)}|^{1/k} = 0$$

so that the functions $\Phi_1(z)$, $\Phi_2(z)$ and $\Psi(z)$ are entire functions. We can also determine the order and type of these functions.

Let $\theta(z) = \sum\limits_{k=0}^{\infty} c_k z^k$ be an entire function. It is then known (see Appendix D) that the order ρ and type τ of $\theta(z)$ can be expressed in terms of the coefficients c_k of $\theta(z)$ and are given by

$$(5.8.12a) \qquad \rho = \limsup_{k\to\infty} \frac{k \log k}{\log |c_k|^{-1}}$$

and

$$(5.8.12b) \qquad \tau = \frac{1}{e\rho}\limsup_{k\to\infty} k|c_k|^{\rho/k}$$

respectively. We substitute in these formulae for the c_k the expressions for the $a_k^{(j)}$ and see after a simple computation (again involving Stirling's formula) that $\Phi_1(z)$ and $\Phi_2(z)$ are entire functions of finite order $\rho = 1/(1-\alpha)$ and type $\tau = (1-\alpha)^{\alpha/(1-\alpha)}$. Similarly we see that $\Psi(z)$ is an entire function of order $\rho = \alpha/(\alpha-1)$ and type $(\alpha-1)\alpha^{-\alpha/(\alpha-1)}$.

The determinations of the order and type of the entire functions $\Phi_j(z)$ and $\Psi(z)$ were carried out for the functions associated with the densities $p_{\alpha\gamma}(x)$, that is for the case $\lambda = 1$. Similar results can also be obtained if $\lambda \neq 1$. Expansions analogous to (5.8.8a) and (5.8.8b) can be derived easily; let $a_k^{(j)}(\lambda)$ and $b_k^{(j)}(\lambda)$ be the coefficients in these series. It follows from (5.8.2b) that $a_k^{(j)}(\lambda) = a_k^{(j)}\lambda^k$, while $b_k^{(j)}(\lambda) = b_k^{(j)}\lambda^{-k/\alpha}$. We conclude from (5.8.12a) and (5.8.12b) that the order of the entire functions associated with $p(x; \alpha, \gamma, \lambda)$ is given by $\rho = (1-\alpha)^{-1}$ if $0 < \alpha < 1$ but by $\rho = \alpha(\alpha-1)^{-1}$ if $1 < \alpha \leqslant 2$. The type $\tau = \lambda^\rho(1-\alpha)^{\alpha/(1-\alpha)}$ for $0 < \alpha < 1$, but $\tau = \lambda^{-\rho/\alpha}(\alpha-1)\alpha^{-\alpha/(\alpha-1)}$ in the case where $1 < \alpha \leqslant 2$. It follows easily that the function $\Psi(z)$ is also an entire function of order $\rho = \alpha(\alpha-1)^{-1}$ and type $\tau = \lambda^{-\rho/\alpha}(\alpha-1)\alpha^{-\alpha/(\alpha-1)}$.

We still have to consider the case $\alpha = 1$. Since the representation (5.7.21) is not valid for $\alpha = 1$ we must use the canonical form (5.7.19) as our starting-point. If $\beta = 0$ we have $f(t) = \exp(-c|t|)$; this is the characteristic function of the Cauchy distribution, and the corresponding frequency function[*] is

$$p(x; 1, 0, c) = \frac{c}{\pi(x^2+c^2)}.$$

This is a rational function with poles at the points $x = \pm ic$ and is therefore regular for all real x. The radius of convergence of the Taylor series of $p(x; 1, 0, c)$ around the point $x = 0$ is equal to c.

We study next the case $\beta \neq 0$; in view of the fact that a relation similar to (5.8.2c) is also valid for $\alpha = 1$, it is no restriction to assume that $\beta > 0$. Using the reasoning which yielded the expression (5.8.1b), we see that

$$(5.8.13) \qquad p(x; 1, \beta, c) = \frac{1}{\pi} \operatorname{Re} \int_0^\infty \exp\left\{-itx - ct\left[1 + \frac{2\beta}{\pi} i \log t\right]\right\} dt.$$

We write

$$g(z) = -ixz - cz - \frac{2\beta}{\pi} ciz \log z,$$

where z is a complex variable, and consider again the closed contour Γ used in deriving (5.8.8a). As in the earlier discussion we show that

$$(5.8.14a) \qquad \lim_{r \to 0} \int_{C_r} \exp[g(z)] dz = 0.$$

---

[*] The use of the notation $p(x; 1, 0, c)$ cannot create any confusion since the symbol $p(x; \alpha, \gamma, \lambda)$, introduced on page 138 and based on the representation (5.7.2b), is not defined for $\alpha = 1$.

Subdividing the range $0 \leqslant \phi \leqslant \pi$ of integration along C_R at a sufficiently small ϕ_0, one can also show that

$$(5.8.14b) \qquad \lim_{R \to \infty} \int_{C_R} \exp\,[g(z)]\, dz = 0.$$

The assumption that $\beta > 0$ is needed in deriving (5.8.14b). One concludes finally from Cauchy's theorem, (5.8.14a), (5.8.14b) and (5.8.13) that

$$(5.8.15) \qquad p(x;1,\beta,c) = \frac{1}{\pi} \int_0^\infty [\sin(1+\beta)ct]\exp\left\{-xt - \frac{2\beta}{\pi}ct\log t\right\}dt.$$

We wish to study the analytic character of $p(x;1,\beta,c)$ in the case where $\beta \neq 0$. Without loss of generality we can put $c = 1$; for the sake of brevity we write $p_\beta(x)$ instead of $p(x;1,\beta,1)$. We expand e^{-xt} in (5.8.15) and exchange the order of summation and integration. In this way we obtain

$$p_\beta(x) = \frac{1}{\pi}\sum_{k=0}^\infty \frac{(-1)^k}{k!}x^k \int_0^\infty t^k[\sin(1+\beta)t]\exp\left(-\frac{2\beta}{\pi}t\log t\right)dt$$

or

$$(5.8.16) \qquad p_\beta(x) = \frac{1}{\pi}\sum_{k=0}^\infty a_k\, x^k$$

where

$$(5.8.16a) \qquad a_k = \frac{(-1)^k}{k!}\int_0^\infty t^k[\sin(1+\beta)t]\exp\left(-\frac{2\beta}{\pi}t\log t\right)dt.$$

Let $\eta_1 = (\pi/2\beta)\eta$, where $\eta > 1$ may be chosen arbitrarily large, and put $t_1 = \exp(\eta_1)$. We write the integral in (5.8.16a) as the sum of three integrals J_1, J_2 and J_3, taken over the intervals $(0, 1)$, $(1, t_1)$ and (t_1, ∞) respectively, and estimate J_1, J_2 and J_3. Since $\max[-t\log t] = e^{-1}$ we see that

$$(5.8.17a) \qquad |J_1| \leqslant \frac{C}{k+1} \qquad \left[C = \exp\left(\frac{2\beta}{\pi e}\right)\right]$$

and

$$(5.8.17b) \qquad |J_2| \leqslant \frac{t_1^{k+1}}{(k+1)}$$

(the estimate for J_2 follows from the fact that $t\log t > 0$ for $t > 1$). We have

$$J_3 = \int_{t_1}^\infty t^k \exp\left(-\frac{2\beta}{\pi}t\log t\right)[\sin(1+\beta)t]\,dt$$

so that

$$|J_3| \leqslant \int_{t_1}^\infty t^k \exp\left(-\frac{2\beta}{\pi}t\log t\right)dt.$$

In view of our choice of t_1, we get

$$|J_3| \leqslant \int_{t_1}^{\infty} t^k e^{-\eta t} dt \leqslant \int_{0}^{\infty} t^k e^{-\eta t} dt;$$

therefore

(5.8.17c) $|J_3| \leqslant \eta^{-k-1} k!$

It follows from (4.8.17a), (5.8.17b), (5.8.17c) and (5.8.16a) that

$$|a_k| \leqslant \eta^{-k-1} \left[\frac{C\eta^{k+1}}{(k+1)!} + \frac{t_1^k \eta^{k+1}}{(k+1)!} + 1 \right]$$

or

(5.8.18) $|a_k| \leqslant \eta^{-k-1}[1 + o(1)]$ (as $k \to \infty$).

We see therefore that

$$|a_k|^{1/k} \leqslant \eta^{-1}[1 + o(1)].$$

Since η can be arbitrarily large, we conclude that

$$\limsup_{k \to \infty} |a_k|^{1/k} = 0$$

so that $p_\beta(x)$ is an entire function.

We rewrite (5.8.18) in the form

(5.8.19) $|a_k| = \theta_k \eta^{-k-1}[1 + o(1)]$

where θ_k is a real number such that $0 \leqslant \theta_k \leqslant 1$. Since $p_\beta(x)$ cannot be a polynomial, there exists necessarily a subsequence θ_{k_j} of the θ_k such that $\theta_{k_j} > 0$. In order to simplify the notation we write in the following θ_j instead of θ_{k_j}. Using (5.8.19), we see that

$$\frac{j \log j}{\log |a_j|^{-1}} = \frac{j \log j}{(j+1) \log \eta - \log \theta_j + o(1)} = O(\log j)$$

hence

$$\limsup_{k \to \infty} \frac{k \log k}{\log |a_k|^{-1}} = \infty.$$

Therefore $p_\beta(x)$ is [see (5.8.12a)] an entire function of infinite order.

We summarize these results in the following statements.

Theorem 5.8.5.   *The frequency function of a stable distribution with character-istic exponent* $\alpha < 1$ *has the form*

$$p(x; \alpha, \gamma, \lambda) = \begin{cases} \dfrac{1}{\pi x} \Phi_1(x^{-\alpha}) & \text{for } x > 0 \\[2ex] \dfrac{1}{\pi x} \Phi_2(|x|^{-\alpha}) & \text{for } x < 0, \end{cases}$$

where $\Phi_1(z)$ and $\Phi_2(z)$ are entire functions of order $\rho = (1-\alpha)^{-1}$ and type $\tau = \lambda^\rho (1-\alpha)^{\alpha/(1-\alpha)}$.

The frequency function of a stable distribution with exponent $\alpha > 1$ is an entire function of order $\rho = \alpha(\alpha-1)^{-1}$ and type $\tau = \lambda^{-\rho/\alpha} (\alpha-1)\alpha^{-\alpha/(\alpha-1)}$.

Theorem 5.8.6. *Stable densities with exponent $\alpha = 1$ are entire functions of infinite order if $\beta \neq 0$ but are rational functions if $\beta = 0$. In this case they have poles at the points ic and $-ic$.*

5.9 Asymptotic expansions and integral representations of stable densities

It is sometimes convenient to have asymptotic expansions of stable density functions. In Section 5.10 we will also use a representation of the derivative of a stable density by an integral. In the present section we derive some of these formulae.

As a first example we derive an asymptotic formula for stable densities $p_{\alpha\gamma}(x)$, with exponent $1 < \alpha < 2$, which is valid for large positive values of x. We see from (5.8.1b) and (5.8.7) that

$$p_{\alpha\gamma}(x) = \frac{1}{\pi} \operatorname{Re}\left\{\exp\left(\frac{i\pi\gamma}{2\alpha}\right) \int_0^\infty \exp\left[-ixu \exp\left(\frac{i\pi\gamma}{2\alpha}\right) - u^\alpha\right] du\right\}.$$

We introduce a new variable by putting

$$u = tx^{-1} e^{-i\pi/(2\alpha)}$$

and get

$$(5.9.1) \quad p_{\alpha\gamma}(x) =$$
$$\frac{1}{\pi x} \operatorname{Re}\left\{\exp\left[\frac{i\pi(\gamma-1)}{2\alpha}\right] \int_0^\infty \exp\left[-t \exp\left(\frac{i\pi(\alpha+\gamma-1)}{2\alpha}\right) - t^\alpha x^{-\alpha} e^{-i\pi/2}\right] dt\right\}.$$

According to Taylor's formula we have

$$\exp\left[-t^\alpha x^{-\alpha} e^{-i\pi/2}\right] = \sum_{k=0}^n \frac{1}{k!} (-1)^k x^{-\alpha k} e^{-i\pi k/2} t^{\alpha k} + \theta \frac{t^{\alpha(n+1)} x^{-\alpha(n+1)}}{(n+1)!},$$

where $|\theta| \leqslant 1$. For the sake of brevity we write $\phi_0 = \frac{\pi}{2\alpha}(\alpha+\gamma-1)$ and

$$I_k = \int_0^\infty t^{\alpha k} \exp\left(-t e^{i\phi_0}\right) dt.$$

We then obtain from (5.9.1) the expression

$$(5.9.2) \quad p_{\alpha\gamma}(x) = \frac{1}{\pi x} \operatorname{Re}\left\{\exp\left[\frac{i\pi(\gamma-1)}{2\alpha}\right] \sum_{k=0}^n \frac{1}{k!} (-1)^k x^{-\alpha k} e^{-i\pi k/2} I_k \right.$$
$$\left. + \theta \frac{x^{-\alpha(n+1)}}{(n+1)!} I_{n+1}\right\}.$$

In order to determine the integral I_k we change the path of integration from the positive real axis to the line $t = u e^{-i\phi_0}$, where $0 \leqslant u < \infty$. To show that this is permissible we consider the function

$$g(z) = z^{\alpha k} \exp \left[-z\, e^{i\phi_0} \right]$$

and the circular arc $\Gamma = \{z : z = r\, e^{i\phi}\}$, $-\phi_0 \leqslant \phi \leqslant 0$, and conclude that $\lim\limits_{r \to \infty} \int_\Gamma g(z)\, dz = 0$ and also $\lim\limits_{r \to 0} \int_\Gamma g(z)\, dz = 0$. In this way we see that

$$I_k = \exp \left[-i\phi_0 \alpha k - i\phi_0 \right] \Gamma(\alpha k + 1).$$

We substitute this into (5.9.2) and obtain the asymptotic formula (5.9.3)

$$p_{\alpha\gamma}(x) = \frac{1}{\pi x} \sum_{k=0}^{n} \frac{(-1)^{k-1}\Gamma(\alpha k + 1)}{k!} \left[\sin \frac{k\pi}{2} (\alpha + \gamma) \right] x^{-\alpha k} + O(x^{-\alpha(n+1)})$$

as $x \to \infty$ and $1 < \alpha < 2$.

We compare formula (5.9.3) with (5.8.6) and see that the series in (5.8.6) is convergent for $0 < \alpha < 1$ but is still useful as an asymptotic series if $1 < \alpha < 2$.

It is sometimes of interest to have asymptotic expansions as x tends to zero. We treat as an example the case where $0 < \alpha < 1$ while $x > 0$. In Section 5.8 we had

$$(5.8.1b) \qquad p_{\alpha\gamma}(x) = \frac{1}{\pi} \operatorname{Re} \int_0^\infty e^{-itx} \exp \left(-t^\alpha e^{-i\pi\gamma/2} \right) dt.$$

We again use Taylor's formula and write

$$(5.9.4) \qquad e^{-itx} = \sum_{k=0}^{n} \frac{(-ix)^k}{k!} t^k + \theta \frac{x^{n+1} t^{n+1}}{(n+1)!} \qquad (|\theta| \leqslant 1).$$

We write

$$J_k = \int_0^\infty t^k \exp \left(-t^\alpha e^{-i\pi\gamma/2} \right) dt$$

and obtain from (5.9.4) and (5.8.1b) the equation

$$p_{\alpha\gamma}(x) = \frac{1}{\pi} \operatorname{Re} \left\{ \sum_{k=0}^{n} \frac{(-ix)^k}{k!} J_k + \theta \frac{x^{n+1}}{(n+1)!} J_{n+1} \right\}.$$

We compute J_k by changing the path of integration and justify this change by applying Cauchy's theorem. We choose the line

$$z = u \exp (i\pi\gamma/2\alpha), \quad 0 \leqslant u < \infty,$$

as the new path and see easily that

$$J_k = \alpha^{-1} \Gamma\!\left(\frac{k+1}{\alpha} \right) \exp \left[i\pi\gamma(k+1)/(2\alpha) \right],$$

so that

$$(5.9.5) \quad p_{\alpha\gamma}(x) = \frac{1}{\pi} \sum_{k=0}^{n} \frac{(-1)^k \Gamma\left(\frac{k+1}{\alpha}\right)}{\alpha k!} x^k \cos \frac{\pi}{2}\left[\frac{\gamma}{\alpha}(k+1)+k\right]$$
$$+ O\left[\frac{\Gamma\left(\frac{n+2}{\alpha}\right)}{(n+1)!} x^{n+1}\right].$$

This is an asymptotic formula (for small x) if $0 < \alpha < 1$, and it can be shown that the series (5.9.5) is convergent if $1 < \alpha < 2$. Formula (5.9.5) is due to H. Bergström (1952). The asymptotic behaviour of stable density functions was also studied by Yu. V. Linnik (1954) and by A. V. Skorohod (1954). A. V. Skorohod (1954) and I. A. Ibragimov–Yu. V. Linnik (1965) also gave comprehensive surveys of these formulae.

In the same way one can derive formulae for the derivatives of stable frequencies. As an example[*] we mention

$$(5.9.6) \quad p'_{\alpha\gamma}(x) = \frac{1}{\pi} \sum_{k=0}^{n} \frac{(-1)^{k+1} \Gamma\left(\frac{k+2}{\alpha}\right)}{\alpha k!} x^k \cos \left[\frac{\pi}{2}(k+1)\left(\frac{\gamma}{\alpha}+1\right)+\frac{\pi\gamma}{2\alpha}\right]$$
$$+ O\left[\frac{\Gamma\left(\frac{n+3}{\alpha}\right)}{(n+1)!} x^{n+1}\right].$$

We note that (5.9.6) can be obtained from (5.9.5) by formal differentiation.

In Section 5.10 we shall need also the representation of the derivative $p'_{\alpha\alpha}(x)$ of a stable density $p_{\alpha\alpha}(x)$ by an integral taken over a finite interval, and we now derive the following result.

Theorem 5.9.1. *Let* $0 < \alpha < 1$; *then for* $x > 0$,

$$(5.9.7) \quad p'_{\alpha\alpha}(x) = \frac{1}{\pi} x^{2/(\alpha-1)} \int_0^\pi b(\phi) \exp\left[-x^{\alpha/(\alpha-1)} a(\phi)\right] d\phi$$

where $a(\phi) = \left(\dfrac{\sin \alpha\phi}{\sin \phi}\right)^{1/(1-\alpha)} \dfrac{\sin (1-\alpha)\phi}{\sin \alpha\phi}$ *and*

$$b(\phi) = \left(\frac{\sin \alpha\phi}{\sin \phi}\right)^{2/(1-\alpha)} \left(\frac{2\alpha \cos \phi \sin (1-\alpha)\phi}{(1-\alpha) \sin \alpha\phi} - 1\right)$$

while $p'_{\alpha\alpha}(x) \equiv 0$ *for* $x < 0$.

The last statement follows from theorem 5.8.3, so that we have only to prove (5.9.7).

---

[*] We write here and in the following $p_{\alpha\gamma}(x)$ for the derivative of $p_{\alpha\gamma}(x)$ with respect to the variable x.

We differentiate (5.8.1a) to get an expression for $p'_{\alpha\gamma}(x)$ which is similar to (5.8.1b) and see that

$$(5.9.8) \qquad p'_{\alpha\gamma}(x) = \frac{1}{\pi} \operatorname{Re} \int_0^\infty (-it) \exp\left[-itx - t^\alpha e^{-i\pi\gamma/2}\right] dt,$$

provided that $\alpha \neq 1$. We introduce the new variable $t = vx^{1/(\alpha-1)}$ and obtain

$$(5.9.8a) \qquad p'_{\alpha\gamma}(x) =$$
$$\frac{1}{\pi} x^{2/(\alpha-1)} \operatorname{Re} \int_0^\infty (-iv) \exp\left\{-x^{\alpha/(\alpha-1)}\left[iv + v^\alpha e^{-i\pi\gamma/2}\right]\right\} dv$$

or

$$(5.9.8b) \qquad p'_{\alpha\gamma}(x) = \frac{1}{\pi} x^{2/(\alpha-1)} \operatorname{Re} \int_0^\infty (iv) \exp\left\{x^{\alpha/(\alpha-1)}\left[iv - v^\alpha e^{i\pi\gamma/2}\right]\right\} dv.$$

According to the assumptions of theorem 5.9.1 we have $0 < \alpha < 1$; in this case $|\gamma| \leqslant \alpha$. We substitute $\gamma = \alpha$ in (5.9.8b) and obtain

$$p'_{\alpha\alpha}(x) = \frac{1}{\pi} x^{2/(\alpha-1)} \operatorname{Re} \int_0^\infty (iv) \exp\left\{x^{\alpha/(\alpha-1)}\left[iv - v^\alpha e^{i\pi\alpha/2}\right]\right\} dv.$$

Let

$$g(z) = iz - z^\alpha e^{i\pi\alpha/2} \quad (z \text{ complex})$$

and put

$$h(z) = \frac{1}{\pi} x^{2/(\alpha-1)} iz \exp\left[x^{\alpha/(\alpha-1)} g(z)\right]$$

so that

$$p'_{\alpha\alpha}(x) = \operatorname{Re} \int_0^\infty h(z)\, dz$$

where the integral is to be taken along the positive real axis. Our next aim is the computation of the expression $\operatorname{Re} \int_0^\infty h(z)\, dz$. This will be greatly facilitated by showing that the path of integration can be replaced by a curve along which the function $g(z)$ is real. It is easy to determine such a curve. Let $z = \rho e^{i\phi}$; then

$$\operatorname{Im} g(z) = \rho \sin\left(\phi + \frac{\pi}{2}\right) - \rho^\alpha \sin \alpha\left(\phi + \frac{\pi}{2}\right).$$

Clearly $\operatorname{Im} g(z) = 0$ if $z = \rho e^{i\phi}$, where

$$(5.9.9) \qquad \rho = \rho(\phi) = \left[\frac{\sin \alpha\left(\phi + \dfrac{\pi}{2}\right)}{\sin\left(\phi + \dfrac{\pi}{2}\right)}\right]^{1/(1-\alpha)}.$$

F

We note that $\rho\left(+\dfrac{\pi}{2}\right) = \infty$ while $\lim\limits_{\phi \to -\pi/2} \rho(\phi) = \alpha^{1/(1-\alpha)}$ and denote the

path $z = \rho(\phi)\,e^{i\phi}$, $-\pi/2 \leqslant \phi \leqslant \pi/2$, by Γ. The curve Γ has the point $z_1 = -i\alpha^{1/(1-\alpha)}$ of the imaginary axis as its initial point and intersects the real axis in the point $z_0 = [\sin \alpha\pi/2]^{1/(1-\alpha)} \leqslant 1$. Let z_n be the point of intersection of Γ with the circle of radius n and centre at the origin. We denote the arc of the circle $z = n\,e^{i\phi}$ located in the first quadrant and having the points $z = n$ and z_n as endpoints by Q_n, and we write Γ_n for the part of Γ located between the points z_1 and z_n. Let

$$C_r = \{z : z = r\,e^{i\phi},\ 0 \geqslant \phi \geqslant -\pi/2\}$$

be the arc of the circle with centre at $z = 0$ and radius r which is located in the fourth quadrant. We consider the contour K which consists of the arc C_r, the segment $\Delta_r = [-ir, -i\alpha^{1/(1-\alpha)}]$ of the imaginary axis, the arcs Γ_n and Q_n and the segment $[n, r]$ of the real axis. It follows from Cauchy's theorem that

$$\int_K h(z)\,dz = 0.$$

so that

(5.9.10)$\quad \displaystyle\int_{C_r} h(z)\,dz + \int_{\Delta_r} h(z)\,dz + \int_{\Gamma_n} h(z)\,dz + \int_{Q_n} h(z)\,dz = \int_r^n h(z)\,dz.$

It is easily seen that

(5.9.11a)$\quad \displaystyle\lim_{r \to 0} \int_{C_r} h(z)\,dz = 0.$

We show next that

(5.9.11b)$\quad \displaystyle\lim_{n \to \infty} \int_{Q_n} h(z)\,dz = 0.$

Since

$$\left| \int_{Q_n} h(z)\,dz \right| \leqslant n \int_0^{\pi/2} \left| h(n\,e^{i\phi}) \right| d\phi$$

we see that

$$\left| \int_{Q_n} h(z)\,dz \right| \leqslant$$
$$\frac{1}{\pi} x^{2/(\alpha-1)} n^2 \int_0^{\pi/2} \exp\left\{ -x^{\alpha/(\alpha-1)}\left[n \sin\phi + n^\alpha \cos\alpha\left(\phi + \frac{\pi}{2}\right) \right] \right\} d\phi.$$

We select a ϕ_0 such that

$$0 < \phi_0 < \min\left(\frac{\pi}{2}, \frac{\pi(1-\alpha)}{2\alpha} \right)$$

and conclude that

$$\left| \int_{Q_n} h(z)\, dz \right| \leqslant \frac{1}{\pi}\, x^{2/(\alpha-1)}\, n^2\, \phi_0 \exp\left\{ -x^{\alpha/(\alpha-1)}\, n^\alpha \cos\alpha\left(\phi_0 + \frac{\pi}{2}\right) \right\}$$

$$+ \frac{1}{\pi}\, x^{2/(\alpha-1)}\, n^2 \int_{\phi_0}^{\pi/2} \exp\left\{ -n x^{\alpha/(\alpha-1)} \sin\phi \left[1 + \frac{\cos\alpha\left(\phi+\frac{\pi}{2}\right)}{\sin\phi}\, n^{-(1-\alpha)} \right] \right\} d\phi.$$

This means that

$$\left| \int_{Q_n} h(z)\, dz \right| = o(1) \quad \text{as } n \to \infty,$$

so that (5.9.11b) is proved. We finally note that $g(-iy)$ is real for real y; therefore

(5.9.11c) $\operatorname{Re} \displaystyle\int_{\Delta_r} h(z)\, dz = 0.$

It follows from (5.9.10), (5.9.11a), (5.9.11b) and (5.9.11c) that

(5.9.12) $p'_{\alpha\alpha}(x) = \operatorname{Re} \displaystyle\int_0^\infty h(z)\, dz = \operatorname{Re} \displaystyle\int_{\Gamma_n} h(z)\, dz.$

In view of the definition of the contour Γ we know that

$$g[e^{i\phi} \rho(\phi)] = \operatorname{Re} g[e^{i\phi} \rho(\phi)],$$

so that

(5.9.13) $g[e^{i\phi}\rho(\phi)] = \rho(\phi) \cos\left(\phi + \dfrac{\pi}{2}\right) - [\rho(\phi)]^\alpha \cos\alpha\left(\phi + \dfrac{\pi}{2}\right).$

We substitute into (5.9.13) for $\rho(\phi)$ the expression given in (5.9.9) and see, after an elementary computation, that

(5.9.14) $g[e^{i\phi}\rho(\phi)] = -\left[\dfrac{\sin\alpha\left(\phi+\frac{\pi}{2}\right)}{\sin\left(\phi+\frac{\pi}{2}\right)} \right]^{1/(1-\alpha)} \dfrac{\sin\left[(1-\alpha)\left(\phi+\frac{\pi}{2}\right)\right]}{\sin\alpha\left(\phi+\frac{\pi}{2}\right)}$

$$= -a\left(\phi + \frac{\pi}{2}\right)$$

where the function $a(\phi)$ is defined in the statement of theorem 5.9.1. Since $z = \rho(\phi)\, e^{i\phi}$ on the contour Γ we see easily that

$$\operatorname{Re}(iz\, dz) = -[\rho\rho' \sin 2\phi + \rho^2 \cos 2\phi]\, d\phi$$

and obtain from (5.9.9) the expression

$$\operatorname{Re}(iz\, dz) = [\rho(\phi)]^2\, B\left(\phi + \frac{\pi}{2}\right) d\phi,$$

where

$$B(\phi) = \frac{2\alpha \cos\alpha\phi \sin\phi - 2\cos\phi \sin\alpha\phi}{(1-\alpha)\sin\alpha\phi} \cos\phi + \cos 2\phi.$$

It follows from (5.9.12) and (5.9.14) that

(5.9.15) $p'_{\alpha\alpha}(x) =$

$$\frac{1}{\pi} x^{2/(\alpha-1)} \int_0^\pi \left[\rho\left(\phi - \frac{\pi}{2}\right) \right]^2 B(\phi) \exp\{-x^{\alpha/(\alpha-1)} a(\phi)\} d\phi.$$

A simple computation yields the expression

(5.9.16) $B(\phi) = \dfrac{2\alpha \cos \phi \sin (1-\alpha)\phi}{(1-\alpha) \sin \alpha\phi} - 1.$

We put

(5.9.17)

$$b(\phi) = \left[\rho\left(\phi - \frac{\pi}{2}\right) \right]^2 B(\phi) = \left[\frac{\sin \alpha\phi}{\sin \phi} \right]^{2/(1-\alpha)} \left\{ \frac{2\alpha \cos \phi \sin (1-\alpha)\phi}{(1-\alpha) \sin \alpha\phi} - 1 \right\}$$

and obtain the statement of theorem 5.9.1. The following alternative expression for $B(\phi)$ is easily obtained from (5.9.16):

(5.9.16a) $B(\phi) = \dfrac{1}{1-\alpha} \left\{ \dfrac{\alpha \sin (2-\alpha)\phi}{\sin \alpha\phi} - 1 \right\}$

and this will also be used.

Corollary 1 to theorem 5.9.1.   *The function $a(\phi)$, defined in theorem* 5.9.1, *is strictly increasing in the interval* $[0, \pi]$.

Let, for ϕ fixed, $\psi(\alpha) = \alpha \cot \alpha\phi - \cot \phi$. Clearly $\psi(1) = 0$ while $\dfrac{d\psi}{d\alpha} \leqslant 0$,

so that

$$\alpha \cot \alpha\phi > \cot \phi$$

for $0 < \alpha < 1$. Moreover, it is easily seen that

$$\frac{d}{d\phi} \log a(\phi) = \frac{1}{1-\alpha} \{\alpha^2 \cot \alpha\phi - \cot \phi + (1-\alpha)^2 \cot (1-\alpha)\phi\}$$

$$> (1-\alpha) \cot (1-\alpha)\phi - \cot \phi > 0,$$

which proves the corollary.

Corollary 2 to theorem 5.9.1.   *The function $b(\phi)$, in the statement of theorem* 5.9.1, *has exactly one change of sign in the interval* $[0, \pi]$.

In view of (5.9.17) and (5.9.16a) it is sufficient to show that

$$u(\phi) = \frac{\alpha \sin (2-\alpha)\phi}{\sin \alpha\phi} - 1$$

has exactly one change of sign in $[0, \pi]$. We note that $u(0) = 1 - \alpha$ while $u(\pi) = -(1+\alpha)/(1-\alpha) < 0$, so that at least one change of sign occurs in the interval. An elementary computation shows that

$$u'(\phi) = \frac{\alpha}{\sin^2 \alpha\phi} v(\phi)$$

where

$$v(\phi) = (1-\alpha) \sin 2\phi - \sin 2(1-\alpha)\phi$$

so that

$$v'(\phi) = 2(1-\alpha)[\cos 2\phi - \cos 2(1-\alpha)\phi].$$

It is then easily seen that there exists a unique value ϕ_0 such that

$$0 < \phi_0 < \pi,$$

while $v'(\phi_0) = 0$, and we get $\phi_0 = \pi/(2-\alpha)$. It follows that $v(\phi)$ has exactly one minimum inside $[0, \pi]$, so that $v(\phi)$ and therefore also $u(\phi)$ has at most one change of sign in this interval. The statement of the corollary follows immediately from (5.9.17).

It is also necessary to derive a result similar to theorem 5.9.1 for the case where the exponent $\alpha > 1$.

Theorem 5.9.2. Let $1 < \alpha < 2$; then for $x > 0$,

$$(5.9.18) \qquad p'_{\alpha,\alpha-2}(x) = \frac{1}{\pi} x^{2/(\alpha-1)} \int_{\pi/\alpha}^{\pi} b_1(\theta) \exp \{x^{\alpha/(\alpha-1)} a_1(\theta)\} \, d\theta,$$

while for $x < 0$,

$$(5.9.18a) \qquad p'_{\alpha,\alpha-2}(x) = \frac{1}{\pi} |x|^{2/(\alpha-1)} \int_0^{\pi/\alpha} b_2(\theta) \exp \{-|x|^{\alpha/(\alpha-1)} a_2(\theta)\} \, d\theta,$$

where

$$a_1(\theta) = \left[\frac{-\sin \theta}{\sin \alpha\theta}\right]^{1/(\alpha-1)} \frac{\sin (\alpha-1)\theta}{\sin \alpha\theta}; \quad a_2(\theta) = \left[\frac{\sin \theta}{\sin \alpha\theta}\right]^{1/(\alpha-1)} \frac{\sin (\alpha-1)\theta}{\sin \alpha\theta}$$

and

$$b_1(\theta) = \left[\frac{-\sin \theta}{\sin \alpha\theta}\right]^{2/(\alpha-1)} \left\{1 - \frac{2\alpha \cos \theta \sin (\alpha-1)\theta}{(\alpha-1) \sin \alpha\theta}\right\}$$

$$b_2(\theta) = \left[\frac{\sin \theta}{\sin \alpha\theta}\right]^{2/(\alpha-1)} \left\{\frac{2\alpha \cos \theta \sin (\alpha-1)\theta}{(\alpha-1) \sin \alpha\theta} - 1\right\}.$$

In order to simplify the notation we write $p'(x)$ instead of $p'_{\alpha,\alpha-2}(x)$ in the proof of theorem 5.9.2. We consider first the case $x > 0$ and substitute $\gamma = \alpha-2$ into (5.9.8b) and see that

$$p'(x) = \frac{1}{\pi} x^{2/(\alpha-1)} \operatorname{Re} \int_0^{\infty} (iz) \exp \{x^{\alpha/(\alpha-1)} g(z)\} \, dz$$

where

$$g(z) = iz + z^{\alpha} e^{i\pi\alpha/2}.$$

We determine first, as in the proof of theorem 5.9.1, a curve along which $g(z)$ is real. It is easily seen that the curve Γ_1, given by

$$z = \rho e^{i\phi} \quad \text{with} \quad \rho = \rho(\phi) = \left[\frac{-\cos\phi}{\sin\alpha\left(\phi+\dfrac{\pi}{2}\right)}\right]^{1/(\alpha-1)} \quad \left(\frac{\pi}{\alpha}-\frac{\pi}{2} \leqslant \phi \leqslant \frac{\pi}{2}\right)$$

satisfies this requirement. Moreover, $\rho\left(\dfrac{\pi}{2}\right) = 0$ while $\rho\left(\dfrac{\pi}{\alpha}-\dfrac{\pi}{2}\right) = \infty$. Let

$z_n = n e^{i\phi_n}$ be the point of intersection of Γ_1 and the circle of radius n with centre at the origin and write C_n for the arc of this circle which is located in the first quadrant between the real axis and the point z_n. It is not difficult to show that

$$\left|\int_{C_n} (iz)\exp\{x^{\alpha/(\alpha-1)}g(z)\}\,dz\right| = o(1)$$

as $n \to \infty$, and we conclude from Cauchy's theorem that

$$\int_0^\infty (iz)\exp\{x^{\alpha/(\alpha-1)}g(z)\}\,dz$$
$$+ \int_{\pi/\alpha-\pi/2}^{\pi/2} (i\rho\rho'-\rho^2)e^{2i\phi}\exp[x^{\alpha/(\alpha-1)}g(\rho e^{i\phi})]\,d\phi = 0.$$

We use the fact that $g[\rho(\phi)e^{i\phi}]$ is real and introduce the new variable $\theta = \phi+\dfrac{\pi}{2}$ and obtain after a somewhat tedious but quite elementary computation formula (5.9.18).

We consider next the case $x < 0$ and see from (5.8.2c) that

$$p'_{\alpha,\gamma}(x) = -p'_{\alpha,-\gamma}(|x|)(x = -|x| < 0).$$

We put $\gamma = \alpha-2$ and write again $p'(x)$ for $p'_{\alpha,\alpha-2}(x)$ and see from (5.9.8a) that

$$(5.9.19) \qquad p'(x) = \frac{1}{\pi}|x|^{2/(\alpha-1)}\,\mathrm{Re}\int_0^\infty (iz)\exp\{-|x|^{\alpha/(\alpha-1)}g(z)\}\,dz$$

where

$$g(z) = iz - z^\alpha e^{i\pi\alpha/2}.$$

Again it is easily seen that $\mathrm{Im}\,g(\rho e^{i\phi}) = 0$ if $z = \rho e^{i\phi}$ is on the curve Γ_2 defined by

$$\rho(\varphi) = \left[\frac{\sin\left(\phi+\dfrac{\pi}{2}\right)}{\sin\alpha\left(\phi+\dfrac{\pi}{2}\right)}\right]^{1/(\alpha-1)} \quad \left(-\frac{\pi}{2} \leqslant \phi \leqslant \frac{\pi}{\alpha}-\frac{\pi}{2}\right)$$

so that $g(z)$ is real along Γ_2. We have $\rho\left(-\dfrac{\pi}{2}\right) = \left(\dfrac{1}{\alpha}\right)^{1/(\alpha-1)}$, $\rho\left(\dfrac{\pi}{\alpha}-\dfrac{\pi}{2}\right) = \infty$, so that Γ_2 goes through the point $-i\alpha^{-1/(\alpha-1)}$ of the imaginary axis and approaches asymptotically the line $z = r \exp\left[i\left(\dfrac{\pi}{\alpha} - \dfrac{\pi}{2}\right)\right]$, $(0 \leqslant r < \infty$.

We also note that $g(-iy) = y - y^\alpha$ for real and positive y, so that the integral in (5.9.19) is purely imaginary along the negative imaginary axis. Let $z_n = n\, e^{i\phi_n}$ be the point of intersection of Γ_2 and the circle of radius n with centre at the origin, and let C_n be the arc of this circle located in the first quadrant between the real axis and the point z_n. Then

$$\left| \int_{C_n} (iz) \exp\left\{ -|x|^{\alpha/(\alpha-1)} g(z) \right\} dz \right| = o(1) \quad (n \to \infty).$$

We consider the contour which consists of the segment $[0, -i\alpha^{-1/(\alpha-1)}]$ of the imaginary axis, the arc of Γ_2 between the origin and z_n, the arc C_n and the segment $[n, 0]$ of the real axis. We apply Cauchy's theorem and let n tend to infinity and conclude that

$$\mathrm{Re}\left\{ \int_{\Gamma_2} (iz) \exp\left[-|x|^{\alpha/(\alpha-1)} g(z) \right] dz + \int_\infty^0 (iz) \exp\left[-|x|^{\alpha/(\alpha-1)} g(z) \right] dz \right\}$$
$$= 0.$$

It follows that

$$p'(x) = \frac{1}{\pi} |x|^{2/(\alpha-1)} \int_{\Gamma_2} (iz) \exp\left[-|x|^{\alpha/(\alpha-1)} g(z) \right] dz.$$

Using the argument which we employed before, we obtain (5.9.18a).

Corollary 1 to theorem 5.9.2. Let $1 < \alpha < 2$; then $p'_{\alpha,\alpha-2}(x) < 0$ for $x > 0$.

To prove the lemma we need only show that $b_1(\theta) < 0$ for $\pi/\alpha < \theta < \pi$. Since $\sin \alpha\theta < 0$ in this interval it is sufficient to show that

$$y(\theta) = (\alpha - 1) \sin \alpha\theta - 2\alpha \cos \theta \sin (\alpha - 1)\theta > 0$$

for $\pi/\alpha < \theta < \pi$. A simple computation shows that

$$y(\theta) = \alpha \sin (2 - \alpha)\theta - \sin \alpha\theta > 0.$$

Corollary 2 to theorem 5.9.2. The function $a_2(\theta)$ which occurs in (5.9.18a) is strictly increasing in the interval $[0, \pi/\alpha]$.

Corollary 3 to theorem 5.9.2. The function $b_2(\theta)$ which occurs in (5.9.18a) has exactly one change of sign in the interval $[0, \pi/\alpha]$.

The proof of the last two corollaries is analogous to the proof of corollaries 1 and 2 to theorem 5.9.1.

Theorems 5.9.1 and 5.9.2 expressed the derivatives of stable frequency functions in terms of certain integrals. V. M. Zolotarev (1964) derived somewhat similar representations for stable distribution functions. In the next theorem we present his result; we use here the notation of formula (5.7.23) for stable characteristic functions. The characteristic function of a stable distribution with exponent $\alpha \neq 1$ and parameters $a = 0, \lambda = 1$, $\gamma = K(\alpha)\delta$ is then given by

$$\log f(t; \alpha, \delta) = -|t|^\alpha \exp\left\{-i\frac{t}{|t|}\frac{\pi K(\alpha)}{2}\delta\right\}.$$

We write $F(x; \alpha, \delta)$ for the corresponding distribution function.

Theorem 5.9.3.   If $\alpha \neq 1$ and $x > 0$ then

$$F(x; \alpha, \delta) = \begin{cases} \frac{1}{2}(1-\delta) + \frac{1}{\pi}\int_{-\pi\delta/2}^{\pi/2} \exp\left\{-V_\alpha(x, \phi)\right\}d\phi, & \text{if } \alpha < 1 \\[2mm] 1 - \frac{1}{\pi}\int_{-\pi\delta K(\alpha)/2\alpha}^{\pi/2} \exp\left\{-V_\alpha(x, \phi)\right\}d\phi, & \text{if } \alpha > 1 \end{cases}$$

where

$$V_\alpha(x, \phi) = x^{\alpha/(\alpha-1)}\left[\frac{\sin\left(\alpha\phi + \frac{\pi}{2}\delta K(\alpha)\right)}{\cos\phi}\right]^{\alpha/(1-\alpha)} \frac{\cos\left[(\alpha-1)\phi + \frac{\pi}{2}\delta K(\alpha)\right]}{\cos\phi}.$$

If $\alpha \neq 1$ but $x = 0$ one has

$$F(0; \alpha, \delta) = \frac{1}{2}[1 - \delta K(\alpha)/\alpha].$$

In the case where $x < 0$ one obtains the corresponding representations from the above formulae and the relation

$$1 - F(-x; \alpha, \delta) = F(x; \alpha, -\delta).$$

For the proof we refer the reader to Zolotarev's paper, quoted above. This paper also contains a similar formula for $\alpha = 1$.

5.10   Unimodality of stable distributions

In this section we prove the following theorem which is due to I. A. Ibragimov–K. E. Czernin.

Theorem 5.10.1.   All stable distributions are unimodal.

The proof is carried out in several steps. We first study symmetric stable distributions (i.e. $\gamma = 0$); then asymmetric stable distributions with extreme values of the parameter γ [i.e., $|\gamma| = K(\alpha)$ or equivalently $|\delta| = 1$, respectively $|\beta| = 1$]; and finally arbitrary stable distributions.

Lemma 5.10.1.   All symmetric stable distributions are unimodal.

Theorem 4.5.3 states that the function

$$f(t) = \frac{1}{1 + |t|^\alpha} \quad (0 < \alpha \leqslant 2)$$

is the characteristic function of a symmetric unimodal distribution. According to theorem 4.5.5 this is also true for the function

$$f_n(t) = [f(n^{-1/\alpha} t)]^n = \frac{1}{\left(1 + \dfrac{|t|^\alpha}{n}\right)^n}.$$

We conclude finally from theorem 4.5.4 that

$$f(t) = \lim_{n \to \infty} f_n(t) = \exp\left(-|t|^\alpha\right)$$

is also the characteristic function of a symmetric unimodal distribution, so that the lemma is proved.

Lemma 5.10.2. *Stable distributions with* $|\gamma| = K(\alpha)$ *and* $\alpha \neq 1$ *are unimodal.*

We consider first the case $\alpha < 1$. The function $b(\phi)$, which occurs in the statement of theorem 5.9.1, has, according to corollary 2 to theorem 5.9.1, exactly one zero in the interval $(0, \pi)$. Let σ be this zero and write formula (5.9.7) in the form

$$p'_{\alpha\alpha}(x) = \frac{1}{\pi} x^{2/(\alpha-1)} \left\{ \int_0^\sigma b(\phi) \exp\left[-x^{\alpha/(\alpha-1)} a(\phi)\right] d\phi \right.$$

$$\left. + \int_\sigma^\pi b(\phi) \exp\left[-x^{\alpha/(\alpha-1)} a(\phi)\right] d\phi \right\}.$$

Let x_0 be an arbitrary zero of the function $p'_{\alpha\alpha}(x)$; we differentiate $p'_{\alpha\alpha}(x)$ with respect to x and see easily from corollary 1 to theorem 5.9.1 that (5.10.1)

$$p''_{\alpha\alpha}(x_0) < \frac{1}{\pi} \frac{\alpha}{\alpha-1} x_0^{3/(\alpha-1)} a(\sigma) \left\{ \int_0^\pi b(\phi) \exp\left[-x_0^{\alpha/(\alpha-1)} a(\phi)\right] d\phi \right\} = 0.$$

We see from (5.10.1) that there exists only one value x_0 in the interval $(0, \infty)$ at which $p'_{\alpha\alpha}(x)$ becomes zero. The corresponding distribution is therefore unimodal. We have treated the case $\gamma = K(\alpha) = \alpha$; the validity of the lemma for $\gamma = -\alpha$ follows from the relation (5.8.2c).

In the case where $2 \geqslant \alpha > 1$ we use theorem 5.9.2 and its corollaries instead of theorem 5.9.1. Corollary 1 of theorem 5.9.2 shows that (when $\gamma = -K(\alpha) = \alpha-2$), $p_{\alpha,\alpha-2}(x)$ is decreasing and never vanishes for $x > 0$. The argument given for the case $\alpha < 1$ can again be applied if one replaces corollaries 1 and 2 to theorem 5.9.1 by corollaries 2 and 3 to theorem 5.9.2. If $\gamma = 2-\alpha$ the result follows again from (5.8.2c).

For the discussion of the case where $|\gamma| < K(\alpha)$ we need two lemmas. The first expresses a stable density with parameters (α, γ) in terms of densities with parameters $(\alpha, 0)$ and (α, α), while the second deals with a transformation of $x^2 p'_{\alpha\gamma}(x)$.

Lemma 5.10.3.   *Let* $\alpha < 1$ *and* $0 < \gamma < \alpha$; *then*

$$p'_{\alpha\gamma}(x) = \frac{1}{a^2 b} \int_0^\infty p'_{\alpha 0}\left(\frac{x-y}{a}\right) p_{\alpha\alpha}\left(\frac{y}{b}\right) dy$$

where $a = \left[\dfrac{\sin \dfrac{\pi}{2}(\alpha-\gamma)}{\sin \dfrac{\pi}{2}\alpha}\right]^{1/\alpha}$ *and* $b = \left[\dfrac{\sin \dfrac{\pi\gamma}{2}}{\sin \dfrac{\pi\alpha}{2}}\right]^{1/\alpha}.$

Since $\log f_{\alpha\gamma}(t) = -|t|^\alpha \exp\left[-i\dfrac{t}{|t|}\dfrac{\pi\gamma}{2}\right]$ we can easily verify that

$$(5.10.2) \qquad p_{\alpha\gamma}(x) = \frac{1}{ab}\int_{-\infty}^\infty p_{\alpha 0}\left(\frac{x-y}{a}\right) p_{\alpha\alpha}\left(\frac{y}{b}\right) dy.$$

We note (see theorem 5.9.1) that $p_{\alpha\alpha}(u) = 0$ for $u < 0$ and differentiate (5.10.2) with respect to x and obtain the statement of the lemma.

Lemma 5.10.4.   *The function* $A(\tau, \sigma)$ *obtained by substituting* $x = e^{-\tau}$, $\gamma = \dfrac{2\alpha}{\pi}\sigma$ *into* $x^2 p'_{\alpha\gamma}(x)$ *is a harmonic function in the strip* $-\infty < \tau < \infty$, $|\sigma| < \dfrac{\pi K(\alpha)}{2\alpha}.$

We use formula (5.9.8) and put $v = tx$ and obtain

$$x^2 p'_{\alpha\gamma}(x) = \frac{1}{\pi}\,\mathrm{Re}\int_0^\infty (iv)\exp\left[iv - v^\alpha x^{-\alpha} e^{i\pi\gamma/2}\right] dv$$

so that

$$(5.10.3) \qquad A(\tau, \sigma) = \frac{1}{\pi}\,\mathrm{Re}\int_0^\infty (iv)\exp\left[iv - v^\alpha e^{\tau\alpha} e^{i\alpha\sigma}\right] dv.$$

An elementary computation shows that

$$\frac{\partial^2 A}{\partial\tau^2} + \frac{\partial^2 A}{\partial\sigma^2} = 0$$

so that the lemma is proved.

In our discussion we consider first the case $0 < \alpha < 1$ and assume also that $0 < \gamma < \alpha$. We conclude from the unimodality of $p_{\alpha,0}(x)$ [lemma 5.10.1] and lemma 5.10.3 that $p'_{\alpha\gamma}(x) > 0$ for $x \leqslant 0$. We denote the smallest zero of $p'_{\alpha\gamma}(x)$ by $x_0 = x_0(\gamma)$. Clearly $x_0(0) = 0$ while $x_0(\gamma) > 0$.

We consider the strip $0 \leqslant x < \infty$, $0 \leqslant \gamma \leqslant \alpha$ and denote by $\mathfrak{D}$ the set of all points (x, γ) in this strip for which $x > x_0(\gamma)$ and $p'_{\alpha\gamma}(x) > 0$. In order to prove that $p_{\alpha\gamma}(x)$ is unimodal, we must show that the set $\mathfrak{D}$ is empty. Let $\overline{\mathfrak{D}}$ be the closure of $\mathfrak{D}$. The set $\overline{\mathfrak{D}}$ is obviously bounded. The mapping $x = e^{-\tau}$, $\gamma = \dfrac{2\alpha}{\pi}\sigma$ takes the strip $0 \leqslant x < \infty$, $0 \leqslant \gamma \leqslant \alpha$ into the strip $-\infty < \tau < \infty, 0 \leqslant \sigma \leqslant \dfrac{\pi}{2}$, and a set $\mathfrak{D}_1$ corresponds in this mapping to $\overline{\mathfrak{D}}$. The function $x^2 p'_{\alpha\gamma}(x)$ is transformed by this mapping into the harmonic function $A(\tau, \sigma)$. Suppose now that the set $\mathfrak{D}$ is not empty. It follows then from the definition of $\mathfrak{D}$ that the function $A(\tau, \sigma)$ vanishes on the boundary of $\mathfrak{D}_1$. Since $A(\tau, \sigma)$ is harmonic we have then necessarily $A(\tau, \sigma) = 0$ for $(\tau, \sigma) \in \mathfrak{D}_1$. In view of the definition of $\mathfrak{D}$ this is impossible, so that $\mathfrak{D}$ is necessarily empty. This proves that stable distributions with $0 < \alpha < 1$ and $\gamma \geqslant 0$ are unimodal; formula (5.8.2c) shows that the statement is also true for $\gamma < 0$. We consider next the case $1 < \alpha \leqslant 2$. We conclude from (5.8.8b) that $\gamma p'_{\alpha\gamma}(0) > 0$ for $\gamma \neq 0$ and use the mapping of lemma 5.10.4 in the same way as in the case where $\alpha < 1$ to show that the stable distributions corresponding to parameter values $1 < \alpha \leqslant 2, \gamma \neq 0$, $|\gamma| \neq K(\alpha)$ are also unimodal.

We still have to consider the case $\alpha = 1$. We write $f(t \,|\, \alpha, C_1, C_2)$ for stable characteristic functions in the Lévy canonical representation (see theorem 5.7.2) and have

$$(5.10.4) \quad \log f(t \,|\, \alpha, C_1, C_2) = C_1 \alpha \int_{-\infty}^{0} \left(e^{itu} - 1 - \frac{itu}{1+u^2}\right) \frac{du}{|u|^{\alpha+1}}$$

$$+ C_2 \alpha \int_{0}^{\infty} \left(e^{itu} - 1 - \frac{itu}{1+u^2}\right) \frac{du}{u^{\alpha+1}}$$

for $0 < \alpha < 2$. We see from formula (5.10.4) that

$$(5.10.5) \quad \lim_{n \to \infty} f\left(t \,\Big|\, 1 - \frac{1}{n}, C_1, C_2\right) = f(t \,|\, 1, C_1, C_2).$$

Since we have already shown that stable distributions with exponent $\alpha \neq 1$ are unimodal, we conclude from (5.10.5) and from theorem 4.4.4 that stable distributions with exponent $\alpha = 1$ are also unimodal, so that theorem 5.10.1 is completely proved.

5.11 Self-decomposable distributions

We defined stable distributions by means of the functional equation (5.7.2). It is possible to introduce other classes of characteristic functions in a somewhat similar manner. As an example we mention the characteristic functions $f(t)$ which obey the relation

$$(5.11.1) \quad f(t) = f(ct) f_c(t)$$

for every c $(0 < c < 1)$, where $f_c(t)$ is some characteristic function. The functions (5.11.1) were introduced by P. Lévy and A. Ya. Khinchine [see Lévy (1937a), p. 192, or second edition (1954), p. 195], and one calls this family of characteristic functions the class of self-decomposable characteristic functions[*] [Loève (1955)]. In the present section we discuss some properties of this class.

Theorem 5.11.1.   All self-decomposable characteristic functions are infinitely divisible.

We first show that a function which satisfies (5.11.1) never vanishes. We give an indirect proof and assume that $f(t)$ has zeros. Then there exists a t_0 such that $f(t_0) = 0$ while $f(t) \neq 0$ for $|t| < t_0$. It follows from (5.11.1) that $f_c(t_0) = 0$ while $f_c(t) \neq 0$ for $|t| < t_0$. We see from theorem 4.1.2, putting $n = 1$ and $t = t_0/2$, that

$$4\left[1 - \left|f_c\left(\frac{t_0}{2}\right)\right|^2\right] \geqslant 1 - |f_c(t_0)|^2 = 1.$$

Since $f_c\left(\dfrac{t_0}{2}\right) = \dfrac{f(t_0/2)}{f(ct_0/2)}$ is continuous in c, we obtain a contradiction by choosing c sufficiently close to 1, so that the functions $f(t)$ and $f_c(t)$ never vanish.

To prove the theorem we note that

$$f_{k,n}(t) = f_{(k-1)/k}\left(\frac{k}{n}t\right) = \frac{f\left(\dfrac{k}{n}t\right)}{f\left(\dfrac{k-1}{n}t\right)}$$

and see that

(5.11.2) $\displaystyle\prod_{k=1}^{n} f_{k,n}(t) = f(t).$

Since $f(t)$ is continuous and never vanishes, we conclude that $\lim_{n\to\infty} f_{k,n}(t) = 1$ uniformly in k $(1 \leqslant k \leqslant n)$ and in every finite t-interval. It then follows from the corollary to theorem 5.6.1 that $f(t)$ is infinitely divisible.

Corollary to theorem 5.11.1.   Let $f(t)$ be a self-decomposable characteristic function; then $f_c(t)$ is infinitely divisible.

Let $m < n$; we rewrite (5.11.2) in the form

$$\prod_{k=1}^{m} f_{(k-1)/k}\left(\frac{m}{n}\cdot\frac{k}{m}t\right) \prod_{k=m+1}^{n} f_{(k-1)/k}\left(\frac{k}{n}t\right) = f(t).$$

Suppose that m increases as n increases in such a manner that $\dfrac{m}{n} \to c$

---

[*] Some authors [e.g. B. V. Gnedenko and A. N. Kolmogorov (1954) and others] refer to this family as the "L-class". We do not use this terminology in order to avoid confusion with the $\mathscr{L}$-class introduced in Chapter 9.

as $n \to \infty$. The first factor then tends to $f(ct)$ while the second factor tends to a characteristic function $f_c(t)$, which by the argument used in the proof of the theorem is infinitely divisible.

Our next aim is the determination of the canonical representation of self-decomposable characteristic functions $f(t)$.

Since $f(t)$ is infinitely divisible, we can write it in the Lévy canonical form (theorem 5.5.2) and see that

$$(5.11.3) \quad \log f(t) = ita - \sigma^2 t^2/2 + \int_{-\infty}^{-0} \left(e^{itu} - 1 - \frac{itu}{1+u^2} \right) dM(u)$$

$$+ \int_{+0}^{\infty} \left(e^{itu} - 1 - \frac{itu}{1+u^2} \right) dN(u),$$

where σ^2, $M(u)$ and $N(u)$ satisfy the conditions of theorem 5.5.2.

Substituting tc for t in (5.11.3), we obtain after a simple change of the variable of integration

$$(5.11.4) \quad \log f(ct) = ita_1 - \sigma^2 c^2 t^2/2 + \int_{-\infty}^{-0} \left(e^{itu} - 1 - \frac{itu}{1+u^2} \right) dM \left(\frac{u}{c} \right)$$

$$+ \int_{+0}^{\infty} \left(e^{itu} - 1 - \frac{itu}{1+u^2} \right) dN \left(\frac{u}{c} \right)$$

where $0 < c < 1$ and

$$a_1 = ca + c \int_{-\infty}^{-0} \frac{(1-c^2)u^3}{(1+c^2 u^2)(1+u^2)} dM(u) + c \int_{+0}^{\infty} \frac{(1-c^2)u^3}{(1+c^2 u^2)(1+u^2)} dN(u).$$

We see from (5.11.3) and (5.11.4) that

$$(5.11.5) \quad \log \frac{f(t)}{f(ct)} = ita_2 - \sigma^2 (1-c^2) t^2/2$$

$$+ \int_{-\infty}^{-0} \left(e^{itu} - 1 - \frac{itu}{1+u^2} \right) d\left[M(u) - M\left(\frac{u}{c} \right) \right]$$

$$+ \int_{+0}^{\infty} \left(e^{itu} - 1 - \frac{itu}{1+u^2} \right) d\left[N(u) - N\left(\frac{u}{c} \right) \right]$$

where $a_2 = a - a_1$. According to the corollary of theorem 5.11.1,

$$f_c(t) = f(t)/f(ct)$$

is infinitely divisible; therefore (5.11.5) is its canonical representation and we conclude from the uniqueness of this representation that $M(u) - M(u/c)$ and $N(u) - N(u/c)$ must be non-decreasing. Therefore

$$(5.11.6) \quad \begin{cases} M(u_1) - M(u_1/c) \leqslant M(u_2) - M(u_2/c) \\ N(v_1) - N(v_1/c) \leqslant N(v_2) - N(v_2/c) \end{cases}$$

whenever

$$(5.11.7) \quad u_1 < u_2 < 0 \quad \text{and} \quad 0 < v_1 < v_2.$$

Conversely, if the inequalities (5.11.6) hold for every c $(0 < c < 1)$ then $f(t)/f(ct)$ is the characteristic function of an infinitely divisible distribution, so that $f(t)$ is self-decomposable. Suppose now that $M(u)$ and $N(u)$ satisfy (5.11.6) for all u_1, u_2, v_1, v_2 for which (5.11.7) holds. We then have

(5.11.8) $\qquad N(u_2/c) - N(u_1/c) \leqslant N(u_2) - N(u_1)$.

Let $a < b$ and $h > 0$ and choose a and b so that $c = e^{a-b}$. We put $v_2 = e^{a+h}$, $v_1 = e^a$ so that $v_2/c = e^{b+h}$, $v_1/c = e^b$. It then follows from (5.11.8) that $N(e^{b+h}) - N(e^b) \leqslant N(e^{a+h}) - N(e^a)$. We write $N(e^v) = A(v)$; then

$$A(b+h) - A(b) \leqslant A(a+h) - A(a)$$

or if we put $b = a+h = x$ (say)

$$A(x) \geqslant \tfrac{1}{2}[A(x+h) + A(x-h)].$$

The function $A(x)$ is therefore concave and has everywhere finite left-hand and right-hand derivatives. The right-hand derivative never exceeds the left-hand derivative, and both are non-increasing as x increases. Since $A(v) = N(e^v)$ we have

$$A'(v) = e^v N'(e^v).$$

Putting $u = e^v$, we see that $uN'(u)$ is a non-increasing function. In exactly the same way one shows that $uM'(u)$ is non-increasing.

Suppose conversely that the functions $M(u)$ and $N(u)$ have the property that $uM'(u)$ and $uN'(u)$ are non-increasing and that $0 < c < 1$. Then

$$\frac{u}{c} M'\left(\frac{u}{c}\right) \geqslant uM'(u) \quad \text{for } u < 0$$

$$\frac{u}{c} N'\left(\frac{u}{c}\right) \leqslant uN'(u) \quad \text{for } u > 0.$$

From these inequalities we obtain (5.11.6) by integration, so that the infinitely divisible distributions determined by the functions $M(u)$ and $N(u)$ are self-decomposable. We have therefore obtained the following result:

Theorem 5.11.2. An infinitely divisible characteristic function is self-decomposable if, and only if, the functions $M(u)$ and $N(u)$ in its Lévy canonical representation have left- and right-hand derivatives everywhere and if the function $uM'(u)$ is non-increasing for $u < 0$ while $uN'(u)$ is non-increasing for $u > 0$. Here $M'(u)$ and $N'(u)$ denote either the right or left derivatives, possibly different ones at different points.

Corollary to theorem 5.11.2. All stable characteristic functions are self-decomposable.

The corollary follows immediately from theorems 5.11.2 and 5.7.2.

For some time it was believed that all distribution functions of self-decomposable characteristic functions are unimodal. K. L. Chung showed in Appendix II of his translation of Gnedenko–Kolmogorov (1954) that the proof given there for this statement is not valid. I. A. Ibragimov (1957) gave an example intended to show that there exist self-decomposable distributions which are not unimodal. However, T. C. Sun (1967) pointed out that Ibragimov's construction contained an error, so that the question of the unimodality of this class is still open. The only known result at present is due to A. Wintner (1956) who proved that all symmetric self-decomposable distributions are unimodal. L. Kubik (1961/62, 1962/63) studied certain analogies which exist between the family of infinitely divisible characteristic functions and the class of self-decomposable characteristic functions. He characterized the latter class of functions in a manner which is similar to the way in which theorem 5.4.2 characterizes infinitely divisible characteristic functions.

We finally mention the semi-stable distributions introduced by P. Lévy (1937a). They are defined by means of the functional equation

$$\phi(qt) = q^{\alpha} \phi(t) \quad (q \neq 0, q \neq 1)$$

for the second characteristic.

V. M. Zolotarev (1963) investigated the smoothness properties (absolute continuity, differentiability, analyticity) of self-decomposable distribution functions. These properties depend on the functions M and N and on the presence or absence of a normal component.

6 FACTORIZATION PROBLEMS—GENERAL THEOREMS FROM THE ARITHMETIC OF DISTRIBUTION FUNCTIONS

In the preceding chapter we discussed a number of examples which indicated that the analogy between the factorization of integers and the decomposition of characteristic functions is rather limited. While a great number of remarkable decompositions of characteristic functions is known, we have only few general results, and one has the impression that the arithmetic of distribution functions has not yet reached a final stage in its development. In this chapter we present the most important general theorems concerning the factorization of characteristic functions, and this treatment will be supplemented by Chapters 8 and 9. The separation is justified by the different tools used: in the present chapter we deal with problems which can be handled without using the theory of functions of a complex variable, while complex variable methods are essential in deriving the results discussed in Chapters 8 and 9.

6.1 Some notations and lemmas

For the investigation of the general factorization theorems we need certain lemmas which we discuss in this section.

Lemma 6.1.1. *Let $f(t)$ be the characteristic function of a symmetric distribution, then*

$$1 - f(2t) \leqslant 4[1 - f(t)]$$

for any real t.

Since the characteristic function of a symmetric distribution is real (theorem 3.1.2), the assertion of lemma 6.1.1 follows immediately from theorem 4.1.2.

Corollary to lemma 6.1.1. *Let $f(t)$ be a characteristic function and suppose that $|f(t)| = 1$ in some neighbourhood $|t| \leqslant \delta$ of the origin. Then $f(t)$ is the characteristic function of a degenerate distribution.*

To prove the corollary we apply repeatedly the lemma to the function $|f(t)|^2$ and see that $|f(t)| = 1$ in every finite interval.

We next introduce an operation which is applicable to any characteristic function. Let $f(t)$ be an arbitrary characteristic function; then there exists

a real number a such that
$$|f(t)| > 0 \quad \text{for } 0 \leqslant t \leqslant a.$$
For a fixed a satisfying this relation we define

(6.1.1) $\qquad N_a[f(t)] = N_a(f) = -\int_0^a \log|f(t)|\,dt.$

The following properties of this operator are easily established:

      (i) $N_a(f) \geqslant 0$

      (ii) $N_a(e^{itm}) = 0$

      (iii) If $f(t) = f_1(t)\,f_2(t)$ then $N_a(f) = N_a(f_1) + N_a(f_2)$

      (iv) $N_a(f) \geqslant \int_0^a [1 - |f(t)|]\,dt$

      (v) $N_a(f) = 0$ if, and only if, $f(t)$ is the characteristic function of a degenerate distribution.

Properties (i), (ii) and (iii) follow immediately from (6.1.1); (iv) is a consequence of the inequality
$$-\log|f(t)| = -\log[1 - (1 - |f(t)|)] \geqslant 1 - |f(t)|$$
while (v) is easily obtained from (ii) and from (iv).

The quantity $N_a(f)$ is a measure of the departure of the distribution belonging to $f(t)$ from a degenerate distribution. We will refer to $N_a(f)$ as the N_a-value of $f(t)$.

The main object of this section is the proof of the following lemma:

Lemma 6.1.2. *Let $\{F_n(x)\}$ be a sequence of distribution functions and denote by $\{f_n(t)\}$ the corresponding sequence of characteristic functions. Suppose that $x = 0$ is a median of $F_n(x)$ $(n = 1, 2, \ldots)$ and that there exists a real $a > 0$ such that*

(6.1.2) $\qquad \lim_{n \to \infty} N_a(f_n) = 0,$

then

$$\operatorname{Lim}_{n \to \infty} F_n(x) = \varepsilon(x).$$

We say that the point $x = m$ is a median of the distribution function $F(x)$ if the inequalities $F(m - \varepsilon) \leqslant \frac{1}{2}$, $F(m + \varepsilon) \geqslant \frac{1}{2}$ hold for any $\varepsilon > 0$.

The assumptions of the lemma imply that for n sufficiently large $f_n(t) \neq 0$ for $0 \leqslant t \leqslant a$. Using (iv) we see that
$$\int_0^a [1 - |f_n(t)|^2]\,dt \leqslant 2 \int_0^a [1 - |f_n(t)|]\,dt \leqslant 2N_a(f_n).$$
Moreover it follows from lemma 6.1.1 that
$$\int_0^{2a} [1 - |f_n(t)|^2]\,dt = 2 \int_0^a [1 - |f_n(2t)|^2]\,dt \leqslant 8 \int_0^a [1 - |f_n(t)|^2]\,dt.$$

We combine the last two inequalities and conclude from assumption (6.1.2) of the lemma that

$$\lim_{n\to\infty} \int_0^{2a} [1-|f_n(t)|^2]\, dt = 0.$$

It is then easily seen that for n sufficiently large $f_n(t) \neq 0$ for $0 \leqslant t \leqslant 2a$, so the argument which we used can be repeated. In this way we see that, for every $T > 0$,

(6.1.3) $$\lim_{n\to\infty} \int_0^T [1-|f_n(t)|^2]\, dt = 0.$$

We denote by $\tilde{F}_n(x) = 1 - F_n(-x-0)$ the conjugate distribution of $F_n(x)$ and write

(6.1.4) $$\hat{F}_n(x) = \tilde{F}_n(x) * F_n(x)$$

for the symmetric distribution whose characteristic function is $|f_n(t)|^2$. We denote by

$$\Phi(x) = \frac{1}{\sqrt{2\pi}} \int_{-\infty}^{x} e^{-y^2/2}\, dy$$

the standardized normal distribution and consider the distribution defined by

(6.1.5) $$G_n(x) = \hat{F}_n(x) * \Phi(x)$$

whose characteristic function is

$$g_n(t) = e^{-t^2/2} |f_n(t)|^2.$$

From the inversion formula we see that

$$G_n(x) - G_n(-x) = \frac{1}{\pi} \int_{-\infty}^{\infty} \frac{\sin tx}{t} e^{-t^2/2} |f_n(t)|^2\, dt.$$

Since $G_n(x)$ is a symmetric distribution this can be written as

$$G_n(x) - \tfrac{1}{2} = \frac{1}{\pi} \int_0^{\infty} \frac{\sin tx}{t} e^{-t^2/2} |f_n(t)|^2\, dt$$

$$= \frac{1}{\pi} \int_0^{\infty} \frac{\sin tx}{t} e^{-t^2/2}\, dt + \frac{1}{\pi} \int_0^{\infty} \frac{\sin tx}{t} e^{-t^2/2} [|f_n(t)|^2 - 1]\, dt.$$

We write

$$I_n(x) = \frac{1}{\pi} \int_0^{\infty} \frac{\sin tx}{t} e^{-t^2/2} [|f_n(t)|^2 - 1]\, dt$$

and see that

$$G_n(x) = \Phi(x) + I_n(x).$$

Since for any $T > 0$

$$\left| \frac{1}{\pi} \int_0^T \frac{\sin tx}{t} e^{-t^2/2} [|f_n(t)|^2 - 1]\, dt \right| \leqslant \frac{|x|}{\pi} \int_0^T [1 - |f_n(t)|^2]\, dt,$$

we conclude from (6.1.3) that

$$\lim_{n\to\infty} I_n(x) = 0$$

so that

(6.1.6) $\qquad \text{Lim}_{n\to\infty} G_n(x) = \Phi(x).$

It follows from the continuity theorem that

$$\lim_{n\to\infty} g_n(t) = e^{-t^2/2} \lim_{n\to\infty} |f_n(t)|^2 = e^{-t^2/2}$$

so that

$$\lim_{n\to\infty} |f_n(t)|^2 = 1$$

and therefore

(6.1.7) $\qquad \text{Lim}_{n\to\infty} \hat{F}_n(x) = \varepsilon(x).$

We write (6.1.4) in the form

$$\hat{F}_n(x) = \int_{-\infty}^{\infty} F_n(x-y)\,d\tilde{F}_n(y)$$

and get

$$\hat{F}_n(x) \geqslant \int_{-\infty}^{\varepsilon} F_n(x-y)\,d\tilde{F}_n(y) \geqslant F_n(x-\varepsilon)\tilde{F}_n(\varepsilon)$$
$$= F_n(x-\varepsilon)[1 - F_n(-\varepsilon-0)],$$

where ε is an arbitrary positive number. Since by assumption $x = 0$ is a median of $F_n(x)$ we see that

$$\hat{F}_n(x) \geqslant \tfrac{1}{2} F_n(x-\varepsilon).$$

We conclude from the last relation and (6.1.7) that for any $x < 0$

(6.1.8) $\qquad \lim_{n\to\infty} F_n(x) = 0.$

On the other hand, we see by a similar reasoning that

$$1 - \hat{F}_n(x) \geqslant \int_{-\varepsilon}^{\infty} [1 - F_n(x-y)]\,d\tilde{F}_n(y) \geqslant \tfrac{1}{2}[1 - F_n(x+\varepsilon)]$$

so that for any $x > 0$

(6.1.9) $\qquad \lim_{n\to\infty} F_n(x) = 1.$

Formulae (6.1.9) and (6.1.8) imply the assertion of the lemma.

6.2 General decomposition theorems

In this section we discuss three general theorems concerning the factorization of distribution functions and characteristic functions. The first two of these theorems are due to A. Ya. Khinchine, the last is due to H. Cramér.

Theorem 6.2.1. *Every characteristic function can be represented as the product of at most two characteristic functions which have the following property: one does not have any indecomposable factors while the other is the convergent product of a finite or denumerable sequence of indecomposable factors.*

Let $f(t)$ be an arbitrary characteristic function and denote the corresponding distribution function by $F(x)$. Since $f(t)$ is continuous and $f(0) = 1$, there exists a real a such that $f(t) \neq 0$ if $|t| \leqslant a$; in the following we fix such a value a and write $N_a(f) = \alpha$.

If $f(t)$ does not have any indecomposable factors then the theorem holds. We suppose therefore that $f(t)$ has indecomposable factors. Then it is possible that $f(t)$ has a prime factor[*] $p_1(t)$ such that $N_a(p_1) > \alpha/2$; it follows then from (iii) [see p. 167] that one can write

$$f(t) = p_1(t) f_1(t)$$

where $N_a(p_1) > \alpha/2$ while $N_a(f_1) < \alpha/2$. In this case we repeat the procedure with $f_1(t)$ but use $\alpha/4$ instead of $\alpha/2$ as the lower bound for the N_a-value of its prime factor. If $f_1(t)$ has an indecomposable factor whose N_a-value exceeds $\alpha/4$, then one obtains a decomposition

$$f(t) = p_1(t) p_2(t) f_2(t)$$

where $N_a(p_j) > \alpha/4$ $(j = 1, 2)$[†] while every indecomposable factor $g(t)$ of $f_2(t)$ has the property that $N_a(g) < \alpha/4$. In the case where no indecomposable factor with N_a-value greater than $\alpha/2$ exists, we search for prime factors $p(t)$ which satisfy the relation $N_a(p) > \alpha/4$. In the case where such factors exist one obtains a decomposition into at most four factors

$$f(t) = p_1(t) \ldots p_{n_2}(t) f_2(t)$$

where $1 \leqslant n_2 \leqslant 3$. Here the $p_j(t)$ are indecomposable factors and satisfy the inequality $N_a(p_j) > \alpha/4$, while every prime factor $g(t)$ of $f_2(t)$ has the property that $N_a(g) < \alpha/4$.

We repeat this procedure and see that $f(t)$ can be decomposed in the following manner:

$$(6.2.1) \qquad f(t) = p_1(t) p_2(t) \ldots p_{n_k}(t) f_k(t)$$

where the $p_j(t)$ are indecomposable factors such that $N_a(p_j) > \alpha/2^k$ $(j = 1, 2, \ldots, n_k; 1 \leqslant n_k \leqslant 2^k - 1)$ and where every prime factor $g(t)$ of $f_k(t)$ has the property that $N_a(g) < \alpha/2^k$.

It can happen that for some $k \geqslant 1$ the characteristic function $f_k(t)$ has no indecomposable factors. Then our process terminates and we see that the theorem holds. We must therefore prove the theorem only in the case

---

[*] We use the terms "prime factor" and indecomposable factor synonymously.
[†] Note that according to our construction $N_a(p_1) > \alpha/2$.

where the factorization process does not terminate; the factors $p_j(t)$ then form an infinite sequence. Since

$$\sum_{=1} N_a(p_j) < N_a(f)$$

we see that the series

$$\sum_{j=1}^{\infty} N_a(p_j)$$

is convergent, so that the sum

$$\sum_{j=k+1}^{k+m} N_a(p_j)$$

converges to zero as k tends to infinity; this convergence is uniform in m ($m > 0$). We now apply lemma 6.1.2 and see that there exist real numbers $A_{v,v'}$, such that

$$\lim_{v \to \infty} e^{itA_{v,v'}} \prod_{k=v} p_k(t) = 1$$

uniformly in every finite t-interval $|t| \leqslant T$ and $v' > v$. We write $p_k(t) = \rho_k(t) \exp[i\omega_k(t)]$ and see that

$$(6.2.2) \qquad tA_{v,v'} + \sum_{k=v}^{v'} \omega_k(t) = 2\pi B_{v,v'}(t) + o(1) \quad \text{as} \quad v \to \infty$$

where $B_{v,v'}(t)$ assumes only integer values. The left-hand side of (6.2.2) is continuous, moreover $B_{v,v'}(0) = 0$; hence $B_{v,v'}(t) = 0$ for sufficiently large v and we have

$$tA_{v,v'} + \sum_{k=v} \omega_k(t) = o(1) \quad \text{as} \quad v \to \infty.$$

It is no restriction[*] to assume that $\omega_k(1) = 0$ so that $A_{v,v'} = o(1)$ and

$$\sum_{k=v}^{v'} \omega_k(t) = o(1) \quad \text{as} \quad v \to \infty.$$

We see therefore that

$$(6.2.3) \qquad \lim_{v \to \infty} \prod_{k=v}^{v'} p_k(t) = 1$$

uniformly in $|t| \leqslant T$ and $v' > v$.

The infinite product

$$\prod_{j=1}^{\infty} p_j(t)$$

is then convergent; let $v(t)$ be its limit. It follows from (6.2.3) that

$$v(t) = \lim_{k \to \infty} \prod_{j=1}^{k} p_j(t)$$

---

[*] This can be seen if one multiplies each $p_k(t)$ by $\exp[-it\omega_k(1)]$.

where the convergence is uniform in every finite t-interval. We see then from the second version of the continuity theorem (theorem 3.6.2) that $v(t)$ is a characteristic function. Let $\varepsilon > 0$ be an arbitrary positive number; according to (6.2.3) we have

$$\left| \prod_{j=k+1}^{k+m} p_j(t) - 1 \right| < \varepsilon \quad (m > 0, |t| \leqslant T)$$

if k is sufficiently large. Since

$$f_k(t) = f_{k+m}(t) \prod_{j=n_k+1}^{n_k+m} p_j(t)$$

one can conclude easily that

$$|f_k(t) - f_{k+m}(t)| < \varepsilon \quad (m > 0, |t| \leqslant T).$$

This means that the sequence $\{f_k(t)\}$ also converges to a characteristic function. Denote

$$u(t) = \lim_{k \to \infty} f_k(t).$$

It follows from (6.2.1) that

$$f(t) = v(t) u(t).$$

The function $u(t)$ has no indecomposable factor; this follows easily from the fact that each indecomposable factor of $u(t)$ must be a prime factor of $f_k(t)$ for all k. But such a factor cannot exist since the N_a-values of the prime factors of $f_k(t)$ tend to zero as k goes to infinity. This completes the proof of theorem 6.2.1.

The second decomposition theorem supplements the preceding result by characterizing the distributions which have no indecomposable factor.

Theorem 6.2.2.[*] *A characteristic function which has no indecomposable factor is infinitely divisible.*

Let $f(t)$ be a characteristic function which has no indecomposable factors and denote by D

$$(D) \qquad f(t) = f_1(t) f_2(t) \ldots f_n(t)$$

an arbitrary decomposition of $f(t)$ where all $f_j(t)$ are characteristic functions. Suppose that a is a positive number such that $f(t) \neq 0$ if $|t| \leqslant a$; we write then

$$\nu(D) = \max_{1 \leqslant j \leqslant n} N_a(f_j)$$

and denote by ν the greatest lower bound of the $\nu(D)$ for all possible decompositions D of $f(t)$.

We first derive a lemma:

Lemma 6.2.1. *Let $f(t)$ be a characteristic function which has no indecomposable factor, then $\nu = 0$.*

----

[*] The converse of theorem 6.2.2 is not true. This will be shown later.

It follows from the definition of ν that there exists a sequence of decompositions $\{D_n\}$, say

(D_n) $\qquad f(t) = f_{n,1}(t)f_{n,2}(t)\ldots f_{n,k_n}(t) \quad (n = 1, 2, \ldots)$

for which $\nu(D_n)$ converges to ν so that

$$\nu \leqslant \nu(D_n) < \nu + 1/n \quad (n = 1, 2, \ldots).$$

Let $f_1^{(n)}(t)$ be the factor of D_n for which $\nu(D_n) = N_a(f_1^{(n)})$ and write $f_2^{(n)}(t)$ for the product of all other factors of D_n. Then

(6.2.4)
$$\nu \leqslant N_a(f_1^{(n)}) < \nu + 1/n \quad (n = 1, 2, \ldots)$$
$$f(t) = f_1^{(n)}(t)f_2^{(n)}(t).$$

Let $F_1^{(n)}(x)$, $F_2^{(n)}(x)$ and $F(x)$ be the distribution functions corresponding to $f_1^{(n)}$, $f_2^{(n)}$ and f respectively; it is no restriction[*] to assume that $x = 0$ is a median of $F_2^{(n)}(x)$. According to Helly's first theorem the sequence $F_1^{(n)}(x)$ contains a convergent subsequence, it is only a simplification of our notation if we assume that the sequence $F_1^{(n)}(x)$ itself is a convergent sequence. We prove next that the limit of this sequence is necessarily a distribution function; this is established if we can show that for every $\eta > 0$ and sufficiently large values of $a > 0$ and n one has

$$F_1^{(n)}(-a) < \eta \quad \text{while} \quad F_1^{(n)}(a) > 1 - \eta.$$

We carry the proof indirectly and assume that one of these inequalities, for instance the second, is not satisfied for $a > 0$ and arbitrarily large n. Then for any $b > 0$

$$1 - F(b) = \int_{-\infty}^{\infty} [1 - F_1^{(n)}(b-y)] \, dF_2^{(n)}(y)$$
$$\geqslant \int_{-1}^{\infty} [1 - F_1^{(n)}(b-y)] \, dF_2^{(n)}(y)$$
$$\geqslant [1 - F_1^{(n)}(b+1)][1 - F_2^{(n)}(-1)] \geqslant \tfrac{1}{2}\eta.$$

This however contradicts the assumption that $F(x)$ is a distribution function. The proof of the inequality $F_1^{(n)}(-a) < \eta$ for sufficiently large $a > 0$ and n is carried in a similar manner and so we have shown that

$$\underset{n \to \infty}{\text{Lim}} \, F_1^{(n)}(x) = F_1(x)$$

is a distribution function. We write $f_1(t)$ for the corresponding characteristic function. We consider next the sequence $F_2^{(n)}(x)$; it also contains a convergent subsequence and we use again the notation $F_2^{(n)}(x)$ for this convergent subsequence. Let

$$F_2(x) = \underset{n \to \infty}{\text{Lim}} \, F_2^{(n)}(x);$$

---

[*] This can always be accomplished by a translation which does not affect the N_a-values.

we show that $F_2(x)$ is also a distribution function. We have for any $a > 0$ and $b > 0$

$$1 - F(a) \geqslant \int_{a+b}^{\infty} [1 - F_1^{(n)}(a-y)] \, dF_2^{(n)}(y)$$
$$\geqslant [1 - F_1^{(n)}(-b)][1 - F_2^{(n)}(a+b)].$$

For sufficiently large b we have

$$\text{Lim}_{n \to \infty} F_1^{(n)}(-b) = F_1(-b) < \tfrac{1}{2}$$

and therefore

$$1 - F_2^{(n)}(a+b) \leqslant 2[1 - F(a)].$$

This indicates that the left-hand member of this inequality tends to zero as a increases; in a similar manner one can show that $F_2^{(n)}(x)$ tends to zero as x goes to $-\infty$ provided that n is sufficiently large. Thus $F_2(x)$ is a distribution function and

$$f_2(t) = \lim_{n \to \infty} f_2^{(n)}(t)$$

is its characteristic function. It follows from (6.2.4) that

$$f(t) = f_1(t)f_2(t)$$

while

$$N_a(f_1) = \nu.$$

We next show by an indirect proof that $\nu < \tfrac{1}{2}N_a(f)$. Let us therefore suppose that $\nu \geqslant \tfrac{1}{2}N_a(f)$; it follows from (iii) (page 167) that $N_a(f_2) \leqslant \nu$. If we decompose f_1 and f_2 once more, we obtain a decomposition

$(D^*) \qquad f = g_1 \, g_2 \, g_3 \, g_4$

which has the property that $\nu(D^*) < \nu$. But this contradicts the definition of ν, so we can conclude that

$$\nu < \tfrac{1}{2}N_a(f).$$

Therefore there exists a decomposition D of $f(t)$ such that

$$\nu(D) < \tfrac{1}{2}N_a(f).$$

Each factor of D is a characteristic function without indecomposable factors and we can apply the result to a factor of D and see that

$$\nu < \tfrac{1}{2}\nu(D) < \tfrac{1}{4}N_a(f).$$

We iterate this procedure to obtain the statement of the lemma.

We proceed to prove theorem 6.2.2. Let $\{\varepsilon_n\}$ be a sequence of decreasing positive numbers such that

$$\lim_{n \to \infty} \varepsilon_n = 0.$$

It follows from lemma 6.2.1 that there exists, for each n, a decomposition

$(D_n) \qquad f(t) = f_{n,1}(t)f_{n,2}(t) \ldots f_{n,k_n}(t)$

such that

$$N_a(f_{n,j}) < \varepsilon_n$$

for $j = 1, 2, \ldots, k_n$ while

$$\lim_{n \to \infty} k_n = \infty.$$

Using lemma 6.1.2 we conclude that it is possible to find constants $\alpha_{n,j}$ ($j = 1, \ldots, k_n; n = 1, 2, \ldots$) such that

$$\lim_{n \to \infty} \{f_{n,j}(t) \exp [it\alpha_{n,j}]\} = 1$$

where the convergence is uniform for $1 \leqslant j \leqslant k_n$ and in every finite interval $|t| \leqslant T$.

We write

$$(6.2.5) \qquad \begin{cases} f_{n,j}(t) = \rho_{n,j}(t) \exp [i\omega_{n,j}(t)] \\ f(t) = \rho(t) \exp [i\omega(t)] \end{cases}$$

where $\omega_{n,j}(0) = \omega(0) = 0$.

Then

$$\lim_{n \to \infty} \rho_{n,j}(t) = 1 \quad \text{and} \quad \lim_{n \to \infty} [\omega_{n,j}(t) + t\alpha_{n,j}] = 0$$

(uniformly in $|t| \leqslant T$ and for $1 \leqslant j \leqslant k_n$). We see then that

$$\lim_{n \to \infty} [\omega_{n,j}(1) + \alpha_{n,j}] = 0,$$

hence also

$$\lim_{n \to \infty} [\omega_{n,j}(t) - t\omega_{n,j}(1)] = 0.$$

Writing

$$g_{n,j}(t) = f_{n,j}(t) \exp \left\{ it \left[\frac{\omega(1)}{k_n} - \omega_{n,j}(1) \right] \right\}$$

we see that

$$(6.2.6) \qquad g_{n,j}(t) = \rho_{n,j}(t) \exp \left\{ i \left[\omega_{n,j}(t) - t\omega_{n,j}(1) + t\frac{\omega(1)}{k_n} \right] \right\}$$

and conclude that

$$(6.2.7) \qquad \lim_{n \to \infty} g_{n,j}(t) = 1;$$

the convergence here is uniform in $|t| \leqslant T$ and for $j = 1, 2, \ldots, k_n$.
From the relation

$$f(t) = \prod_{j=1}^{k_n} f_{n,j}(t)$$

and from (6.2.5) and (6.2.6) we can easily see that

$$f(t) = \prod_{j=1}^{k_n} g_{n,j}(t).$$

It follows from (6.2.7) that the assumptions of the corollary to theorem 5.6.1 are satisfied; we finally conclude from this corollary that $f(t)$ is infinitely divisible.

The first two theorems discussed in this section show that there are three possibilities for the product representation of an arbitrary characteristic function $f(t)$:

(I) $f(t)$ has no indecomposable factor (in this case it is necessarily infinitely divisible);

(II) $f(t)$ is the product of a finite or denumerable sequence of indecomposable factors;

(III) $f(t)$ is the product of two characteristic functions $f_1(t)$ and $f_2(t)$ where $f_1(t)$ has no indecomposable factors, while $f_2(t)$ is the finite or denumerable product of indecomposable factors.

The decomposition is in general not unique; this is illustrated by the example discussed in Section 5.1 (p. 104) and also by the multiple factorization of the characteristic function $g(t)$, defined by (5.5.12). The first of these examples refers to a purely discrete distribution, while the function (5.5.12) is the characteristic function of an absolutely continuous distribution. In the next section we will find some further examples of multiple factorizations of absolutely continuous distributions.

The converse of theorem 6.2.2 is not true. We have already given (page 124, Section 5.5) an example of an infinitely divisible characteristic function which is the product of an indecomposable characteristic function and an infinitely divisible characteristic function. The characteristic function

$$f(t) = \frac{p-1}{p-e^{it}} \quad (p > 1)$$

of the geometric distribution which we considered at the end of Section 5.4 permits an even more remarkable factorization. It is easily seen that

$$\frac{p-1}{p-e^{it}} = \prod_{k=0}^{\infty} \frac{p^{2^k}+e^{it2^k}}{1+p^{2^k}}.$$

We see therefore that the characteristic function of the geometric distribution is infinitely divisible but admits nevertheless a representation as a product of an enumerable sequence of indecomposable characteristic functions.

Our next theorem indicates that the existence of infinitely divisible distributions with indecomposable factors is not a rare occurrence.

Theorem 6.2.3. An infinitely divisible characteristic function $g(t)$ whose Lévy canonical representation is determined by the constants $a = \sigma = 0$ and *by the functions*

$$N(u) = \begin{cases} k(u-c) & \text{if } 0 < u < c \\ 0 & \text{otherwise} \end{cases} \quad \text{and } M(u) \equiv 0$$

always has an indecomposable factor. Here k > 0 and c > 0 are arbitrary real constants.

The characteristic function $g(t)$ is then given by

$$\log g(t) = k \int_0^c \left(e^{itu} - 1 - \frac{itu}{1+u^2} \right) du.$$

Let ε be a real number such that $0 < \varepsilon < \frac{1}{2}$ and introduce the functions

(6.2.8a) $\quad \alpha_1(u) = \begin{cases} -\varepsilon & \text{if } (\frac{1}{2}-\varepsilon)c < u < (\frac{1}{2}+\varepsilon)c \\ 1 & \text{elsewhere in } (0, c) \\ 0 & \text{outside } (0, c) \end{cases}$

(6.2.8b) $\quad \alpha_2(u) = \begin{cases} 1+\varepsilon & \text{if } (\frac{1}{2}-\varepsilon)c < u < (\frac{1}{2}+\varepsilon)c \\ 0 & \text{if } |u-c/2| \geqslant \varepsilon c \end{cases}$

(6.2.8c) $\quad \log g_j(t) = k \int_0^c \left(e^{itu} - 1 - \frac{itu}{1+u^2} \right) \alpha_j(u) \, du \quad (j = 1, 2).$

Clearly $k[\alpha_1(u) + \alpha_2(u)] = N'(u)$ so that

(6.2.9) $\quad \log g(t) = \log g_1(t) + \log g_2(t).$

The function $g_2(t)$ is, according to the representation theorem 5.5.2, the characteristic function of an infinitely divisible distribution. We show next that $g_1(t)$ is also a characteristic function provided that ε is sufficiently small.

We define a sequence of functions $\beta_v(x)$ by means of the recurrence relations

$$\beta_1(x) = k\alpha_1(x)$$

$$\beta_n(x) = \int_{-\infty}^{\infty} \beta_{n-1}(x-t)\beta_1(t) \, dt = \int_0^c \beta_{n-1}(x-t)\beta_1(t) \, dt.$$

We conclude from these relations and from (6.2.8a) that $\beta_n(x) = 0$ if either $x \leqslant 0$ or $x \geqslant nc$ and note also that

$$|\beta_n(x)| \leqslant k^n c^{n-1}.$$

We remark that $\beta_n(x)$ is the n-fold convolution of $\beta_1(x)$ with itself so that

$$\int_0^{nc} e^{itx} \beta_n(x) \, dx = k^n \left[\int_0^c e^{itx} \alpha_1(x) \, dx \right]^n.$$

The series

$$\sum_{n=1}^{\infty} (1/n!) \beta_n(x)$$

is absolutely and uniformly convergent; therefore

(6.2.10) $\quad \int_0^{\infty} e^{itx} \left[\sum_{n=1}^{\infty} \frac{1}{n!} \beta_n(x) \right] dx = \exp\left[k \int_0^c e^{itx} \alpha_1(x) \, dx \right] - 1.$

We write

$$\lambda = k \int_0^c \alpha_1(x)\,dx \quad \text{and} \quad \eta = k \int_0^c \frac{x}{1+x^2}\alpha_1(x)\,dx$$

and obtain from (6.2.8c) and (6.2.10)

$$g_1(t) = \left[1 + \int_0^\infty e^{itx}\left(\sum_{n=1}^\infty \frac{1}{n!}\beta_n(x)\right)dx\right]\exp\left(-\lambda - it\eta\right).$$

Let

$$G_1(x) = e^{-\lambda}\left\{\varepsilon(x+\eta) + \int_{-\infty}^x \left[\sum_{n=1}^\infty \frac{1}{n!}\beta_n(y+\eta)\right]dy\right\},$$

then

$$g_1(t) = \int_{-\infty}^\infty e^{itx}\,dG_1(x).$$

In order to show that $g_1(t)$ is a characteristic function we must prove that $G_1(x)$ is a distribution function. Clearly $G_1(-\infty) = 0$, while we see from (6.2.8c) that $G_1(+\infty) = g_1(0) = 1$. We must still show that $G_1(x)$ is non-decreasing; we do this by proving that

$$\sum_{n=1}^\infty \frac{1}{n!}\beta_n(x)$$

is non-negative for all x, provided that ε is chosen sufficiently small.

We first remark that $\beta_1(x)$ is non-negative except in the interval $(\frac{1}{2}-\varepsilon)c < x < (\frac{1}{2}+\varepsilon)c$; moreover it is easily seen that $\beta_2(x)$ tends to $k^2(c-|c-x|)$ uniformly in the interval $0 < x < 2c$ as ε tends to zero. One can also show that $\beta_2(x)$ and $\beta_3(x)$ as well as

$$\beta_1(x) + \frac{1}{2!}\beta_2(x) + \frac{1}{3!}\beta_3(x)$$

are non-negative for all real x if ε is sufficiently small. Let $\varepsilon = \varepsilon_0$ be such a value. For $n \geq 4$ we can rewrite the relations defining the $\beta_n(x)$ in the form

$$\beta_{n+2}(x) = \int_0^{2c} \beta_n(x-t)\beta_2(t)\,dt \quad (n = 2, 3, \ldots)$$

and see that $\beta_{n+2}(x) \geq 0$ for all x and all $n \geq 2$ if $\varepsilon = \varepsilon_0$.

Therefore

$$\sum_{n=1}^\infty \frac{1}{n!}\beta_n(x) \geq 0,$$

and $G_1(x)$ is the distribution function whose characteristic function is $g_1(t)$. We show next by means of an indirect proof that $g_1(t)$ is not infinitely divisible. Let us then assume tentatively that $g_1(t)$ is an infinitely divisible characteristic function. Then $g_1(t)$ admits a Lévy canonical representation with some non-decreasing function $N_1(t)$. The derivative $N_1'(t)$ of $N_1(t)$ exists almost everywhere and is non-negative. It follows from the uniqueness of the canonical representation that the relation

$$N'(x) = k = N_1'(x) + k\alpha_2(x) \geqslant k\alpha_2(x)$$

is valid almost everywhere in the interval $(0, c)$; but this contradicts (6.2.8b). Hence $g_1(t)$ cannot be infinitely divisible. It follows from theorem 6.2.2 that $g_1(t)$ must have an indecomposable factor, and we see from (6.2.9) that this is also true for $g(t)$, so that theorem 6.2.3 is proved.

In exactly the same way in which we proved theorem 6.2.3 it can be shown that an infinitely divisible characteristic function whose Lévy canonical representation is determined by the constants $a = \sigma = 0$ and by the functions $N(u) \equiv 0$ and $M(u) = k(u+c)$ for $-c < u < 0$ and $M(u) = 0$ for $u \leqslant -c$ or $u > 0$ always has an indecomposable factor. We can therefore reformulate our result:

Corollary 1 to theorem 6.2.3.   Let $f(t)$ be an infinitely divisible characteristic function and suppose that the functions $M(u)$ and $N(u)$ which occur in its canonical representation satisfy the following condition: there exist two positive constants k and c such that at least one of the relations $M'(u) > k$ almost everywhere in $(-c, 0)$ or $N'(u) > k$ almost everywhere in $(0, c)$ holds. Then $f(t)$ has an indecomposable factor.

We consider only the case where the condition is satisfied in the interval $(0, c)$. Then $f(t)$ has an infinitely divisible factor of the form required by theorem 6.2.3, so that the corollary is established.

Let $f(t)$ now be a characteristic function which satisfies the conditions of this corollary. The function $f(t)$ can be written as an infinite product

$$f(t) = \prod_{s=1}^{\infty} [f(t)]^{2^{-s}}.$$

Each factor $[f(t)]^{2^{-s}}$ also satisfies the conditions of the corollary, so that we obtain the following result:

Corollary 2 to theorem 6.2.3.   Suppose that the infinitely divisible characteristic function $f(t)$ satisfies the condition of the corollary 1, then it is divisible by the product of an infinite sequence of indecomposable characteristic functions.

We finally remark that the conditions of corollary 1 are satisfied by the Gamma distribution and also by all non-normal stable distributions.

Generalizations of theorem 6.2.3 were given by R. Shimizu (1964) [see also B. Ramachandran (1967)]. We mention here only one of his results to which we shall refer later.

Theorem 6.2.4.   An infinitely divisible characteristic function $g(t)$ whose Lévy *canonical representation is determined by the constants $a = \sigma = 0$ and the functions*

$$N(u) = \begin{cases} k(b-c) & \text{for } 0 < u \leqslant b \\ k(u-c) & \text{for } b < u < c \quad \text{and} \quad M(u) \equiv 0 \\ 0 & \text{for } u \geqslant c \end{cases}$$

always has an indecomposable factor. Here $k > 0$ is an arbitrary constant, while the constant c satisfies the inequality $0 < 2b < c$.

The proof is similar to the proof of theorem 6.2.3. We select first a point d such that $2b < d < c$ and a number $\varepsilon > 0$ so that

$$2b < d(1-\varepsilon) < d(1+\varepsilon) < c.$$

We define

$$\alpha_1(u) = \begin{cases} -\varepsilon & \text{if } d(1-\varepsilon) < u < d(1+\varepsilon) \\ 1 & \text{elsewhere in } (b, c) \\ 0 & \text{outside } (b, c) \end{cases}$$

$$\alpha_2(u) = \begin{cases} 1+\varepsilon & \text{if } d(1-\varepsilon) < u < d(1+\varepsilon) \\ 0 & \text{otherwise.} \end{cases}$$

The functions $\alpha_1(u)$ and $\alpha_2(u)$ determine again—according to formula (6.2.8c)—two functions $g_1(t)$ and $g_2(t)$. The function $g_2(t)$ is an infinitely divisible characteristic function, while it can be shown that $g_1(t)$ is, for sufficiently small ε, a characteristic function but not infinitely divisible.

6.3   Indecomposable characteristic functions

We have already given several examples of indecomposable characteristic functions, and we showed at the end of the last section that a rather wide class of infinitely divisible characteristic functions has indecomposable factors. This, however, is almost the only general theorem concerning indecomposable characteristic functions which we know at present. There is no general method for finding the prime factors of a given characteristic function; our knowledge consists mostly of interesting special examples. In the present section we will make a few general remarks about prime factors and also list a number of remarkable decompositions.

We consider next an arbitrary distribution function $F(x)$ (which is not assumed to be of a pure type) and suppose that it is the convolution of two distribution functions $F_1(x)$ and $F_2(x)$:

$$F(x) = \int_{-\infty}^{\infty} F_1(x-t) \, dF_2(t).$$

Suppose that ξ is a point of increase of $F_1(x)$ and η a point of increase of $F_2(x)$; it is then easy to see that $\xi + \eta$ is a point of increase of $F(x)$. Similarly, if ξ is a discontinuity point of $F_1(x)$ and η a discontinuity point of $F_2(x)$

then $\xi+\eta$ is a discontinuity point of $F(x)$.(†) It can also be shown that every discontinuity point ζ of $F(x)$ can be written in the form $\zeta = \xi+\eta$ where ξ is a discontinuity point of $F_1(x)$ while η is a discontinuity point of $F_2(x)$.

Let $\{\xi_i\}$ and $\{\eta_j\}$ be the (finite or enumerable) sets of discontinuity points of $F_1(x)$ and $F_2(x)$ respectively and denote the discontinuity points of $F(x) = F_1(x)*F_2(x)$ by $\{\zeta_k\}$. Since the elements of the set $\{\zeta_k\}$ can be written in the form $\{\xi_i+\eta_j\}$ we see that every difference $\xi_j-\xi_k$ must occur among the differences of $\zeta_j-\zeta_k$ at least as many times as there are different η-values.

From these considerations we obtain easily the following results:

(1) Suppose that all the differences $\zeta_j-\zeta_k$ between the discontinuity points of a purely discrete function $F(x)$ are different. Then $F(x)$ is an indecomposable distribution function.(§)

(2) Suppose that the purely discrete distribution function $F(x)$ has at least n^2 discontinuity points and that it is not possible to find n pairs of discontinuity points which differ by the same number. Then $F(x)$ is indecomposable.

(3) A finite distribution which has two discontinuity points, one at each extremity, is always indecomposable.

The last statement follows from the earlier remarks and from the relations

$$\text{lext}\,[F_1*F_2] = \text{lext}\,[F_1]+\text{lext}\,[F_2]$$
$$\text{rext}\,[F_1*F_2] = \text{rext}\,[F_1]+\text{rext}\,[F_2]$$

which hold for the convolution of two finite distributions F_1 and F_2.

In Chapter 3 (corollary to theorem 3.3.3) we showed that the number N of discontinuity points of a purely discrete distribution function has lower and upper bounds which are determined by the numbers of discontinuities of its factors. It can be shown that this corollary is also true if the distribution is not purely discrete, the same limits $(n+m-1 \leqslant N \leqslant nm)$ are valid also in the general case. We then obtain by induction the following result:

(4) A purely discrete distribution which has exactly $n+1$ discontinuity points has at most n indecomposable factors. This maximum can only be attained if the discontinuity points are the $(n+1)$ consecutive terms of an arithmetic series.

(†) These statements follow from the inequality
$$F(\xi+\eta+h_2)-F(\xi+\eta-h_1) \geqslant [F_1(\xi+h_2-k_2)-F_1(\xi-h_1+k_1)][F_2(\eta+k_2)-F_2(\eta-k_1)].$$
Here
$$h_1 > 0, \quad h_2 > 0, \quad k_1 > 0, \quad k_2 > 0.$$
(§) We say that the distribution function $F(x)$ is indecomposable if its characteristic function is indecomposable.

We consider next a purely discrete distribution whose discontinuity points are the consecutive terms of a finite arithmetic series. It is then no restriction[*] to assume that this series consists of the integers $0, 1, 2, \ldots, n$. In studying this class of distributions it is more convenient to use the probability generating function than the characteristic function. Let a_k be the saltus of the distribution at the point k $(k = 0, 1, \ldots, n)$; the probability generating function is then the polynomial

$$(6.3.1) \qquad P(y) = \sum_{k=0}^{n} a_k y^k \quad (a_k > 0, \ \sum_{k=0}^{n} a_k = 1).$$

The substitution $y = e^{it}$ transforms $P(y)$ into the characteristic function $f(t) = P(e^{it})$; the corresponding distribution function is given by

$$F(x) = \sum_{k=0}^{n} a_k \varepsilon(x-k).$$

Each decomposition of $f(t)$ corresponds to a factorization of the generating function $P(y)$ into the product of polynomials with non-negative coefficients. If no such decomposition exists then $f(t)$ is indecomposable. The number of factors of $F(x)$ reaches its possible maximum if, and only if, the generating function has n real, negative zeros. We assume next that all coefficients of the polynomial (6.3.1) are equal and write

$$P_n(y) = \frac{1}{n} \sum_{k=0}^{n-1} y^k = \frac{1-y^n}{n(1-y)}$$

for the generating functions of this sub-class. Since

$$P_{nm}(y) = P_n(y) P_m(y^n) = P_m(y) P_n(y^m)$$

we see that the distributions of this class admit multiple decompositions, provided that the index n is not a prime number. Using the present notation we could rewrite the example at the end of Section 5.1 in the form $P_6(y) = P_2(y) P_3(y^2) = P_3(y) P_2(y^3)$. If

$$n = p_1^{\alpha_1} p_2^{\alpha_2} \ldots p_s^{\alpha_s} \quad (\alpha_1 + \alpha_2 + \ldots + \alpha_s = h)$$

is the decomposition of n into prime factors, then one can obtain in this way

$$\frac{h!}{\alpha_1! \, \alpha_2! \ldots \alpha_s!}$$

different decompositions of $P_n(y)$ into prime factors. M. Krasner–B. Ranulac (1937) have shown that these are the only decompositions of $P_n(y)$.

The problem of decomposition into prime factors is therefore com-

---

[*] Since the decomposition properties of distribution functions are invariant under linear transformations.

pletely solved[*] for the family of distributions with equal and equally-spaced jumps.

The indecomposable distributions which we have so far studied all had a finite set of discontinuity points. We show now that an indecomposable distribution can have an enumerable set of discontinuity points and can also be absolutely continuous or purely singular.

Let $\{p_v\}$ be the sequence of prime numbers and suppose that the distribution function $F(x)$ has its discontinuity points at $\xi_v = \log p_v$ $(v = 1, 2, \ldots)$. It is then clear that the differences between discontinuity points are all different, so that $F(x)$ is necessarily indecomposable.

The following lemma will be used in our construction of a characteristic function which belongs to an absolutely continuous, indecomposable distribution function.

Lemma 6.3.1. Let $p(x)$ be a frequency function which has a normal component, then $p(0) > 0$.

If $p(x)$ has a normal component then it can be written in the form

$$p(x) = \frac{1}{\sigma\sqrt{2\pi}} \int_{-\infty}^{\infty} \exp\left[-\frac{(x-\mu-y)^2}{2\sigma^2}\right] dF(y)$$

where $F(y)$ is a distribution function. Hence

$$p(0) = \frac{1}{\sigma\sqrt{2\pi}} \int_{-\infty}^{\infty} \exp\left[-\frac{(\mu+y)^2}{2\sigma^2}\right] dF(y) > 0$$

and the lemma is proved.

Let now

$$(6.3.2) \qquad f(t) = (1-t^2)e^{-t^2/2} = -\frac{d^2}{dt^2}(e^{-t^2/2}).$$

Since

$$e^{-t^2/2} = \frac{1}{\sqrt{2\pi}} \int_{-\infty}^{\infty} \exp\left[itx-\frac{x^2}{2}\right] dx,$$

we see that

$$f(t) = \frac{1}{\sqrt{2\pi}} \int_{-\infty}^{\infty} x^2 \exp\left[itx-\frac{x^2}{2}\right] dx.$$

It follows then that $f(t)$ is the characteristic function of the density

$$p(x) = \frac{1}{\sqrt{2\pi}} x^2 e^{-x^2/2}.$$

---

[*] According to a remark by J. Hadamard, which is appended to the paper by Krasner–Ranulac, this problem was also solved independently and simultaneously by A. Liénard and D. A. Raikov.

G

Since $p(0) = 0$ we see from lemma 6.3.1 that $f(t)$ has no normal component and therefore also no component of the form

$$(1-t^2) \exp(-\sigma^2 t^2/2) \quad (\sigma^2 < 1).$$

The only possible factors[*] have either the form $(1-t)e^{-t^2/2}$ or the form $(1+t)e^{-t^2/2}$. These factors do not satisfy the necessary conditions of theorem 2.1.1 and cannot therefore be characteristic functions. Hence $f(t)$ is indecomposable.

We have thus demonstrated that an absolutely continuous distribution function can be indecomposable. We add a few remarks which refer to the presence of normal components.

Since the characteristic function (6.3.2) is indecomposable we see that

$$h(t) = (1 - \tfrac{1}{2}t^2)e^{-t^2/4}$$

is also an indecomposable characteristic function. We consider next the characteristic function

$$(6.3.3) \qquad g(t) = [h(t)]^2 = (1 - t^2 + \tfrac{1}{4}t^4)e^{-t^2/2}$$

and show that it has a normal component.

This is the case if

$$g_1(t) = (1 - t^2 + \tfrac{1}{4}t^4) \exp(-A^2 t^2/2)$$

is a characteristic function for some A such that $|A| < 1$. Let

$$p_1(x) = \frac{1}{2\pi} \int_{-\infty}^{\infty} e^{-itx} g_1(t)\, dt;$$

it is easily seen that

$$(6.3.4) \qquad p_1(x) =$$

$$\frac{1}{A\sqrt{2\pi}} \left[\frac{1}{4}\left(\frac{x}{A^2}\right)^4 + \left(1 - \frac{3}{2A^2}\right)\left(\frac{x}{A^2}\right)^2 + 1 - \frac{1}{A^2} + \frac{3}{4A^4} \right] \exp\left[-\frac{x^2}{2A^2} \right]$$

The function $p_1(x)$ is a frequency function if, and only if, the polynomial

$$\tfrac{1}{4}z^4 + \left(1 - \frac{3}{2A^2}\right)z^2 + \left(1 - \frac{1}{A^2} + \frac{3}{4A^4}\right)$$

is non-negative for all real z. It is easy to see that this is the case if $A^2 \geqslant \tfrac{3}{4}$. Moreover, for $A^2 = \tfrac{3}{4}$ we see that $p_1[\pm(3\sqrt{2})/4] = 0$ so that $g_1(t)$ can have no normal component. It follows then that for $A^2 = \tfrac{3}{4}$ the characteristic function

$$g_1(t) = (1 - t^2 + \tfrac{1}{4}t^4) \exp(-3t^2/8)$$

is indecomposable.

We have just shown that the product of two characteristic functions

---

[*] This follows from theorem 8.1.2.

without normal components can have a normal component and have also obtained the factorization

$$g(t) = (1 - t^2 + \tfrac{1}{4}t^4) e^{-t^2/2} = [(1 - \tfrac{1}{2}t^2) e^{-t^2/4}]^2$$
$$= [(1 - t^2/2)^2 e^{-3t^2/8}][e^{-t^2/8}],$$

where the factors $(1 - \tfrac{1}{2}t^2) e^{-t^2/4}$ and $(1 - t^2/2)^2 e^{-3t^2/8}$ are indecomposable characteristic functions.

Our next example will show that the Poisson distribution has a similar property. The product of two characteristic functions which have no Poissonian factor may have a Poissonian component.

Let $\lambda > 1$;

$$f_1(t) = \frac{\lambda}{\lambda+1} + \frac{1}{\lambda+1} e^{it}$$

and

$$f_2(t) = \left(\frac{\lambda^2 - 1}{\lambda^2 - e^{2it}} \right)^{1/2}.$$

Clearly $f_1(t)$ is the characteristic function of an indecomposable law, and it is not difficult to show that $f_2(t)$ is also a characteristic function. Moreover we can write

$$f_1(t) = \frac{\lambda}{\lambda+1} \exp\left[\sum_{v=1}^{\infty} (-1)^{v-1} \frac{e^{itv}}{v\lambda^v} \right]$$

$$f_2(t) = \sqrt{(1 - \lambda^{-2})} \exp\left[\sum_{v=1}^{\infty} \frac{e^{2vit}}{2v\lambda^{2v}} \right].$$

Then

$$f_1(t) f_2(t) = \sqrt{\left(\frac{\lambda - 1}{\lambda + 1} \right)} \exp\left[\sum_{v=1}^{\infty} \frac{e^{i(2v-1)t}}{(2v-1)\lambda^{2v-1}} \right]$$

is a characteristic function which has the Poisson factor

$$\exp\{(1/\lambda)(e^{it} - 1)\}$$

while neither $f_1(t)$ nor $f_2(t)$ have Poisson factors. This is trivial for the indecomposable characteristic function $f_1(t)$. If, on the other hand, $f_2(t)$ would have a Poissonian factor $\exp[\mu(e^{it} - 1)]$ $(\mu > 0)$, then

$$f_2(t) \exp[-\mu(e^{it} - 1)] = e^{\mu}\sqrt{(1 - \lambda^{-2})} \exp\left[-\mu e^{it} + \sum_{v=1}^{\infty} \frac{e^{2vit}}{2v\lambda^{2v}} \right]$$

would be a characteristic function; if we expand the right-hand side of this equation according to powers of e^{it} we then see that the coefficient of e^{it} is negative, so that $f_2(t) \exp[-\mu(e^{it} - 1)]$ cannot be a characteristic function. This shows that $f_2(t)$ has no Poissonian component.

The characteristic function (6.3.2) is an example of a characteristic function of an absolutely continuous, unbounded distribution function which is indecomposable.

We next derive a theorem which enables us to construct certain interesting examples of indecomposable distribution functions.

Theorem 6.3.1.   *Let* $F(x)$ *be a distribution function and n be an integer. Write*

(6.3.5) $p_n = F(n+1-0) - F(n-0)$

and define the distribution function $\hat{F}(x)$ *by*

(6.3.6) $\hat{F}(x) = \sum_{n=-\infty}^{\infty} p_n \varepsilon(x-n)$

and introduce for n, for which $p_n > 0$, *distribution functions* $F_n(x)$ *by*

(6.3.7) $F_n(x) = \begin{cases} 0 & \text{if } x < 0 \\ \dfrac{1}{p_n}[F(x+n) - F(n-0)] & \text{if } 0 \leqslant x < 1 \\ 1 & \text{if } x \geqslant 1. \end{cases}$

Suppose that

   (a) $p_{2k+1} = 0$ *for all* k;
   (b) $p_0 > 0$;
   (c) $\hat{F}(x)$ *is indecomposable*;
   (d) *the distribution functions* $F_{2k}(x)$ *have no common, non-degenerate factor.*

Then the distribution function $F(x)$ *is indecomposable.*

We give an indirect proof and assume that $F(x)$ admits a decomposition

(6.3.8) $F = G * H,$

where G and H are both non-degenerate distributions. We introduce the quantities

$q_n = G(n+1-0) - G(n-0)$ and $r_n = H(n+1-0) - H(n-0)$

and define the distribution functions $\hat{G}(x)$ and $G_n(x)$ [respectively $\hat{H}(x)$ and $H_n(x)$] corresponding to $G(x)$ [respectively $H(x)$] by replacing, in formulae (6.3.6) and (6.3.7), p_n and F by q_n and G [respectively r_n and H]. In view of (b), we can assume without loss of generality that

(6.3.9) $q_0 > 0$ and $r_0 > 0.$

We next show that

(6.3.10) $\hat{F} = \hat{G} * \hat{H}.$

It follows from (a) and (6.3.8) that

$$p_{2k} = F(2k+2-0) - F(2k-0) = \iint\limits_{2k < x+y < 2k+2} dG(x)\, dH(y).$$

On the other hand it is easily seen that

$$\sum_{m+n=2k} q_m r_n = \iint_{2k \leqslant x+y < 2k+2} dG(x)\, dH(y)$$

so that

(6.3.11) $\qquad p_{2k} = \sum_{m+n=2k} q_m r_n$

and (6.3.10) follows. We conclude from (c) that one of the factors in (6.3.10) must be degenerate. Let $\hat{H}$ be this factor. We see from (6.3.9) that

(6.3.12) $\qquad r_0 = 1; r_j = 0 \quad \text{for } j \neq 0$

and

(6.3.13) $\qquad p_{2k} = q_{2k}.$

In view of (6.3.12) we have

(6.3.14a) $\qquad r_0 = H(1-0) - H(-0) = 1.$

Moreover we see from (6.3.13) and assumption (a) that $q_{2k-1} = 0$ or

$$G(2k-0) - G(2k-1-0) = 0;$$

hence

(6.3.14b) $\qquad G(2k-y-0) = G(2k-0) \quad \text{for } 0 \leqslant y < 1.$

We next show that for a k such that $p_{2k} > 0$ the relation

(6.3.15) $\qquad F_{2k} = G_{2k} * H$

holds. We have

$$G_{2k} * H = \int_{-\infty}^{\infty} G_{2k}(x-y)\, dH(y)$$

or, using (6.3.14a) and (6.3.14b),

$$G_{2k} * H = \frac{1}{q_{2k}} \int_0^1 [G(x-y+2k) - G(2k-y-0)]\, dH(y)$$

$$= \frac{1}{q_{2k}} [F(x+2k) - F(2k-0)] = F_{2k}(x),$$

so that (6.3.15) holds. We conclude from assumption (d) that $H(x)$ is degenerate and the statement of the theorem is proved.

We use the theorem to construct examples of indecomposable distributions which are absolutely continuous or purely singular.

Let A and B be real numbers such that $0 < A < 1, 0 < B < 1$ and A/B is irrational. The function

$$F(x) = \begin{cases} 0 & \text{if } 0 > x \\ x/2 & \text{if } 0 \leqslant x < A \\ A/2 & \text{if } A \leqslant x < 2 \\ [AB + (2-A)(x-2)]/(2B) & \text{if } 2 \leqslant x < 2+B \\ 1 & \text{if } x \geqslant 2+B \end{cases}$$

is then an absolutely continuous distribution. We have

$$p_0 = A/2, \quad p_2 = 1 - A/2, \quad p_j = 0 \quad (j \neq 0, j \neq 2).$$

$\hat{F}(x) = \dfrac{A}{2}\varepsilon(x) + \left(1 - \dfrac{A}{2}\right)\varepsilon(x-2)$, so that conditions (a), (b) and (c) of

theorem 6.3.1 are satisfied. We also have

$$F_0(x) = \begin{cases} 0 & \text{if } x < 0 \\ \dfrac{x}{A} & \text{if } 0 \leqslant x < A \\ 1 & \text{if } A \leqslant x \end{cases} \quad \text{and} \quad F_2(x) = \begin{cases} 0 & \text{if } x < 0 \\ \dfrac{x}{B} & \text{if } 0 \leqslant x < B \\ 1 & \text{if } B \leqslant x. \end{cases}$$

The corresponding characteristic functions are

$$f_0(t) = e^{itA/2}\,\frac{\sin At/2}{At/2} \quad \text{and} \quad f_2(t) = e^{itB/2}\,\frac{\sin Bt/2}{Bt/2}$$

respectively. Since A/B is irrational we see that $f_0(t)$ and $f_2(t)$ have no common zeros, and therefore also no common factor, so that condition (d) is also satisfied. Therefore $F(x)$ is indecomposable. This example has already been given by P. Lévy (1952), and theorem 6.3.1 is a modification of his construction.

We now construct an indecomposable, purely singular distribution. Let

$$c(t) = e^{it/2} \prod_{j=1}^{\infty} \cos \frac{t}{3^j}$$

be the characteristic function of the singular distribution constructed in Chapter 2 over Cantor's ternary set [see pp. 8 to 9 and formula (2.1.7)]. We write $C(x)$ for the corresponding distribution and put

$$c_A(t) = c(At)$$

and write $C_A(x)$ for the distribution function of $c_A(t)$. Let again A and B be two real numbers such that $0 < A < 1$, $0 < B < 1$ and A/B irrational. Let p_0 and p_2 be two positive numbers such that $p_0 + p_2 = 1$. Then it is easily seen that

$$F(x) = p_0 C_A(x) + p_2 C_B(x-2)$$

is a purely singular distribution function. Moreover it satisfies the conditions of theorem 6.3.1 and is therefore indecomposable.

We next discuss several factorizations of the rectangular distributions. The characteristic function of the rectangular distribution over the range $(-1, +1)$ is

$$r(t) = \frac{\sin t}{t}.$$

Clearly

$$\frac{\sin t}{t} = \frac{2 \sin (t/2) \cos (t/2)}{t} = \cos (t/2) \cdot \frac{\sin (t/2)}{t/2}.$$

We iterate this procedure and get

$$r(t) = \frac{\sin t}{t} = \left(\prod_{k=1}^{n} \cos \frac{t}{2^k}\right) \frac{\sin (t/2^n)}{t/2^n}.$$

Since

$$\lim_{n \to \infty} \frac{\sin (t/2^n)}{t/2^n} = 1$$

we see that $r(t)$ can be written as the product of an infinite sequence of indecomposable factors:

$$(6.3.16) \qquad r(t) = \frac{\sin t}{t} = \prod_{k=1}^{\infty} \cos \frac{t}{2^k}.$$

We know that the rectangular distribution is not infinitely divisible; formula (6.3.16) indicates that it is possible to decompose a characteristic function which is not infinitely divisible into a product of infinitely many indecomposable factors. The decomposition (6.3.16) is not unique. It is easy to verify that

$$\frac{\sin t}{t} = \frac{\sin (t/3)}{t/3} \left[\frac{2 \cos (2t/3)+1}{3}\right].$$

We repeat the procedure which led to (6.3.16) and obtain

$$(6.3.17) \qquad r(t) = \frac{\sin t}{t} = \left[\frac{2 \cos (2t/3)+1}{3}\right] \prod_{k=1}^{\infty} \cos \frac{t}{3 \cdot 2^k}.$$

We have therefore obtained two different representations of the characteristic function $r(t)$ as an infinite product of indecomposable factors.

We give next another interesting decomposition of the rectangular distribution. Let

$$(6.3.19) \qquad \begin{cases} f_1(t) = \displaystyle\prod_{k=1}^{\infty} \cos \frac{t}{2^{2k+1}} \\[2ex] f_2(t) = \displaystyle\prod_{k=1}^{\infty} \cos \frac{t}{2^{2k}} \end{cases}$$

It follows from the corollary to theorem 3.7.9 that $f_1(t)$ and $f_2(t)$ are characteristic functions of convergent symmetric Bernoulli convolutions. Moreover we conclude from the corollary to theorem 3.7.10 that $f_1(t)$ as well as $f_2(t)$ are characteristic functions of purely singular distributions. The product

$$f_1(t) f_2(t) = \prod_{k=1}^{\infty} \cos \frac{t}{2^{k+1}},$$

and we see from (6.3.16) that

$$(6.3.20) \qquad r\left(\frac{t}{2}\right) = f_1(t) f_2(t).$$

Formulae (6.3.19) and (6.3.20) show that it is possible to represent the rectangular distribution as the convolution of two purely singular distributions.

Several authors have raised the question whether it is possible to represent the rectangular distribution as a convolution of two absolutely continuous distributions. T. Lewis (1967) showed that this is not possible, and that the convolution of two absolutely continuous distributions cannot be a rectangular distribution.

We also note that $r(t)$ is the characteristic function of a finite distribution; we will show later [corollary 3 to theorem 8.4.1] that the characteristic function of a finite distribution is always the product of a finite or of a denumerable sequence of indecomposable factors.

Using the examples of decompositions discussed so far, we are in a position to summarize the Lebesgue properties of convolutions:

(A) The convolution of two discrete distributions is always discrete.
(B) A convolution which contains one absolutely continuous component is absolutely continuous.
(C) The convolution of a discrete and a singular distribution is always singular.
(D) The convolution of two singular distributions is continuous. It is either purely singular or purely absolutely continuous, or a mixture of a singular and an absolutely continuous component.

Remarks. Statements (A) and (B) follow from theorem 3.3.2. (C) is a consequence of some results contained in a paper by H. Tucker (1965). In connection with (D) it is interesting to note that H. Tucker constructed an infinitely divisible distribution $F(x)$, produced by a purely discrete function $\theta(x)$ in the Lévy–Khinchine representation, such that F is purely singular while $F * F$ is absolutely continuous. Theorems 3.7.9 and 3.7.10 can also be used to construct examples of purely singular distributions whose convolution is singular. It would be interesting to have a necessary and sufficient condition which assures that the convolution of two singular distributions is absolutely continuous. No such condition is known at present.

7 ANALYTIC CHARACTERISTIC FUNCTIONS

We now introduce the class of analytic characteristic functions. This class includes many characteristic functions which are important in probability theory and in mathematical statistics. In the present chapter we consider the general theory, and in Chapters 8 and 9 we study factorization problems.

In the following sections we will denote real variables by t and y and a complex variable by $z = t + iy$. We introduce the following definition.

A characteristic function $f(t)$ is said to be an analytic characteristic function if there exists a function $A(z)$ of the complex variable z which is regular in the circle $|z| < \rho$ ($\rho > 0$) and a constant $\Delta > 0$ such that $A(t) = f(t)$ for $|t| < \Delta$. We can express this in an informal manner by saying that an analytic characteristic function is a characteristic function which coincides with a regular analytic function in some neighbourhood of the origin in the complex z-plane.

As examples of distributions with analytic characteristic functions we mention: the Normal distribution, the Gamma distribution, and the Poisson distribution. Stable distributions with exponent $\alpha < 2$ provide examples of characteristic functions which are not analytic.

7.1 The strip of regularity and the integral representation

From now on we assume that $f(t)$ is an analytic characteristic function. We know (corollary to theorem 2.3.2) that all moments of the corresponding distribution exist and that it admits a Maclaurin expansion

$$(7.1.1) \qquad f(z) = \sum_{k=0}^{\infty} \frac{i^k \alpha_k}{k!} z^k \quad \text{for } |z| < \rho \ (z \text{ complex})$$

where $\rho > 0$ is the radius of convergence of the series.

We write for the even part of $f(z)$

$$f_0(z) = \tfrac{1}{2}[f(z) + f(-z)]$$

and for the odd part of $f(z)$

$$f_1(z) = \tfrac{1}{2}[f(z) - f(-z)]$$

Then the two series

$$f_0(z) = \sum_{k=0}^{\infty} \frac{(-1)^k \alpha_{2k}}{(2k)!} z^{2k}$$

$$(7.1.2)$$

$$f_1(z) = \sum_{k=1}^{\infty} \frac{i^{2k-1} \alpha_{2k-1}}{(2k-1)!} z^{2k-1}$$

also converge in circles about the origin. We denote the radii of convergence of these series by ρ_0 and ρ_1.

From the inequality

$$|x^{2k-1}| \leqslant \tfrac{1}{2}(x^{2k}+x^{2k-2})$$

we see that

$$(7.1.3) \qquad \frac{\alpha_{2k-1}}{(2k-1)!} \leqslant \frac{\beta_{2k-1}}{(2k-1)!} \leqslant \frac{1}{2}\left[\frac{\alpha_{2k}}{(2k)!}\,(2k)+\frac{\alpha_{2k-2}}{(2k-2)!}\right].$$

Here and in the following we write again α_k and β_k for the algebraic and absolute moments of order k.

We conclude from (7.1.3) that $\rho_1 \geqslant \rho_0 \geqslant \rho$ and also that the series

$$\sum_{k=0}^{\infty} \beta_k \frac{z^k}{k!}$$

converges for $|z| < \rho_0$.

Let ξ be a real number and denote the radius of convergence of the Taylor series of $f_0(z)$ [respectively of $f_1(z)$] around ξ by $\rho_0(\xi)$ [respectively $\rho_1(\xi)$]. According to corollary 2 to theorem 2.3.1 we have

$$|f^{(2k)}(\xi)| \leqslant \alpha_{2k} \quad \text{and} \quad |f^{(2k-1)}(\xi)| \leqslant \beta_{2k-1}$$

so that

$$\rho_0(\xi) \geqslant \rho_0(0) = \rho_0 \geqslant \rho \quad \text{and} \quad \rho_1(\xi) \geqslant \rho_1(0) = \rho_1 \geqslant \rho.$$

The Taylor series of $f_0(z)$ and of $f_1(z)$ around ξ therefore converge in circles of radii at least equal to ρ. The same is therefore true for the expansion of $f(z)$ around ξ, so that $f(z)$ is regular at least in the strip $|\operatorname{Im}(z)| < \rho$.

We have already mentioned that the series

$$\sum_{k=0}^{\infty} \frac{\beta_k}{k!} |y|^k$$

converges for $|y| < \rho$. Clearly

$$\sum_{k=0}^{\infty} \frac{\beta_k}{k!} |y|^k \geqslant \sum_{k=0}^{\infty} \frac{|y|^k}{k!} \int_{-A}^{A} |x|^k \, dF(x) = \int_{-A}^{A} e^{|yx|} \, dF(x)$$

for any A and $|y| < \rho$. Therefore the integral

$$\int_{-\infty}^{\infty} e^{|yx|} \, dF(x)$$

exists for $|y| < \rho$, hence the integral

$$\int_{-\infty}^{\infty} e^{izx} \, dF(x)$$

is convergent whenever $|e^{izx}| \leqslant e^{|yx|}$, where $z = t+iy$. This means that the integral

$$\int_{-\infty}^{\infty} e^{izx} \, dF(x)$$

is convergent for any t and $|y| < \rho$. This integral is a regular function in its strip of convergence and agrees with $f(z)$ for real z, therefore it must agree with $f(z)$ also for complex values $z = t+iy$, provided that $|y| < \rho$.

The integral $\int_{-\infty}^{\infty} e^{izx} dF(x)$ converges in a strip $-\alpha < \text{Im}(z) < +\beta$

where $\alpha \geqslant \rho$, $\beta \geqslant \rho$ and is regular inside this strip. We write

$$f(z) = \int_0^{\infty} e^{izx} dF(x) + \int_{-\infty}^0 e^{izx} dF(x) = \mathcal{L}_1(z) + \mathcal{L}_2(z).$$

The functions $\mathcal{L}_1(z)$ and $\mathcal{L}_2(z)$ are Laplace integrals, convergent in the half-planes $y > -\alpha$ and $y < \beta$ respectively. Let $z = iw$; then $w = -iz = -it+y$ and $\mathcal{L}_1(iw) = \int_0^{\infty} e^{-wx} dF(x) = \Phi(w)$ is convergent for $\text{Re}(w) = y > -\alpha$.

It is known that the Laplace transform $g(s) = \int_0^{\infty} e^{-st} dG(t)$ of a monotonic function $G(t)$ has a singularity at the real point of its axis of convergence. For a proof we refer the reader to D. V. Widder (1946) (p. 58, theorem 5b). Since $F(x)$ is non-decreasing we can apply this result to $\Phi(w)$ and we conclude that $-\alpha$ is a singular point of $\Phi(w)$. Thus $-i\alpha$ is a singular point of $f(z)$. In the same way it is also seen that $i\beta$ is a singular point of $f(z)$. We summarize these results and obtain the following theorem:

Theorem 7.1.1. *If a characteristic function $f(z)$ is regular in a neighbourhood of the origin, then it is also regular in a horizontal strip and can be represented in this strip by a Fourier integral. This strip is either the whole plane, or it has one or two horizontal boundary lines. The purely imaginary points on the boundary of the strip of regularity (if this strip is not the whole plane) are singular points of $f(z)$.*

From theorem 7.1.1 we obtain immediately the following result:

Corollary to theorem 7.1.1. *A necessary condition that a function, analytic in some neighbourhood of the origin, be a characteristic function is that in either half-plane the singularity nearest to the real axis be located on the imaginary axis.*

The corollary can sometimes be used to decide whether a given function could be a characteristic function. We illustrate this by an example. Let

$$f_1(t) = \left[\left(1-\frac{it}{a}\right)\left(1-\frac{it}{a+ib}\right)\left(1-\frac{it}{a-ib}\right)\right]^{-1}$$

and

$$f_2(t) = \left[1-\frac{it}{a}\right]^{-1}$$

with $a \geqslant b > 0$.

It is easy to see that both these functions are analytic characteristic functions. Their quotient

$$f(t) = \frac{f_1(t)}{f_2(t)}$$

satisfies the elementary necessary conditions for characteristic functions, $f(-t) = \overline{f(t)}, |f(t)| \leqslant f(0) = 1$ for real t. However the condition of the corollary to theorem 7.1.1 is violated since $f(t)$ has no singularity on the imaginary axis while it has a pair of conjugate complex poles $\pm b - ia$. Therefore $f(t)$ cannot be a characteristic function.

Suppose that a distribution function $F(x)$ has an analytic characteristic function $f(z)$ whose strip of regularity is

$$-\alpha < \operatorname{Im}(z) < \beta.$$

It is then possible to express α and β in terms of $F(x)$. Using classical results [see Widder (1946) pp. 42 ff.] concerning the abscissa of convergence of a Laplace integral, one obtains

$$\alpha = -\limsup_{x \to \infty} \left\{ \frac{\log [1 - F(x)]}{x} \right\} \qquad \beta = -\limsup_{x \to \infty} \frac{\log F(-x)}{x}.$$

Let $f(z)$ be an analytic characteristic function; according to theorem 7.1.1 it can be represented as the Fourier integral

$$f(z) = \int_{-\infty}^{\infty} e^{izx} dF(x) \quad [-\alpha < \operatorname{Im}(z) < \beta].$$

Therefore

$$f^{(r)}(z) = \frac{d^r}{dz^r} f(z) = i^r \int_{-\infty}^{\infty} x^r e^{izx} dF(x).$$

We write $z = a + iy$ where a and y are real and where $-\alpha < y < \beta$, then

$$|f^{(r)}(a + iy)| \leqslant \int_{-\infty}^{\infty} |x|^r e^{-xy} dF(x).$$

If $r = 2k$ ($k = 0, 1, 2, \ldots$) is an even integer, then this becomes

$$|f^{(2k)}(a + iy)| \leqslant \int_{-\infty}^{\infty} x^{2k} e^{-xy} dF(x) = |f^{(2k)}(iy)|,$$

so that

$$\max_{-\infty < a < \infty} |f^{(2k)}(a + iy)| = |f^{(2k)}(iy)|.$$

We have therefore derived the following result:

Theorem 7.1.2. *Let $f(z)$ be an analytic characteristic function. Then $|f(z)|$ attains its maximum along any horizontal line contained in the interior of its strip of regularity on the imaginary axis. The derivatives $f^{(2k)}(z)$ of even order of $f(z)$ have the same property.*

The relation
$$|f(t+iy)| \leqslant f(iy)$$
is very important in the theory of analytic characteristic functions. We say that functions satisfying this inequality have the "ridge property" and we refer to them as "ridge functions".

Corollary to theorem 7.1.2.   An analytic characteristic function has no zeros on the segment of the imaginary axis inside its strip of regularity. The zeros and the singular points of an analytic characteristic function are located symmetrically with respect to the imaginary axis.

The first part of the corollary follows immediately from theorem 7.1.2; we obtain the statement about the location of the zeros and of the singularities of the characteristic function $f(z)$ if we observe that the functional relation

(7.1.4) $\overline{f(z)} = f(-\bar{z})$

holds not only in the strip of convergence of the Fourier integral but in the entire domain of regularity of $f(z)$.

It is in general possible to continue an analytic characteristic function beyond the strip of regularity. However, an analytic characteristic function may have a natural boundary. I. V. Ostrovskii (1966) showed that the boundary of any region which satisfies certain conditions can be the natural boundary of an analytic characteristic function. These conditions are consequences of the ridge property and of the relation (7.1.4) $\overline{f(z)} = f(-\bar{z})$ which all analytic characteristic functions satisfy.

The strip of regularity of an analytic characteristic function $f(z)$ can also be the whole z-plane; in this case $f(z)$ is an entire (integral) function. We next derive a result concerning the order[*] of an entire function.

Let $f(z)$ be an entire characteristic function. We denote by
$$M(r;f) = \max_{|z| \leqslant r} |f(z)|$$
the maximum modulus of $f(z)$ in the circle $|z| \leqslant r$. This value is assumed on the perimeter of this circle[*] and we see from theorem 7.1.2 that $M(r;f) = \max [f(ir), f(-ir)]$. We formulate this result in a slightly different way.

Lemma 7.1.1.   If $f(z)$ is an entire characteristic function, then
$$[f(ir)+f(-ir)] \geqslant M(r;f) \geqslant \tfrac{1}{2}[f(ir)+f(-ir)].$$

If $f(z)$ is an entire characteristic function, then the integral representation is valid in the whole plane so that

(7.1.5) $f(ir)+f(-ir) = 2 \displaystyle\int_{-\infty}^{\infty} \cosh rx \, dF(x).$

_____

[*] See Appendix D.

It follows from (7.1.5) and the lemma that

$$M(r;f) \geqslant \int_{|x|>\delta} \cosh rx \, dF(x) \geqslant \tfrac{1}{2}(e^{\delta r}+e^{-\delta r}) \int_{|x|>\delta} dF(x)$$

$$\geqslant \tfrac{1}{2}e^{\delta r} \int_{|x|>\delta} dF(x)$$

where δ is an arbitrary positive constant. We write $\alpha = \int_{|x|>\delta} dF(x) \geqslant 0$
and note that $\alpha = 0$ for every $\delta > 0$ if, and only if, $F(x) = \varepsilon(x)$ where
$\varepsilon(x)$ denotes the degenerate distribution. From the preceding inequality
we obtain

(7.1.6) $M(r;f) \geqslant \tfrac{1}{2}\alpha e^{\delta r}$.

Since the order ρ of an entire function $f(z)$ is (see Appendix D)

(7.1.7) $\rho = \limsup\limits_{r\to\infty} \dfrac{\log \log M(r;f)}{\log r}$

we see from (7.1.6) that $\rho \geqslant 1$, provided that $\alpha > 0$, and have proved the
following theorem:

*Theorem 7.1.3.   The order of an entire characteristic function which does
not reduce to a constant is at least equal to 1.*

We will resume the study of entire characteristic functions in the next
section, but proceed now to discuss some convexity properties of analytic
characteristic functions. We introduced in Section 1.4 the moment
generating function

(7.1.8) $M(y) = \displaystyle\int_{-\infty}^{\infty} e^{yx} \, dF(x).$

This function is defined for distributions for which the integral (7.1.8)
exists for all $|y| < R$, where R is some positive constant. If $f(z)$ is an
analytic characteristic function, then we can take $R = \min(\alpha, \beta)$ and see
that its moment generating function exists and that $M(y) = f(-iy)$. We
see from (7.1.8) that $M(y)$ is real and positive while $M''(y) \geqslant 0$. Therefore
$f(-iy)$ is real and positive and is a convex function of y for all y for which
the representation by a Fourier integral is valid. Moreover $M(y) = f(-iy)$
is strictly convex unless $f(z) \equiv 1$.

We next discuss a less trivial convexity property of analytic characteristic functions and their derivatives of even order. Let $f(z)$ be an analytic
characteristic function which has $-\alpha < \operatorname{Im}(z) < \beta$ as its strip of regularity; according to theorem 7.1.2

(7.1.9) $|f^{(2k)}(t+iy)| \leqslant |f^{(2k)}(iy)|$.

Suppose that for some y_0 such that $-\alpha < y_0 < \beta$ we have $f^{(2k)}(iy_0) = 0$.
It follows from (7.1.9) that $f^{(2k)}(z) \equiv 0$, so that $f(z)$, and therefore also

$f(t)$ for real t, is a polynomial of degree $2k$. Since $f(t)$ is bounded, this is only possible if $k = 0$ and $f(t) \equiv 1$. We see therefore that the derivative $f^{(2k)}(z)$ of even order of an analytic characteristic function has no zeros on the segment of the imaginary axis contained in its strip of regularity unless $f(z) \equiv 1$. Each point iy of this segment has a neighbourhood in which $f^{(2k)}(z)$ is regular and different from zero. In this neighbourhood $\log f^{(2k)}(z)$ is defined and regular. We can therefore write $f^{(2k)}(z) = e^{g_k(z)}$, where $g_k(z)$ is regular in every point of the line segment $-\alpha < \text{Im}(z) < \beta$. Let $A_k(t, y)$ and $B_k(t, y)$ be the real and imaginary parts respectively of $g_k(z)$, so that

$$f^{(2k)}(z) = \exp[A_k(t, y) + iB_k(t, y)].$$

Then $A_k(t, y) = \log |f^{(2k)}(z)|$ while $B_k(t, y) = \arg f^{(2k)}(z)$. We can therefore write (7.1.9) as $A_k(t, y) \leqslant A_k(0, y)$ and see that for fixed y $(-\alpha < y < \beta)$ the function $A_k(t, y)$ has a maximum at $t = 0$ so that

$$\frac{\partial A_k(t, y)}{\partial t}\bigg]_{t=0} = 0, \qquad \frac{\partial^2 A_k(t, y)}{\partial t^2}\bigg]_{t=0} \leqslant 0.$$

Since $g_k(z)$ is regular at the point $z = iy$ we see from the Cauchy–Riemann equations and from Laplace's equation that

$$\frac{\partial B_k(t, y)}{\partial y}\bigg]_{t=0} = 0, \qquad \frac{\partial^2 A_k(t, y)}{\partial y^2}\bigg]_{t=0} \geqslant 0.$$

We therefore obtain the following result:

Theorem 7.1.4. Let $f(z)$ be an analytic characteristic function which has the strip $-\alpha < \text{Im}(z) = y < \beta$ as its strip of regularity and let k be a non-negative integer. Then $\arg f^{(2k)}(iy) = B_k(0, y)$ is independent of y while $\log |f^{(2k)}(iy)| = A_k(0, y)$ is convex for all y such that $-\alpha < y < \beta$. Moreover, for all such y, the function $f(iy)$ is real-valued, non-negative and convex and is even strictly convex, except in the case where $f(z) \equiv 1$.

7.2 Analytic characteristic functions and their distribution functions

In this section we deal with the relation between the properties of an analytic characteristic function and its distribution function. As a first step we will derive a necessary and sufficient condition which a distribution function must satisfy in order that its characteristic function be an analytic characteristic function.

In the preceding section we have seen that the moment generating function (7.1.8) exists for every distribution function $F(x)$ which has an analytic characteristic function. The converse statement follows from the argument used in the proof of theorem 7.1.1. Thus distribution functions $F(x)$ which have analytic characteristic functions are exactly those for which the moment generating function exists. This remark leads to a rather obvious criterion:

The distribution function $F(x)$ has an analytic characteristic function if, and only if, the following two conditions are satisfied:

(i) the distribution $F(x)$ has moments α_k of all orders k

(ii) $\limsup_{k \to \infty} [|\alpha_k|/k!]^{1/k} = 1/\rho$ is finite.

These conditions are equivalent to the statement that the series

$$f(z) = \sum_{k=0}^{\infty} \frac{\alpha_k}{k!} (iz)^k$$

represents a function which is regular in the circle $|z| < \rho$ ($\rho > 0$) and which agrees with the characteristic function of $F(x)$ for real values of z.

We note that it is easy to construct distributions which have moments of all orders but do not have analytic characteristic functions. Such a distribution then necessarily violates condition (ii). As an example we mention the distribution whose frequency function is

$$p(x) = \begin{cases} \frac{1}{2} \exp(-|\sqrt{x}|) & \text{for } x > 0 \\ 0 & \text{for } x < 0. \end{cases}$$

The corresponding moments are easily computed. We find $\alpha_k = (2k+1)!$ so that

$$\left[\frac{|\alpha_k|}{k!} \right]^{1/k} = k^{(k+1)/k} \sqrt[k]{\left(1 + \frac{1}{k}\right) \cdots \left(1 + \frac{k+1}{k}\right)} > k.$$

Hence all moments exist but do not satisfy (ii).

This distribution has another interesting property. Although its moment generating function does not exist, it is completely determined by its moments. It is known [see Shohat–Tamarkin (1943), theorem 1.11] that a distribution function is completely determined by the sequence $\{\alpha_k\}$ of its moments, if the sum $\sum_{k=1}^{\infty} \alpha_k^{-1/2k}$ diverges. Since $\alpha_k = (2k+1)! < (2k+1)^{2k}$ it is easily seen that this condition is satisfied.

Our next result is more useful and is directly applicable to the distribution function $F(x)$.

Theorem 7.2.1. The characteristic function $f(t)$ of a distribution function $F(x)$ is an analytic characteristic function if, and only if, there exists a positive constant R such that the relation

(7.2.1) $1 - F(x) + F(-x) = O(e^{-rx})$ *as $x \to \infty$*

holds for all positive $r < R$. The strip of regularity of $f(z)$ then contains the strip $|\operatorname{Im}(z)| < R$.

Remark. The positive constant R may be infinite. In this case (7.2.1) holds for all positive real r and $f(z)$ is an entire function.

We first note that (7.2.1) is equivalent to the simultaneous validity of the relations

(i) $1 - F(x) = O(e^{-rx})$ as $x \to \infty$

(ii) $F(-x) = O(e^{-rx})$ as $x \to \infty$.

We prove first the sufficiency of these conditions. Let y be a real number such that $|y| < R$ and choose a positive r so that $|y| < r < R$. Let k be a positive integer; then

$$\int_{k-1}^{k} e^{|y|x} dF(x) \leqslant e^{|y|k}[1 - F(k-1)].$$

Using condition (i), we see that $1 - F(k-1) = O(e^{-r(k-1)})$ as $k \to \infty$, so that there exists a constant C_1 such that $1 - F(k-1) \leqslant C_1 e^{-rk}$ for sufficiently large k, say for $k \geqslant K_1$, so that

$$\int_{k-1}^{k} e^{|y|x} dF(x) \leqslant C_1 e^{-k(r-|y|)} \quad \text{for } k \geqslant K_1.$$

We choose an integer $K \geqslant K_1$ and real numbers $a \geqslant K, b > 0$. Then

$$\int_{a}^{a+b} e^{|y|x} dF(x) \leqslant \sum_{k=K}^{\infty} \int_{k-1}^{k} e^{|y|x} dF(x)$$

$$\leqslant C_1 \sum_{k=K}^{\infty} e^{-k(r-|y|)} = \frac{C_1 e^{-(r-|y|)K}}{1 - e^{-(r-|y|)}}.$$

The last expression can be made arbitrarily small by choosing K sufficiently large; therefore the integral $\int_{a}^{a+b} e^{|y|x} dF(x)$ can be made arbitrarily small—no matter what b is—by choosing a sufficiently large. Thus the integral

$$\int_{0}^{\infty} e^{|y|x} dF(x) = \int_{0}^{\infty} e^{|y x|} dF(x)$$

exists and is finite.

We also have

$$\int_{-k}^{-k+1} e^{|y x|} dF(x) \leqslant e^{|y|k} F(-k+1),$$

and we conclude from (ii) that there exists a constant C_1' such that $F(-k+1) \leqslant C_1' e^{-rk}$ for sufficiently large k, say for $k > K_1'$. We choose now an integer $K' > K_1'$ and two real numbers $c > K', d > 0$. We see then that

$$\int_{-c-d}^{-c} e^{|y x|} dF(x) \leqslant \frac{C_1' e^{-(r-|y|)K'}}{1 - e^{-(r-|y|)}}$$

and apply an argument, similar to the one used above, to show that the integral $\int_{-\infty}^{0} e^{|y x|} dF(x)$ exists and is finite. Combining this with our earlier result we see that $\int_{-\infty}^{\infty} e^{|ux|}\,dF(x)$, and therefore also $\int_{-\infty}^{\infty} e^{yx}\,dF(x)$, exists and is finite for all y such that $|y| < R$. Let $z = t+iy$, then the integral $f(z) = \int_{-\infty}^{\infty} e^{izx}\,dF(x)$ is also convergent for any t and $|y| < R$ and represents a regular analytic function, so that the sufficiency of our condition is established.

We next prove that the condition (7.2.1) [or (i) and (ii)] is necessary, and suppose that the characteristic function $f(z) = \int_{-\infty}^{\infty} e^{izx}\,dF(x)$ is an analytic characteristic function whose strip of regularity is the strip $-\alpha < \operatorname{Im}(z) < \beta$. Let $R = \min(\alpha, \beta)$ and let $x > 0$ be a real number; then the two integrals

$$\int_{x}^{-\infty} e^{yu}\,dF(u) \quad \text{and} \quad \int_{-\infty}^{-x} e^{yu}\,dF(u)$$

exist and are finite for all $|y| < R$. We choose a number $r < R$ and let r_1 be such that $r < r_1 < R$. Then there exists a constant C such that

$$C > \int_{x}^{\infty} e^{r_1 u}\,dF(u) \geqslant e^{r_1 x}[1-F(x)] \geqslant 0$$

or

$$0 \leqslant [1-F(x)]e^{rx} \leqslant C\,e^{-(r_1-r)x}.$$

Since $r_1 > r$, the expression on the right of the last inequality goes to zero as x tends to infinity, so that $1-F(x) = O(e^{-rx})$ as $x \to \infty$. In the same way we see that (ii) is satisfied.

If $F(x)$ is a finite distribution then $1-F(x)+F(-x) = 0$ for sufficiently large x, so that (7.2.1) is satisfied for all positive r. Every finite distribution has therefore an entire characteristic function. However, it is possible to make more precise statements concerning finite distributions. These are closely related to properties of one-sided distributions with analytic characteristic functions which we shall discuss first.

Theorem 7.2.2.   Let $F(x)$ be a distribution function with an analytic characteristic function. $F(x)$ is bounded to the left [respectively to the right] if, and only if, its characteristic function is regular in the upper [respectively lower] half-plane and if there exists a finite positive constant c such that

$$|f(z)| \leqslant e^{c|z|}$$

provided that $\operatorname{Im}(z) > 0$ *[respectively* $\operatorname{Im}(z) < 0$*].*

We first show that our condition is necessary and we suppose that[*]

$a = \text{lext}\,[F]$ and consider the integral $\int_{a}^{\infty} e^{izx}\,dF(x)$ where $z = t+iy$. In

---

[*] The symbol lext is defined in Section 5.8, page 142.

the case where $a \geqslant 0$ it is clear that this integral is regular in the half-plane $y = \mathrm{Im}\,(z) > 0$. If $a < 0$ we write

$$\int_a^\infty e^{izx}\,dF\,(x) = \int_a^0 e^{izx}\,dF\,(x) + \int_0^\infty e^{izx}\,dF\,(x);$$

the first integral is an entire function while the second is regular in the upper half-plane. We assume that $f(z)$ is an analytic characteristic function. Therefore $f(z)$ is regular in a horizontal strip containing the real axis in its interior and admits in this strip the integral representation

$$f(z) = \int_{-\infty}^\infty e^{izx}\,dF\,(x).$$

Since $f(z)$ is regular in the upper half-plane we see that the region of validity of this representation contains the half-plane $\mathrm{Im}\,(z) > 0$ in its interior. Therefore

$$|f(z)| = \left| \int_{-\infty}^\infty e^{ilx-xy}\,dF\,(x) \right| \leqslant \int_a^\infty e^{-yx}\,dF\,(x)$$

for $y = \mathrm{Im}\,(z) > 0$ and we can show easily that

(7.2.2) $\qquad |f(z)| \leqslant e^{-ay} \leqslant e^{|a|y} \leqslant e^{|a||z|},$

provided that $y > 0$.

We next prove the sufficiency of the condition and assume that $f(z)$ is an analytic characteristic function which is regular in the upper half-plane and which satisfies the inequality

$$|f(z)| \leqslant e^{c|z|} \quad (c > 0),$$

provided that $\mathrm{Im}\,(z) > 0$. Let here $z = iy\,(y > 0)$; then it can be shown that

$$h = -\limsup_{y \to \infty} \frac{1}{y} \log f(iy)$$

is finite. Let ε be an arbitrary positive number and let x_1 and x_2 be two real numbers such that $x_1 < x_2$ and $h - x_2 = 2\varepsilon$. We then see from the representation of $f(z)$ as a Fourier integral that

$$f(iy) = \int_{-\infty}^\infty e^{-yx}\,dF\,(x) \geqslant \int_{x_1}^{x_2} e^{-yx}\,dF\,(x) \geqslant e^{-yx_2}[F\,(x_2) - F\,(x_1)].$$

The definition of h implies that $-h + \varepsilon > y^{-1} \log f(iy)$ or that

$$f(iy) < e^{-y(h-\varepsilon)} = e^{-y(x_2+\varepsilon)}.$$

Therefore $e^{-y\varepsilon} > F\,(x_2) - F\,(x_1) \geqslant 0$ for arbitrary $\varepsilon > 0$ and sufficiently large y. This, however, is only possible if $F\,(x_2) - F\,(x_1) = 0$ whenever $x_1 < x_2 = h - 2\varepsilon$; this means that $F\,(x)$ is bounded to the left and that

$$\mathrm{lext}\,[F] \geqslant h.$$

This completes the proof concerning distributions which are bounded from the left. However, we see from (7.2.2) that $\log f(iy) \leqslant -ay$, hence the inequality $h \geqslant a = \text{lext}\,[F]$ also holds and we have $h = a$ or

$$(7.2.3) \qquad \text{lext}\,[F] = -\limsup_{y \to \infty} \frac{1}{y} \log f(iy).$$

We can therefore state

Corollary to thereom 7.2.2. If $F(x)$ is a distribution function which is bounded to the left and has an analytic characteristic function, then

$$(7.2.3) \qquad \text{lext}\,[F] = -\limsup_{y \to \infty} \frac{1}{y} \log f(iy);$$

if $F(x)$ is bounded to the right and has an analytic characteristic function, then

$$(7.2.4) \qquad \text{rext}\,[F] = \limsup_{y \to \infty} \frac{1}{y} \log f(-iy).$$

The proof has been given only for distributions which are bounded to the left; the proof of the statements concerning distributions which are bounded from the right is quite similar and is therefore omitted.

Remark. Let $k(x)$ be an arbitrary convex function such that $k(0) = 0$; it is then easily seen that $k(x)/x$ is a non-decreasing function for $x > 0$. Let $f(z)$ be a characteristic function which is regular in the half-plane $-\alpha < \text{Im}\,(z) = y$ $(\alpha > 0)$. According to theorem 7.1.4, the function $\log f(iy)$ is a convex function of y for $y > 0$, and we conclude that $[\log f(iy)]/y$ is a non-decreasing function of y. Therefore it is possible to replace in the formula for the left extremity the lim sup by lim, and to write instead of (7.2.3)

$$(7.2.3a) \qquad \text{lext}\,[F] = -\lim_{y \to \infty} \frac{1}{y} \log f(iy).$$

Using a similar argument one obtains

$$(7.2.4a) \qquad \text{rext}\,[F] = \lim_{y \to \infty} \frac{1}{y} \log f(-iy).$$

These limits will of course be infinite if the distribution function $F(x)$ is unbounded either to the left or to the right.

If the distribution $F(x)$ is finite, then we can combine the results of theorem 7.2.2 and its corollary and obtain the following statement:

Theorem 7.2.3. Let $F(x)$ be a non-degenerate and finite distribution function. The characteristic function $f(t)$ of $F(x)$ is then an entire function of exponential type $\tau > 0$ and of order 1 which has infinitely many zeros. Con-

versely, an entire characteristic function of exponential type $\tau > 0$ *and of order* 1 *belongs always to a finite distribution. Moreover the two extremities of* $F(x)$ *are given by* (7.2.3) *and* (7.2.4).

Let $a = \text{lext}[F], b = \text{rext}[F], c = \max(|a|, |b|)$. We see then from theorem 7.2.2 that $|f(z)| \leqslant e^{c|z|}$, so that $M(r; f) \leqslant e^{cr}$. It follows from theorem 7.1.3 that $f(z)$ is an entire function of order 1 of exponential type not exceeding c. According to Hadamard's factorization theorem[*] $f(z) = G(z)e^{az}$ where $G(z)$ is the canonical product formed with the zeros of $f(z)$. Since $|f(t)| \leqslant 1$ for real t, we see that $G(z)$ cannot be a polynomial and must therefore have infinitely many zeros. The second statement of theorem 7.2.3 as well as the formulae for the extremities follow immediately from theorem 7.2.2.

Remark 1. A one-sided distribution does not necessarily have an analytic characteristic function. As examples we mention the stable distributions with exponent $0 < \alpha < 1$ and $\beta = \pm 1$ which were treated in theorem 5.8.3. A specific example was given by formula (5.8.9).

Remark 2. A one-sided distribution may have an entire characteristic function, and the order of this function can exceed 1. As an example we mention the characteristic function which is obtained by truncating the standardized normal distribution at the point zero.

Remark 3. An interesting modification of the continuity theorem for characteristic functions of one-sided distributions was established by A. Zygmund (1951). He showed that in the case of one-sided distributions the condition that the sequence of characteristic functions should converge over every finite interval can be replaced by convergence over a fixed interval around $t = 0$. For a precise statement as well as for the proof we refer the reader to A. Zygmund's paper.

Remark 4. The characteristic function of a finite distribution necessarily has infinitely many zeros. These need not, however, be real [Example: $f(t) = (p + q e^{it})$].

Remark 5. Entire characteristic functions of order 1 and maximal type do not belong to finite distributions.

Remark 6. If $B(x)$ is a non-decreasing function of bounded variation such that its spectrum S_B is contained in the finite interval $[a, b]$ then its Fourier–Stieltjes transform

$$b(t) = \int_{-\infty}^{\infty} e^{itx} dB(x) = \int_{a}^{b} e^{itx} dB(x)$$

---

[*] See Copson (1935), pp. 174–175.

is an entire function of order 1 and exponential type not exceeding

$$\max (|a|, |b|).$$

Remark 7. If a distribution function $F(x)$ has an entire characteristic function of order 1 and exponential type τ then

$$-\tau \leqslant \operatorname{lext} [F] < \operatorname{rext} [F] \leqslant \tau.$$

A similar statement is true if $F(x)$ is a function of bounded variation whose Fourier–Stieltjes transform is an entire function of order 1 and exponential type τ.

We next study the order and type of entire characteristic functions. For this purpose we need three lemmas:

Lemma 7.2.1. *Let $\alpha > 0$ and $k > 0$; then the integral*

$$I(z) = \int_0^\infty \exp (izx - kx^{1+\alpha})\, dx$$

is an entire function of order $\rho = 1 + 1/\alpha$ and type $\tau = \dfrac{\alpha}{k^{1/\alpha}(1+\alpha)^{1+1/\alpha}}.$

We expand the factor e^{izx} into a power series, and since the order of integration and summation may be exchanged we see that

$$I(z) = \sum_{n=0}^\infty \frac{(iz)^n}{n!} \int_0^\infty x^n e^{-kx^{1+\alpha}}\, dx.$$

We introduce the new variable $y = kx^{1+\alpha}$ in the integral and obtain

$$I(z) = \sum_{n=0}^\infty c_n z^n$$

where

$$c_n = \frac{i^n}{n!} \Gamma\!\left(\frac{n+1}{1+\alpha}\right) \frac{1}{(1+\alpha)\, k^{(n+1)/(1+\alpha)}}.$$

We use Stirling's formula and the expressions (D4) and (D5) of Appendix D and obtain the statement of the lemma.

The order and type of entire characteristic functions depends on the "tail behaviour" of the corresponding distribution function. In order to study this behaviour it is convenient to introduce three functions. Let $F(x)$ be a distribution function; we write for $x > 0$

$$(7.2.5) \quad \begin{cases} T(x) = 1 - F(x) + F(-x) \\[2mm] T_1(x) = \dfrac{\log [T(x)]^{-1}}{x^{1+\alpha}} \quad (\alpha > 0) \\[2mm] T_2(x) = \dfrac{\log \log [T(x)]^{-1}}{\log x} \end{cases}$$

We note that $T_1(x)$ depends on the positive parameter α.

Lemma 7.2.2. Let $F(x)$ be a distribution function and $\alpha > 0$ and $k > 0$. Suppose that there exists an $x_0 > 0$ such that

$$T(x) \leqslant \exp\left(-kx^{1+\alpha}\right)$$

for $x \geqslant x_0$. Then $F(x)$ has an entire characteristic function $f(z)$ which is either of order equal to $1+\alpha^{-1}$ and type $\tau \leqslant \alpha[k^{1/\alpha}(1+\alpha)^{1+1/\alpha}]^{-1}$ or of order less than $1+\alpha^{-1}$.

Let $A > x_0$ and $r > 0$; we see then (integrating by parts) that

$$\int_{x_0}^{A} e^{rx}\, dF(x) = -\int_{x_0}^{A} e^{rx}\, d\,[1-F(x)]$$

$$= e^{rx_0}[1-F(x_0)] - e^{rA}[1-F(A)] + r\int_{x_0}^{A}[1-F(x)]\,e^{rx}\,dx.$$

We let A tend to infinity and conclude from the assumption of the lemma that

$$\int_{x_0}^{\infty} e^{rx}\, dF(x) \leqslant e^{rx_0}[1-F(x_0)] + r\int_{x_0}^{\infty}\exp\left(rx - kx^{1+\alpha}\right)dx.$$

Since $\displaystyle\int_{-\infty}^{x_0} e^{rx}\, dF(x) \leqslant e^{rx_0} F(x_0)$, we have

(7.2.6) $$\int_{-\infty}^{\infty} e^{rx}\, dF(x) \leqslant e^{rx_0} + r\int_{0}^{\infty}\exp\left(rx - kx^{1+\alpha}\right)dx.$$

Similarly one can show that

(7.2.7) $$\int_{-\infty}^{\infty} e^{-rx}\, dF(x) \leqslant e^{rx_0} + r\int_{0}^{\infty}\exp\left(rx - kx^{1+\alpha}\right)dx.$$

Since $M(r, f) = \max\left[f(ir), f(-ir)\right]$ we see from (7.2.6) and (7.2.7) that

$$M(r, f) \leqslant e^{rx_0} + r\int_{0}^{\infty}\exp\left(rx - kx^{1+\alpha}\right)dx.$$

The statement of lemma 7.2.2 follows easily from lemma 7.2.1 and from the last inequality.

Lemma 7.2.3. Let $F(x)$ be a distribution function with characteristic function $f(t)$ and let $\lambda > 0$, $\mu > 0$ be two constants. Suppose that there exists a constant R such that

$$M(r; f) \leqslant \exp[\lambda r^{1+\mu}]$$

for $r \geqslant R$. Then

$$\liminf_{x\to\infty} T_2(x) \geqslant 1 + 1/\mu$$

and

$$T(x) \leqslant \exp\left(-x^{1+\mu^{-1}-\varepsilon}\right)$$

for any $\varepsilon > 0$ and sufficiently large x.

We see from (7.1.6) that for $x > 0$ and $r \geqslant R$

$$T(x) \leqslant 2\exp\left(-rx + \lambda r^{1+\mu}\right).$$

We put $x \geqslant x_0 = 2R^\mu$ and $r = (\frac{1}{2}x)^{1/\mu}$ so that $r \geqslant R$; then we get

$$T(x) \leqslant 2 \exp\left[-(2-\lambda)(\tfrac{1}{2}x)^{1+\mu^{-1}}\right]$$

and we conclude from formula (7.2.5) that

$$\liminf_{x \to \infty} T_2(x) \geqslant 1 + 1/\mu.$$

For any $\varepsilon > 0$ and sufficiently large x, one then has

$$T_2(x) \geqslant 1 + \frac{1}{\mu} - \varepsilon.$$

Using again (7.2.5), one obtains the statement of the lemma.

We study next entire characteristic functions of order greater than 1.

Theorem 7.2.4.   The distribution function $F(x)$ has an entire characteristic function $f(z)$ of order $1 + \alpha^{-1}$ ($\alpha > 0$) and of intermediate type τ if, and only if, the following two conditions are satisfied:

(i) $\displaystyle \liminf_{x \to \infty} T_1(x) = \frac{(\alpha\tau^{-1})^\alpha}{(1+\alpha)^{1+\alpha}}$

(ii) $T(x) > 0$

for all $x > 0$.

We first prove that the condition is necessary, and assume that $f(z)$ is an entire function of order $1 + \alpha^{-1}$ and finite type $\tau > 0$. Clearly (ii) is necessary, since $T(x) = 0$ means that $F(x)$ is finite, so that $f(z)$ would have order 1. Moreover it is possible to find for any $\varepsilon > 0$ a value $R = R(\varepsilon)$ such that

$$(7.2.8) \qquad M(r; f) \leqslant \exp\left[(\tau+\varepsilon)\,r^{1+\alpha^{-1}}\right],$$

provided that $r \geqslant R$. It follows from (7.1.6) and (7.2.8) that

$$(7.2.9) \qquad T(x) \leqslant 2 \exp\left[-rx + (\tau+\varepsilon)\,r^{1+\alpha^{-1}}\right]$$

for $x > 0$, $r \geqslant R$.

Let a be an arbitrary positive number and let $x \geqslant x_0 = \left(\dfrac{R}{a}\right)^{1/\alpha}$ and $r = ax^\alpha$; then $r \geqslant R$. It follows from (7.2.9) that

$$\log \frac{1}{T(x)} \geqslant -\log 2 + x^{\alpha+1}\left[a - (\tau+\varepsilon)\,a^{1+\alpha^{-1}}\right]$$

so that

$$T_1(x) \geqslant a - (\tau+\varepsilon)\,a^{1+\alpha^{-1}} + o(1)$$

as $x \to \infty$. Therefore

$$(7.2.10) \qquad \liminf_{x \to \infty} T_1(x) \geqslant a - (\tau+\varepsilon)\,a^{1+\alpha^{-1}}.$$

This relation holds for any $a > 0$ and in particular for that value of a which maximizes the right-hand side of (7.2.10), that is for

$$a = \{\alpha/[(\tau+\varepsilon)(1+\alpha)]\}^{\alpha}.$$

We substitute this value of a into (7.2.10) and get

$$\liminf_{x\to\infty} T_1(x) \geqslant \frac{[\alpha(\tau+\varepsilon)^{-1}]^{\alpha}}{(1+\alpha)^{1+\alpha}}.$$

Since $\varepsilon > 0$ is arbitrary we see that

$$(7.2.11) \qquad \liminf_{x\to\infty} T_1(x) \geqslant \frac{(\alpha\tau^{-1})^{\alpha}}{(1+\alpha)^{1+\alpha}}.$$

We show next by means of an indirect proof that the inequality sign cannot hold in (7.2.11). Suppose therefore that

$$\liminf_{x\to\infty} T_1(x) > \frac{(\alpha\tau^{-1})^{\alpha}}{(1+\alpha)^{1+\alpha}}.$$

Then it is possible to find a $k > \dfrac{(\alpha\tau^{-1})^{\alpha}}{(1+\alpha)^{1+\alpha}}$ such that $T_1(x) \geqslant k$ for x

sufficiently large. Using (7.2.5), we see that $T(x) \leqslant \exp(-kx^{1+\alpha})$ for sufficiently large x and conclude from lemma 7.2.2 that

$$(7.2.12) \qquad M(r;f) \leqslant \exp[(\tau'+\varepsilon)r^{1+\alpha^{-1}}]$$

for any $\varepsilon > 0$ and sufficiently large r, where $\tau' = [k^{1/\alpha}(1+\alpha)^{1+1/\alpha}]^{-1}\alpha < \tau$. Since the order of $f(z)$ is, by assumption, $1+\alpha^{-1}$, it follows from (7.2.12) that the type of $f(z)$ is at most equal to τ', hence less than τ. This contradicts the assumptions of the theorem; therefore the inequality sign cannot hold in (7.2.11), so that the necessity of (i) is established.

We still have to show that conditions (i) and (ii) are sufficient. Clearly (ii) implies that $f(z)$ is not a function of exponential type and that $T_1(x)$ is defined for $x > 0$. Let

$$(7.2.13) \qquad k < (\alpha\tau^{-1})^{\alpha}(1+\alpha)^{-1-\alpha}.$$

In view of (i), there exists a value $x_1 = x_1(k)$ such that $T_1(x) \geqslant k$ for $x \geqslant x_1$. It follows from (7.2.5) that

$$(7.2.14) \qquad T(x) \leqslant \exp(-kx^{1+\alpha})$$

for $x \geqslant x_1$, and we conclude from lemma 7.2.2 that $f(z)$ is an entire function whose order ρ and type τ' are such that either

$$(7.2.15) \qquad \rho = 1+\alpha^{-1} \quad \text{and} \quad \tau' \leqslant \alpha/[k^{1/\alpha}(1+\alpha)^{1+1/\alpha}]$$

or

$$(7.2.16) \qquad \rho < 1+\alpha^{-1}.$$

We show next that (7.2.16) cannot hold. We give an indirect proof and assume therefore tentatively the validity of (7.2.16). It is then possible to find a number $\gamma > \alpha$ such that

$$M(r; f) \leqslant \exp{(r^{1+1/\gamma})}$$

for sufficiently large r, say $r \geqslant R$. It follows from this inequality and lemma 7.2.3 that for any $\varepsilon > 0$

$$T(x) \leqslant \exp{(-x^{1+\gamma-\varepsilon})},$$

provided that x is taken sufficiently large. We again apply lemma 7.2.2 and see that $f(z)$ is an entire function whose order ρ cannot exceed $1 + (\gamma - \varepsilon)^{-1}$. Since ε is arbitrary, we see that

$$\rho \leqslant 1 + \gamma^{-1} < 1 + \alpha^{-1}.$$

But then

$$M(r; f) \leqslant \exp{(r^{1+\gamma^{-1}})},$$

and we see from lemma 7.2.3 that

$$(7.2.17) \qquad \liminf_{x \to \infty} T_2(x) \geqslant 1 + \gamma > 1 + \alpha.$$

We also see from (7.2.14) and (7.2.5) that

$$(7.2.18) \qquad T_1(x) = x^{T_2(x) - (1+} \; .$$

Since α and τ are finite and positive, (i) implies that $\liminf_{x \to \infty} T_1(x)$ is finite and positive. Equation (7.2.18) indicates that this is only possible if

$$(7.2.19) \qquad \liminf_{x \to \infty} T_2(x) = 1 + \alpha.$$

Relation (7.2.17), derived under the tentative assumption (7.2.16), contradicts (7.2.19), so that necessarily (7.2.15) is valid and $\rho = 1 + \alpha^{-1}$, as stated in the theorem. Since k is only subject to condition (7.2.13) but is otherwise arbitrary, we deduce easily from (7.2.15) that

$$(7.2.20) \qquad \tau' \leqslant \tau.$$

We show, again by an indirect proof, that the inequality sign in (7.2.20) leads to a contradiction. Suppose therefore that $\tau' < \tau$. Then there exists a τ'' such that $\tau' < \tau'' < \tau$ and

$$M(r; f) \leqslant \exp{(\tau'' r^{1+\alpha^{-1}})}$$

for sufficiently large r. The last inequality has the same form as (7.2.8). We use the reasoning which led from (7.2.8) to (7.2.11) and see that

$$\liminf_{x \to \infty} T_1(x) \geqslant \frac{(\alpha/\tau'')^\alpha}{(1+\alpha)^{1+\alpha}} > \frac{(\alpha/\tau)^\alpha}{(1+\alpha)^{1+\alpha}}.$$

This contradicts assumption (i) of the theorem, so that $\tau' = \tau$ and the proof is completed.

It is also possible to derive conditions which assure that a distribution function has an entire characteristic function of a given order greater than 1 and of intermediate but unspecified type, or of maximal or minimal type.

Theorem 7.2.5. *The distribution function $F(x)$ has an entire characteristic function $f(z)$ of order $1+\alpha^{-1}$ ($\alpha > 0$) if, and only if, the following two conditions are satisfied:*

    (i) $\liminf_{x \to \infty} T_2(x) = 1+\alpha$

    (ii) $T(x) > 0$ *for all $x > 0$.*

In view of theorem 7.2.4 it is clear that the conditions are necessary. To prove that they are sufficient, we note that (i) implies that $T(x) \leqslant \exp(-x^{1+\alpha-\varepsilon})$ for any $\varepsilon > 0$ and sufficiently large x. Using the argument which we employed in the proof of theorem 7.2.4, we can show that $f(z)$ has order $1+\alpha^{-1}$.

Theorem 7.2.6. *The distribution function $F(x)$ has an entire characteristic function of order $1+\alpha^{-1}$ ($\alpha > 0$) and of minimal type if, and only if, the following three conditions are satisfied:*

    (i) $\liminf_{x \to \infty} T_2(x) = 1+\alpha$

    (ii) $T(x) > 0$ *for all $x > 0$*

    (iii) $\lim_{x \to \infty} T_1(x)$ *exists and* $\lim_{x \to \infty} T_1(x) = +\infty$.

Theorem 7.2.7. *The distribution function $F(x)$ has an entire characteristic function of order $1+\alpha^{-1}$ ($\alpha > 0$) and of maximal type if, and only if, the following three conditions are satisfied:*

    (i) $\liminf_{x \to \infty} T_2(x) = 1+\alpha$

    (ii) $T(x) > 0$ *for all $x > 0$*

    (iii) $\liminf_{x \to \infty} T_1(x) = 0$.

It is also possible to obtain results concerning distributions whose characteristic functions are entire functions of order 1. The method of proof is similar to that used in proving theorem 7.2.4. We therefore list here only the relevant results.

Theorem 7.2.8. *The distribution function $F(x)$ has an entire characteristic function of order 1 and maximal type if, and only if,*

    (i) $T(x) > 0$ *for all $x > 0$*

    (ii) $\lim_{x \to \infty} T_2(x)$ *exists and* $\lim_{x \to \infty} T_2(x) = +\infty$.

Theorem 7.2.9. *An entire function of order 1 and minimal type cannot be a characteristic function.*

The last theorem is only a reformulation of a result from the theory of entire functions which asserts that a non-constant entire function of at most first order and minimal type cannot be bounded on some line [see B. Ya. Levin (1964), p. 51]. For a detailed proof of theorems 7.2.5 to 7.2.9 we refer to B. Ramachandran (1962).

Order and type of entire functions provide means of studying their growth. This study can be refined by introducing proximate orders and types with respect to proximate orders [see e.g. Levin (1964), pp. 31 ff.]. It is also possible to investigate the behaviour of characteristic functions having given proximate orders. For these studies we refer the reader to H. J. Rossberg (1966), (1967a), (1967b).

We finally remark that there exist entire characteristic functions of infinite order. Let $f(t)$ be an arbitrary characteristic function; it follows from lemma 5.4.1 that $\exp[f(t)-1]$ is also a characteristic function. We define the sequence of functions

$$(7.2.21) \quad \begin{cases} f_{(1)}(t) = f(t) \\ f_{(n)}(t) = \exp[f_{(n-1)}(t)-1] \quad (n = 2, 3, \ldots) \end{cases}$$

and see, again using lemma 5.4.1, that all functions of the sequence $f_{(n)}(t)$ are characteristic functions. Suppose now that $f(t)$ is an entire characteristic function of finite order, then the functions $f_{(n)}(t)$ are entire functions of infinite order if $n > 1$. As an example we mention the sequence of functions which starts with $f_{(1)}(t) = e^{it}$; this yields a sequence of entire characteristic functions of infinite order of more and more rapid growth. The second function in this sequence is the characteristic function of the Poisson distribution.

7.3 Criteria for analytic characteristic functions

In Chapter 4 we discussed various criteria for characteristic functions. We have seen that the necessary and sufficient conditions developed by Bochner, Cramér and Khinchine are not easily applicable. It is therefore desirable to derive less general results which are applied more readily. These results are usually restricted to certain classes of functions; in this connection the problem arises whether it is possible to characterize those functions which are regular in a (complex) neighbourhood of the origin and are characteristic functions. This problem is still unsolved, but a number of results, giving sometimes necessary and sometimes sufficient conditions for analytic functions to be characteristic functions, were found. The present section deals with these criteria. In some instances we only mention conditions and give appropriate references, but a very important criterion for a class of entire characteristic functions will be studied in detail.

We note first that some of the results treated in Section 7.1 can be regarded as criteria for analytic characteristic functions. Thus theorems 7.1.1, 7.1.2 and their corollaries give necessary conditions which a function regular in a neighbourhood of the origin must satisfy in order to be a characteristic function. The same is true of theorem 7.1.4 or of P. Lévy's result (theorem 7.1.3) that a non-constant entire function of finite order must have at least order 1 and must have infinitely many zeros if its order is equal to 1.

It is easy to establish a condition similar to the one listed in theorem 4.1.2. Let $f(z)$ be an analytic characteristic function; then

$$\operatorname{Re}\left[f(iy) - f(t+iy)\right] = \int_{-\infty}^{\infty} e^{-yx}(1 - \cos tx)\, dF(x)$$

$$\geqslant \tfrac{1}{2} \int_{-\infty}^{\infty} e^{-yx} \sin^2 tx\, dF(x) = \tfrac{1}{4} \int_{-\infty}^{\infty} e^{-yx}(1 - \cos 2tx)\, dF(x).$$

Therefore

$$\operatorname{Re}\left[f(iy) - f(t+iy)\right] \geqslant \tfrac{1}{4}\operatorname{Re}\left[f(iy) - f(2t+iy)\right].$$

We iterate this procedure and obtain the following result:

Theorem 7.3.1. *Let n be a non-negative integer; the inequality*

$$\operatorname{Re}\left[f(iy) - f(t+iy)\right] \geqslant 4^{-n} \operatorname{Re}\left[f(iy) - f(2^n t + iy)\right]$$

is then satisfied for every analytic characteristic function $f(z)$, provided that the point $z = iy$ is in the interior of the strip of regularity of $f(z)$.

The ridge property gives an upper bound for the values of an analytic characteristic function along a line which is parallel to the real axis and is located in the interior of the strip of regularity. It is also possible to derive a lower bound for the values of an analytic characteristic function along the imaginary axis in the strip.

Let $f(z)$ be an analytic characteristic function which has the strip $-\alpha < \operatorname{Im}(z) < \beta$ as its strip of regularity ($\alpha > 0$, $\beta > 0$, $z = t+iy$). Since

$$1 - f\left(\frac{iy}{2}\right) = \int_{-\infty}^{\infty}\left[1 - e^{-yx/2}\right] dF(x)$$

we conclude from Schwarz's inequality that

$$\left|1 - f\left(\frac{iy}{2}\right)\right|^2 \leqslant \int_{-\infty}^{\infty}\left[1 - 2e^{-yx/2} + e^{-yx}\right] dF(x)$$

or

$$\left[f\left(\frac{iy}{2}\right)\right]^2 \leqslant f(iy) \quad (-\alpha < y < \beta).$$

We apply this inequality repeatedly and see that for any positive integer n,

$$(7.3.1) \qquad f(iy) \geqslant \left[f\left(\frac{iy}{2^n}\right)\right]^{2^n} \quad (-\alpha < y < \beta).$$

It follows from the corollary to theorem 7.1.2 that $\log f(z)$ is defined in a region which contains the segment $-\alpha < \operatorname{Im} z < \beta$. It is easily seen that in this region

$$\log f(z) = \sum_{j=1}^{\infty} \frac{\kappa_j}{j!} (iz)^j,$$

where κ_j is the cumulant of order j. We then have

$$2^n \log \left[f\!\left(\frac{iy}{2^n}\right) \right] = -y\kappa_1 + \sum_{j=2}^{\infty} \frac{(-1)^j}{j!} \frac{\kappa_j}{2^{n(j-1)}} y^j.$$

We combine the last equation with the inequality (7.3.1), and letting n tend to infinity we see that

$$\log f(iy) \geqslant -y\kappa_1$$

or

$$f(iy) \geqslant \exp(-y\kappa_1).$$

We therefore obtain the following result:

Theorem 7.3.2.   Let $f(z)$ be an analytic characteristic function which has the strip $-\alpha < \operatorname{Im}(z) = y < \beta$ as its strip of regularity. Then $f(iy) \geqslant \exp(-y\kappa_1)$, provided that $-\alpha < y < \beta$. Here $\kappa_1 = i^{-1} f'(0)$ is the cumulant of order 1 (first moment) of the distribution corresponding to $f(z)$.

Theorem 7.3.2 is also a necessary condition which an analytic characteristic function must satisfy. It will be used in Chapter 8.

We next discuss a sufficient condition which is applicable to certain analytic functions.

Let θ be a real number; the function $[1-(it/\theta)]^{-1}$ is always a characteristic function (it belongs either to an exponential distribution or to the conjugate of such a distribution). Since the product of two characteristic functions is always a characteristic function, we see that the reciprocal of a polynomial which has only purely imaginary roots is always a characteristic function. It follows from the continuity theorem that the reciprocals of canonical products[*] of genus zero or 1 which have only purely imaginary roots are characteristic functions. Necessary conditions for rational functions were given by E. Lukacs–O. Szász (1954a) and for reciprocals of polynomials by K. Takano (1951); the last paper also contains a necessary and sufficient condition for the reciprocals of polynomials of degree not exceeding 3. Sufficient conditions for a special class of rational functions are given by E. Lukacs–O. Szász (1954b) and by A. Zemanian (1959), (1961).

The most important result concerning criteria for analytic characteristic functions refers to a class of entire functions which we now introduce.

---

[*] See Titchmarsh (1939), p. 250.

It is convenient to adopt the following notation for iterated exponential functions:

$$e_1(z) = e^z, \quad e_2(z) = e^{e_1(z)}, \ldots, e_k(z) = \exp[e_{k-1}(z)].$$

Our object is to derive the following theorem:

Theorem 7.3.3. Let

$$P(t) = \sum_{v=0}^{m} c_v t^v$$

be a polynomial of degree m > 2 and denote by

$$f_n(t) = K_n e_n[P(t)]$$

where $K_n^{-1} = e_n(c_0)$. Then $f_n(t)$ cannot be a characteristic function.

The constant K_n is determined by the fact that every characteristic function equals 1 for $t = 0$.

A particular case of theorem 7.3.3 is of great interest and is quite often useful. If we put $n = 1$ in theorem 7.3.3, then we obtain the following corollary:

Corollary to theorem 7.3.3 (Theorem of Marcinkiewicz). Let $P_m(t)$ be a polynomial of degree m > 2 and denote by $f(t) = \exp[P_m(t)]$. Then $f(t)$ cannot be a characteristic function.

The corollary to theorem 7.3.3 was first given by J. Marcinkiewicz (1938) and is therefore frequently called the Theorem of Marcinkiewicz. It is often useful and has been applied by many authors in studies concerning the characterization of the normal distribution. Marcinkiewicz derived his result in a different manner; he obtained it as a special case of a more general theorem (see theorem 7.3.4) which will be discussed later.

We introduce first the following notation which will be used throughout the proof of theorem 7.3.3. Let

$$\phi_1(z) = \sum_{v=1}^{m} c_v z^v$$

denote a polynomial of degree m without constant term and with $c_m \neq 0$. The coefficients $c_1, c_2, \ldots, c_m$ are arbitrary, real or complex, numbers. Define the real functions $\alpha_1(t, y)$ and $\beta_1(t, y)$ as the real and imaginary parts, respectively, of $\phi_1(z)$ so that $\phi_1(z) = \alpha_1(t, y) + i\beta_1(t, y)$ where $z = t + iy$. Moreover define $A_1(t, y) = \alpha_1(t, y) - \alpha_1(0, y)$.

We write $c_v = \alpha_v + i\beta_v$ $(v = 1, 2, \ldots, m; \alpha_v, \beta_v$ real) and obtain for the polynomial $\phi_1(z)$ the expression

$$(7.3.2) \qquad \phi_1(z) = \sum_{v=1}^{m} (\alpha_v + i\beta_v)(t + iy)^v.$$

We expand the powers of $(t+iy)$ according to the binomial theorem and get

$$(t+iy)^{2v} = (-1)^v\, y^{2v}\left\{ \sum_{k=0}^{v}\binom{2v}{2k}\left(\frac{-t^2}{y^2}\right)^k - i\,\frac{t}{y}\sum_{k=1}^{v}\binom{2v}{2k-1}\left(\frac{-t^2}{y^2}\right)^{k-1}\right\}$$

and

$$(t+iy)^{2v-1} = (-1)^{v-1}\, y^{2v-1}\left\{\frac{t}{y}\sum_{k=1}^{v}\binom{2v-1}{2k-1}\left(\frac{-t^2}{y^2}\right)^{k-1}\right.$$
$$\left. +i\sum_{k=0}^{v-1}\binom{2v-1}{2k}\left(\frac{-t^2}{y^2}\right)^k\right\}.$$

We note that the expressions in the braces are functions of t/y and see that they contain certain polynomials in t^2/y^2. It is convenient to introduce formally these polynomials. We denote by

(7.3.3) $$V_s(\xi) = \sum_{k=1}^{[s/2]}\binom{s}{2k}(-\xi)^{k-1} \quad \text{for } s \geqslant 2 \text{ and } V_1(\xi) \equiv 1$$

(7.3.4) $$W_s(\xi) = \sum_{k=1}^{[(s+1)/2]}\binom{s}{2k-1}(-\xi)^{k-1} = \sum_{k=0}^{[(s-1)/2]}\binom{s}{2k+1}(-\xi)^k$$
$$\text{for } s \geqslant 1.$$

The symbol $[x]$ denotes here, as usual, the greatest integer contained in x. In this way we obtain

(7.3.5)
$$\begin{cases}(t+iy)^{2v} = (-1)^v\, y^{2v}\left\{\left[1-\frac{t^2}{y^2}\,V_{2v}\left(\frac{t^2}{y^2}\right)\right] - i\,\frac{t}{y}\,W_{2v}\left(\frac{t^2}{y^2}\right)\right\}\\[2mm](t+iy)^{2v-1}\\[1mm]\qquad =(-1)^{v-1}\, y^{2v-1}\left\{\frac{t}{y}\,W_{2v-1}\left(\frac{t^2}{y^2}\right) + i\left[1-\frac{t^2}{y^2}\,V_{2v-1}\left(\frac{t^2}{y^2}\right)\right]\right\}.\end{cases}$$

We write in the following

(7.3.6) $$\gamma_{2v} = \alpha_{2v}, \quad \gamma_{2v-1} = \beta_{2v-1}, \quad \delta_{2v} = \beta_{2v}, \quad \delta_{2v-1} = \alpha_{2v-1}$$

and obtain from (7.3.5) and (7.3.6) by means of elementary computations

(7.3.7) $$(\alpha_s+i\beta_s)(t+iy)^s$$

$$= \left\{(-1)^{[(s+1)/2]}\gamma_s\left[1-\frac{t^2}{y^2}\,V_s\left(\frac{t^2}{y^2}\right)\right] + (-1)^{[s/2]}\delta_s\,\frac{t}{y}\,W_s\left(\frac{t^2}{y^2}\right)\right\}y^s$$

$$+ i\left\{(-1)^{[(s-1)/2]}\gamma_s\,\frac{t}{y}\,W_s\left(\frac{t^2}{y^2}\right) + (-1)^{[s/2]}\delta_s\left[1-\frac{t^2}{y^2}\,V_s\left(\frac{t^2}{y^2}\right)\right]\right\}y^s$$

for $s = 1, 2, \ldots, m$.

The last formula permits the computation of $\alpha_1(t, y)$ and of $\beta_1(t, y)$; one obtains immediately

$$(7.3.8) \qquad \alpha_1(t, y) = \sum_{s=1}^{m} \left\{ (-1)^{[(s+1)/2]} \gamma_s \left[1 - \frac{t^2}{y^2} V_s\left(\frac{t^2}{y^2}\right) \right] \right.$$
$$\left. + (-1)^{[s/2]} \delta_s \frac{t}{y} W_s\left(\frac{t^2}{y^2}\right) \right\} y^s$$

and

$$(7.3.9) \qquad \beta_1(t, y) = \sum_{s=1}^{m} \left\{ (-1)^{[(s-1)/2]} \gamma_s \frac{t}{y} W_s\left(\frac{t^2}{y^2}\right) \right.$$
$$\left. + (-1)^{[s/2]} \delta_s \left[1 - \frac{t^2}{y^2} V_s\left(\frac{t^2}{y^2}\right) \right] \right\} y^s.$$

Since $A_1(t, y) = \alpha_1(t, y) - \alpha_1(0, y)$ we obtain from (7.3.8)

$$(7.3.10)$$
$$A_1(t, y) = \sum_{v=1}^{m} \left\{ (-1)^{[(v-1)/2]} \gamma_v \frac{t^2}{y^2} V_v\left(\frac{t^2}{y^2}\right) + (-1)^{[v/2]} \delta_v \frac{t}{y} W_v\left(\frac{t^2}{y^2}\right) \right\} y^v.$$

We introduce a new variable $\xi = (t^2/y^2)$ $(\xi \geq 0)$ and write

$$(7.3.11) \qquad \begin{cases} A_v(\xi) = (-1)^{[(v-1)/2]} \gamma_v \xi V_v(\xi) + (-1)^{[v/2]} \delta_v \xi^{1/2} W_v(\xi) \\ B_v(\xi) = (-1)^{[(v-1)/2]} \gamma_v \xi^{1/2} W_v(\xi) + (-1)^{[v/2]} \delta_v [1 - \xi V_v(\xi)]; \end{cases}$$

with this notation(†) we have

$$(7.3.12) \qquad \begin{cases} A_1[y\sqrt{\xi}, y] = \sum_{v=1}^{m} A_v(\xi) y^v \\ \beta_1[y\sqrt{\xi}, y] = \sum_{v=1}^{m} B_v(\xi) y^v. \end{cases}$$

For the proof of theorem 7.3.3 we need several lemmas and formulate next the following two statements concerning the coefficients of the highest power of y in the polynomials $A_1[y\sqrt{\xi}, y]$ and $\beta_1[y\sqrt{\xi}, y]$.

Lemma 7.3.1. Let $m \geq 4$; then it is possible to find a real number $\xi_m > 0$ such that $A_m(\xi_m) > 0$ while $B_m(\xi_m) \neq 0$.

Lemma 7.3.2. Let $m = 3$ and $\gamma_3 \neq 0$; then there exists a $\xi_3' > 0$ such that $\gamma_3 A_3(\xi_3') < 0$ and $B_3(\xi_3') \neq 0$. If $m = 3$ and $\gamma_3 = 0$ then there exists a $\xi_3' > 0$ such that $A_3(\xi_3') > 0$ and $B_3(\xi_3') \neq 0$.

In order to prove these statements we study the polynomials $V_s(\xi)$ and $W_s(\xi)$ and show that they can be expressed in terms of Chebyshev polynomials or trigonometric functions of an auxiliary variable.

(†) $\xi^{1/2}$ is here and in the following the positive square root of ξ.

H

We consider the expression $(1+i\sqrt{\xi})^s$, where s is a positive integer and $\xi \geqslant 0$, and set $\phi = $ arc tan $\sqrt{\xi}$ with $|\phi| < \pi/2$. Then

(7.3.13) $(1+i\sqrt{\xi})^s = (1+\xi)^{s/2}(\cos s\phi + i \sin s\phi)$.

For $s \geqslant 2$ we expand $(1+i\sqrt{\xi})^s$ according to the binomial theorem and obtain

(7.3.14) $(1+i\sqrt{\xi})^s = 1 - \xi V_s(\xi) + i\sqrt{\xi} W_s(\xi)$.

We note that $(1+\xi)^{s/2} = (\cos \phi)^{-s}$ and get from (7.3.13) and (7.3.14)

(7.3.15)
$$\begin{cases} 1 - \xi V_s(\xi) = (\cos s\phi)/(\cos \phi)^s = (1+\xi)^{s/2} T_s \left(\frac{1}{\sqrt{(1+\xi)}} \right) \\[3mm] \sqrt{\xi} W_s(\xi) = (\sin s\phi)/(\cos \phi)^s = (1+\xi)^{s/2} U_{s-1} \left(\frac{1}{\sqrt{(1+\xi)}} \right) \end{cases}$$

where $T_s(x) = \cos(s \text{ arc} \cos x)$ and

$$U_{s-1}(x) = \frac{\sin(s \text{ arc} \cos x)}{\sqrt{(1-x^2)}}$$

are the Chebyshev polynomials of the first and of the second kind respectively.

We introduce for the sake of brevity the notation

(7.3.16) $\begin{cases} \gamma = (-1)^{[(m-1)/2]} \gamma_m \\ \delta = (-1)^{[m/2]} \delta_m \end{cases}$

and express the functions $A_m(\xi)$ and $B_m(\xi)$ in terms of the variable ϕ. If we write

(7.3.17) $\begin{cases} \xi = \tan^2 \phi \\ C(\phi) = A_m(\tan^2 \phi) \\ D(\phi) = B_m(\tan^2 \phi), \end{cases}$

then we get from (7.3.11), (7.3.15) and (7.3.16)

(7.3.18) $C(\phi) = \gamma \left[1 - \dfrac{\cos m\phi}{(\cos \phi)^m} \right] + \delta \dfrac{\sin m\phi}{(\cos \phi)^m}$

(7.3.19) $D(\phi) = \gamma \dfrac{\sin m\phi}{(\cos \phi)^m} + \delta \dfrac{\cos m\phi}{(\cos \phi)^m}$.

We next prove lemma 7.3.1 by showing that it is always possible to find a ϕ_0 such that $C(\phi_0) > 0$ while $D(\phi_0) \neq 0$. We give the following rules for the selection of ϕ_0:

   (I) If $\gamma > 0$ and $\delta \geqslant 0$, select ϕ_0 so that $\pi/2m < \phi_0 < \pi/m$ while $\tan m\phi_0 \neq - \delta/\gamma$.

   (II) If $\gamma > 0$ and $\delta < 0$, select ϕ_0 so that $\pi/m < \phi_0 < 5\pi/4m$ while $\tan m\phi_0 \neq -\delta/\gamma$.

(III) If $\gamma = 0$ and $\delta > 0$, select ϕ_0 so that $\pi/2m < \phi_0 < \pi/m$.

(IV) If $\gamma = 0$ and $\delta < 0$, select ϕ_0 so that $\pi/m < \phi_0 < 5\pi/4m$.

(V) If $\gamma < 0$, select a value ϕ_0 which satisfies the following three conditions:

(a) $\dfrac{\pi}{m} < \phi_0 < \dfrac{2\pi}{m}$,

(b) $\tan m\phi_0 \neq -\delta/\gamma$,

(c) $h(\phi_0) = \gamma(\cos^m \phi_0 - \cos m\phi_0) + \delta \sin m\phi_0 > 0$.

We must still show that it is possible to select ϕ_0 in case (V) so that condition (c) is satisfied. We first observe that $h(\phi) = \gamma(\cos^m \phi - \cos m\phi) + \delta \sin m\phi$ is a continuous function and that $h(2\pi/m) > 0$. Hence the function $h(\phi)$ is positive in some neighbourhood of $\phi = 2\pi/m$, so that a selection in accordance with (c) is possible.

The assumption $c_m \neq 0$ implies that γ and δ cannot vanish simultaneously, so that our selection rule covers all possibilities. Using this fact as well as the assumption $m \geqslant 4$, it is easily seen that the value ϕ_0 whose selection we have just described satisfies the conditions $C(\phi_0) > 0$ and $D(\phi_0) \neq 0$. But then it follows from (7.3.17) that $\xi_m = \tan^2 \phi_0$ satisfies the assertion of lemma 7.3.1.

We next prove lemma 7.3.2. We see from (7.3.11) that

$$A_3(\xi') = -3\gamma_3\xi' - \delta_3\sqrt{(\xi')}(3-\xi')$$
$$B_3(\xi') = -\gamma_3\sqrt{(\xi')}(3-\xi') - \delta_3(1-3\xi').$$

If $\gamma_3 \neq 0$ and $\gamma_3\delta_3 < 0$ we choose $\xi'_3 > 3$, and if $\gamma_3\delta_3 \geqslant 0$ we choose $0 < \xi'_3 < 3$. If $\gamma_3 = 0$ and $\delta_3 > 0$ we select $\xi'_3 > 3$; if $\delta_3 < 0$ we select $0 < \xi'_3 < 3$. Obviously it is possible to select ξ'_3 in agreement with this rule so that $B_3(\xi'_3) \neq 0$. This completes the proof of lemma 7.3.2.

In the following we assume that $m \geqslant 3$ and choose ξ_m and ξ'_3 in accordance with lemma 7.3.1 and 7.3.2 respectively. We write

(7.3.20) $\qquad A_v = A_v(\xi_m), \quad B_v = B_v(\xi_m)$

and obtain from (7.3.12)

(7.3.21) $\qquad A_1[y\sqrt{(\xi_m)}, y] = A_m y^m + \sum_{v=1}^{m-1} A_v y^v.$

Now let $m \geqslant 4$; then

$$A_1[y\sqrt{(\xi_m)}, y] = A_m y^m [1 + o(1)] \quad \text{as } y \to \infty.$$

We see from lemma 7.3.1 that $A_m > 0$, so that $A_1[y\sqrt{(\xi_m)}, y]$ is positive for sufficiently large positive values of y.

We consider next the case $m = 3$ and write $\varepsilon = \operatorname{sgn} y = y/|y|$. We choose ε so that $\varepsilon\gamma_3 < 0$. Then

$$A_1[y\sqrt{(\xi'_3)}, y] = A_3\varepsilon|y|^3 + A_2 y^2 + A_1\varepsilon|y| = A_3\varepsilon|y|^3[1+o(1)]$$
$$\text{as } |y| \to \infty.$$

We know from lemma 7.3.2 that $\varepsilon A_3 > 0$, so that $A_1[y\sqrt{\xi_3'}, y]$ becomes positive if the sign of y is opposite to the sign of γ_3 and if $|y|$ is sufficiently large. We summarize our findings in the following statement:

Lemma 7.3.3A. *Let $m \geqslant 3$ and suppose that one or the other of the following two conditions is satisfied:*

    (i) $m > 3$ *or* $m = 3$ *and* $\gamma_3 = \beta_3 = 0$

    (ii) $m = 3$ *and* $\gamma_3 = \beta_3 \neq 0$.

Then there exists a $\xi_m \geqslant 0$ and an $\tilde{A} > 0$ such that

$$A_1[y\sqrt{\xi_m}, y] = \tilde{A}|y|^m[1+o(1)]$$

where the estimate holds in case (i) *as $y \to \infty$, but in case* (ii) *as $(-\operatorname{sgn}\gamma_3)y \to \infty$. Then there exists also a value $Y = Y(m)$ such that*

$$A_1[y\sqrt{\xi_m}, y] > 0$$

provided that in case (i) *$y \geqslant Y$ while in case* (ii) *one must require*

$$(-\operatorname{sgn}\gamma_3)y \geqslant Y.$$

The chief instrument in the proof of theorem 7.3.3 is the following lemma:

Lemma 7.3.3. *Let θ be an arbitrary real number. If $m \geqslant 3$, then it is possible to find real numbers $\xi_m \geqslant 0$ and y^* such that for $t^* = y^*\sqrt{\xi_m}$ and some integer g_1 the relations*

$$A_1(t^*, y^*) > 0, \quad \beta_1(t^*, y^*) - 2g_1\pi = \theta$$

are satisfied.

To prove lemma 7.3.3 we must study the function $\beta_1(t, y)$. We choose again ξ_m in accordance with lemmas 7.3.1 and 7.3.2 respectively and consider the polynomial

$$(7.3.22)\quad B(y) = \beta_1[y\sqrt{\xi_m}, y] = \sum_{v=1}^{m} B_v y^v.$$

Here B_v is given by (7.3.20). Let Y be the number determined by lemma 7.3.3A; since $B_m \neq 0$ we conclude from (7.3.22) that

$$B(y) = B_m y^m[1+o(1)] \quad \text{as } |y| \to \infty.$$

This means that $B(y)$ is monotone if y is sufficiently large. We can therefore find a $Y_0 > Y$ such that $B(y)$ is monotone for $|y| \geqslant Y_0$. In view of lemma 7.3.3A it is always possible to find a real y_0 such that $|y_0| > Y_0$ and $A_1[y_0\sqrt{\xi_m}, y_0] > 0$. Let θ be an arbitrary real number, then there exists an integer g such that

$$\theta + 2\pi g \leqslant B(y_0) < \theta + 2\pi(g+1).$$

We consider from now on only such values of y for which $yy_0 > 0$ and $|y| \geqslant |y_0|$. For such values of y, $B(y)$ is either monotone increasing or monotone decreasing. In the first case we can find a real number y_1 such that $B(y_1) = \theta + 2(g+1)\pi$; in the second case there exists a y_1 for which $B(y_1) = \theta + 2g\pi$. Since $|y_1| \geqslant |y_0|$ and $y_1 y_0 > 0$, we see from lemma 7.3.3A that $A_1[y_1\sqrt{\xi_m}, y_1] > 0$, while $B(y_1) - \theta = \beta_1[y_1\sqrt{\xi_m}, y_1] - \theta$ is an integer multiple of 2π. To complete the proof of lemma 7.3.3 we need only put $y^* = y_1$ and $t^* = y_1\sqrt{\xi_m}$. We are now ready to prove theorem 7.3.1.

Let

$$P(t) = \sum_{v=0}^{m} c_v t^v$$

be a polynomial of degree $m > 2$ ($c_m \neq 0$) and $K_n^{-1} = e_n(c_0)$. We carry an indirect proof of the theorem and suppose therefore that

$$f_n(t) = K_n e_n[P(t)]$$

is a characteristic function. The function $f_n(t)$ agrees for real values of z with the function $A(z) = K_n e_n[P(z)]$ so that it is an entire characteristic function. From now on we consider this characteristic function also for complex values of the argument $z = t + iy$ and apply the ridge property (theorem 7.1.2) of analytic characteristic functions. This theorem indicates that necessarily

$$(7.3.23) \qquad R(t, y) = \left| \frac{f_n(t+iy)}{f_n(iy)} \right| \leqslant 1$$

for all real t and y.

We now introduce the functions

$$(7.3.24) \qquad f_v(z) = K_v e_v[P(z)] \quad (v = 1, 2, \ldots, n)$$

where $K_v = [e_v(c_0)]^{-1}$ and note that $f_v(0) = 1$ ($v = 1, 2, \ldots, n$) and that $f_1(z) = \exp[\phi_1(z)]$. We obtain easily from definition (7.3.24) of the functions $f_v(z)$ the recursion formula

$$(7.3.25) \qquad f_v(z) = \exp\{K_{v-1}^{-1}[f_{v-1}(z) - 1]\} \quad (v = 2, \ldots, n).$$

We now introduce the functions

$$(7.3.25a) \qquad \phi_v(z) = K_{v-1}^{-1}[f_{v-1}(z) - 1] \quad (v = 2, 3, \ldots, n).$$

and write $\alpha_v(t, y)$ for the real part, $\beta_v(t, y)$ for the imaginary part of $\phi_v(z)$, so that

$$(7.3.25b) \qquad \phi_v(z) = \alpha_v(t, y) + i\beta_v(t, y) \quad (v = 1, 2, \ldots, n)$$

and

$$(7.3.25c) \qquad f_v(z) = \exp[\phi_v(z)] \quad (v = 1, 2, \ldots, n).$$

We set

$$(7.3.26) \qquad K_v^{-1} = \exp(\rho_v + i\lambda_v) \quad (v = 2, \ldots, n).$$

Since $K_{v-1}^{-1} = e_{v-1}(c_0)$ we see that $K_v^{-1} = \exp(K_{v-1}^{-1})$ or

$$\exp(\rho_v + i\lambda_v) = e_2(\rho_{v-1} + i\lambda_{v-1}),$$

therefore

(7.3.27) $\rho_v + i\lambda_v = \exp(\rho_{v-1} + i\lambda_{v-1}) + 2g_v \pi i$

where g_v is an integer. It follows from (7.3.27) that

(7.3.28) $\lambda_v = \exp(\rho_{v-1}) \sin \lambda_{v-1} + 2g_v \pi.$

We combine (7.3.25a), (7.3.25c) and (7.3.26) to get

$$\phi_v(z) = \exp[\rho_{v-1} + i\lambda_{v-1}]\{\exp[\alpha_{v-1}(t, y) + i\beta_{v-1}(t, y)] - 1\}$$
$$(v = 2, 3, \ldots, n).$$

We separate real and imaginary parts in the last formula and obtain recursion formulae for $\alpha_v(t, y)$ and $\beta_v(t, y)$:

(7.3.29a) $\alpha_v(t, y) = \exp[\rho_{v-1} + \alpha_{v-1}(t, y)] \cos[\lambda_{v-1} + \beta_{v-1}(t, y)] -$
$$- \exp(\rho_{v-1}) \cos \lambda_{v-1} \quad (v = 2, 3, \ldots, n)$$

(7.3.29b) $\beta_v(t, y) = \exp[\rho_{v-1} + \alpha_{v-1}(t, y)] \sin[\lambda_{v-1} + \beta_{v-1}(t, y)] -$
$$- \exp(\rho_{v-1}) \sin \lambda_{v-1} \quad (v = 2, 3, \ldots, n).$$

We now define the functions

$$A_v(t, y) = \alpha_v(t, y) - \alpha_v(0, y) \quad (v = 1, 2, \ldots, n)$$

and see from (7.3.29a) that

(7.3.30) $A_v(t, y) = \{\exp[A_{v-1}(t, y)] \cos[\lambda_{v-1} + \beta_{v-1}(t, y)] -$
$$- \cos[\lambda_{v-1} + \beta_{v-1}(0, y)]\} \exp[\rho_{v-1} + \alpha_{v-1}(0, y)]$$
$$(v = 2, 3, \ldots, n).$$

We apply lemma 7.3.3 and select $\theta = -\lambda_1$. Then it is possible to find a pair of real numbers t^*, y^* such that

(7.3.31) $A_1(t^*, y^*) > 0$

while

(7.3.32) $\beta_1(t^*, y^*) + \lambda_1 = 2g_1 \pi \quad (g_1 \text{ integer}).$

We show next that a similar relation holds for all functions $\beta_v(t, y,)$ namely

(7.3.33) $\beta_v(t^*, y^*) + \lambda_v = 2g_v \pi$

where t^*, y^* are the numbers determined according to lemma 7.3.3 and used in (7.3.31) and (7.3.32); λ_v is given by (7.3.28) and g_v is an integer. We prove (7.3.33) by induction. Formula (7.3.32) indicates that (7.3.33) is valid for $v = 1$; we suppose now that it holds for all subscripts inferior to v. We then have in particular

$$\beta_{v-1}(t^*, y^*) + \lambda_{v-1} = 2g_{v-1} \pi.$$

Substituting this into (7.3.29b) and using (7.3.28) we see that

$$\beta_v(t^*, y^*) = -\exp(\rho_{v-1}) \sin \lambda_{v-1} = -\lambda_v + 2g_v \pi.$$

Thus (7.3.33) is generally valid.

We see from (7.3.30) and (7.3.33) that

$$A_v(t^*, y^*) = \{\exp [A_{v-1}(t^*, y^*)] - \cos [\lambda_{v-1} + \beta_{v-1}(0, y^*)]\}$$
$$\times \exp [\rho_{v-1} + \alpha_{v-1}(0, y^*)]$$

for $v = 2, 3, \ldots, n$. From this formula we see that the relation

$$A_{v-1}(t^*, y^*) > 0$$

implies that

$$A_v(t^*, y^*) > 0.$$

We can therefore conclude from (7.3.31) that

(7.3.34) $A_n(t^*, y^*) > 0.$

We defined earlier the function $R(t, y)$ as

$$R(t, y) = \left| \frac{f_n(t + iy)}{f_n(iy)} \right|;$$

it follows from (7.3.25b) and (7.3.25c) that

$$R(t, y) = \exp \{A_n(t, y)\}.$$

We have therefore determined a pair of real numbers t^*, y^* such that

(7.3.35) $R(t^*, y^*) > 1.$

But this contradicts (7.3.23) which must be satisfied if $f_n(t)$ is a characteristic function. This contradiction completes the proof of theorem 7.3.3 since it shows that $f_n(t)$ cannot be a characteristic function if $m > 2$.

In the case where $m \leqslant 2$ the iterated exponentials $f_n(t) = e_n[P(t)]$ can be characteristic functions. The function $f_1(t) = \exp [-a_2 t^2 + ia_1 t]$ where a_1 and a_2 are both real, $a_2 \geqslant 0$, is a characteristic function (of a normal or of a degenerate distribution). It follows from the recursion formula (7.3.25) and from lemma 5.4.1 that $f_v(z)$ as defined by (7.3.24) is a characteristic function for all values of v.

We note that for $m = 1$ and $c_1 = 1$ we obtain for $n = 2$ a Poisson distribution and for $n = 3$ a Neyman type A distribution,

$$f_3(t) = \exp \{\mu [\exp (\lambda(e^{it} - 1)) - 1]\}.$$

We have already mentioned that Marcinkiewicz derived a particular case of theorem 7.3.3 in a different manner. He obtained it as a special case of a more general theorem which gives a necessary condition which an entire function of finite order must satisfy if it is a characteristic function. We now state this theorem of Marcinkiewicz.

Theorem 7.3.4.   An entire function of finite order $\rho > 2$ whose exponent of convergence ρ_1 is less than ρ cannot be a characteristic function.

In the proof of theorem 7.3.4 we use a number of theorems from the theory of functions of a complex variable. The results needed may be found, for instance, in Copson (1935), pp. 165–175.

Let $f(z)$ be an entire function of finite order ρ. By Hadamard's factorization theorem we can write $f(z)$ in the form

(7.3.36) $f(z) = G(z) \exp [H(z)]$

where $G(z)$ is the canonical product of the zeros of $f(z)$ and where $H(z)$ is a polynomial of degree $m \leqslant \rho$. We denote by ρ_1 the exponent of convergence of the zeros of $f(z)$; it is easily seen that $\rho = \max (\rho_1, m)$. If $\rho_1 < \rho$ then necessarily $\rho = m$. It is known that the order of a canonical product equals its exponent of convergence. Let $G(z)$ be a canonical product of order ρ_1; then for any $\varepsilon > 0$ the modulus $|G(z)| \leqslant \exp [|z|^{\rho_1 + \varepsilon}]$, provided that $|z|$ is sufficiently large. We will also use the following result which is due to E. Borel.

If $G(z)$ is a canonical product of order ρ_1 and if ε is an arbitrary positive number, then there exists an infinite number of circles of arbitrarily large radius on each of which the inequality

$$|G(z)| > \exp (-|z|^{\rho_1 + \varepsilon})$$

holds.

Let $z = t + iy$ and denote by $r = |z| = \sqrt{t^2 + y^2}$. We see then that there exist arbitrarily large values of r such that

$$|G(t + iy)| > \exp (-r^{\rho_1 + \varepsilon}).$$

On the other hand we know that for arbitrary $\varepsilon > 0$ and sufficiently large y

$$|G(iy)| \leqslant \exp (r^{\rho_1 + \varepsilon}).$$

We combine the last two inequalities and see that there exists an increasing sequence $\{r_k\}$ of positive real numbers such that

$$\lim_{k \to \infty} r_k = \infty$$

which has the property that for arbitrary $\varepsilon > 0$ and sufficiently large k

(7.3.37) $R_1(t, y) = \left| \dfrac{G(t + iy)}{G(iy)} \right| > \exp (-2r_k^{\rho_1 + \varepsilon})$

provided that $t^2 + y^2 = r_k^2$.

We consider next $f_2(z) = \exp [H(z)]$ and write

(7.3.38) $R_2(t, y) = |\exp [H(t + iy) - H(iy)]|$

so that

(7.3.39) $R(t, y) = \left| \dfrac{f(t + iy)}{f(iy)} \right| = R_1(t, y) R_2(t, y).$

We give an indirect proof for theorem 7.3.4 and assume therefore that $f(z)$ is an entire characteristic function of order $\rho > 2$ and suppose that the exponent of convergence ρ_1 of the zeros of $f(z)$ is less than ρ, $\rho_1 < \rho$. We again apply theorem 7.1.2 and see that necessarily

(7.3.40) $R(t, y) \leqslant 1$

for all real t and y.

Since $\rho_1 < \rho$ we have $\rho = m$, where m is the degree of the polynomial $H(z)$. We see also that $H(0) = 0$ (since $f(0) = 1$) and use the notation of the preceding proof and write

$$\phi_1(z) = H(z) = \sum_{v=1}^{m} (\alpha_v + i\beta_v)z^v$$

so that

(7.3.41) $\qquad R_2(t, y) = \exp[A_1(t, y)].$

We see then from (7.3.37), (7.3.39) and (7.3.41) that there exists an infinite sequence of indefinitely increasing positive numbers r_k such that for an arbitrary $\varepsilon > 0$

(7.3.42) $\qquad R(t, y) > \exp[-2r_k^{\rho_1+\varepsilon} + A_1(t, y)],$

provided that k is sufficiently large and that $t^2 + y^2 = r_k^2$.

We next define an infinite sequence of points (t_k, y_k) in the z-plane. In order to be able to apply lemma 7.3.3A we subject these points to the following restrictions:

(i) $t_k = y_k \sqrt{\xi_m}$
(ii) $|t_k + iy_k| = r_k$
(iii) if $m > 3$ or $m = 3$ while $\gamma_3 = \beta_3 = 0$, then $y_k > 0$
(iv) if $m = 3$ and $\gamma_3 = \beta_3 \neq 0$, then $(-\operatorname{sgn}\gamma_3)y_k > 0$.

From (i) and (ii) it is seen that all these points are located in the same quadrant and that $|y_k| = r_k/\sqrt{(1+\xi_m)}$. We deduce from lemma 7.3.3A that

(7.3.43) $\qquad A_1(t_k, y_k) = \tilde{A}|y_k|^m [1+o(1)] \quad$ as $k \to \infty$

where $\tilde{A} > 0$.

We denote by $\mathfrak{A} = \tilde{A}(1+\xi_m)^{-m/2}$ and obtain from (7.3.42) and (7.3.43)

$$R(t_k, y_k) > \exp\{-2r_k^{\rho_1+\varepsilon} + \mathfrak{A}r_k^m[1+o(1)]\} \quad \text{as } k \to \infty.$$

Since by assumption $\rho = m > \rho_1$, we can choose the arbitrary positive quantity ε so that $\rho_1 + \varepsilon < m$. We conclude from the last inequality that

$$R(t_k, y_k) > \exp\{\mathfrak{A}r_k^m[1+o(1)]\} \quad \text{as } k \to \infty.$$

Since $\mathfrak{A} > 0$ we can determine k so large that $R(t_k, y_k) > 1$. This, however, contradicts (7.3.40) and we see therefore that $f(z)$ cannot be a characteristic function and have thus completed the proof of theorem 7.3.4.

In conclusion we mention, without proof, another theorem of this type.

Theorem 7.3.5. Let

$$P_m(t) = \sum_{v=0}^{m} c_v t^v$$

be a polynomial of degree m. The function

$$f(t) = \exp[\lambda_1(e^{it}-1) + \lambda_2(e^{-it}-1) + P_m(t)]$$

is a characteristic function if, and only if, $\lambda_1 \geq 0$, $\lambda_2 \geq 0$, $m \leq 2$ and if $P_2(t) = a_1(it) - a_2 t^2$ where a_1 and a_2 are real and $a_2 \geq 0$.

This theorem contains again as a special case the theorem of Marcin-kiewicz (corollary to theorem 7.3.3). Marcinkiewicz's theorem is obtained by putting $\lambda_1 = \lambda_2 = 0$. For the proof, which is similar to the demonstration of theorem 7.3.3, the reader is referred to Lukacs (1958).

Several authors have discussed related necessary conditions for entire or meromorphic functions to be characteristic functions. These conditions can all be considered to be extensions of Marcinkiewicz's theorem. I. F. Christensen (1962) studied functions of the form

$$f(t) = K_n g(t) \, e_n \, [P_m(t)],$$

where $g(t)$ is a characteristic function subject to certain restrictions. R. Cairoli (1964) investigated similar problems for meromorphic functions of finite order. H. D. Miller (1967) studied entire functions of the form $g(t) f \{\exp [P(t)]\}$ or $f \{\exp [P(t)]\}$, where $g(t)$ and $f(t)$ are entire functions while $P(t)$ is a polynomial. The method in all these cases is similar to that used in proving theorem 7.3.2; the principal tool is the ridge property

(7.3.44) $\quad |f(t+iy)| \leqslant f(iy)$

which is valid for all y if $f(z)$ is an entire characteristic function.[*]

Far-reaching generalizations of Marcinkiewicz's theorem were obtained by I. V. Ostrovskii (1963). His work is based on a careful study of entire functions which belong to families characterized by the following inequalities:

(7.3.45a) $\quad |f(t+iy)| \leqslant M(|y|;f) \quad (-\infty < t, y < \infty)$

(7.3.45b) $\quad \mathrm{Re}\, f(t+iy) \leqslant M(|y|;f) \quad (-\infty <, y < \infty)$

It is easily seen that the class described by (7.3.45b) contains the class described by (7.3.45a) which in turn is wider than the family of ridge functions. The basic results of Ostrovskii's paper are theorems on entire functions belonging to these classes. These theorems are interesting on account of their applicability to the theory of characteristic functions. The reasoning which yields these results on entire functions is tedious, and the discussion would exceed the scope of this monograph. We therefore list, as a lemma, only one of Ostrovskii's results and also indicate its application.

Lemma 7.3.4. *Let $A(w)$ and $b(z)$ be entire functions and suppose that $A(w)$ does not reduce to a constant. Let $f(z) = A[b(z)]$. If the function $f(z)$ satisfies (7.3.45a) then $b(z)$ is either a polynomial of degree not exceeding 2 or an entire function of not less than order 1 and of normal type.*

We deduce from the lemma the following results concerning characteristic functions:

---

[*] I. F. Christensen and R. Cairoli also considered functions which are not entire. However, they had to assume that these functions are regular in a half-plane which contains the origin in its interior. Inequality (7.3.44) is then valid in this half-plane.

Theorem 7.3.5.   Suppose that an entire characteristic function $f(t)$ is the superposition of two functions $A(w)$ and $b(z)$, that is, $f(z) = A[b(z)]$. Then $b(z)$ is either a polynomial of degree not exceeding 2 or an entire function of not less than order 1 and of normal type.

Remark. Theorem 7.3.2, and therefore also Marcinkiewicz's theorem, are particular cases of theorem 7.3.5.

Corollary 1 to theorem 7.3.5.   Let $b(z)$ be an entire function of order 1 and minimal type; then $f(z) = \exp [b(z)]$ cannot be a characteristic function.

Corollary 2 to theorem 7.3.5.   Let $b(z)$ be an entire function of order less than 1, then $f(z) = \exp [b(z)]$ cannot be a characteristic function.

Corollary 1 answers a question raised by Yu. V. Linnik, while corollary 2 solves a problem posed by D. Dugué.

I. V. Ostrovskii's paper also contains a generalization of theorem 7.3.4.

7.4 Periodic analytic characteristic functions

The characteristic function of a lattice distribution which has the origin as a lattice point has the form

$$(7.4.1) \qquad f(t) = \sum_v p_v e^{itrv}$$

where r is a real number and

$$p_v \geqslant 0, \quad \sum_v p_v = 1.$$

Let k be an arbitrary integer; it follows from (7.4.1) that $\omega = 2\pi k/r$ is a period of $f(t)$. We see therefore that a characteristic function can be a periodic function; however, a periodic characteristic function is **not** necessarily analytic. The characteristic functions discussed in theorem 4.3.2 are examples of periodic characteristic functions which are **not** analytic.

In the present section we discuss briefly the properties of analytic characteristic functions $f(z)$ which are single-valued and periodic. We consider first the case where $f(z)$ has a purely imaginary period $\omega = i\eta$ (η real); it is then no restriction to assume that $\eta > 0$.

We wish to avoid the discussion of trivial cases and suppose therefore that $f(z) \not\equiv 1$. Let $-\alpha < \text{Im}(z) < \beta$, $(\alpha > 0, \beta > 0)$, be the strip of regularity of $f(z)$; we first show that necessarily $\eta \geqslant \min(\alpha, \beta)$. We give an indirect proof and assume that $\eta < \min(\alpha, \beta)$. The points $z_1 = i\eta$, $z_2 = -i\eta$ are then in the interior of the strip of regularity of $f(z)$ and it follows from theorem 7.1.4 that

$$(7.4.2) \qquad f(0) < \frac{f(i\eta) + f(-i\eta)}{2}.$$

On the other hand it follows from the periodicity of $f(z)$ that $f(0) = f(i\eta) = f(-i\eta) = 1$ so that $f(0) = [f(i\eta)+f(-i\eta)]/2 = 1$ in contradiction with (7.4.2). The indirect proof is therefore completed and we have always $\eta \geqslant \min(\alpha, \beta)$. But the equality sign would imply that the origin is a singular point of $f(z)$ so that always $\eta > \min(\alpha, \beta)$. But then at least one of the inequalities $\eta > \alpha$ or $\eta > \beta$ holds. If $\eta > \alpha$ [respectively $\eta > \beta$] then $i(\eta-\alpha)$ [respectively $-i(\eta-\beta)$] is a singular point of $f(z)$ located in the upper [respectively lower] half-plane. Therefore $\eta-\alpha \geqslant \beta$, and we have established the following result:

Theorem 7.4.1. *If a non-constant analytic characteristic function has a purely imaginary period $\omega = i\eta$ ($\eta > 0$), then this period is at least equal to the width of the strip of regularity of $f(z)$, that is $|\omega| = \eta \geqslant \alpha+\beta$.*

We consider next the case where $f(z)$ has a complex period $\omega = \xi+i\eta$. The case $\xi = 0$ (purely imaginary period) has just been treated, so that we may assume $\xi \neq 0$. Using (7.1.4) and the assumption that ω is a period of $f(z)$, we conclude easily that $\bar{\omega}$ and $-\bar{\omega}$ are also periods. Therefore 2ξ and $2\eta i$ are also periods of $f(z)$ so that

(7.4.3) $\qquad f(2\xi) = 1.$

We conclude then from theorem 2.1.4 that $f(z)$ is the characteristic function of a lattice distribution whose lattice points are the points where $1 - \cos 2\xi x$ vanishes. Therefore $f(z)$ is given by

(7.4.4) $\qquad f(z) = \sum_{s=-\infty}^{s=\infty} p_s \exp(iz\pi s/\xi)$

where

(7.4.5) $\qquad p_s \geqslant 0, \quad \sum_{s=-\infty}^{\infty} p_s = 1.$

If $\eta = 0$, then $f(z)$ is simply periodic and has a real period ξ, so that $f(0) = f(\xi) = 1$, and we see by the same argument that it can be written as

(7.4.6) $\qquad f(z) = \sum_{s=-\infty}^{\infty} p_s \exp(2\pi izs/\xi)$

where the p_s satisfy again (7.4.5). If $\eta \neq 0$ then $f(z)$ is given by (7.4.4) and is a doubly periodic function which necessarily has a real and also a purely imaginary period. We summarize this in the following manner:

Theorem 7.4.2. *An analytic characteristic function which is single-valued and simply periodic has either a real or a purely imaginary period. The period is real if, and only if, the characteristic function belongs to a lattice distribution which has the origin as a lattice point.*

Let $f(z)$ be an entire characteristic function which does not reduce to a constant and assume that it is periodic. From theorem 7.4.1 we see that it cannot be doubly periodic, and we can conclude that it must have a real period and have the form (7.4.6).

Theorem 7.4.3. *If a characteristic function is an entire periodic function then it is necessarily the characteristic function of a lattice distribution which has the origin as a lattice point.*

It is easy to give examples of analytic characteristic functions which are periodic. We mention the Poisson distribution whose characteristic function has the real period 2π; the distribution with frequency function $p(x) = [2 \cosh (\pi x/2)]^{-1}$ has the characteristic function $f(z) = 1/(\cosh z)$ which is regular in the strip $|\operatorname{Im}(z)| < \pi/2$ and which has the purely imaginary period $2\pi i$. A doubly periodic characteristic function was constructed by M. Girault (1955) who showed that the elliptic function

$$f(z) = \prod_{n=-\infty}^{\infty} \frac{1-k^{2n-1}}{1+k^{2n-1}} \frac{1+k^{2n-1}e^{iz}}{1-k^{2n-1}e^{iz}}$$

is a characteristic function. This function has the real period 2π, the purely imaginary period $4i \log k$ and the strip of regularity $|\operatorname{Im}(z)| < |\log k|$.

In conclusion we remark that one could regard theorems 7.4.1, 7.4.2 and 7.4.3 also as conditions which a single-valued, periodic analytic function must satisfy in order to be a characteristic function.

7.5 Analytic characteristic functions as solutions of certain differential equations

Regression problems lead sometimes to a differential equation for the characteristic function. After all solutions of this equation are found, one has to determine those which can be characteristic functions. This is often the most difficult part of the problem and it is therefore desirable to find general properties of characteristic functions which satisfy certain differential equations.

In the present section we discuss a result due to A. A. Zinger and Yu. V. Linnik, which is of great theoretical interest.

We write $f^{(s)}(t)$ for the derivative of order s of $f(t)$ and consider the differential equation

(7.5.1) $\qquad \sum A_{j_1 \dots j_n} i^{-(j_1 + \dots + j_n)} f^{(j_1)}(t) \dots f^{(j_n)}(t) = c[f(t)]^n.$

The $A_{j_1 \dots j_n}$ are real constants while the sum is here taken over all non-negative integers $j_1, j_2, \dots, j_n$ which satisfy the condition

(7.5.1a) $\qquad j_1 + j_2 + \dots + j_n \leqslant m \quad (j_s \geqslant 0; \quad s = 1, \dots, n).$

We assume that at least one coefficient with $j_1 + j_2 + \dots + j_n = m$ is different from zero and denote by m the order of this differential equation.

We adjoin to the differential equation (7.5.1) the polynomial

$$(7.5.2) \qquad A(x_1, \ldots, x_n) = \frac{1}{n!} \sum_{(s_1, \ldots, s_n)} \sum A_{j_1 \ldots j_n} x_{s_1}^{j_1} \ldots x_{s_n}^{j_n}.$$

The first summation is here to be extended over all permutations $(s_1, s_2, \ldots, s_n)$ of the numbers $(1, 2, \ldots, n)$; the second summation over all integers $j_1, \ldots, j_n$ satisfying (7.5.1a).

The differential equation (7.5.1) is said to be positive definite if its adjoint polynomial (7.5.2) is non-negative. We can now state the result of A. A. Zinger and Yu. V. Linnik.

Theorem 7.5.1. Suppose that the function $f(t)$ is, in a certain neighbourhood of the origin, a solution of the positive definite differential equation (7.5.1) and assume that $m \geqslant n-1$. If the solution $f(t)$ is a characteristic function then it is necessarily an entire function.

We state first a lemma, which uses only some of the assumptions of theorem 7.5.1 and which therefore yields less information concerning the solutions of (7.5.1).

Lemma 7.5.1. Suppose that the characteristic function $f(t)$ is, in a certain neighbourhood of the origin, a solution of the positive definite equation (7.5.1). Then $f(t)$ has derivatives of all orders at the origin.

Lemma 7.5.1 is certainly true if the distribution function $F(x)$ of $f(t)$ is a finite distribution [see theorem 7.2.3]. We therefore assume in the following that for all $x > 0$

$$(7.5.3) \quad F(-x)+1-F(x) > 0.$$

We remark that the assumptions of the lemma imply that $f(t)$ can be differentiated at least m times. Moreover, m is necessarily an even number if $A(x_1, x_2, \ldots, x_n)$ is non-negative. Since $f(t)$ is the characteristic function of $F(x)$, we know that

$$(7.5.4) \qquad f^{(j)}(t) = i^j \int_{-\infty}^{\infty} x^j e^{itx} dF(x) \quad (j = 0, 1, \ldots, m).$$

In view of (7.5.2) and (7.5.4) we can write (7.5.1) in the form
(7.5.5)

$$\int_{-\infty}^{\infty} \ldots \int_{-\infty}^{\infty} A(x_1, \ldots, x_n) \exp\left[it(x_1+\ldots+x_n)\right] dF(x_1) \ldots dF(x_n)$$

$$= c \int_{-\infty}^{\infty} \ldots \int_{-\infty}^{\infty} \exp\left[it(x_1+\ldots+x_n)\right] dF(x_1) \ldots dF(x_n).$$

We give an indirect proof for the lemma and assume therefore that $f(t)$ has only a finite number of derivatives. Then there exists an even integer

$2p$ such that $f(t)$ can be differentiated at the origin $2p$ times but not $(2p+2)$ times. Clearly, one has

$$2p \geqslant m \geqslant 2.$$

The function on the right of (7.5.5) can then be differentiated $2p-m+2$ times. Since $A(x_1, \ldots, x_n)$ is non-negative we can conclude from Fatou's lemma [see Titchmarsh (1939) p. 346] that

$$\int_{-\infty}^{\infty} \ldots \int_{-\infty}^{\infty} A(x_1, \ldots, x_n)(x_1 + \ldots + x_n)^{2p-m+2} \exp\left[it(x_1 + \ldots + x_n)\right]$$
$$\times dF(x_1) \ldots dF(x_n)$$
$$= c \int_{-\infty}^{\infty} \ldots \int_{-\infty}^{\infty} (x_1 + \ldots + x_n)^{2p-m+2} \exp\left[it(x_1 + \ldots + x_n)\right]$$
$$\times dF(x_1) \ldots dF(x_n)$$

or, putting $t = 0$,

$$(7.5.6) \quad \int_{-\infty}^{\infty} \ldots \int_{-\infty}^{\infty} A(x_1, \ldots, x_n)(x_1 + \ldots + x_n)^{2p-m+2}$$
$$\times dF(x_1) \ldots dF(x_n)$$
$$= c \int_{-\infty}^{\infty} \ldots \int_{-\infty}^{\infty} (x_1 + \ldots + x_n)^{2p-m+2} dF(x_1) \ldots dF(x_n).$$

The differential equation (7.5.1) has by assumption the order m so that the polynomial $A(x_1, \ldots, x_n)$ contains the mth power of at least one variable. It is evidently no restriction to assume that x_1 is this variable; one can then write

$$(7.5.7) \quad A(x_1, \ldots, x_n) = A_0(x_2, \ldots, x_n)x_1^m + A_1(x_2, \ldots, x_n)x_1^{m-1}$$
$$+ \ldots + A_m(x_2, \ldots, x_n).$$

Since $A(x_1, \ldots, x_n)$ is non-negative we conclude that $A_0(x_2, \ldots, x_n)$ is also a non-negative polynomial.

It is always possible to find a bounded region Ω_{n-1} in the $(n-1)$-dimensional space R_{n-1} of the variables $(x_2, \ldots, x_n)$ such that

$$(7.5.8a) \quad \int_{\Omega_{n-1}} dF(x_2) dF(x_3) \ldots dF(x_n) = \alpha > 0$$

while

$$(7.5.8b) \quad \min_{\Omega_{n-1}} A_0(x_2, x_3, \ldots, x_n) \geqslant C_1 > 0.$$

This follows from (7.5.3) and the fact that the equation $A_0(x_2, \ldots, x_n) = 0$ determines an algebraic surface in R_{n-1}. We use here, and in the following, the symbols $C_1, C_2, \ldots$ to denote arbitrary positive constants.

We see from (7.5.7) that it is possible to find a sufficiently large $C_2 > 0$ such that for $|x_1| > C_2$ and $(x_2, \ldots, x_n) \in \Omega_{n-1}$ the relations

$$(7.5.9) \quad \begin{cases} A(x_1, \ldots, x_n) \geqslant C_3 x_1^m \\ |x_1 + x_2 + \ldots + x_n| \geqslant C_4 |x_1| \end{cases}$$

hold.

Let Ω_n be the set of all the points $(x_1, \ldots, x_n)$ of the n-dimensional space which satisfy the condition

(7.5.10) $|x_1| > C_2$ and $(x_2, \ldots, x_n) \in \Omega_{n-1}$.

Since m is even and $A(x_1, x_2, \ldots, x_n) \geqslant 0$ we conclude from (7.5.6) that

(7.5.11) $\displaystyle\int_{\Omega_n} A(x_1, \ldots, x_n)(x_1 + \ldots + x_n)^{2p-m+2} \, dF(x_1) \ldots dF(x_n) \leqslant K$

where

$$K = c \int_{-\infty}^{\infty} \ldots \int_{-\infty}^{\infty} (x_1 + \ldots + x_n)^{2p-m+2} \, dF(x_1) \ldots dF(x_n)$$

is a (finite) positive constant. Substituting (7.5.9) into (7.5.11), we see that

$$C_3 C_4^{2p-m+2} \int_{\Omega_n} x_1^{2p+2} \, dF(x_1) \ldots dF(x_n) = C_5 \int_{|x_1| > C_2} x_1^{2p+2} \, dF(x_1) \leqslant K.$$

This inequality indicates that the moment of order $2p+2$ of $F(x)$ exists; this is in contradiction with the assumption concerning p, so that the indirect proof of lemma 7.5.1 is completed.

We proceed now to prove theorem 7.5.1. As a first step we show that $f(t)$ is an analytic characteristic function. We need the following lemma.

Lemma 7.5.2. Let G be a positive integer; then $e^G > G^G/G!$.

To prove the lemma we note that

$$e^G = \sum_{j=0}^{\infty} \frac{G^j}{j!} > \frac{G^G}{G!}.$$

Let N and m be two positive integers; according to lemma 7.5.2 we have

$$\frac{(2N+m)^{2N+m}}{(2N+m)!} < e^{2N+m}$$

or

(7.5.12) $\displaystyle\frac{2N+m}{[(2N+m)!]^{1/(2N+m)}} < e.$

We again use the region Ω_{n-1} introduced in the proof of lemma 7.5.1 and write

$$b_j = \int_{\Omega_{n-1}} |x_2 + x_3 + \ldots + x_n|^j \, dF(x_2) \ldots dF(x_n).$$

It is then possible to find a positive number b such that

(7.5.13) $b_j < b^j b_0$ $(j = 1, 2, \ldots, 2N)$.

We consider also the set of those points $(x_1, x_2, \ldots, x_n)$ of the n-dimensional space which satisfy the relations

(7.5.14) $|x_1| \leqslant C_2$ and $(x_2, x_3, \ldots, x_n) \in \Omega_{n-1}$.

This set is bounded, therefore there exists a positive constant C_6 such that

$$(7.5.15) \qquad I = \int_{|x_1| < C_2} x_1^m \left[\int_{\Omega_{n-1}} (|x_1| - |x_2 + \ldots + x_n|)^{2N} \right.$$

$$\left. \times dF(x_2) \ldots dF(x_n) \right] dF(x_1) < b_0 C_6^{2N+m}.$$

The constant C_2 was introduced in the proof of lemma 7.5.1. We write

$$\beta_k = \int_{-\infty}^{\infty} |x|^k dF(x)$$

for the absolute moment of order k of $F(x)$. Clearly it is possible to find a sufficiently large positive constant M_1 such that the inequalities

$$(7.5.16) \qquad \beta_k \leqslant k! \, M_1^k \exp \{[1 - (-1)^k]/2\}$$

hold for $k = 0, 1, \ldots, m-2$.

We next prove the following lemma:

Lemma 7.5.3. Suppose that the conditions of theorem 7.5.1 are satisfied and that M_2 is a positive constant such that

$$M_2^{-m} e^n C_7 b_0^{-1} + (C_6/M_2)^m + e(e^{b/M_2} - 1) < \tfrac{1}{2},$$

where $C_7 = c/C_3$ while b_0, b, C_6 and C_3 were defined earlier.

Let $M = \max (M_1, M_2, C_6, 2be)$ and assume that

$$(7.5.17) \qquad \beta_k \leqslant k! \, M^k \exp \{[1 - (-1)^k]/2\}$$

for $k = 0, 1, 2, \ldots, 2N + m - 2$. Then

$$\beta_{2N+m} \leqslant (2N+m)! \, M^{2N+m}.$$

We differentiate equation (7.5.5) $2N$ times with respect to t, and putting $t = 0$ we obtain

$$(7.5.18) \qquad \int_{-\infty}^{\infty} \ldots \int_{-\infty}^{\infty} A(x_1, x_2, \ldots, x_n)(x_1 + \ldots + x_n)^{2N}$$

$$\times dF(x_1) \ldots dF(x_n)$$

$$= c \int_{-\infty}^{\infty} \ldots \int_{-\infty}^{\infty} (x_1 + \ldots + x_n)^{2N} dF(x_1) \ldots dF(x_n).$$

It follows from the first relation (7.5.9) and from the obvious inequality

$$|x_1 + x_2 + \ldots + x_n| \geqslant \left| |x_1| - |x_2 + \ldots + x_n| \right|$$

that

$$(7.5.19)$$

$$\int_{|x_1| > C_2} x_1^m \left[\int_{\Omega_{n-1}} (|x_1| - |x_2 + \ldots + x_n|)^{2N} dF(x_2) \ldots dF(x_n) \right] dF(x_1)$$

$$\leqslant C_7 J$$

where

$$(7.5.19a) \qquad J = \int_{-\infty}^{\infty} \ldots \int_{-\infty}^{\infty} (x_1 + x_2 + \ldots + x_n)^{2N} dF(x_1) \ldots dF(x_n).$$

We add the integral I, defined in (7.5.15), to both sides of (7.5.19) and see easily that

$$0 \leqslant \sum_{j=0}^{2N} \binom{2N}{j}(-1)^j \beta_{2N+m-j} b_j \leqslant C_7 J + I.$$

It follows from this inequality, and (7.5.15), that
(7.5.20)

$$|b_0 \beta_{2N+m} - 2Nb_1 \beta_{2N+m-1}| \leqslant C_7 J + b_0 C_6^{2N+m} + \sum_{j=2}^{2N} \binom{2N}{j} \beta_{2N+m-j} b_j.$$

We estimate next the expressions on the right of (7.5.20).

We see from (7.5.13) and (7.5.17) that

$$\sum_{j=2}^{2N} \binom{2N}{j} \beta_{2N+m-j} b_j \leqslant M^{2N+m} e b_0 \sum_{j=2}^{2N} (2N+m-j)! \binom{2N}{j} (b/M)^j.$$

We note that

$$(2N+m-j)! \binom{2N}{j} = \frac{2N(2N-1)\ldots(2N-j+1)}{j!}(2N+m-j)!$$

$$< \frac{1}{j!}(2N+m)!$$

so that
(7.5.21)

$$\sum_{j=2}^{2N} \binom{2N}{j} \beta_{2N+m-j} b_j \leqslant (2N+m)! \, M^{2N+m} e b_0 (e^{b/M}-1).$$

We turn now to the expression (7.5.19a) and see that

$$J \leqslant \sum_{j_1+\ldots+j_n=2N} \frac{(2N)!}{j_1!\ldots j_n!} \beta_{j_1} \beta_{j_2} \ldots \beta_{j_n}.$$

We again use (7.5.17) to show that

$$J \leqslant (2N)! \, M^{2N} e^n \sigma$$

where σ is the number of terms in the multinomial expansion of $(x_1+x_2+\ldots+x_n)^{2N}$. It is not difficult to show that the number of terms in a homogeneous polynomial of degree p in n variables cannot exceed

$$\binom{p+n-1}{n-1};$$

using this fact we conclude that
(7.5.22) $J \leqslant (2N+n-1)! \, M^{2N} e^n/(n-1)!$

It follows then from (7.5.20), (7.5.21) and (7.5.22) that

$$|\beta_{2N+m} - 2Nb_1 b_0^{-1} \beta_{2N+m-1}| \leqslant (2N+n-1)! \, M^{2N} e^n C_7 b_0^{-1}/(n-1)!$$
$$+ C_6^{2N+m} + (2N+m)! \, M^{2N+m} e(e^{b/M}-1).$$

According to the assumptions of theorem 7.5.1 we have

$$n-1 \leqslant m$$

so that

$$|\beta_{2N+m} - 2Nb_1 b_0^{-1}\beta_{2N+m-1}|$$
$$\leqslant (2N+m)!\, M^{2N+m}\{M^{-m}\,e^n\,C_7 b_0^{-1} + (C_6/M)^{2N+m} + e(e^{b/M}-1)\}.$$

In view of the definition of M we then have

(7.5.23) $|\beta_{2N+m} - 2Nb_1 b_0^{-1}\beta_{2N+m-1}| \leqslant \tfrac{1}{2}(2N+m)!\, M^{2N+m}.$

For the further discussion of (7.5.23) we consider two mutually exclusive possibilities described by the inequalities

(7.5.24) $2Nb_1 b_0^{-1}\beta_{2N+m-1} \leqslant \tfrac{1}{2}\beta_{2N+m}$

(7.5.25) $2Nb_1 b_0^{-1}\beta_{2N+m-1} > \tfrac{1}{2}\beta_{2N+m}.$

We examine first the case where (7.5.24) holds. Then

$$\beta_{2N+m} - 2Nb_1 b_0^{-1}\beta_{2N+m-1} \geqslant \tfrac{1}{2}\beta_{2N+m}.$$

We see then from (7.5.23) that

(7.5.26) $\beta_{2N+m} \leqslant (2N+m)!\, M^{2N+m}.$

We consider next the second case and assume that (7.5.25) holds. It is known [see (1.4.7)] that

(7.5.27) $\beta_{2N+m-1} \leqslant (\beta_{2N+m})^{[1-1/(2N+m)]}.$

We substitute this into (7.5.25) and see easily that

$$\beta_{2N+m} < (4Nb)^{2N+m}$$

or, using (7.5.12),

$$\beta_{2N+m} < (2N+m)!\,(2be)^{2N+m} < (2N+m)!\, M^{2N+m}.$$

It follows that (7.5.26) is also valid in the second case, so that lemma 7.5.3 is proved.

We show next that condition (7.5.17) holds for any positive integer k. We establish this fact by induction; in view of lemma 7.5.3 it is only necessary to show that condition (7.5.17) holds also for $k = 2N+m-1$.

We substitute the expression (7.5.26) into (7.5.27) and see that

$$\beta_{2N+m-1} \leqslant (\beta_{2N+m})^{(2N+m-1)/(2N+m)} \leqslant \frac{(2N+m)!\, M^{2N+m-1}}{[(2N+m)!]^{1/(2N+m)}}$$

It follows from (7.5.12) that

$$\beta_{2N+m-1} \leqslant e(2N+m-1)!\, M^{2N+m-1}.$$

Thus condition (7.5.17) holds for $k = 2N+m-1$ and therefore also for all positive integers k. We have then

$$\left(\frac{|\alpha_k|}{k!}\right)^{1/k} \leqslant \left(\frac{\beta_k}{k!}\right)^{1/k} \leqslant Me^{1/k}$$

and conclude that $f(t)$ is an analytic characteristic function which is regular at least in the strip $|\operatorname{Im}(z)| < 1/M$. We write as usual $f(z)$ for the function of the complex argument $z = t+iy$ (t, y real) which agrees with the characteristic function $f(t)$ on the real axis.

We complete the proof of the theorem by showing that $f(z)$ is an entire function. This is accomplished by proving that the integral

$$(7.5.28) \qquad \int_{-\infty}^{\infty} e^{vx}\, dF(x)$$

exists and is finite for arbitrary real y. We give an indirect proof and suppose that the least upper bound η of all $|y|$ for which the integral (7.5.28) exists is finite. Then

$$\frac{1}{M} \leqslant \eta < \infty.$$

We now select a real $y_0 > 0$ such that

$$(7.5.29) \qquad \eta - \frac{1}{M} < y_0 < \eta.$$

Since $f(z)$ is regular in the strip $|\operatorname{Im}(z)| < \eta$, the relation (7.5.5) is also valid if we replace the real variable t by the complex argument $z = t + iy$ with $|y| < \eta$. We do this and differentiate the new relation $2N$ times with respect to z and then put $z = -iy_0$. In this way we obtain the equation

$$(7.5.30) \qquad \int_{-\infty}^{\infty} \cdots \int_{-\infty}^{\infty} A(x_1, \ldots, x_n)(x_1 + \ldots + x_n)^{2N}$$
$$\times \exp\left[y_0(x_1 + \ldots + x_n)\right] dF(x_1) \ldots dF(x_n)$$
$$= c \int_{-\infty}^{\infty} \cdots \int_{-\infty}^{\infty} (x_1 + \ldots + x_n)^{2N} \exp\left[y_0(x_1 + \ldots + x_n)\right] dF(x_1) \ldots dF(x_n).$$

We divide both sides of (7.5.30) by Λ^n where

$$\Lambda = \int_{-\infty}^{\infty} e^{y_0 x}\, dF(x)$$

and introduce the distribution function

$$(7.5.31) \qquad G(x) = \frac{1}{\Lambda} \int_{-\infty}^{x} e^{y_0 v}\, dF(v).$$

We see then from (7.5.30) that $G(x)$ satisfies a relation which corresponds to the equation (7.5.18) for $F(x)$. We conclude as before that the characteristic function $g(t)$ of $G(x)$ is regular at least in the strip $|\operatorname{Im}(z)| < 1/M$ so that

$$\int_{-\infty}^{\infty} e^{ux}\, dG(x)$$

exists and is finite if $|u| < 1/M$.

We see from (7.5.29) that it is always possible to select a real u_0 such that

$$\eta - y_0 < u_0 < \frac{1}{M}.$$

Then the integral

$$\int_{-\infty}^{\infty} \exp\left[(u_0+y_0)x\right] dF(x) = \Lambda \int_{-\infty}^{\infty} \exp\left(u_0 x\right) dG(x)$$

exists and is finite. In a similar manner one can show also that the integral

$$\int_{-\infty}^{\infty} \exp\left[-(u_0+y_0)x\right] dF(x)$$

exists and is finite. In view of the definition of η this is impossible, so that the proof of theorem 7.5.1 is completed.

A. A. Zinger and Yu. V. Linnik (1957) also give in their paper further conditions on the polynomial $A(x_1, x_2, \ldots, x_n)$ and on the solution $f(t)$ which ensure that the only positive definite solutions of the equation (7.5.1) are the characteristic functions of normal distributions.

8 FACTORIZATION OF ANALYTIC CHARACTERISTIC FUNCTIONS

In Chapter 6 we dealt with the factorization of distribution functions and of characteristic functions and derived several general theorems. In the present chapter we restrict ourselves to the study of decompositions of analytic characteristic functions. This specialization permits us to obtain further results by applying the tools furnished by the theory of functions of a complex variable.

8.1 Properties of the factors of an analytic characteristic function

Let $f(z)$ be an analytic characteristic function which has the strip
$$-\alpha < \text{Im}\,(z) < \beta \quad (\alpha > 0, \beta > 0)$$
as its strip of regularity. Suppose that $f(z)$ is decomposable and has the two non-degenerate characteristic functions $f_1(t)$ and $f_2(t)$ as factors. Then

(8.1.1) $f(t) = f_1(t) f_2(t)$

for real t; the corresponding distribution functions then satisfy the relation

(8.1.2) $\displaystyle F(x) = \int_{-\infty}^{\infty} F_1(x-y)\,dF_2(y) = \int_{-\infty}^{\infty} F_2(x-y)\,dF_1(y).$

Let $A > 0$, $B > 0$ and $\xi_2 > \xi_1$ be four real numbers; it follows from (8.1.2) that

(8.1.3) $\displaystyle F(\xi_2) - F(\xi_1) \geqslant \int_{-A}^{B} [F_1(\xi_2 - y) - F_1(\xi_1 - y)]\,dF_2(y).$

We choose a fixed real number v such that $-\alpha < v < \beta$; since $f(z)$ is an analytic characteristic function we know that the integral

$$\int_{-\infty}^{\infty} e^{vx}\,dF(x)$$

exists and is finite and that

$$\int_{-\infty}^{\infty} e^{vx}\,dF(x) \geqslant \int_{a}^{b} e^{vx}\,dF(x)$$

where a and b $(b > a)$ are two real numbers. We next consider the integral $\displaystyle \int_{a}^{b} e^{vx}\,dF(x)$ and represent it as the limit of Darboux sums. We construct a sequence of subdivisions of the interval $[a, b]$ by defining

$$x_j^{(n)} = a + \frac{b-a}{2^n}(j-1) \quad \{j = 1, 2, \ldots, (2^n+1) \quad \text{and} \quad n = 1, 2, \ldots\}$$

so that

(8.1.4) $x_{2k-1}^{(n+1)} = x_k^{(n)}$ for $k = 1, 2, \ldots, (2^n+1)$.

We can then write

(8.1.5) $\int_a^b e^{vx}\, dF(x) = \lim_{n\to\infty} \sum_{j=1}^{2^n} \exp\left(vx_j^{(n)}\right)[F(x_{j+1}^{(n)}) - F(x_j^{(n)})]$

$= \lim_{n\to\infty} \sum_{j=1}^{2^n} \exp\left(vx_{j+1}^{(n)}\right)[F(x_{j+1}^{(n)}) - F(x_j^{(n)})].$

We denote by

$h_{j,n}(y; v) = \begin{cases} \exp\left(vx_j^{(n)}\right)[F_1(x_{j+1}^{(n)}-y) - F_1(x_j^{(n)}-y)] & \text{if } v > 0 \\ \exp\left(vx_{j+1}^{(n)}\right)[F_1(x_{j+1}^{(n)}-y) - F_1(x_j^{(n)}-y)] & \text{if } v < 0 \end{cases}$

for $j = 1, 2, \ldots, 2^n$ and by

$g_n(y; v) = \sum_{j=1}^{2^n} h_{j,n}(y; v).$

We see then from (8.1.3) and (8.1.5) that

(8.1.6) $\int_a^b e^{vx}\, dF(x) \geqslant \lim_{n\to\infty} \int_{-A}^B g_n(y; v)\, dF_2(y).$

Using (8.1.4) together with the inequality

$x_{2j-1}^{(n+1)} < x_{2j}^{(n+1)} < x_{2j+1}^{(n+1)}$

we see that

$h_{j,n}(y; v) \leqslant h_{2j,n+1}(y; v) + h_{2j-1,n+1}(y; v)$

so that

$g_n(y; v) \leqslant g_{n+1}(y; v).$

From the definition of the functions $g_n(y)$ it follows that they are Darboux sums and that

$\lim_{n\to\infty} g_n(y; v) = \int_{a-y}^{b-y} e^{v(y+z)}\, dF_1(z).$

We then apply to (8.1.6) the monotone convergence theorem [Loève (1955), p. 124] and conclude that

$\int_a^b e^{vx}\, dF(x) \geqslant \int_{-A}^B [\lim_{n\to\infty} g_n(y; v)]\, dF_2(y)$

or

$\infty > \int_{-\infty}^\infty e^{vx}\, dF(x) \geqslant \int_a^b e^{vx}\, dF(x) \geqslant \int_{-A}^B e^{vy}\left[\int_{a-y}^{b-y} e^{vz}\, dF_1(z)\right] dF_2(y).$

We note that

$\int_{a-y}^{b-y} e^{vz}\, dF_1(z) \geqslant \int_{a+A}^{b-B} e^{vz}\, dF_1(z)$

so that

$$\int_{-\infty}^{\infty} e^{vx}\, dF(x) \geqslant \left[\int_{-A}^{B} e^{vy}\, dF_2(y)\right]\left[\int_{a+A}^{b-B} e^{vz}\, dF_1(z)\right].$$

The integral on the left of this inequality is finite and independent of a, b, A, B. Carrying out the necessary passages to the limit, we see that the integrals

(8.1.7)
$$\begin{cases} \int_{-\infty}^{\infty} e^{vx}\, dF_1(x) \quad \text{and} \\ \int_{-\infty}^{\infty} e^{vy}\, dF_2(y) \end{cases}$$

exist and are finite and that

(8.1.8) $$\int_{-\infty}^{\infty} e^{vx}\, dF(x) \geqslant \int_{-\infty}^{\infty} e^{vy}\, dF_1(y) \int_{-\infty}^{\infty} e^{vy}\, dF_2(y).$$

Here v is a real number such that $-\alpha < v < \beta$, so that the integrals (8.1.7) exist for all such v. But then the integrals

$$f_1(z) = \int_{-\infty}^{\infty} e^{izx}\, dF_1(x) \quad \text{and} \quad f_2(z) = \int_{-\infty}^{\infty} e^{izx}\, dF_2(x)$$

exist and are finite for all complex z such that $-\alpha < \mathrm{Im}\,(z) < \beta$, and we see that $f_1(z)$ and $f_2(z)$ are analytic characteristic functions whose strip of regularity is at least the strip of $f(z)$. Moreover equation (8.1.1), which holds for real t, is also valid (by analytic continuation) in the entire strip of regularity of $f(z)$. We summarize this result as

Theorem 8.1.1.   Let $f(z)$ be an analytic characteristic function which has the strip $-\alpha < \mathrm{Im}\,(z) < \beta$ as its strip of regularity. Then any factor $f_1(z)$ of $f(z)$ is also an analytic characteristic function which is regular, at least in the strip of regularity of $f(z)$.

We now turn back to inequality (8.1.8). There exist two real numbers a_1 and a_2 such that $0 < F_2(a_1)$ while $1 > F_2(a_2)$. Then

$$\int_{-\infty}^{\infty} e^{vy}\, dF_2(y) \geqslant \begin{cases} \int_{a_2}^{\infty} e^{vx}\, dF_2(x) \geqslant e^{a_2 v}[1 - F_2(a_2)] & \text{if } v > 0 \\ \int_{-\infty}^{a_1} e^{vx}\, dF_2(x) \geqslant e^{a_1 v}\, F_2(a_1) & \text{if } v < 0. \end{cases}$$

Let $C^{-1} = \min\,[F_2(a_1),\, 1 - F_2(a_2)]$ and $a = \max\,[|a_1|,\, |a_2|]$; we then see that

$$\int_{-\infty}^{\infty} e^{vx}\, dF_1(x) \leqslant C\, e^{a|v|} \int_{-\infty}^{\infty} e^{vx}\, dF(x).$$

Corollary to theorem 8.1.1.   Let $f(z)$ be a decomposable analytic characteristic function with strip of regularity $-\alpha < \mathrm{Im}\,(z) < \beta$ and suppose that

$f_1(z)$ is a factor of $f(z)$. Then there exist positive constants C and a such that

$$f_1(-iv) \leqslant C e^{a|v|} f(-iv)$$

for all v satisfying $-\alpha < v < \beta$.

We next consider an important particular case and suppose that $f(z)$ is an entire characteristic function.

Theorem 8.1.2. *Every factor $f_1(z)$ of an entire characteristic function $f(z)$ is an entire characteristic function. The order of the factors of an entire characteristic function $f(z)$ cannot exceed the order of $f(z)$.*

The first part of this statement follows immediately from theorem 8.1.1. The second part is a consequence of the relation $M(r; f_1) \leqslant c e^{ar} M(r; f)$ which is easily obtained from the corollary and from the equation $M(r; f)$ $= \max [f(ir), f(-ir)]$ which was derived in Section 7.1.

Corollary to theorem 8.1.2. *Let $f(z)$ be an entire characteristic function of order $\rho > 1$ and type τ and suppose that $f_1(z)$ is a factor of $f(z)$. If the order of $f_1(z)$ is also ρ, then the type τ_1 of $f_1(z)$ cannot exceed the type τ of $f(z)$, $\tau_1 \leqslant \tau$.*

The statement of the corollary is obtained in the same way as the statement of the theorem, using the definition of the type given in Appendix D.

Remark 1. The statement of the corollary does not hold if either $\rho = 1$ or if $\rho_1 < \rho$, where ρ_1 is the order of $f_1(z)$.

Remark 2. Let $f(z)$ be an entire characteristic function without zeros so that $f(z) = e^{\phi(z)}$ [$\phi(z)$ entire, $z = t+iy$]. Then every factor $f_1(z)$ of $f(z)$ is also an entire characteristic function without zeros and therefore has the form $f_1(z) = e^{\phi_1(z)}$ where $\phi_1(z)$ is an entire function.

We conclude this section by deriving a property of entire characteristic functions without zeros.

Theorem 8.1.3. *Let $f(z)$ be an entire characteristic function without zeros which has a factor $f_1(z)$. The entire functions $\phi(z) = \log f(z)$ and $\phi_1(z) = \log f_1(z)$ then satisfy the relation $M(r; \phi_1) \leqslant 6rM(r+1; \phi)+Cr(r+1)$, where C is a positive constant.*

For the proof of the theorem we need two lemmas.[*]

Lemma 8.1.1. *Let $f(z)$ be a function which is regular in a region G, let $z_0 = t_0+iy_0$ be an interior point of G, and let Δ be the distance between z_0 and the boundary of G. Then*

$$(8.1.9) \quad f(z) = \frac{1}{2\pi} \int_0^{2\pi} u(t_0+\rho \cos \theta, y_0+\rho \sin \theta) \frac{\rho e^{i\theta}+(z-z_0)}{\rho e^{i\theta}-(z-z_0)} d\theta + i\beta_0 .$$

---

[*] Let $w = \xi+i\eta$ be a complex number and let $f(w)$ be a function which is regular in a certain region. We write then $u(\xi, \eta)$ for the real part of $f(w)$.

Moreover,

(8.1.9a) $f'(z_0) = \dfrac{1}{\pi\rho} \displaystyle\int_0^{2\pi} u(t_0+\rho\cos\theta, y_0+\rho\sin\theta)\, e^{-i\theta}\, d\theta.$

Here z_0 is an interior point of the region G; z is a point in the interior of the circle with centre z_0 and radius ρ such that $|z-z_0| < \rho < \Delta$, while $\beta_0 = \mathrm{Im}\,[f(z_0)]$.

The representation (8.1.9) is known as Schwarz's formula; for its proof see Markushevich (1965) [vol. 2, p. 151]. If we differentiate (8.1.9) with respect to z and put $z = z_0$ we obtain (8.1.9a).

Lemma 8.1.2.   Let $f(z)$ be an entire characteristic function $[z = t+iy;\ t,\ y$ real$]$, then there exists a positive constant $M = M_f$, which depends on f but is independent of y, such that $\log f(iy) \geqslant -M|y|$.

According to theorem 7.3.2 we have $\log f(iy) \geqslant -y\kappa_1$, where $\kappa_1 = if'(0)$. The statement of the lemma follows from the fact that $-y\kappa_1 \geqslant -|\kappa_1||y|$ if $\kappa_1 \neq 0$, so that in this case $M = |\kappa_1|$. If $\kappa_1 = 0$, M is an arbitrary positive number.

We proceed to the proof of theorem 8.1.3 and write

(8.1.10) $\begin{cases} u(t, y) = \mathrm{Re}\,[\phi(t+iy)] \\ u_1(t, y) = \mathrm{Re}\,[\phi_1(t+iy)] \end{cases}$

It follows easily from theorem 7.1.2 that

(8.1.11) $0 \leqslant u_1(0, y)-u_1(t, y) \leqslant u(0, y)-u(t, y) \leqslant 2M(r; \phi),$

where $r = |t+iy|$.

Since $f_1(z)$ is a factor of $f(z)$ there exists an entire characteristic function $f_2(z)$ without zeros such that $f(z) = f_1(z) f_2(z)$. We write $\phi_2(z) = \log f_2(z)$ and $u_2(t, y) = \mathrm{Re}\,[\phi_2(t+iy)]$, so that

(8.1.12) $u_1(t, y) = u(t, y)-u_2(t, y).$

We conclude from lemma 8.1.2 that there exist positive constants M_1 and M_2 such that

$$\log f_j(iy) \geqslant -M_j|y| \quad (j = 1, 2)$$

and note that

$$u_j(0, y) = \log |f_j(iy)| = \log f_j(iy).$$

Hence

(8.1.13) $u_j(0, y) \geqslant -M_j|y| \quad (j = 1, 2).$

It is also easily seen that

(8.1.14) $u(t, y) = \log |f(t, y)| \leqslant M(r; \phi),$

where $r = (t^2+y^2)^{1/2}$. It follows from (8.1.12), (8.1.13) and (8.1.14) that

$$-M_1|y| \leqslant u_1(0, y) = u(0, y)-u_2(0, y) \leqslant u(0, y)+M_2|y|$$

or
$$-M_1|y| \leqslant u_1(0, y) \leqslant M(y; \phi) + M_2|y|.$$
Therefore there exists a positive constant C such that
(8.1.15) $$|u_1(0, y)| \leqslant M(y; \phi) + C|y|.$$
Clearly
$$|u_1(t, y)| \leqslant |u_1(0, y)| + |u_1(0, y) - u_1(t, y)|$$
or, using (8.1.11) and (8.1.15),
$$|u_1(t, y)| \leqslant M(y; \phi) + C|y| + 2M(r; \phi).$$
Since $|y| \leqslant r$ we have
(8.1.16) $$|u_1(t, y)| \leqslant 3M(r; \phi) + C|y|.$$

We apply formula (8.1.9a) of lemma 8.1.1 to $\phi_1(z)$. Since $\phi_1(z)$ is an entire function we may put $\rho = 1$ and we write also z, t and y instead of z_0, t_0 and y_0, respectively. We obtain

$$\phi_1'(z) = \frac{1}{\pi} \int_0^{2\pi} u_1(t + \cos\theta, y + \sin\theta) e^{-i\theta} d\theta.$$

It follows from (8.1.16) that
$$|\phi_1'(z)| \leqslant 6M(r+1; \phi) + 2C(r+1).$$
Since

$$|\phi_1(z)| = \left| z \int_0^1 \phi_1'(zv) dv \right| \leqslant |z| \max_{0 < v \leqslant 1} |\phi_1'(zv)|$$

we see that
$$|\phi_1(z)| \leqslant 6rM(r+1; \phi) + 2Cr(r+1).$$
This is the estimate given in theorem 8.1.3.

Corollary 1 to theorem 8.1.3. Let $f(z)$ be an entire characteristic function without zeros which has a factor $f_1(z)$ and write $\phi(z) = \log f(z)$, $\phi_1(z) = \log f_1(z)$. The order ρ_1 of $\phi_1(z)$ cannot exceed the order ρ of $\phi(z)$. Moreover, if $\rho_1 = \rho$ then the type of $\phi_1(z)$ cannot exceed the type of $\phi(z)$.

The statement of the corollary follows immediately from the theorem and the definitions of order and type of an entire function given in Appendix D.

Remark. The estimate of theorem 8.1.3 can sometimes be improved, namely if it is possible to find for $u_1(0, y)$ and $u_1(0, y) - u_1(t, y)$ better bounds than those of formulae (8.1.11) and (8.1.15).
Suppose that we have
(8.1.11a) $$0 \leqslant u_1(0, y) - u_1(t, y) \leqslant A(t, y)$$
(8.1.15a) $$|u_1(0, y)| \leqslant B(y)$$

where $A(t, y)$ and $B(y)$ are non-decreasing functions. Repeating the previous argument we get

$$|u_1(t, y)| \leqslant A(t, y) + B(y)$$

and

(8.1.17) $|\phi_1(z)| \leqslant 2|z|A(t+1, y+1) + 2|z|B(y+1)$ $(z = t+iy)$.

We give an example which we shall use in the next section. Let

$$f(z) = \exp\{\lambda(e^{iz}-1) + i\mu z - \gamma z^2\},$$

where μ is real, while $\gamma \geqslant 0$ and $\lambda \geqslant 0$. We suppose that $f(z)$ admits the decomposition,

$$f(z) = f_1(z)f_2(z).$$

The function $f(z)$ is an entire characteristic function without zeros; we write again $u(t, y) = \mathrm{Re}\,[\log f(t+iy)] = \mathrm{Re}\,[\phi(t+iy)]$ and use analogous notations for the factors $f_1(z)$ and $f_2(z)$. Then

(8.1.18) $u(0, y) - u(t, y) = \log\left|\dfrac{f(iy)}{f(t+iy)}\right| = 2\lambda e^{-y}\sin^2\dfrac{t}{2} + \gamma t^2$,

so that we see from (8.1.11) that

(8.1.19) $A(t, y) = 2\lambda\,e^{|y|} + \gamma t^2$.

According to lemma 8.1.2 there exist two positive constants M_1 and M_2 such that

$$\phi_k(iy) \geqslant -M_k|y| (k = 1, 2)$$

and we see that

(8.1.20a) $u_1(0, y) = \mathrm{Re}\,[\phi_1(iy)] = \phi_1(iy) \geqslant -M_1|y|$.

According to our assumptions we have

$$\phi_1(iy) = \log f(iy) - \phi_2(iy)$$

so that

(8.1.20b) $u_1(0, y) \leqslant \lambda(e^{-y}-1) - \mu y + \gamma y^2 + M_2|y|$.

Hence

$$|u_1(0, y)| \leqslant \lambda e^{|y|} + \gamma y^2 + O(|y|),$$

so that

(8.1.21) $B(y) = \lambda e^{|y|} + \gamma y^2 + O(|y|)$.

We see therefore from (8.1.17), (8.1.19) and (8.1.21) that

(8.1.22) $|\phi_1(z)| = O\{|z|\exp[|\,\mathrm{Im}\,(z)\,|] + |z|^3\}$ $(|z| \to \infty)$

and have obtained the following result:

Corollary 2 to theorem 8.1.3.   Let $f(z)$ be the characteristic function of the convolution of a normal and a Poisson distribution,

$$f(z) = \exp[\lambda(e^{iz}-1) + i\mu z - \gamma z^2].$$

If $f_1(z) = \exp[\phi_1(z)]$ is a factor of $f(z)$, then

$$\phi_1(z) = O\{|z| \exp[|\operatorname{Im}(z)|] + |z|^3\}$$

as $|z| \to \infty$.

8.2 Factorization of certain entire characteristic functions

Certain entire characteristic functions have interesting factorization properties. We next prove an important theorem concerning the decomposition of the normal distribution; this theorem was first conjectured by P. Lévy and somewhat later proved by H. Cramér.

Theorem 8.2.1 (Cramér's theorem). The characteristic function $f(t)$ $= \exp[i\mu t - \sigma^2 t^2/2]$ of the normal distribution has only normal factors. Moreover, if $f(t) = f_1(t)f_2(t)$ with $f_j(t) = \exp[i\mu_j t - \sigma_j^2 t^2/2]$ $(j = 1, 2)$, then $\mu_1 + \mu_2 = \mu$ and $\sigma_1^2 + \sigma_2^2 = \sigma^2$.

The function $f(t)$ is an entire function without zeros; it follows then from theorem 8.1.2 that the same is true for its factors and that the order of these factors cannot exceed 2. Therefore $f_1(z)$ has the form

$$f_1(z) = \exp[g_1(z)]$$

and it follows from Hadamard's factorization theorem that $g_1(z)$ is a polynomial of degree not exceeding 2. Let for real argument t, $g_1(t) = a_0 + a_1 t + a_2 t^2$; since $f(0) = 1$ we see that $a_0 = 0$. From the relation $g_1(-t) = \overline{g_1(t)}$ we conclude that $a_1 = i\mu_1$ is purely imaginary and that a_2 is real. Since a characteristic function is bounded for real values of its argument we deduce finally from $|f_1(t)| = \exp[a_2 t^2]$ that $a_2 \leqslant 0$ and set $a_2 = -\frac{1}{2}\sigma_1^2$. Thus $f_1(t) = \exp[i\mu_1 t - \frac{1}{2}\sigma_1^2 t^2]$ is the characteristic function of a normal distribution. The same argument applies to $f_2(t)$ while the relation between the parameters of $f(t)$ and those of its factors is established by elementary reasoning.

We discussed in Section 6.2, without giving any examples, characteristic functions which have no indecomposable factors. Cramér's theorem shows that the characteristic function of the normal distribution belongs to the class of characteristic functions without indecomposable factors. Our next theorem indicates that the characteristic function of the Poisson distribution also belongs to this class. The following factorization theorem was derived by D. A. Raikov and is in some respects similar to Cramér's theorem.

Theorem 8.2.2 (Raikov's theorem). The characteristic function $f(t)$ $= \exp[\lambda(e^{it} - 1)]$ of the Poisson distribution has only Poissonian factors. Moreover if $f(t) = f_1(t)f_2(t)$ with $f_j(t) = \exp[\lambda_j(e^{it} - 1)]$ $(j = 1, 2)$ then $\lambda_1 + \lambda_2 = \lambda$.

To prove the theorem we suppose that

$$(8.2.1) \qquad f(t) = \exp[\lambda(e^{it} - 1)] = f_1(t)f_2(t)$$

is decomposed into two non-degenerate factors. Since the convolution of a discrete and a continuous distribution is always continuous, we see that $f_1(t)$ and $f_2(t)$ are necessarily characteristic functions of discrete distributions. The Poisson distribution $f(t)$ has its discontinuity points at the non-negative integers; it is then no restriction to assume that the discontinuity points of $f_1(t)$ and $f_2(t)$ are also non-negative integers. Then

$$f_1(t) = \sum_{v=0}^{\infty} a_v e^{itv} \quad \text{and} \quad f_2(t) = \sum_{v=0}^{\infty} b_v e^{itv} \quad \text{with } a_v \geqslant 0,\ b_v \geqslant 0,$$

$$\sum_{v=0}^{\infty} a_v = \sum_{v=0}^{\infty} b_v = 1 \quad \text{and where } f(t) = e^{-\lambda} \sum_{v=0}^{\infty} \frac{\lambda^v}{v!} e^{itv}.$$

Since $f(t)$ is an entire function without zeros, the same is also true for $f_1(t)$ and $f_2(t)$, so that these series also converge for arbitrary complex values of the argument. We now introduce a new variable $w = e^{it}$; this transforms the characteristic functions $f_1(t), f_2(t)$ and $f(t)$ into the generating functions $g_1(w), g_2(w)$ and $g(w)$ respectively. Here

$$g(w) = e^{-\lambda} \sum_{v=0}^{\infty} \frac{\lambda^v}{v!} w^v, \quad g_1(w) = \sum_{v=0}^{\infty} a_v w^v, \quad g_2(w) = \sum_{v=0}^{\infty} b_v w^v$$

and $g(w) = g_1(w)g_2(w)$. The coefficients of these power series satisfy the equation

$$(8.2.2) \qquad a_0 b_v + a_1 b_{v-1} + \ldots + a_{v-1} b_1 + a_v b_0 = e^{-\lambda} \frac{\lambda^v}{v!}$$

and it follows from the non-negativity of the a_v and b_v and from the relation

$$a_0 b_0 = e^{-\lambda} \neq 0$$

that

$$(8.2.3) \qquad a_v \leqslant b_0^{-1} e^{-\lambda} \frac{\lambda^v}{v!}.$$

Since $g(w) = \exp[\lambda(w-1)]$ is an entire function, we conclude from (8.2.3) that $g_1(w)$ is also an entire function, and we see that for real t

$$g_1(t) \leqslant b_0^{-1} g(t).$$

It is also easy to verify that

$$M(r; g) \geqslant b_0 M(r, g_1)$$

so that the order of $g_1(w)$ cannot exceed the order of $g(w)$. The function $g(w)$ is an entire function of order 1 without zeros; therefore $g_1(w)$ has the same property. We conclude from Hadamard's factorization theorem that $g_1(w)$ has exactly the order 1. Since $g_1(1) = 1$ we see that $g_1(w) = \exp[\lambda_1(w-1)]$ so that $f_1(t) = \exp[\lambda_1(e^{it}-1)]$ is the characteristic function of a Poisson distribution. A similar argument applies to $f_2(t)$ and it is easily seen that $\lambda_1 \geqslant 0,\ \lambda_2 \geqslant 0,\ \lambda_1 + \lambda_2 = \lambda$.

The following corollary follows almost immediately from Raikov's theorem.

Corollary to theorem 8.2.2. A Poisson-type distribution[*] has only Poisson type factors.

One can summarize theorems 8.2.1 and 8.2.2 by introducing the following definition. A family of characteristic functions (or distribution functions) is said to be factor-closed if the factors of every element of the family belong necessarily to the family. The preceding results mean that the normal family, as well as the family of Poisson type distributions, is factor-closed. H. Teicher (1954) showed that a family which contains the binomial distributions is factor-closed. For the binomial distributions this fact was already noted by N. A. Sapogov (1951). In this connection we mention an interesting result which describes another family of characteristic functions which is factor-closed. Yu. V. Linnik (1957) derived the following generalization of the theorems of Cramér and Raikov.

Theorem 8.2.3. Let
$$f(t) = \exp \{\lambda(e^{it}-1)+i\mu t - \tfrac{1}{2}\sigma^2 t^2\}$$
(μ real, $\sigma^2 \geqslant 0$, $\lambda \geqslant 0$) be the characteristic function of the convolution of a normal and of a Poisson distribution. Suppose that $f(t)$ has the decomposition $f(t) = f_1(t)f_2(t)$. Then
$$f_j(t) = \exp \{\lambda_j(e^{it}-1)+i\mu_j t - \tfrac{1}{2}\sigma_j^2 t^2\} \quad (j = 1, 2)$$
where $\lambda = \lambda_1+\lambda_2$ and $\sigma^2 = \sigma_1^2+\sigma_2^2$.

We note that theorems 8.2.1 and 8.2.2 can be obtained from this result as particular cases. However, the proof of theorem 8.2.3 requires more powerful analytical tools than theorems 8.2.1 and 8.2.2. This is explained by the fact that theorem 8.2.1 deals with an entire function of finite order while theorem 8.2.2 treats the characteristic function of a lattice distribution. Under the assumptions of theorem 8.2.3 both these advantages are lost and the proof becomes much more complicated.

For the proof of theorem 8.2.3 we need certain results from the theory of analytic functions which we state as lemmas.

Lemma 8.2.1. Let $f(z)$ be a function which is regular in the angle $\mathcal{D} = \{z : 0 \leqslant |z| < \infty, \alpha \leqslant \arg(z) \leqslant \beta\}$ and which satisfies the following conditions:

(i) $|f(z)| \leqslant M_1 \exp(|z|^\rho)$ for $z \in \mathcal{D}$ where $\rho < \pi/(\beta-\alpha)$.

(ii) $|f(z)| \leqslant M$ on the lines $z = x e^{i\alpha}$ and $z = x e^{i\beta}$ forming the boundary of $\mathcal{D}$.

Then $|f(z)| \leqslant M$ for all $z \in \mathcal{D}$.

---

[*] That is a distribution with characteristic function of the form
$$f(t) = \exp [t i\mu + \lambda(e^{it\sigma}-1)].$$

Lemma 8.2.1 is a special case of the Phragmén–Lindelöf theorem; for its proof we refer the reader to Titchmarsh (1939) [p. 176] or to Markushevich (1965) [vol. 2, p. 214].

Lemma 8.2.2.   Let $f(z)$ be an entire periodic function with period T, such that the inequality $|f(z)| \leqslant K e^{a|z|}$ (K and a are real and positive constants) holds. Then

$$f(z) = \sum_{k=-\tau}^{\tau} c_k \exp\left\{\frac{2\pi i}{T} zk\right\}$$

is a trigonometric polynomial with $\tau = [a \mid T \mid / 2\pi]$.

Lemma 8.2.2 is a consequence of the theorem [see Markushevich (1967), vol. 3, p. 143] which states that a non-constant, periodic entire function of exponential type is necessarily a trigonometric polynomial.

We proceed to prove theorem 8.2.3 and suppose that the characteristic function

(8.2.4) $f(t) = \exp\{\lambda(e^{it}-1) + i\mu t - \tfrac{1}{2}\sigma^2 t^2\}$

admits a decomposition

(8.2.5) $f(t) = f_1(t)f_2(t).$

We see from theorem 8.1.2 and the fact that $f(t)$ is an entire characteristic function without zeros that $f_1(t)$ and $f_2(t)$ are entire characteristic functions without zeros. Therefore

$$f_j(z) = \exp\left[\phi_j(z)\right] \quad (j = 1, 2)$$

where the $\phi_j(z)$ are entire functions which are real for $z = iy$ ($-\infty < y < \infty$, y real) and have the property that $\phi_1(0) = 0$. We see from corollary 2 to theorem 8.1.3 that

(8.2.6) $\phi_1(z) = O\{|z| \exp[|\operatorname{Im}(z)|] + |z|^3\}$ $(|z| \to \infty).$

Up to this point we have considered $u_1(t, y) = \operatorname{Re}[\phi_1(z)]$ as a function of the real variables t and y. For the completion of the proof it is necessary to fix y and to continue $u_1(t, y)$ into the complex plane. It will be convenient to introduce the function

(8.2.7) $g(z) = \phi_1(-iz).$

We note that $g(z)$ is an entire function which is real for real z. Therefore $g(z)$ admits an expansion

$$g(z) = \sum_{k=0}^{\infty} a_k z^k$$

where the coefficients a_k are real. Let $z = t + iy$ (t, y real) then

$$\operatorname{Re}[g(z)] = \operatorname{Re}[g(t+iy)] = \tfrac{1}{2}[g(t+iy) + g(t-iy)].$$

On the other hand, we see from (8.2.7) that

$$\operatorname{Re}[g(z)] = \operatorname{Re}[\phi_1(-iz)] = \operatorname{Re}[\phi_1(y-it)] = u_1(y, -t)$$

so that

(8.2.8) $u_1(y, -t) = \frac{1}{2}[g(t+iy)+g(t-iy)]$.

The right-hand side of equation (8.2.8) is, for fixed y, an entire function of t and can be continued into the complex plane. In the following we write $u_1(y, w)$ if we consider also complex values of the second variable. Since

$$g(w+iy) = \phi_1(y-iw)$$
$$g(w-iy) = \phi_1(-y-iw),$$

we see from (8.2.8) and (8.2.6) that

(8.2.9) $u_1(y, w) = O(|w|e^{|\text{Re}(w)|}+|w|^3)$ $(|w| \to \infty)$.

We now introduce the function

$$K(w) = u_1(0, w)-u_1(2\pi, w).$$

Since $u_1(0, w)$ and $u_1(2\pi, w)$ are entire functions, we see that $K(w)$ is an entire function. It follows from (8.1.11) and (8.1.18) that

(8.2.10a) $K(w) = O(1)$ if $\text{Im}(w) = 0$ and $|w| \to \infty$,

while one sees from (8.2.9) that

(8.2.10b) $K(w) = O(|w|^3)$ if $\text{Re}(w) = 0$ and $|w| \to \infty$.

Moreover, one has for all w

(8.2.10c) $K(w) = O[\exp(|w|^{3/2})]$ as $|w| \to \infty$.

We use the last three estimates to prove the following statement.

Lemma 8.2.3.   The function $K(w)$ reduces to a constant.

We consider the function

$$\vartheta(w) = K(w)(w+1)^{-3}.$$

This function is analytic in the half-plane $\text{Re}(w) \geqslant 0$; in view of the estimates (8.2.10a), (8.2.10b) and (8.2.10c), it satisfies the conditions[*] of lemma 8.2.1 in each of the angles $-\frac{\pi}{2} \leqslant \arg(w) \leqslant 0$ and $0 \leqslant \arg(w) \leqslant \frac{\pi}{2}$.

We conclude from lemma 8.2.1 that for $\text{Re}(w) \geqslant 0$,

(8.2.11) $K(w) = O(|w|^3)$ as $|w| \to \infty$.

We use the function

$$\vartheta_1|w| = K(w)(w-1)^{-3},$$

which is analytic in the half-plane $\text{Re}(w) \leqslant 0$, to show in the same way that (8.2.11) is valid also for $\text{Re}(w) \leqslant 0$. Therefore the entire function $K(w)$ satisfies (8.2.11) for all w, so that it is necessarily a polynomial of degree not exceeding 3. We conclude from the estimate (8.2.10a) that $K(w)$ is necessarily a constant.

---

[*] with $\rho = 3/2$, $\beta - \alpha = \pi/2$.

I

We are now ready to complete the proof of theorem 8.2.3. It follows from the definition of the function $K(w)$ and from (8.2.8) that

$$-2K(-w) = g(w+2\pi i)+g(w-2\pi i)-2g(w).$$

Since, according to lemma 8.2.5, the function $K(w)$ is a constant, we see that $g(z)$ satisfies the relation

$$g(z+2\pi i)+g(z-2\pi i)-2g(z) = c,$$

where c is a constant. We put

(8.2.12) $g_1(z) = g(z)-g(z-2\pi i)-\dfrac{cz}{2\pi i}$

and see from the preceding equation that $g_1(z)$ is periodic with period $2\pi i$. Moreover we see from (8.2.6) that

$$g_1(z) = O[\exp(3|z|/2)] \quad \text{as } |z| \to \infty.$$

The function $g(z)$ satisfies the conditions of lemma 8.2.2 (with $T = 2\pi i$, $a = 3/2 = \tau$), and applying it we get

$$g_1(z) = A_0+A_1 e^z+A_2 e^{-z},$$

where A_0, A_1, A_2 are constants. We see from (8.2.6) that $g(z) = O(|z|^3)$ as $\text{Re}(z) \to -\infty$; the same is therefore true for $g_1(z)$, so that $A_2 = 0$ and

(8.2.13) $g_1(z) = A_0+A_1 e^z.$

In view of (8.2.12) and (8.2.13) we have

$$g(z)-g(z-2\pi i) = B_0+B_1 z+B_2 e^z$$

with B_0, B_1 and B_2 constant. We put

$$g_2(z) = g(z)-\frac{B_0+iB_1}{2\pi i}z-\frac{B_1}{4\pi i}z^2-\frac{B_2}{2\pi i}ze^z.$$

Repeating the reasoning which led to (8.2.13), we see that

$$g_2(z) = C_0+C_1 e^z,$$

where C_0 and C_1 are constants. Using the definition of $g_2(z)$ we conclude that

(8.2.14) $g(z) = D_0+D_1 z+D_2 z^2+D_3 e^z+D_4 ze^z$

where the coefficients D_j $(j = 0, 1, 2, 3, 4)$ are constants. These constants are real, since $g(z)$ is real for real z. We see from (8.2.7) that $g(0) = 0$; therefore,

$$D_0 = -D_3.$$

We put $z = y+it$ and separate the real and imaginary parts in (8.2.14) and obtain

$$u_1(y, t) = D_1 y+D_2(y^2-t^2)+D_3(e^y \cos t-1)+D_4 e^y(y \cos t-t \sin t).$$

It follows from the estimate (8.1.20b) that $D_4 = 0$. Therefore

$$u_1(y, 0)-u_1(y, t) = D_2 t^2+2D_3 e^y \sin^2 \frac{t}{2}.$$

This expression must be non-negative for all real y and t. If we put $t = \pi$ and let y tend to $+\infty$ we see that $D_3 \geqslant 0$, and if we put $t = \pi$ and let y tend to $-\infty$ we see that $D_2 \geqslant 0$. Therefore

$$g(z) = D_1 z + D_2 z^2 + D_3 (e^z - 1) \quad (D_2 \geqslant 0, D_3 \geqslant 0).$$

If we write $D_1 = \mu_1$, $D_2 = \gamma = \frac{1}{2}\sigma_1^2$, $D_3 = \lambda_1$ we see that $\phi_1(z) = g(-iz)$ has the form

$$\phi_1(z) = i\mu_1 z - \sigma_1^2 z^2/2 + \lambda_1 (e^{iz} - 1)$$

so that the theorem is proved.

Some of the factorization theorems for analytic characteristic functions admit interesting generalizations which we discuss in Chapter 9.

The results of Raikov's theorem can also be extended in another direction. P. Lévy (1937b) and D. A. Raikov (1938) studied the multiplicative structure of finite convolutions of Poisson type distributions and obtained a number of interesting results. We now introduce certain notations which will be used in formulating these results.

Let $\lambda \geqslant 0$ be a real constant; we denote by

(8.2.15) $F(x; \lambda) = e^{-\lambda} \sum\limits_{k=0}^{\infty} \dfrac{\lambda^k}{k!} \varepsilon(x - k)$

the distribution function of the Poisson distribution with parameter λ. We write therefore $F[(x-\gamma)/\sigma; \lambda]$ for distributions of the type of (8.2.15); clearly the characteristic function of Poisson type distributions is $f(t) = \exp[i\gamma t + \lambda(e^{it\sigma} - 1)]$ where $\lambda \geqslant 0$, $\sigma > 0$ and γ are real numbers.

Let $\sigma_1 < \sigma_2 < \ldots < \sigma_n$ be n positive numbers; we write $\Lambda(\sigma_1, \sigma_2, \ldots, \sigma_n)$ for the set of real numbers which can be represented in the form

$$g_1 \sigma_1 + g_2 \sigma_2 + \ldots + g_n \sigma_n,$$

where the $g_1, g_2, \ldots, g_n$ are arbitrary non-negative integers such that $g_1 + g_2 + \ldots + g_n > 0$. The set $\Lambda(\sigma_1, \sigma_2, \ldots, \sigma_n)$ has no finite accumulation point; it is therefore possible to arrange its elements in an increasing sequence

$$\Lambda_1 = \sigma_1 < \Lambda_2 < \ldots < \Lambda_n \ldots.$$

We say that the n numbers $\sigma_1, \sigma_2, \ldots, \sigma_n$ are rationally independent if no relation

(8.2.16) $r_1 \sigma_1 + r_2 \sigma_2 + \ldots + r_n \sigma_n = 0$

holds where the $r_1, r_2, \ldots, r_n$ are rational numbers such that

$$|r_1| + |r_2| + \ldots + |r_n| > 0.$$

In other words a linear relation (8.2.16) with rational coefficients between the $\sigma_1, \ldots, \sigma_n$ can only hold if all the coefficients are zero.

We now state Raikov's results.

Theorem 8.2.4. *Let* $\gamma_1, \gamma_2, \ldots, \gamma_n$ *be* n *arbitrary real numbers, and let* $\lambda_1, \lambda_2, \ldots, \lambda_n$ *be* n *non-negative numbers while* $\sigma_1, \sigma_2, \ldots, \sigma_n$ *are* n *positive numbers. The characteristic function of the distribution*

$$F(x) = F\left(\frac{x-\gamma_1}{\sigma_1}; \lambda_1\right) * F\left(\frac{x-\gamma_2}{\sigma_2}; \lambda_2\right) * \ldots * F\left(\frac{x-\gamma_n}{\sigma_n}; \lambda_n\right)$$

then has only factors of the form

$$\exp\left[i\gamma t + \sum_{\Lambda_k \leqslant \sigma_n} \alpha_{\Lambda_k}(e^{i\Lambda_k t} - 1)\right]$$

where the Λ_k *are the elements of* $\Lambda(\sigma_1, \ldots, \sigma_n)$ *and where* γ *and* α_{Λ_k} *are real numbers.*

We note that the factors of $F(x)$ are not necessarily convolutions of Poisson type distributions since the coefficient α_{Λ_k} may be negative. We will give later an example of such a characteristic function.

Theorem 8.2.5. *Let* $\sigma_1, \sigma_2, \ldots, \sigma_n$ *be* n *rationally independent positive numbers. The distribution*

$$F(x) = F\left(\frac{x-\gamma_1}{\sigma_1}; \lambda_1\right) * F\left(\frac{x-\gamma_2}{\sigma_2}; \lambda_2\right) * \ldots * F\left(\frac{x-\gamma_n}{\sigma_n}; \lambda_n\right)$$

then has only factors of the same form, namely

$$F_1(x) = F\left(\frac{x-\delta_1}{\sigma_1}; \mu_1\right) * F\left(\frac{x-\delta_2}{\sigma_2}; \mu_2\right) * \ldots * F\left(\frac{x-\delta_n}{\sigma_n}; \mu_n\right)$$

where $\delta_j \gtreqless 0$ *while* $0 \leqslant \mu_j \leqslant \lambda_j (j = 1, \ldots, n)$.

Paul Lévy (1938b) has shown that theorems 8.2.3 and 8.2.4 are valid even if the numbers $\sigma_1, \sigma_2, \ldots, \sigma_n$ have arbitrary signs.

Theorem 8.2.6. *Let* $\sigma_1, \sigma_2, \ldots, \sigma_n$ *be* n *positive numbers which satisfy the condition*

$$0 < \sigma_1 < \sigma_2 < \ldots < \sigma_n \leqslant 2\sigma_1.$$

The distribution

$$F(x) = F\left(\frac{x-\gamma_1}{\sigma_1}; \lambda_1\right) * F\left(\frac{x-\gamma_2}{\sigma_2}; \lambda_2\right) * \ldots * F\left(\frac{x-\gamma_n}{\sigma_n}; \lambda_n\right)$$

has only components of the same form, namely

$$F_1(x) = F\left(\frac{x-\delta_1}{\sigma_1}; \mu_1\right) * F\left(\frac{x-\delta_2}{\sigma_2}; \mu_2\right) * \ldots * F\left(\frac{x-\delta_n}{\sigma_n}; \mu_n\right)$$

where $\delta_j \gtreqless 0$ *while* $0 \leqslant \mu_j \leqslant \lambda_j (j = 1, 2, \ldots, n)$.

For the proof of the last three theorems the reader is referred to the paper by Raikov (1938).(†)

(†) We prove in the next chapter two theorems [theorems 9.4.2 and 9.4.4] which are generalizations of Raikov's theorems 8.2.6 and 8.2.5 respectively.

In his remarkable paper P. Lévy (1937b) studied convolutions of Poisson type distributions of a somewhat more specialized character. He considered real polynomials $P(x)$ and the entire functions $\exp [P(x)]$. If the coefficients of $P(x)$ are all non-negative, then the coefficients in the Taylor series expansion of $\exp [P(x)]$ about the origin are also non-negative so that $M(t) = \exp [P(e^t) - P(1)]$ is a moment generating function. However, $M(t)$ can be a generating function even if $P(x)$ has negative coefficients. P. Lévy derived a necessary and sufficient condition which the polynomial $P(x)$ must satisfy in order that $\exp [P(x) - P(1)]$ should be a probability generating function. The generating functions studied by P. Lévy belong to distributions of the form

$$F_1\left(\frac{x}{\sigma_1}; \lambda_1\right) * F_2\left(\frac{x}{\sigma_2}; \lambda_2\right) * \ldots * F_n\left(\frac{x}{\sigma_n}; \lambda_n\right)$$

where the positive numbers $\sigma_1, \sigma_2, \ldots, \sigma_n$ are all integers.

We conclude this section with the discussion of an example which was studied by D. A. Raikov as well as by P. Lévy.

We consider the polynomial

(8.2.17) $P(x) = 1 + ax - \beta x^2 + cx^3 + dx^4$

of degree four. The numbers a, β, c, d are assumed to be positive. We compute $[P(x)]^2$ and $[P(x)]^3$ and see that it is possible to determine the coefficients a, β, c, d in such a way that $[P(x)]^2$ and $[P(x)]^3$ have no negative coefficients.(†) Then $[P(x)]^{2k} = \{[P(x)]^2\}^k$ and $[P(x)]^{2k+1} = [P(x)]^3\{[P(x)]^2\}^{k-1}$ also have non-negative coefficients for $k \geqslant 1$. We form

(8.2.18) $\exp [P(x)] = \sum_{=0}^{\infty} \frac{[P(x)]^j}{j!}$

and see that under these conditions only the quadratic term in $\exp [P(x)]$ can have a negative coefficient. The coefficient of the quadratic term of $\exp [P(x)]$ is easily determined; it is $[(a^2/2) - \beta]e$. If we suppose that

(8.2.19) $\beta \leqslant \dfrac{a^2}{2}$

then $\exp [P(x)]$ has only non-negative coefficients. The function $\exp [P(x) - P(1)]$ is then a generating function, so that

(8.2.20) $g(t) = \exp \{a e^{it} - \beta e^{2it} + c e^{3it} + d e^{4it} - a - c - d + \beta\}$

is a characteristic function. The function (8.2.20) cannot be an infinitely divisible characteristic function. To show this we note that the coefficients of the linear and of the quadratic term of the polynomial in the exponent of $[g(t)]^{1/n}$ are a/n and β/n respectively. The condition corresponding to (8.2.19) will therefore be violated for large n so that $[g(t)]^{1/n}$

(†) These conditions are for instance satisfied if $a = c = d$ and $\beta = \frac{1}{4}$.

cannot be a characteristic function if n is chosen sufficiently large. The function $g(t)$ can be used to construct an interesting decomposition. The characteristic function of the distribution

$$F(x) = F(x; a) * F(\tfrac{1}{3}x; c) * F(\tfrac{1}{4}x; d)$$

is then

$$f(t) = \exp \{a\,e^{it} + c\,e^{3it} + d\,e^{4it} - a - c - d\}.$$

This convolution of three Poisson type distributions also admits the factorization

$$f(t) = g(t) \exp [\beta(e^{2it} - 1)].$$

We conclude from theorem 6.2.2 that $g(t)$ must have an indecomposable factor and see that a convolution of three Poisson type distributions can have indecomposable factors. Since every factor of $g(t)$ is also a factor of $f(t)$ we conclude from theorem 8.2.4 and from a result of P. Lévy(†) that there exist indecomposable characteristic functions of the form (8.2.20).

P. Lévy (1937b) considered polynomials of the form

$$P_1(x) = ax + \beta x^2 - \gamma x^3 + bx^4 + cx^5$$

and

$$P_2(x) = a'x - \beta x^2 + \gamma x^3 + b'x^4$$

and showed that it is possible to determine the coefficients in such a way that

$$f_1(t) = \exp \{P_1(e^{it}) - P_1(1)\}$$

and

$$f_2(t) = \exp \{P_2(e^{it}) - P_2(1)\}$$

are both indecomposable characteristic functions. Therefore $f(t) = f_1(t) f_2(t)$ is the characteristic function of a convolution of three Poisson type distributions and provides an example of the factorization of an infinitely divisible characteristic function into two indecomposable factors.

We conclude this section by listing several theorems which indicate that certain functions can be characteristic functions, provided a parameter is suitably chosen. These theorems are somewhat similar to theorem 6.2.3 since they can also be used to prove the existence of infinitely divisible characteristic functions having an indecomposable factor.

Theorem 8.2.7.   Let $\alpha = p/q$ be a rational number and suppose that the integers p and q are relatively prime and that $1 < p < q$. For given positive numbers λ_1, λ_2 and γ it is possible to select a sufficiently small positive number ν so that

$$f_1(t) = \exp \{-\gamma t^2 + \lambda_1 (e^{it} - 1) + \lambda_2 (e^{\alpha it} - 1) - \nu(e^{it/q} - 1)\}$$

is a characteristic function.

(†) P. Lévy (1937b) has shown that a function of the form $\exp [P(x) - P(1)]$ ($P(x)$ a polynomial) cannot be a generating function unless a term with negative coefficient is preceded by one term and followed by at least two terms with positive coefficients.

Theorem 8.2.8. *Let* α *be an irrational number,* $0 < \alpha < 1$. *For given positive numbers* λ_1, λ_2 *and* γ *it is possible to select sufficiently small positive numbers* ν *and* η *so that the function*

$$f_2(t) = \exp\{-\gamma t^2 + \lambda_1(e^{it} - 1) + \lambda_2(e^{\alpha it} - 1) - \nu(e^{\eta it} - 1)\}$$

is a characteristic function.

Theorem 8.2.9. *Let* $G(u)$ *be a function which is continuous and non-decreasing in the interval* $[b_1, b_2]$ *and suppose that* $G(b_2) - G(b_1) > 0$ *and let* γ *be a positive constant. Then it is possible to select sufficiently small positive numbers* ν *and* η *so that the function*

$$f_3(t) = \exp\left\{-\gamma t^2 + \int_{b_1}^{b_2}(e^{itu} - 1)\,dG(u) - \nu(e^{it\eta} - 1)\right\}$$

is a characteristic function.

Theorems 8.2.7, 8.2.8 and 8.2.9 are due to Yu. V. Linnik; for their proof we refer the reader to Chapter 8 of Linnik (1964).

Remark. We see from the Remark 1 following theorem 5.5.1 that the characteristic functions $f_1(t)$, $f_2(t)$ and $f_3(t)$ are not infinitely divisible and therefore have indecomposable factors.

We mention here another open problem of the arithmetic of distribution functions. It is known that many infinitely divisible characteristic functions have indecomposable factors; however, it is only possible to determine these factors in a few cases. It would be interesting to study methods which would permit the determination of indecomposable factors of infinitely divisible characteristic functions.

8.3 Determination of certain entire characteristic functions by properties of their factors

In studying factorizations we disregard the trivial degenerate factors. It is therefore convenient to introduce the following terminology. We say that two characteristic functions $f_1(t)$ and $f_2(t)$ are equivalent and write

$$f_1(t) \sim f_2(t)$$

if $f_1(t) = e^{iat} f_2(t)$ where a is a real number. Similarly we say that the second characteristics $\phi_1(t) = \log f_1(t)$ and $\phi_2(t) = \log f_2(t)$ are equivalent (in symbols $\phi_1(t) \sim \phi_2(t)$) if

$$\phi_1(t) = ait + \phi_2(t).$$

With this notation we can express the fact that two characteristic functions $f_1(t)$ and $f_2(t)$ belong to distributions of the same type(†) by stating that there exists a constant $\sigma > 0$ such that $f_1(t) \sim f_2(t/\sigma)$.

In this section we show that certain entire characteristic functions can be

---

(†) For the sake of brevity we will say that $f_1(t)$ and $f_2(t)$ are of the same type.

characterized by properties of their factors. We derive first a theorem which is the converse of Cramér's theorem.

Theorem 8.3.1. Let $f(t)$ be a decomposable characteristic function and suppose that all factors of $f(t)$ are of the type of $f(t)$. Then $f(t)$ is the characteristic function of a normal distribution.

We prove first that $f(t)$ is infinitely divisible. Let

$$f(t) = f_1(t) f_2(t)$$

be a decomposition of $f(t)$. It follows then from the assumptions of the theorem that there exist two positive constants c_1 and c_2 such that

$$(8.3.1) \qquad f(t) \sim f(c_1 t) f(c_2 t).$$

We apply the same decomposition to each factor on the right-hand side of (8.3.1) and see that

$$f(t) \sim f(c_1^2 t) f(c_1 c_2 t) f(c_1 c_2 t) f(c_2^2 t)$$

so that $[f(c_1 c_2 t)]^2$ is a factor of $f(t)$. According to the assumption of the theorem there exists then a positive constant c_3 such that

$$[f(c_1 c_2 t)]^2 \sim f(c_3 t)$$

or

$$f(t) \sim \left[f\left(\frac{c_1 c_2}{c_3} t \right) \right]^2.$$

But this means that $f(t)$ is the square of a characteristic function. We repeat this argument to show that for any positive integer k, $f(t)$ is the 2^kth power of some characteristic function. It follows (see the remark following the corollary to theorem 5.3.3) that $f(t)$ is infinitely divisible.

Therefore $f(t)$ has the canonical representation

$$(8.3.2) \qquad \log f(t) \sim \int_{-\infty}^{\infty} \left(e^{itx} - 1 - \frac{itx}{1+x^2} \right) \frac{1+x^2}{x^2} \, d\theta(x).$$

We show next, by means of an indirect proof, that the only point of increase of $\theta(x)$ is the point $x = 0$. Let us therefore assume tentatively that $x = a \neq 0$ is a point of increase of $\theta(x)$. Select $\varepsilon > 0$ so that $|a| > \varepsilon$, then the three numbers a, $a-\varepsilon$ and $a+\varepsilon$ have the same sign. We introduce the function

$$H_\varepsilon(x) = \begin{cases} 0 & \text{if } x < a-\varepsilon \\ \frac{1}{2}[\theta(x) - \theta(a-\varepsilon)] & \text{if } a-\varepsilon \leqslant x < a+\varepsilon \\ \frac{1}{2}[\theta(a+\varepsilon) - \theta(a-\varepsilon)] & \text{if } a+\varepsilon \leqslant x. \end{cases}$$

The functions $H_\varepsilon(x)$ and $\theta(x) - H_\varepsilon(x)$ are then both bounded and non-decreasing functions; therefore

$$h_\varepsilon(t) \sim \exp \left[\int_{-\infty}^{\infty} \left(e^{itx} - 1 - \frac{itx}{1+x^2} \right) \frac{1+x^2}{x^2} \, dH_\varepsilon(x) \right]$$

is a factor of $f(t)$; hence there exists a $c > 0$ such that

$$h_\varepsilon(t) \sim f\!\left(\frac{t}{c}\right)$$

or

$$\int_{-\infty}^{\infty}\left(e^{itx}-1-\frac{itx}{1+x^2}\right)\frac{1+x^2}{x^2}\,dH_\varepsilon(x)$$

$$\sim \int_{-\infty}^{\infty}\left(e^{itx/c}-1-\frac{itx/c}{1+x^2}\right)\frac{1+x^2}{x^2}\,d\theta(x).$$

By a simple transformation of the integral on the right-hand side of this relation we see that

$$\int_{-\infty}^{\infty}\left(e^{itx}-1-\frac{itx}{1+x^2}\right)\frac{1+x^2}{x^2}\,dH_\varepsilon(x)$$

$$\sim \int_{-\infty}^{\infty}\left(e^{ity}-1-\frac{ity}{1+y^2}\right)\frac{1+y^2}{y^2}\frac{1+c^2y^2}{c^2(1+y^2)}\,d\theta(cy).$$

It follows that

$$H_\varepsilon(x) = C + \int_{-\infty}^{x}\frac{1+c^2y^2}{c^2(1+y^2)}\,d\theta(cy)$$

where C is a constant. The function $H_\varepsilon(x)$ increases only in the interval $[a-\varepsilon,\ a+\varepsilon]$, therefore $\theta(x)$ grows only in $[c(a-\varepsilon),\ c(a+\varepsilon)]$. Since a is a point of increase of $\theta(x)$, it must lie in this interval, i.e.,

$$c(a-\varepsilon) \leqslant a \leqslant c(a+\varepsilon)$$

so that

(8.3.3) $\begin{cases} \dfrac{a}{a+\varepsilon} \leqslant c \leqslant \dfrac{a}{a-\varepsilon} & \text{if } a > 0 \\[2ex] \dfrac{a}{a-\varepsilon} \leqslant c \leqslant \dfrac{a}{a+\varepsilon} & \text{if } a < 0. \end{cases}$

We see from (8.3.3) that c tends to 1 as $\varepsilon \to 0$; at the same time the interval which contains all the points of increase of $\theta(x)$ shrinks to the point $x = a$; hence $x = a$ is the only point of increase of $\theta(x)$, and $\theta(x)$ has the form

$$\theta(x) = \lambda\varepsilon(x-a) \quad (\lambda > 0).$$

Then

$$\log f(t) \sim \lambda\frac{1+a^2}{a^2}(e^{ita}-1)$$

and it is easy to show that $f(t)$ cannot have a proper decomposition (8.3.1). This shows that $a \neq 0$ leads to a contradiction with the assumptions of our theorem, so that $a = 0$ is necessarily the only point of increase of $\theta(x)$. This means that $f(t)$ is the characteristic function of a normal distribution, so that theorem 8.3.1 is proved.

It follows from Cramér's theorem (theorem 8.2.1) that a normal characteristic function has only factors of its own type. Theorem 8.3.1 is therefore the converse of Cramér's theorem and we obtain immediately the following characterization of the normal distribution.

Corollary to theorem 8.3.1.   *The decomposable characteristic function $f(t)$ is the characteristic function of a normal distribution if, and only if, all factors of $f(t)$ are of the type of $f(t)$.*

Our next theorem gives a common property of normal distributions, Poisson type distributions and their conjugates.

Theorem 8.3.2.   *Suppose that the characteristic function $f(t)$ has an infinite set of non-equivalent factors and assume that $f(t)$ has the following property: if $f_1(t)$ and $f_2(t)$ are any two factors of $f(t)$, then either $f_1(t)$ is a factor of $f_2(t)$ or $f_2(t)$ is a factor of $f_1(t)$. Then $f(t)$ is the characteristic function of either the normal distribution or of a Poisson-type distribution or of the conjugate to a Poisson-type distribution.*

For the proof of theorem 8.3.2 we need the following lemma.

Lemma 8.3.1.   *If a characteristic function $f(t)$ is divisible by an arbitrary integer power of a characteristic function $g(t)$, then $g(t)$ belongs necessarily to a degenerate distribution.*

If the conditions of the lemma are satisfied, then
$$f(t) = [g(t)]^n h_n(t) \quad (n = 1, 2, \ldots)$$
where $h_n(t)$ is some characteristic function. Therefore
$$(8.3.4) \qquad |f(t)| = |g(t)|^n |h_n(t)| \leqslant |g(t)|^n \quad (n = 1, 2, \ldots).$$
We now show that the assumption that $g(t)$ is non-degenerate leads to a contradiction. It follows from the corollary to lemma 6.1.1 that there exists a $\delta > 0$ such that $|g(t)| < 1$ for $0 < t < \delta$. We choose such a t and let n tend to infinity in (8.3.4) and see that $|f(t)|$ can be made arbitrarily small, provided $0 < t < \delta$. This contradicts the fact that $f(t)$, as a characteristic function, is continuous at $t = 0$ and $f(0) = 1$, so that the lemma is proved.

We proceed to the proof of theorem 8.3.2 and show first that the characteristic function $f(t)$ has no indecomposable factors. We give an indirect proof and assume therefore tentatively that $f_1(t)$ is an indecomposable factor of $f(t)$. According to the assumptions of the theorem, every other factor $g(t)$ of $f(t)$ is divisible by some power of $f_1(t)$. We see then from lemma 8.3.1 that there exists a highest power of $f_1(t)$ which is a factor of $g(t)$. Let n be the exponent of this power, so that $g(t) = [f_1(t)]^n h(t)$. The factor $h(t)$ is not divisible by $f_1(t)$; it follows from the assumptions of the theorem that $h(t)$ must be a factor of $f_1(t)$, but since $f_1(t)$ is indecomposable, $h(t)$ is necessarily degenerate, so that
$$(8.3.5) \quad g(t) \sim [f_1(t)]^n.$$

If the characteristic function is non-degenerate it can, according to lemma 8.3.1, not be divisible by arbitrarily large powers of $f_1(t)$. On the other hand we see from (8.3.5) that every factor of $f(t)$ is equivalent to some power of $f_1(t)$, so that $f(t)$ can have only a finite number of non-equivalent factors. This contradicts the assumption of the theorem, so we must conclude that $f(t)$ has no indecomposable factors. According to theorem 6.2.2 $f(t)$ is then infinitely divisible. Therefore we can write $f(t)$ in the canonical form

$$(8.3.6) \qquad f(t) \sim \exp\left[\int_{-\infty}^{\infty}\left(e^{itx}-1-\frac{itx}{1+x^2}\right)\frac{1+x^2}{x^2}\,d\theta(x)\right].$$

We show next—again by means of an indirect proof—that $\theta(x)$ has only a single point of increase. Let us therefore assume tentatively that this is not true and that $\theta(x)$ has the points a_1 and a_2 as points of increase. We select $\varepsilon > 0$ so that $a_1+\varepsilon < a_2-\varepsilon$ and construct two functions

$$(8.3.7) \qquad H_j(x) = \begin{cases} 0 & \text{if } x < a_j-\varepsilon \\ \theta(x)-\theta(a_j-\varepsilon) & \text{if } a_j-\varepsilon \leqslant x < a_j+\varepsilon \\ \theta(a_j+\varepsilon)-\theta(a_j-\varepsilon) & \text{if } a_j+\varepsilon \leqslant x \end{cases}$$

for $j = 1, 2$. The functions $\theta(x)-H_j(x)$ $(j = 1, 2)$ are non-decreasing and bounded, so that the functions

$$f_j(t) = \exp\left[\int_{-\infty}^{\infty}\left(e^{itx}-1-\frac{itx}{1+x^2}\right)\frac{1+x^2}{x^2}\,dH_j(x)\right] \quad (j = 1, 2)$$

are characteristic functions. Moreover $f_1(t)$ as well as $f_2(t)$ are factors of $f(t)$. We conclude then from the conditions of the theorem that one of these factors must divide the other. If $f_2(t)$ would be a factor of $f_1(t)$, then

$$(8.3.8) \qquad \frac{f_1(t)}{f_2(t)} = \exp\left\{\int_{-\infty}^{\infty}\left(e^{itx}-1-\frac{itx}{1+x^2}\right)\frac{1+x^2}{x^2}\,d[H_1(x)-H_2(x)]\right\}$$

would be a factor of $f(t)$ and therefore an infinitely divisible characteristic function. However we see from (8.3.7) that $H_1(x)-H_2(x)$ is not monotone, so that the expression (8.3.8) cannot represent an infinitely divisible characteristic function. Therefore $f_2(t)$ cannot be a factor of $f_1(t)$. In the same way we can rule out the possibility that $f_1(t)$ is a factor of $f_2(t)$ and therefore obtain a contradiction with the assumptions of the theorem. This contradiction shows that $\theta(x)$ has exactly one point of increase. Let $x = a$ be this point. If $a = 0$, we see from (8.3.6) that $f(t)$ is the characteristic function of a normal distribution; if $a > 0$ then $f(t)$ is the characteristic function of a Poisson-type distribution; if $a < 0$ then $f(t)$ is the conjugate of a Poisson-type characteristic function.

This completes the proof of theorem 8.3.2. Its converse is trivial, so that it can provide a characterization of the family of all distributions which belong to the type of the normal, the Poisson or the conjugate Poisson distribution.

We finally mention a result due to I. A. Ibragimov (1956b) which gives a characterization of the normal distributions. He considered the class $\mathfrak{F}$ of infinitely divisible distribution functions $F(x)$ which have the following property: if $F(x) \in \mathfrak{F}$ and if the convolution $F * H = Q$ is infinitely divisible then H is infinitely divisible. Ibragimov showed that the class $\mathfrak{F}$ coincides with the family of all normal distributions.

8.4   Infinitely divisible analytic characteristic functions

In this section we discuss analytic characteristic functions which are infinitely divisible. We have seen earlier that an infinitely divisible characteristic function does not vanish for real values of its argument and we now extend this remark.

Theorem 8.4.1.   Let $f(z)$ be an analytic characteristic function and suppose that it is infinitely divisible. Then $f(z)$ has no zeros in the interior of its strip of regularity.

Since $f(t)$ is an infinitely divisible characteristic function, $[f(t)]^{1/n}$ is a characteristic function for any positive integer n and is also a factor of $f(t)$. According to theorem 8.1.1 the function $[f(z)]^{1/n}$ is an analytic characteristic function which is regular at least in the strip of regularity of $f(z)$. If $f(z)$ should have a zero at some point z_0 inside this strip, then $[f(z)]^{1/n}$ would have a singularity at the point z_0 for sufficiently large n, which is impossible.

The statement of theorem 8.4.1 cannot be improved. This is shown by constructing an analytic characteristic function of an infinitely divisible distribution which has zeros on the boundary of its strip of regularity. Let $a > 0$, $b > 0$ be two real numbers and put $w = a + ib$. It is easy to show that

$$f(t) = \frac{(1 - it/w)(1 - it/\bar{w})}{(1 - it/a)^2}$$

is an analytic characteristic function which is regular in the half-plane $\mathrm{Im}\,(z) > -a$ and which has two zeros $-iw$ and $-i\bar{w}$ on the boundary of this region. Moreover it admits the representation

$$\log f(t) = mit + \int_0^\infty \left(e^{itu} - 1 - \frac{itu}{1 + u^2}\right) dN(u)$$

where

$$m = 2 \int_0^\infty e^{-ax}(1 - \cos bx)(1 + x^2)^{-1}\, dx$$

and

$$N(u) = -2 \int_u^\infty e^{-at}(1 - \cos bt)t^{-1}\, dt.$$

According to P. Lévy's representation theorem (theorem 5.5.2) $f(t)$ is infinitely divisible and therefore provides the desired example.

Corollary 1 to theorem 8.4.1. *An infinitely divisible entire characteristic function has no zeros.*

P. Lévy (1938a) raised the question whether an entire characteristic function without zeros is infinitely divisible and solved it [P. Lévy (1937c)] by constructing an example of an entire characteristic function without zeros which is not infinitely divisible. The characteristic function (8.2.20) is such an example. Moreover our argument in Section 8.2 indicates that it is possible to determine the coefficients in such a manner that (8.2.20) represents an entire and indecomposable characteristic function without zeros.

Corollary 2 to theorem 8.4.1. *The characteristic function of a finite distribution cannot be infinitely divisible.*

The corollary follows immediately from theorem 7.2.3 and corollary 1 to theorem 8.4.1.

Corollary 3 to theorem 8.4.1. *The characteristic function $f(t)$ of a finite distribution is always the product of a finite or denumerable number of indecomposable factors.*

From corollary 2 and from theorem 6.2.2 we conclude that $f(t)$ must have indecomposable factors. It is also easily seen that it can have no infinitely divisible factors since all its non-degenerate factors are entire functions of order 1 and cannot therefore be infinitely divisible.

The preceding theorem and its corollaries can be regarded as necessary conditions which an analytic characteristic function must satisfy in order to be infinitely divisible. For instance it follows from theorem 8.4.1 that the characteristic function determined by formula (5.5.12) is not infinitely divisible. We used this fact—without proving it—in an example discussed in Section 5.5. We now give another application of the theorems discussed in the present section.

Let $f(z)$ be an infinitely divisible analytic characteristic function which has the strip of regularity $-\alpha < \text{Im}(z) < \beta$. Then $f(t)$ has no factor of the form $g(t) = p\,e^{it\xi} + (1-p)\,e^{it\eta}$ for which

$$-\alpha < \frac{\log p - \log(1-p)}{\xi - \eta} < \beta.$$

It is easily seen that the existence of such a factor would produce a contradiction with theorem 8.4.1.

We have already remarked that the second characteristic $\phi(t) = \ln f(t)$ is defined for every characteristic function in a (real) neighbourhood of the origin. Let $f(z)$ be an analytic characteristic function which has the strip $-\alpha < \mathrm{Im}\,(z) < \beta$ as its strip of regularity and suppose that $f(z)$ has a zero z_0 in this strip. Then we can only state that $\phi(z)$ is defined and regular in the interior of the circle whose radius is min $(\alpha, \beta, |z_0|)$. If $f(z)$ has no zeros in the interior of the strip, then $\phi(z)$ can be continued analytically in the strip. This is the case if $f(z)$ is an infinitely divisible analytic characteristic function. In this case we obtain the following important result.

Theorem 8.4.2. Let $f(z)$ be an analytic characteristic function and suppose that it is infinitely divisible. Then the canonical representation

$$(8.4.1) \qquad \log f(z) = icz + \int_{-\infty}^{\infty} (e^{izu} - 1 - izu)\,\frac{dK(u)}{u^2}$$

is valid in the interior of the strip of regularity of $f(z)$. Here c is a real constant and $K(u)$ is a non-decreasing bounded function such that $K(-\infty) = 0$ and

$$\int_{-\infty}^{\infty} dK(u) = K(+\infty) < \infty.$$

We assume therefore that $f(z)$ is an infinitely divisible analytic characteristic function with $-\alpha < \mathrm{Im}\,(z) < \beta$ as its strip of regularity. Then the second moment of $f(z)$ exists and $f(z)$ admits, for real values of the argument, the (Kolmogorov) representation (8.4.1). We see from the remarks preceding the statement of the theorem that $\log f(z)$ is defined in the strip of regularity. We denote by $\phi(z) = \log f(z)$ that branch of the function $\log f(z)$ which, for real z, is given by (8.4.1). The function $\phi(z)$ is regular in the strip $-\alpha < \mathrm{Im}\,(z) < \beta$. Now let t be real; we can apply (8.4.1) and see that

$$\phi''(t) = \lim_{h \to 0} \frac{\phi(t+h) + \phi(t-h) - 2\phi(t)}{h^2}$$

or

$$\phi''(t) = -\lim_{h \to 0} \int_{-\infty}^{\infty} e^{itu}\,\frac{1 - \cos hu}{h^2 u^2/2}\,dK(u)$$

so that

$$\phi''(t) = -\int_{-\infty}^{\infty} e^{itu}\,dK(u).$$

Since $K(u)$ is bounded and non-decreasing we see that $\phi''(t)$ is, except for a constant factor, a characteristic function. Moreover, it follows from the analyticity of $\phi(z)$ that $\phi''(z)$ is, except for a constant factor, an analytic characteristic function which is regular in the strip $-\alpha < \mathrm{Im}\,(z) < \beta$.

The integral

$$(8.4.2) \qquad -\phi''(z) = \int_{-\infty}^{\infty} e^{iuz}\,dK(u)$$

converges in this strip and is a regular function of z. Let ζ be a complex number such that $-\alpha < \operatorname{Im}(\zeta) < \beta$ and select $\alpha' > 0, \beta' > 0$ so that $-\alpha < -\alpha' \leqslant \operatorname{Im}(\zeta) \leqslant \beta' < \beta$. Then the integrals

$$\int_{-\infty}^{\infty} e^{-\beta' u} dK(u) \quad \text{and} \quad \int_{-\infty}^{\infty} e^{\alpha' u} dK(u)$$

both exist and are finite. From this it follows easily that (8.4.2) can be integrated under the integral sign from 0 to ζ and we obtain

$$(8.4.3) \qquad -\phi'(\zeta) + \phi'(0) = \int_{-\infty}^{\infty} \frac{e^{i\zeta u} - 1}{iu} dK(u).$$

By a similar argument one can show that it is permissible to integrate the expression on the right-hand side of (8.4.3) under the integral sign from 0 to z, provided that $-\alpha < \operatorname{Im}(z) < \beta$. In this manner one obtains

$$\phi(z) = [\phi'(0)]z + \int_{-\infty}^{\infty} (e^{izu} - 1 - izu) \frac{dK(u)}{u^2}.$$

Since $\phi'(0) = i\kappa_1$, where κ_1—the first cumulant—is real, we see that (8.4.1) holds in the entire strip of regularity of $f(z)$, so that theorem 8.4.2 is established.

9 INFINITELY DIVISIBLE CHARACTERISTIC FUNCTIONS WITHOUT INDECOMPOSABLE FACTORS

Khinchine's theorem (theorem 6.2.2) indicates that a characteristic function which has no indecomposable factors is always infinitely divisible. We have seen from theorem 6.2.3 that the converse is not true; i.e. an infinitely divisible characteristic function can have indecomposable factors. This situation suggests the investigation of the family of infinitely divisible characteristic functions which do not admit indecomposable factors. This family is usually denoted by I_0, and one of the most important problems of the arithmetic of distribution functions is the study of the class I_0. The present chapter deals with this topic.

It follows from theorems 8.2.1, 8.2.2 and 8.2.3 that the class I_0 contains the Normal distribution,[*] the Poisson distribution, and the convolution of a Normal and a Poisson distribution. Theorems 8.2.5 and 8.2.6 provide other examples of members of I_0, while an example given on page 251 shows that not all convolutions of Poisson-type distribution functions belong to I_0.

A systematic study of the class I_0 was carried out by Yu. V. Linnik; his work was first published in a series of papers in the Russian probability journal and later presented in a monograph [Linnik (1964)]. These investigations were continued by other authors.

9.1 The class $\mathscr{L}$

We first introduce some terms which are convenient in the discussion of these studies.

We have shown that every infinitely divisible characteristic function $f(t)$ can be written in the canonical form

(9.1.1)

$$\log f(t) = ita - \gamma t^2 + \int_{-\infty}^{-0} \left(e^{itu} - 1 - \frac{itu}{1+u^2}\right) dM(u)$$
$$+ \int_{+0}^{\infty} \left(e^{itu} - 1 - \frac{itu}{1+u^2}\right) dN(u)$$

where a is real, $\gamma \geqslant 0$, and where the functions $M(u)$ and $N(u)$ satisfy the conditions listed in theorem 5.5.2.

---

[*] We have defined the class I_0 as a family of characteristic functions. We will also speak of distribution functions belonging to I_0, meaning that the corresponding characteristic function is in I_0.

We shall call $M(u)$ and $N(u)$ the spectral functions of $f(t)$, or of the corresponding distribution function $F(x)$; more specifically, we refer to $M(u)$ [respectively $N(u)$] as the spectral function of the negative [respectively positive] spectrum. The negative [respectively positive] Poisson spectrum of the infinitely divisible characteristic function $f(t)$, or of its distribution function $F(x)$, is the set of all points of increase of the function $M(u)$ [respectively $N(u)$]. We write S_M and S_N for the negative and positive Poisson spectrum respectively. We call the set $S_M \cup S_N$ simply the Poisson spectrum of $f(t)$ [or $F(x)$]. An infinitely divisible characteristic function is said to have a bounded negative [positive] Poisson spectrum if there exists a number d [respectively b] such that

$$\int_{-\infty}^{-d} dM(u) = 0 \quad \left[\int_{b}^{\infty} dN(u) = 0 \right].$$

The Poisson spectrum of $f(t)$ is bounded if the positive as well as the negative Poisson spectrum is bounded. An infinitely divisible characteristic function $f(t)$ is said to have a finite spectrum if

$$(9.1.2) \qquad \log f(t) = ait - \gamma t^2 + \sum_{j=1}^{m} \lambda_j (e^{it\mu_j} - 1) + \sum_{j=1}^{n} \lambda_{-j}(e^{-it\nu_j} - 1),$$

where m and n are non-negative integers and $\gamma \geqslant 0$, $\lambda_j > 0$, $\lambda_{-j} > 0$, $\mu_j > 0$, $\nu_j > 0$. If either m or n is equal to zero then the corresponding sum is omitted.

The infinitely divisible characteristic function $f(t)$ is said to have a denumerable Poisson spectrum if

$$(9.1.3) \qquad \log f(t) = ait - \gamma t^2 + \sum_{j=1}^{\infty} \lambda_j \left(e^{it\mu_j} - 1 - \frac{it\mu_j}{1+\mu_j^2} \right)$$
$$+ \sum_{j=1}^{\infty} \lambda_{-j} \left(e^{-it\nu_j} - 1 + \frac{it\nu_j}{1+\nu_j^2} \right)$$

where $\lambda_j > 0$, $\lambda_{-j} > 0$, $\gamma \geqslant 0$ and where the series

$$(9.1.3a) \qquad \sum_{j=1}^{\infty} \frac{\lambda_j \mu_j^2}{1+\mu_j^2} \quad \text{and} \quad \sum_{j=1}^{\infty} \frac{\lambda_{-j} \nu_j^2}{1+\nu_j^2}$$

converge so that

$$(9.1.3b) \qquad \sum_{\mu_j < \varepsilon} \lambda_j \mu_j^2 + \sum_{\nu_j < \varepsilon} \lambda_{-j} \nu^2$$

tends to zero as ε approaches zero. The numbers ν_j and μ_j are called the Poisson frequencies of $f(t)$. The λ_j and λ_{-j} are called the energy parameters of the frequencies μ_j and ν_j respectively.

We also introduce a class[(*)] $\mathscr{L}$ of infinitely divisible characteristic functions which has the following properties:

(i) The Poisson spectrum of a characteristic function $f \in \mathscr{L}$ is

---

(*) This class should not be confused with the class of self-decomposable characteristic functions (L-class) treated in Section 5.11.

either finite or denumerable. Therefore $f(t)$ admits the representation

(9.1.4) $\log f(t) = iat - \gamma t^2 + \sum_{r=1}^{2} \sum_{m=-\infty}^{\infty} \lambda_{m,r} \left(e^{i\mu_{m,r}t} - 1 - \frac{i\mu_{m,r}t}{1+\mu_{m,r}^2} \right)$

where a is real, $\gamma \geqslant 0$, $\lambda_{m,r} \geqslant 0$ $(r = 1, 2; m = 0, \pm 1, \pm 2, \ldots)$, $\mu_{m,1} > 0$, $\mu_{m,2} < 0$.

(ii) $\sum_{r=1}^{2} \sum_{m=-\infty}^{\infty} \lambda_{m,r} \mu_{m,r}^2 (1+\mu_{m,r}^2)^{-1} < \infty$.

(iii) $\sum_{|\mu_{m,r}|<\varepsilon} \lambda_{m,r} \mu_{m,r}^2$ tends to zero as $\varepsilon \to 0$ (*).

(iv) The quotients $\mu_{m+1,r}/\mu_{m,r}$ $(r = 1, 2; m = 0, \pm 1, \pm 2, \ldots)$ are natural numbers greater than 1.

It follows that

$$\ldots \mu_{-1,1} < \mu_{0,1} < \mu_{1,1} < \ldots$$
$$\ldots \mu_{-1,2} > \mu_{0,2} > \mu_{1,2} > \ldots$$

and

$$\lim_{m \to -\infty} \mu_{m,1} = 0, \quad \lim_{m \to +\infty} \mu_{m,1} = +\infty$$
$$\lim_{m \to -\infty} \mu_{m,2} = 0, \quad \lim_{m \to +\infty} \mu_{m,2} = -\infty.$$

In this section we derive the following property of characteristic functions of the class $\mathcal{L}$.

Theorem 9.1.1.   Let $f(t) \in \mathcal{L}$ and suppose that the energy parameters of $f(t)$ satisfy for some $k > 0$ the condition

(9.1.5) $\lambda_{m,r} = O[\exp(-k\mu_{m,r}^2)]$ $(m \to +\infty, r = 1, 2)$;

then $\phi(z) = \log f(z)$ is an entire function, so that the characteristic function $f(z)$ is an entire function without zeros. Moreover,

$$\phi(z) = O\{|z|^2 \exp[N(\operatorname{Im}(z))^2]\} \quad (as \; |z| \to \infty)$$

where $N > 0$ is a constant.

For the proof of theorem 9.1.1 we need several lemmas concerning analytic functions. We now state these lemmas, but since their proofs are not easily accessible in the literature we give them in Appendix E (the motivation for this separation of the statements and of their proofs is our wish to avoid disrupting the discussion of the theorems concerning the characteristic functions of the class I_0).

Lemma 9.1.1.   Suppose that the function $N(u)$ is non-decreasing in the half open interval $0 < u \leqslant a$ $(a < \infty)$ and that $\int_{+0}^{a} u^2 \, dN(u) < \infty$. Then the integral

$$f(z) = \int_{+0}^{a} \left(e^{zu} - 1 - \frac{zu}{1+u^2} \right) dN(u)$$

(*) Condition (iii) is a consequence of (ii).

converges absolutely and uniformly on any bounded set of the z-plane, so that $f(z)$ is an entire function. Moreover the estimate

$$f(z) = O\{|z|^2(1+\exp[a\,\mathrm{Re}\,(z)])\}$$

holds as $|z| \to \infty$.

Lemma 9.1.2A.   Suppose that the function $f(z)$ admits the representation

$$f(z) = \sum_{p=0}^{\infty} d_p \exp\left(\frac{2\pi p}{T}z\right)$$

where the coefficients d_p satisfy, for some $k > 0$, the relation

$$d_p = O[\exp(-kp^2)] \quad (p \to \infty)$$

while $T > 0$. Then $f(z)$ is an entire periodic function with period iT and

(9.1.6) $\log|f(z)| = \begin{cases} O\{[\mathrm{Re}\,(z)]^2\} & \text{if } \mathrm{Re}\,(z) > 0 \\ O(1) & \text{if } \mathrm{Re}\,(z) \leqslant 0. \end{cases}$

Lemma 9.1.2B.   Suppose that the entire function $f(z)$ is periodic with purely imaginary period iT and that

(9.1.7) $\log|f(z)| = \begin{cases} O\{[\mathrm{Re}\,(z)]^2+\log|z|\} & \text{if } \mathrm{Re}\,(z) > 0 \\ O(\log|z|) & \text{if } \mathrm{Re}\,(z) \leqslant 0. \end{cases}$

Then $f(z)$ admits the expansion

$$f(z) = \sum_{p=0}^{\infty} d_p \exp\left(\frac{2\pi p}{T}z\right)$$

where the coefficients d_p satisfy, for some $k > 0$, the relation

$$d_p = O[\exp(-kp^2)] \quad \text{as } p \to \infty.$$

Remark.   The estimate (9.1.7) follows from (9.1.6). It would therefore be possible to use (9.1.7) as a necessary and sufficient condition for the series representation of $f(z)$. In view of the later application of the lemmas it is more convenient to present the necessary and the sufficient condition separately.

We now proceed to the proof of theorem 9.1.1 and suppose that $f(t)$ is a characteristic function of the class $\mathscr{L}$ which satisfies the condition (9.1.5). Then $\phi(t) = \log f(t)$ can be written in the form (9.1.4); we consider first the positive Poisson spectrum of $f(t)$ and write

$$\sum_{m=-\infty}^{\infty} \lambda_{m,1}\left(e^{i\mu_{m,1}t}-1-\frac{i\mu_{m,1}t}{1+\mu_{m,1}^2}\right)$$

$$= \sum_{m=-\infty}^{0} \lambda_{m,1}\left(e^{i\mu_{m,1}t}-1-\frac{i\mu_{m,1}t}{1+\mu_{m,1}^2}\right) + \sum_{m=1}^{\infty} \lambda_{m,1}e^{i\mu_{m,1}t} - \sum_{m=1}^{\infty} \lambda_{m,1}\left(1+\frac{i\mu_{m,1}t}{1+\mu_{m,1}^2}\right)$$

$$= S_1+S_2+S_3 \quad \text{(say)}.$$

Let $N(u) = -\sum_{m=-\infty}^{0} \lambda_{m,1}\varepsilon(u-\mu_{m,1})$. We can then write the first sum S_1 as an integral

$$S_1 = \int_{+0}^{\mu_{0,1}} \left(e^{itu} - 1 - \frac{itu}{1+u^2} \right) dN(u).$$

This integral has (if we put $it = z$) the form of the integral in lemma 9.1.1. We see from (9.1.3b) that the conditions of the lemma are satisfied, and we conclude that S_1 is an entire function. We can therefore consider S_1 also for complex values of the variable t and obtain from lemma 9.1.1 the estimate

$$S_1 = O\{|t^2|(1 + \exp[\mu_{0,1} \operatorname{Im}(t)])\}$$

as $|t| \to \infty$. Since $f(t) \in \mathscr{L}$, the quotients $\mu_{m,1} \mu_{1,1}^{-1}$ are integers greater than 1, and we can write

$$S_2 = \sum_{p=1}^{\infty} d_p \exp(i\mu_{1,1} pt)$$

where

$$d_p = \begin{cases} 0 & \text{if } p \notin \{\mu_{m,1}\mu_{1,1}^{-1}\}_{m=1}^{\infty} \\ \lambda_{m,1} & \text{if } p = \mu_{m,1}\mu_{1,1}^{-1}. \end{cases}$$

We see from (9.1.5) that for $p = \mu_{m,1}/\mu_{1,1}$ the coefficient

$$d_p = \lambda_{m,1} = O[\exp(-k\mu_{m,1}^2)] = O(-k\mu_{1,1}^2 p^2).$$

We apply lemma 9.1.2A and we see that S_2 is an entire function of the complex variable t and that

$$S_2 = O\{\exp[N(\operatorname{Im}(t))^2]\} \quad \text{as } |t| \to \infty$$

for some $N > 0$. The third sum S_3 is a linear function.

We treat the negative Poisson spectrum in the same way and obtain the estimate for $\phi(z)$ stated in theorem 9.1.1.

9.2   A sufficient condition for membership of I_0

The problem of characterizing the class I_0 has not been solved completely at present. We only have some necessary and some sufficient conditions for membership of this class. In this section we prove a sufficient condition; a necessary condition will be given in Section 9.3.

Theorem 9.2.1.   Let $f(t)$ be a characteristic function of the class $\mathscr{L}$ whose energy parameters and frequencies satisfy the following conditions:

(9.2.1) $\lambda_{m,r} = O[\exp[-k(\mu_{m,r}^2)]] \quad (m \to +\infty; r = 1, 2)$

where k is a positive constant. Then $f(t) \in I_0$, that is $f(t)$ has no indecomposable factor.

Condition (9.2.1) is identical with (9.1.5) used in the proof of theorem 9.1.1.

We now assume that the characteristic function $f(t)$ can be factored

$$f(t) = f_1(t) f_2(t).$$

It follows from theorem 9.1.1 that $f(t)$ is an entire characteristic function without zeros, and we see from this fact and from theorem 8.1.2 that $f_1(t)$ and $f_2(t)$ are entire characteristic functions without zeros.

We can therefore write $f(t) = e^{\phi(t)}$, $f_j(t) = e^{\phi_j(t)}$ $(j = 1, 2)$, where $\phi(t)$, $\phi_1(t)$ and $\phi_2(t)$ are entire functions; these functions can be continued into the complex z-plane, $z = t+iy$. We introduce

$$g(z) = \phi_1(-iz) = \phi_1(y-it)$$

and

$$u(t, y) = \operatorname{Re}[g(z)].$$

Then

$$|f_1(-iz)| = |f_1(y-it)| = e^{u(t,y)}$$

and we see from the ridge property of analytic characteristic functions (p. 195) that

$$1 \leqslant \frac{f_1(-it)}{|f_1(y-it)|} \leqslant \frac{f(-it)}{|f(y-it)|}$$

or

(9.2.2) $0 \leqslant u(t, 0) - u(t, y) \leqslant \phi(-it) - \operatorname{Re}[\phi(y-it)].$

Applying the estimate of theorem 9.1.1, we conclude that

(9.2.3) $0 \leqslant u(t, 0) - u(t, y) = O[|z|^2 \exp(Nt^2)]$ as $|z| \to \infty.$

We next derive two similar estimates. We see from (9.1.2) that

$$\phi(-it) - \operatorname{Re}[\phi(y-it)] = \gamma y^2 + 2 \sum_{r=1}^{2} \sum_{m=-\infty}^{\infty} \lambda_{m,r} \left(\sin \frac{\mu_{m,r}\, y}{2}\right)^2 e^{\mu_{m,r}t}.$$

We substitute for $y = 2\pi\, \mu_{s,1}^{-1}$ and obtain (using property (iv) given in the definition of the $\mathscr{L}$-class) that

(9.2.4) $\phi(-it) - \operatorname{Re}[\phi(2\pi\mu_{s,1}^{-1} - it)] = 2 \sum_{m=-\infty}^{s-1} \lambda_{m,1} e^{\mu_{m,1}t} \left(\sin \frac{\mu_{m,1}\pi}{\mu_{s,1}}\right)^2$

$$+ 2 \sum_{m=-\infty}^{\infty} \lambda_{m,2}\, e^{\mu_{m,2}t} \left(\sin \frac{\mu_{m,2}\pi}{\mu_{s,1}}\right)^2 + \gamma \left(\frac{2\pi}{\mu_{s,1}}\right)^2.$$

We note that

$$\sum_{m=-\infty}^{s-2} \lambda_{m,1} e^{\mu_{m,1}t} \left(\sin \frac{\mu_{m,1}\pi}{\mu_{s,1}}\right)^2 \leqslant e^{\mu_{s-1,1}t} \sum_{m=-\infty}^{s-2} \lambda_{m,1} \left(\frac{\mu_{m,1}\pi}{\mu_{s,1}}\right)^2 = o(e^{\mu_{s-1,1}t})$$

as $t \to \infty$ and

$$\sum_{m=-\infty}^{\infty} \lambda_{m,2} e^{\mu_{m,2}t} \left(\sin \frac{\mu_{m,2}\pi}{\mu_{s,1}}\right)^2 \leqslant \sum_{|\mu_{m,2}|<\mu_{s,1}} \lambda_{m,2} \left(\frac{\mu_{m,2}\pi}{\mu_{s,1}}\right)^2$$

$$+ \sum_{|\mu_{m,2}|\geqslant\mu_{s,1}} \lambda_{m,2} = O(1) \text{ as } t \to \infty.$$

We conclude from (9.2.2), (9.2.4) and the last two estimates that
(9.2.5)

$$0 \leqslant u(t, 0) - u(t, 2\pi\mu_{s,1}^{-1}) \leqslant (2\lambda_{s-1,1} + o(1)) \left(\sin \frac{\mu_{s-1,1}\pi}{\mu_{s,1}} \right)^2 \exp\left(\mu_{s-1,1} t \right)$$

$$\text{as } t \to \infty \ (s = 0, \pm 1, \pm 2, \ldots).$$

In the same way we obtain the estimate

$$(9.2.6) \qquad 0 \leqslant u(t, 0) - u(t, 2\pi\mu_{s,2}^{-1})$$

$$\leqslant (2\lambda_{s-1,2} + o(1)) \left(\sin \frac{\mu_{s-1,2}\pi}{\mu_{s,2}} \right)^2 \exp\left(\mu_{s-1,2} t \right) \quad (t \to -\infty).$$

We next derive an estimate for $f(z)$. It follows from theorem 9.1.1 and from the definition of $g(z)$ that

$$(9.2.7) \qquad \phi(-iz) = O\{|z|^2 \exp [N(\mathrm{Re}\,(z))^2]\}.$$

Moreover we see from theorem (8.1.3) that

$$(9.2.8) \qquad M(r; g) \leqslant 6rM(r+1, \phi) + O(r^2)$$

and obtain the following result:

Lemma 9.2.1. *For all complex z ($z = t + iy$; t, y real), the estimate $g(z) = O\{|z|^3 \exp [N(\mathrm{Re}\,(z))^2]\}$ ($|z| \to \infty$) holds. Here N is a positive constant.*

Let q be an integer (positive, negative or zero) and put

$$(9.2.9) \qquad g_{q,r}(z) = g(z) \exp\left(-\mu_{q,r} z \right) \quad (r = 1, 2),$$

and write

$$u_{q,r}(t, y) = \mathrm{Re}\,[g_{q,r}(t + iy)] \quad (t, y \text{ real}).$$

We shall need estimates for the expressions $u_{q,r}(t, 0) - u_{q,r}(t, 2\pi\mu_{q,r}^{-1})$. One has

$$u_{q,r}(t, 0) - u_{q,r}(t, 2\pi\mu_{q,r}^{-1}) =$$

$$= g(t) \exp\left(-\mu_{q,r} t \right) - \mathrm{Re}\,\{g(t + 2\pi i\mu_{q,r}^{-1}) \exp [-\mu_{q,r}(t + 2\pi i\mu_{q,r}^{-1})]\}$$

$$= \{u(t, 0) - u(t, 2\pi\mu_{q,r}^{-1})\} \exp\left(-\mu_{q,r} t \right).$$

We apply the estimate (9.2.5) in the case where $r = 1$ [respectively (9.2.6) for $r = 2$] and conclude that

$$(9.2.7a) \qquad u_{q,1}(t, 0) - u_{q,1}(t, 2\pi\mu_{q,1}^{-1}) = O(1) \quad \text{as } t \to +\infty$$

$$(9.2.7b) \qquad u_{q,2}(t, 0) - u_{q,2}(t, 2\pi\mu_{q,2}^{-1}) = O(1) \quad \text{as } t \to -\infty.$$

Lemma 9.2.2. *The functions $g_{q,r}(z)$ ($r = 1, 2$) can be written as sums*

$$(9.2.10) \qquad g_{q,r}(z) = g_{q,r}^{(+)}(z) + g_{q,r}^{(-)}(z) \quad (r = 1, 2).$$

The summands $g_{q,r}^{(+)}$ and $g_{q,r}^{(-)}$ are entire functions which are real for real z and which admit the estimates (as $|z| \to \infty$)

$$g_{q,r}^{(+)}(z) = \begin{cases} O\{|z|^5 \exp [N(\mathrm{Re}\,(z))^2]\} & \text{if } \mathrm{Re}\,(z) > 0 \\ O(|z|^5) & \text{if } \mathrm{Re}\,(z) \leqslant 0 \end{cases}$$

$$g_{q,r}^{(-)}(z) = \begin{cases} O(|z|^5) & \text{if } \mathrm{Re}\,(z) \geqslant 0 \\ O\{|z|^5 \exp [N(\mathrm{Re}\,(z))^2]\} & \text{if } \mathrm{Re}\,(z) < 0. \end{cases}$$

Here N is a positive constant.

It follows from the definition of the function $g_{q,r}(z)$ that it is real for real z and that

(9.2.11) $g_{q,r}(z) = O\{|z|^3 \exp [N(\mathrm{Re}\,(z))^2]\}.$

Let $0 < a < b$ and $H > 0$ and consider the rectangle which has the points $a+iH$, $b+iH$, $b-iH$ and $a-iH$ as vertices. We integrate the function

$$\frac{z^5 g_{q,r}(\zeta)}{2\pi i \zeta^5 (\zeta - z)}$$

along the contour of this rectangle. According to Cauchy's theorem, this integral is equal to $g_{q,r}(z)$ if z is inside the rectangle, but equals zero if z is outside the rectangle. It follows from the estimate (9.2.11) that the integrals along the horizontal sides of the rectangle tend to zero as H tends to ∞, while a and b are fixed. Therefore

(9.2.12)

$$\frac{z^5}{2\pi i} \int_{b-i\infty}^{b+i\infty} \frac{g_{q,r}(\zeta)\,d\zeta}{\zeta^5(\zeta-z)} - \frac{z^5}{2\pi i} \int_{a-i\infty}^{a+i\infty} \frac{g_{q,r}(\zeta)\,d\zeta}{\zeta^5(\zeta-z)} = \begin{cases} g_{q,r}(z) \\ \text{if}\quad a < \mathrm{Re}\,(z) < b \\ 0 \quad \text{if } \mathrm{Re}\,(z) < a \\ \text{or}\quad \mathrm{Re}\,(z) > b \end{cases}$$

We consider the function $g_{q,r}^{(+)}(z)$ defined by

$$g_{q,r}^{(+)}(z) = \frac{z^5}{2\pi i} \int_{1-i\infty}^{1+i\infty} \frac{g_{q,r}(\zeta)\,d\zeta}{\zeta^5(\zeta-z)} \quad \text{for } \mathrm{Re}\,(z) < 1.$$

We see that the value of the integral defining $g_{q,r}^{(+)}$ does not change if the limits $1-i\infty$ and $1+i\infty$ are replaced by $b-i\infty$ and $b+i\infty$ respectively, where $b > 1$. This means that it is possible to extend $g_{q,r}^{(+)}(z)$ into the half-plane $\mathrm{Re}\,(z) \geqslant 1$; therefore $g_{q,r}^{(+)}(z)$ is an entire function. For values z with $\mathrm{Re}\,(z) > 1$ we select $b > \mathrm{Re}\,(z)$ and obtain the representation

(9.2.13) $g_{q,r}^{(+)}(z) = \dfrac{z^5}{2\pi i} \displaystyle\int_{b-i\infty}^{b+i\infty} \dfrac{g_{q,r}(\zeta)\,d\zeta}{\zeta^5(\zeta-z)} = \dfrac{z^5}{2\pi} \displaystyle\int_{-\infty}^{\infty} \dfrac{g_{q,r}(b+iy)\,dy}{(b+iy)^5(b+iy-z)}.$

It follows easily that $g_{q,r}^{(+)}(z)$ is real for real z. Combining (9.2.12) and (9.2.13), we see that for $\mathrm{Re}\,(z) > 1$

(9.2.14) $g_{q,r}^{(+)}(z) = \dfrac{z^5}{2\pi i} \displaystyle\int_{1-i\infty}^{1+i\infty} \dfrac{g_{q,r}(\zeta)\,d\zeta}{\zeta^5(\zeta-z)} + g_{q,r}(z).$

Moreover

$$\int_{b-i\infty}^{b+i\infty} \frac{g_{q,r}(\zeta)\,d\zeta}{\zeta^5(\zeta-z)} = O(1) \quad (|z| \to \infty)$$

if $|\operatorname{Re}(z)-b| \geqslant 1$. The estimates stated in the lemma for $g_{q,r}^{(+)}(z)$ are obtained from (9.2.14), (9.2.13) and (9.2.11).

We define

$$g_{q,r}^{(-)}(z) = g_{q,r}(z) - g_{q,r}^{(+)}(z)$$

and obtain easily the second estimate of the lemma.

We saw that the functions $g_{q,r}^{(+)}(z)$ and $g_{q,r}^{(-)}(z)$ are entire functions which are real for real z. The Maclaurin expansions of these functions therefore have real coefficients, so that $g_{q,r}^{(+)}(x+iy)$ and $g_{q,r}^{(+)}(x-iy)$ [respectively $g_{q,r}^{(-)}(x+iy)$ and $g_{q,r}^{(-)}(x-iy)$] are complex conjugate for x and y real. Writing

$$u_{q,r}^{(+)}(x,y) = \operatorname{Re}[g_{q,r}^{(+)}(x+iy)], \quad u_{q,r}^{(-)}(x,y) = \operatorname{Re}[g_{q,r}^{(-)}(x+iy)]$$

we have

(9.2.15)
$$\begin{cases} u_{q,r}^{(+)}(x,y) = \tfrac{1}{2}[g_{q,r}^{(+)}(x+iy)+g_{q,r}^{(+)}(x-iy)] \\ u_{q,r}^{(-)}(x,y) = \tfrac{1}{2}[g_{q,r}^{(-)}(x+iy)+g_{q,r}^{(-)}(x-iy)]. \end{cases}$$

The functions on the right-hand side of (9.2.15) are entire functions. One can therefore consider the equations (9.2.15) as definitions of $u_{q,r}^{(+)}(x,y)$ and $u_{q,r}^{(-)}(x,y)$ for complex x (and fixed y). We use the estimates of lemma 9.2.2 and see that

(9.2.16a) $\quad u_{q,r}^{(+)}(x,y) = \begin{cases} O\{|x|^5 \exp[N(\operatorname{Re}(x))^2]\} & \text{if } \operatorname{Re}(x) > 0 \\ O(|x|^5) & \text{if } \operatorname{Re}(x) \leqslant 0 \end{cases}$

(9.2.16b) $\quad u_{q,r}^{(-)}(x,y) = \begin{cases} O(|x|^5) & \text{if } \operatorname{Re}(x) \geqslant 0 \\ O\{|x|^5 \exp[N(\operatorname{Re}(x))^2]\} & \text{if } \operatorname{Re}(x) < 0. \end{cases}$

We introduce the functions

$$K_{q,1}(x) = u_{q,1}^{(+)}(x,0) - u_{q,1}^{(+)}(x, 2\pi\mu_{q,1}^{-1})$$
$$K_{q,2}(x) = u_{q,2}^{(-)}(x,0) - u_{q,2}^{(-)}(x, 2\pi\mu_{q,2}^{-1}).$$

Clearly these are entire functions, and we see from (9.2.16a) and (9.2.16b) that they admit the estimates

(9.2.17a) $\quad K_{q,1}(x) = \begin{cases} O\{|x|^5 \exp[N(\operatorname{Re}(x))^2]\} & \text{if } \operatorname{Re}(x) > 0 \\ O(|x|^5) & \text{if } \operatorname{Re}(x) \leqslant 0 \end{cases}$

(9.2.17b) $\quad K_{q,2}(x) = \begin{cases} O(|x|^5) & \text{if } \operatorname{Re}(x) \geqslant 0 \\ O\{|x|^5 \exp[N(\operatorname{Re}(x))^2]\} & \text{if } \operatorname{Re}(x) < 0 \end{cases}$

as $|x| \to \infty$.

For the study of the functions $K_{q,r}(x)$ $(r = 1, 2)$ we need two analytical results. The first of these can be derived from lemma 8.2.1.

Lemma 9.2.3.   *Suppose that the function $f(z)$ is regular in the half-plane* $\text{Re}(z) \geqslant 0$ *and that it satisfies the conditions*

(i) $|f(z)| \leqslant M_1 |z+1|^a$ *for* $\text{Re}(z) = 0$

(ii) $|f(z)| \leqslant M_2 e^{bz}(z+1)^c$ *for* $\text{Im}(z) = 0$

(iii) $|f(z)| \leqslant M_3 \exp [d (\text{Re}(z))^2]|z+1|^c$ *for* $\text{Re}(z) \geqslant 0$

where M_1, M_2 and M_3 are positive constants, while a, b, c, d are non-negative constants and $c \geqslant a$. Then

$$|f(z)| \leqslant M_1 |z+1|^a \exp [b \, \text{Re}(z)]$$

in the half-plane $\text{Re}(z) \geqslant 0$.

Lemma 9.2.4.   *Let $f(z)$ be an entire function which satisfies the condition*

$$|f(z)| \leqslant \exp \{k \, \text{Re}(z) + O(\log |z|)\} \quad [\text{Re}(z) \geqslant 0]$$

where k is some real constant. Suppose that $f(z)$ can be represented in the form

$$f(z) = \sum_{j=-\infty}^{\infty} (a_j + b_j z) \exp \left(\frac{2\pi j z}{T} \right)$$

with $T > 0$ and where the series converges uniformly on every bounded set. Then $a_j = b_j = 0$ for $j > \omega = [kT(2\pi)^{-1}]$.

The proofs of lemmas 9.2.3 and 9.2.4 are given in Sections E3 and E4 respectively of Appendix E.

We return to the investigation of the functions $K_{q,r}(x)$ and prove the following statement.

Lemma 9.2.5.   *The functions $K_{q,r}(x)$ $(r = 1, 2)$ are polynomials of degree not exceeding 5.*

Since $u_{q,r}(x, y) = u_{q,r}^{(+)}(x, y) + u_{q,r}^{(-)}(x, y)$ we see that

$$K_{q,1}(x) = [u_{q,1}(x, 0) - u_{q,1}(x, 2\pi\mu_{q,1}^{-1})] - [u_{q,1}^{(-)}(x, 0) - u_{q,1}^{(-)}(x, 2\pi\mu_{q,1}^{-1})].$$

In view of (9.2.7a) and (9.2.16b) we obtain for real x the estimate as x tends to $+\infty$,

(9.2.18) $K_{q,1}(x) = O(|x|^5).$

We see from (9.2.17a) that

$$K_{q,1}(x) = O\{|x|^5 \exp [N(\text{Re}(x))^2]\} \quad (|x| \to \infty)$$

in the half-plane $\text{Re}(x) \geqslant 0$. The conditions of lemma 9.2.3 (with $f = K_{q,1}$; $a = c = 5$, $b = 0$, $d = N$) are satisfied, so that (9.2.18) holds in the half-plane $\text{Re}(x) \geqslant 0$. We see from (9.2.17a) that (9.2.18) holds also for $\text{Re}(x) \leqslant 0$, so that (9.2.18) is valid in the entire x-plane. Let

$$K_{q,1}(x) = \sum_{j=0}^{\infty} a_j x^j$$

be the Maclaurin series for $K_{q,1}(x)$ and consider the function

$$H(w) = K_{q,1}(e^w) = \sum_{j=0}^{\infty} a_j e^{wj}.$$

Since (9.2.18) holds for all real or complex x, we conclude that

$$H(w) = O\{\exp[5\,\mathrm{Re}\,(w)]\}.$$

The function $H(w)$ therefore satisfies the conditions of lemma 9.2.4 (with $f = H$, $T = 2\pi$, $b_j = 0$, $k = 5$, $\omega = 5$) so that $a_j = 0$ for $j > 5$. Therefore $K_{q,1}(x)$ is a polynomial of degree not exceeding 5. The statement concerning $K_{q,2}(x)$ is proved in the same way.

The information concerning the $K_{q,r}(x)$ $(r = 1, 2)$ given by lemma 9.2.5 permits us to get more precise results on the functions $g_{q,1}^{(+)}(x)$ and $g_{q,2}^{(-)}(x)$.

Lemma 9.2.6. *The functions $g_{q,1}^{(+)}(x)$ and $g_{q,2}^{(-)}(x)$ admit the expansions*

$$(9.2.19a)\qquad g_{q,1}^{(+)}(x) = \sum_{j=1}^{\infty}(a_{j,1}^{(q)}+b_{j,1}^{(q)}x)\exp[\mu_{q,1}jx]+S_{q,1}(x)$$

$$(9.2.19b)\qquad g_{q,2}^{(-)}(x) = \sum_{j=1}^{\infty}(a_{j,2}^{(q)}+b_{j,2}^{(q)}x)\exp[\mu_{q,2}jx]+S_{q,2}(x)$$

where the real constants $a_{j,r}^{(q)}$ and $b_{j,r}^{(q)}$ satisfy the condition

$$(9.2.19c)\qquad |a_{j,r}^{(q)}|+|b_{j,r}^{(q)}| = O\{\exp(-kj^2)\}\quad(j\to\infty;r = 1, 2)$$

for some $k > 0$. The $S_{q,r}(x)$ are polynomials of degree not exceeding 7 and have real coefficients.

We prove only the statement concerning $g_{q,1}^{(+)}(x)$, since the statement concerning the second function is proved in the same way.

To simplify the notation we write in the proof of formula (9.2.19a) $h(x)$, λ and $S(x)$ instead of $g_{q,1}^{(+)}(x)$, $2\pi i/\mu_{q,1}$ and $S_{q,1}(x)$ respectively. After the completion of the proof we revert to the original notation.

It follows from the definition of the function $K_{q,1}(x)$ and from (9.2.15) that

$$K_{q,1}(x) = g_{q,1}^{(+)}(x)-\tfrac{1}{2}\{g_{q,1}^{(+)}(x+2\pi i\mu_{q,1}^{-1})+g_{q,1}^{(+)}(x-2\pi i\mu_{q,1}^{-1})\}.$$

Since $K_{q,1}(x)$ is a polynomial of at most fifth degree, we obtain (using our simplified notation) the relation

$$h(x+\lambda)-2h(x)+h(x-\lambda) = \sum_{j=0}^{5}c_j x^j$$

where the c_j are constants (which depend on the suppressed subscript q). We choose constants c_j' (also depending on q) such that the polynomial $P(x) = \sum_{j=2}^{7}c_j' x^j$ satisfies the equation

$$P(x+\lambda)-2P(x)+P(x-\lambda) = \sum_{j=0}^{5}c_j x^j.$$

The function

$$(9.2.20)\qquad h_1(x) = h(x)-P(x)$$

then satisfies the equation

$$h_1(x+\lambda)-2h_1(x)+h_1(x-\lambda) = 0$$

so that the function

$$h_2(x) = h_1(x)-h_1(x-\lambda)$$

is periodic with period λ. From the definitions of the functions $h_1(x)$ and $h_2(x)$ and from lemma 9.2.2 we see that $h_2(x)$ is an entire function and that for large $|x|$

$$h_2(x) = \begin{cases} O\{|x|^7 \exp [N(\mathrm{Re}(x))^2]\} & \text{if } \mathrm{Re}(x) > 0 \\ O(|x|^7) & \text{if } \mathrm{Re}(x) \leqslant 0. \end{cases}$$

The conditions of lemma 9.1.2B are satisfied, so that

$$(9.2.21) \qquad h_2(x) = \sum_{j=0}^{\infty} d_j \exp(\mu_{q,1} jx)$$

where $d_j = O[\exp(-kj^2)]$ for some k. (We write here again d_j instead of $d_j^{(q)}$.)

The function $h_1(x)-\lambda^{-1}xh_2(x)$ is periodic with period λ. It is again possible to apply lemma 9.1.2B and we get

$$(9.2.22) \qquad h_1(x)-\lambda^{-1}xh_2(x) = \sum_{j=0}^{\infty} \delta_j \exp(\mu_{q,1} jx)$$

where $\delta_j = \delta_j^{(q)} = O[\exp(-kj^2)]$ for some k. We now return to the original notation and see from (9.2.20), (9.2.21) and (9.2.22) that

$$g_{q,1}^{(+)}(x) = \sum_{j=0}^{\infty} (a_{j,1}^{(q)}+b_{j,1}^{(q)} x) \exp(\mu_{q,1} jx)+\sum_{j=2}^{7} c_j' x^j$$

where

$$|a_{j,1}^{(q)}|+|b_{j,1}^{(q)}| = O[\exp(-kj^2)]$$

for some $k > 0$. The statement of the lemma follows from the fact (established in lemma 9.2.2) that $g_{q,r}^{(+)}(x)$ is real for real x. Let

$$\ell_q(z) = g(z)-g_{q,1}^{(+)}(z) \exp(\mu_{q,1} z)-g_{q,2}^{(-)}(z) \exp(\mu_{q,2} z).$$

Using relations (9.2.9) and (9.2.10), we obtain the following two representations for $\ell_q(z)$:

$$(9.2.23) \qquad \begin{cases} \ell_q(z) = g_{q,1}^{(-)}(z) \exp(\mu_{q,1} z)-g_{q,2}^{(-)}(z) \exp(\mu_{q,2} z). \\ \ell_q(z) = g_{q,2}^{(+)}(z) \exp(\mu_{q,2} z)-g_{q,1}^{(-)}(z) \exp(\mu_{q,1} z). \end{cases}$$

We apply the estimates of lemma 9.2.2 to these representations and see that

$$\ell_q(z) = O\{|z|^5 \exp [\mu_{q,1} \mathrm{Re}(z)]\} \quad \text{if } \mathrm{Re}(z) \geqslant 0$$

$$\ell_q(z) = O\{|z|^5 \exp [\mu_{q,2} \mathrm{Re}(z)]\} \quad \text{if } \mathrm{Re}(z) \leqslant 0$$

as $|z| \to \infty$.

We introduce the expansions (9.2.19a) and (9.2.19b) into (9.2.23) and see that

(9.2.24)
$$\begin{cases} g(z) = \sum_{r=1}^{2} \sum_{j=2}^{\infty} (c_{j,r}^{(q)} + z d_{j,r}^{(q)}) \exp(\mu_{q,r} jz) + L_q(z) \\ \text{where} \\ L_q(z) = \ell_q(z) + S_{q,1}(z) \exp(\mu_{q,1} z) + S_{q,2}(z) \exp(\mu_{q,2} z) \end{cases}$$

where $c_{j,r}^{(q)} = a_{j-1,r}^{(q)}$ and $d_{j,r}^{(q)} = b_{j-1,r}^{(q)}$.

As a consequence of (9.2.19c) we have the estimate

(9.2.24a) $|c_{j,r}^{(q)}| + |d_{j,r}^{(q)}| = O[\exp(-kj^2)] \quad (j \to \infty)$.

We also note that $L_q(z)$ is an entire function which is real for real z. Using the estimates for $\ell_q(z)$ we see that

(9.2.24b) $L_q(z) = \begin{cases} O\{|z|^7 \exp[\mu_{q,1} \operatorname{Re}(z)]\} & \text{for } \operatorname{Re}(z) \geq 0 \\ O\{|z|^7 \exp[\mu_{q,2} \operatorname{Re}(z)]\} & \text{for } \operatorname{Re}(z) \leq 0 \end{cases}$

as $|z| \to \infty$.

We introduce the functions

(9.2.25) $\begin{cases} h_{q,1}(z) = g_{q,1}^{(+)}(z) - S_{q,1}(z) \exp(\mu_{q,1} z) \\ h_{q,2}(z) = g_{q,2}^{(-)}(z) - S_{q,2}(z) \exp(\mu_{q,2} z). \end{cases}$

It follows from (9.2.19a) and (9.2.19b) that

(9.2.26) $h_{q,r}(z) = \sum_{j=2}^{\infty} (c_{j,r}^{(q)} + d_{j,r}^{(q)} z) \exp(\mu_{q,r} jz)$

so that

(9.2.27) $g(z) = \sum_{r=1}^{2} h_{q,r}(z) + L_q(z)$

where $L_q(z)$ is the function defined in (9.2.24). The functions $h_{q,r}(z)$ are entire functions and are real for real z. Let $z = t + iy$ (t, y real) and write

(9.2.28) $H_{q,r}(t, y) = h_{q,r}(t) - \frac{1}{2}[h_{q,r}(t+iy) + h_{q,r}(t-iy)]$.

The right-hand side of this equation is for fixed y an entire function of t. The function $H_{q,r}(t, y)$ can therefore be continued into the complex plane, and we write $H_{q,r}(x, y)$ for its analytical continuation. We consider the function $H_{q,r}(x, y)$ for fixed real y and complex x and use the estimates of lemma 9.2.2 and formulae (9.2.25) and (9.2.28) and see that for $|x| \to \infty$,

(9.2.29a) $H_{q,1}(x, y) = \begin{cases} O\{|x|^7 \exp[N(\operatorname{Re}(x))^2]\} & \text{for } \operatorname{Re}(x) > 0 \\ O(|x|^7) & \text{for } \operatorname{Re}(x) \leq 0 \end{cases}$

(9.2.29b) $H_{q,2}(x, y) = \begin{cases} O(|x|^7) & \text{for } \operatorname{Re}(x) \geq 0 \\ O\{|x|^7 \exp[N(\operatorname{Re}(x))^2]\} & \text{for } \operatorname{Re}(x) < 0. \end{cases}$

Let

$$\Lambda_q(x, y) = L_q(x) - \tfrac{1}{2}[L_q(x+iy) + L_q(x-iy)].$$

The function $\Lambda_q(x, y)$ is, for fixed real y, an entire function of the complex variable x and we see from (9.2.24b) that for $|x| \to \infty$

$$(9.2.30) \qquad \Lambda_q(x, y) = \begin{cases} O\{|x|^7 \exp [\mu_{q,1} \operatorname{Re}(x)]\} & \text{if } \operatorname{Re}(x) \geqslant 0 \\ O\{|x|^7 \exp [\mu_{q,2} \operatorname{Re}(x)]\} & \text{if } \operatorname{Re}(x) \leqslant 0. \end{cases}$$

For real t and real y we have

$$H_{q,r}(t, y) = h_{q,r}(t) - \operatorname{Re}[h_{q,r}(t + iy)]$$
$$\Lambda_q(t, y) = L_q(t) - \operatorname{Re}[L_q(t+iy)].$$

Using these formulae, as well as (9.2.27) and the relation

$$u(t, y) = \operatorname{Re}[g(t+iy)],$$

we see easily that

$$(9.2.31) \qquad u(t, 0) - u(t, y) = \sum_{r=1}^{2} H_{q,r}(t, y) + \Lambda_q(t, y).$$

We see from (9.2.5) that

$$u(t, 0) - u(t, 2\pi\mu_{s,1}^{-1}) = O[\exp(\mu_{s-1,1} t)]$$

as $t \to \infty$. In view of our earlier estimate for $\Lambda_q(t, y)$ and formula (9.2.29b) we see easily that for $s > q+1$

$$(9.2.32a) \qquad H_{q,1}(t, 2\pi\mu_{s,1}^{-1}) = O[\exp(\mu_{s-1,1} t)] \quad (s = q+2, q+3 \ldots)$$

and

$$(9.2.32b) \qquad H_{q,1}(t, 2\pi\mu_{q+1,1}^{-1}) = O[t^7 \exp(\mu_{q,1} t)]$$

as $t \to +\infty$. We see from (9.2.29a), (9.2.32a) and (9.2.32b) that the functions $H_{q,1}(t, 2\pi\mu_{s,1}^{-1})$ satisfy, for integer $s \geqslant q+1$, the conditions of lemma 9.2.3 and we conclude that

$$(9.2.33a) \qquad H_{q,1}(x, 2\pi\mu_{s,1}^{-1}) = O\{|x|^7 \exp [\mu_{s-1,1} \operatorname{Re}(x)]\}$$

$$[\operatorname{Re}(x) \geqslant 0, s = q+1, q+2, \ldots]$$

and we see from (9.2.29a) that, for $|x| \to \infty$,

$$(9.2.33b) \qquad H_{q,1}(x, 2\pi\mu_{s,1}^{-1}) = O(|x|^7) \quad \text{for } \operatorname{Re}(x) \leqslant 0.$$

By means of a simple computation we obtain from (9.2.28) and (9.2.26) the representation

$$(9.2.34) \qquad H_{q,1}(x, y) = 2 \sum_{j=2}^{\infty} (c_{j,1}^{(q)} + d_{j,1}^{(q)} x) \left(\sin \frac{\mu_{q,1} jy}{2} \right)^2 \exp(\mu_{q,1} jx)$$

$$+ \sum_{j=2}^{\infty} y d_{j,1}^{(q)} \sin(\mu_{q,1} jy) \exp(\mu_{q,1} jx).$$

We substitute $y = 2\pi/\mu_{s,1}$ (with $s = q+1, q+2, \ldots$) into (9.2.34) and obtain a series of the form treated in lemma 9.2.4 with coefficients

$$(9.2.35) \quad \begin{cases} a_j = 2c_{j,1}^{(q)}\left(\sin\dfrac{\mu_{q,1}j\pi}{\mu_{s,1}}\right)^2 + d_{j,1}^{(q)}\dfrac{2\pi}{\mu_{s,1}}\sin\dfrac{2\mu_{q,1}j\pi}{\mu_{s,1}} \\[4mm] b_j = 2d_{j,1}^{(q)}\left(\sin\dfrac{\mu_{q,1}j\pi}{\mu_{s,1}}\right)^2 \end{cases}$$

and $T = 2\pi/\mu_{q,1}$. Then $\omega = \mu_{s-1,1}\mu_{q,1}^{-1}$ and the coefficients a_j and b_j vanish if $j > \mu_{s-1,1}\mu_{q,1}^{-1}$ ($s = q+1, q+2, \ldots$). It follows from (9.2.35) that

$$d_{j,1}^{(q)} = 0 \quad \text{for } \mu_{s-1,1}\mu_{q,1}^{-1} < j < \mu_{s,1}\mu_{q,1}^{-1} \quad (s = q+1, q+2, \ldots)$$

and therefore also

$$c_{j,1}^{(q)} = 0 \quad \text{for } \mu_{s-1,1}\mu_{q,1}^{-1} < j < \mu_{s,1}\mu_{q,1}^{-1} \quad (s = q+1, q+2, \ldots).$$

The coefficients $c_{j,1}^{(q)}$ may be different from zero only if j belongs to the set $J_1 = \{\mu_{q+p,1}/\mu_{q,1}\}_{p=1}^{\infty}$. (It follows from the assumptions of the theorem that J_1 is a set of integers.) We show next that $d_{j,1}^{(q)} = 0$ even for $j \in J_1$. We carry an indirect proof and assume that $d_{\cdot 1}^{(q)} \neq 0$. We put $y = 2\pi/\mu_{j,1}$ in (9.2.34) and see that

$$H_{q,1}(t, 2\pi\mu_{j,1}^{-1}) = 2d_{j,1}^{(q)}t(1+o(1))\sin^2\frac{\mu_{j-1}\pi}{\mu_{j,1}}\exp(\mu_{j-1,1}t)$$

$$(t \to \infty).$$

This contradicts (9.2.32a) so that

(9.2.36) $d_{j,1}^{(q)} = 0 \quad \text{for } j = 2, 3, \ldots.$

We next derive an inequality for the coefficients $c_{j,1}^{(q)}$. Let $\lambda_{m,r}$ be the energy parameters of $f(t)$. We show that for $m = q+2, q+3, \ldots$ and $j = \mu_{m-1,1}\mu_{q,1}^{-1}$ the relation

$$(9.2.37) \quad 0 \leqslant c_{j,1}^{(q)} \leqslant \lambda_{m-1,1} \quad \text{for } j = \frac{\mu_{m-1,1}}{\mu_{q,1}}$$

is valid. We give an indirect proof for (9.2.37) and assume that for some integer $m \geqslant q+2$ the inequality (9.2.37) does not hold. Let $p = \mu_{m-1,1}\mu_{q,1}^{-1}$ be the corresponding subscript. Then

$$H_{q,1}\left(t, \frac{2\pi}{\mu_{m,1}}\right) = 2c_{p,1}^{(q)}\left(\sin\frac{\mu_{m-1,1}\pi}{\mu_{m,1}}\right)^2(1+o(1))\exp(\mu_{m-1,1}t) \quad \text{as } t \to \infty.$$

It follows then from (9.2.31), (9.2.30) and (9.2.29b) that

$$0 \leqslant u(t,0) - u\left(t, \frac{2\pi}{\mu_{m,1}}\right) = 2c_{p,1}^{(q)}\left(\sin\frac{\mu_{m-1,1}\pi}{\mu_{m,1}}\right)^2(1+o(1))\exp(\mu_{m-1,1}t)$$

as $t \to +\infty$.

The last relation leads to a contradiction with (9.2.5), so that the validity of (9.2.37) is established.

The function $H_{q,2}(x, y)$ can be treated in a similar manner. One obtains an expansion corresponding to (9.2.34) with coefficients $c_{j,2}^{(q)}$ and $d_{j,2}^{(q)}$. One can again show that

$$d_{j,2}^{(q)} = 0 \quad \text{for } j = 2, 3 \dots$$

while the coefficients $c_{j,2}^{(q)}$ may be different from zero only if j belongs to the set $J_2 = \{\mu_{q+p,2}/\mu_{q,2}\}_{p=1}^{\infty}$ and where

(9.2.37a) $0 \leqslant c_{j,2}^{(q)} \leqslant \lambda_{m-1,2} \quad \text{for } j = \dfrac{\mu_{m-1,2}}{\mu_{q,2}}$

for $m = q+2, q+3 \dots$.

We write $c_{p,r}^{(q)} = \lambda_{m,r}^{(q)} \quad \text{for } p = \mu_{m,r}/\mu_{q,r}$

and $m = q+1, q+2, \dots$ and obtain from (9.2.26) and (9.2.27) the representation

(9.2.38) $$g(z) = \sum_{r=1}^{2} \sum_{m=q+1}^{\infty} \lambda_{m,r}^{(q)} \exp(\mu_{m,r} z) + L_q(z)$$

where

(9.2.38a) $0 \leqslant \lambda_{m,r}^{(q)} \leqslant \lambda_{m,r} \quad (m = q+1, q+2, \dots).$

The representation is valid for each $q = 0, \pm 1, \pm 2, \dots$. We select two arbitrary integers q_1 and q_2, $q_1 < q_2$ and write (9.2.38) for $q = q_1$ and $q = q_2$ and subtracting the two equations we obtain

(9.2.39)

$$\sum_{m=q_2+1}^{\infty} [\lambda_{m,1}^{(q_1)} - \lambda_{m,1}^{(q_2)}] \exp(\mu_{m,1} z) = - \sum_{m=q_2+1}^{\infty} [\lambda_{m,2}^{(q_1)} - \lambda_{m,2}^{(q_2)}] \exp(\mu_{m,2} z)$$

$$- \sum_{r=1}^{2} \sum_{m=q_1+1}^{q_2} \lambda_{m,r}^{(q_1)} \exp(\mu_{m,r} z) - L_{q_1}(z) + L_{q_2}(z).$$

We write $A(z)$ for the sum on the left of (9.2.39) and see from (9.2.38a) and from condition (9.2.1) of theorem 9.2.1 that

$$A(z) = O(1) \quad \text{for } \mathrm{Re}\,(z) \leqslant 0.$$

To estimate $A(z)$ for $\mathrm{Re}\,(z) \geqslant 0$ we use again (9.2.38a), (9.2.1), (9.2.24b) and the fact that $\mu_{m,2} < 0$ and obtain for the four terms on the right of (9.2.39) the estimates

$$O(1), \quad O\{\exp[\mu_{q_2,1}\,\mathrm{Re}\,(z)]\}, \quad O\{|z|^7 \exp[\mu_{q_1,1}\,\mathrm{Re}\,(z)]\}$$

and $O\{|z|^7 \exp[\mu_{q_2,1}\,\mathrm{Re}\,(z)]\}$ respectively. Therefore

$$A(z) = O\{|z|^7 \exp[\mu_{q_2,1}\,\mathrm{Re}\,(z)]\} \quad \text{for } \mathrm{Re}\,(z) \geqslant 0.$$

We see that the function $A(z)$ satisfies the conditions of lemma 9.2.4 with $k = \mu_{q_2,1}$, $a_j = 0$ if j is not one of the integers $\{\mu_{m,1}/\mu_{q_2,1}\}_{m=q_2+1}^{\infty}$, $b_j = 0$ for $j = 0, \pm 1, \pm 2 \dots$; $T = 2\pi/\mu_{q_2,1}$. Then $\omega = 1$ and we see that

$$\lambda_{m,1}^{(q_1)} - \lambda_{m,1}^{(q_2)} = 0 \quad \text{for } m = q_2+1, q_2+2, \dots.$$

Similarly one can prove that

$$\lambda_{m,2}^{(q_1)} - \lambda_{m,2}^{(q_2)} = 0 \quad \text{for } m = q_2+1, q_2+2, \dots.$$

Since q_1 and q_2 are arbitrary we conclude that the $\lambda_{m,r}^{(q)}$ do not depend on q; we therefore write $\tilde{\lambda}_{m,r}$ instead of $\lambda_{m,r}^{(q)}$ and obtain the following representation for $g(z)$:

$$(9.2.40) \qquad g(z) = \sum_{r=1}^{\infty} \sum_{m=q+1}^{\infty} \tilde{\lambda}_{m,r} \exp(\mu_{m,r} z) + L_q(z)$$

where

$$(9.2.40a) \qquad 0 \leqslant \tilde{\lambda}_{m,r} \leqslant \lambda_{m,r} \quad (m = 0, \pm 1, \pm 2, \ldots)$$

and where this representation holds for all integers q.

We introduce the function

$$(9.2.41) \qquad \tilde{\phi}(z) = \sum_{r=1}^{2} \sum_{m=-\infty}^{\infty} \tilde{\lambda}_{m,r} \left(e^{z\mu_{m,r}} - 1 - \frac{z\mu_{m,r}}{1+\mu_{m,r}^2} \right).$$

We repeat the reasoning used in the proof of theorem 9.1.1 and see that $\tilde{\phi}(z)$ is an entire function and that

$$(9.2.42) \qquad \tilde{\phi}(z) = O\{|z|^2 \exp[N(\text{Re}(z))^2]\}$$

where $N > 0$ is a constant.

We introduce the function

$$L(z) = g(z) - \tilde{\phi}(z).$$

To prove theorem 9.2.1 we must show that

$$L(z) = \tilde{\gamma}z^2 + \tilde{\beta}z$$

where $\tilde{\beta}$ is real while $\tilde{\gamma} \geqslant 0$.

The first step in the proof is the demonstration that $L(z)$ is a polynomial of degree not exceeding 3.

We see from (9.2.42) and lemma 9.2.1 that there exists a positive constant A such that

$$|L(z)| \leqslant A|z|^3 \quad \text{for Re}(z) = 0.$$

According to formulae (9.2.40) and (9.2.40a) we can represent $L(z)$, for each $q = 0, \pm 1, \pm 2, \ldots$, as

$$L(z) = \sum_{r=1}^{2} \sum_{m=q+1}^{\infty} \tilde{\lambda}_{m,r} \left(1 + \frac{\mu_{m,r} z}{1+\mu_{m,r}^2} \right)$$
$$- \sum_{r=1}^{2} \sum_{m=-\infty}^{q} \tilde{\lambda}_{m,r} \left(e^{\mu_{m,r} z} - 1 - \frac{\mu_{m,r} z}{1+\mu_{m,r}^2} \right) + L_q(z)$$
$$= \Sigma_1 + \Sigma_2 + L_q \quad \text{(say)}.$$

The sum Σ_1 is a linear function of z and we have

$$\Sigma_1 = O(|z|) \quad \text{as } |z| \to \infty.$$

We next use lemma 9.1.1 and estimate Σ_2 in the same way in which we estimated S_1 in the proof of theorem 9.1.2, and obtain

$$\Sigma_2 = O\{|z|^2 \exp[\mu_{q,1} \text{Re}(z)]\} + O\{|z|^2 \exp[\mu_{q,2} \text{Re}(z)]\} \quad (|z| \to \infty).$$

Using these estimates for Σ_1 and Σ_2 and the estimate (9.2.24b) for $L_q(z)$, we conclude that

$$(9.2.43) \qquad L(z) = \begin{cases} O\{|z|^7 \exp[\mu_{q,1}\operatorname{Re}(z)]\} & \text{if } \operatorname{Re}(z) \geqslant 0 \\ O\{|z|^7 \exp[\mu_{q,2}\operatorname{Re}(z)]\} & \text{if } \operatorname{Re}(z) \leqslant 0, \end{cases}$$

as $|z| \to \infty$.

We apply lemma 9.2.3 to the function $L(z)$ (with $M_1 = A$, $a = 3$, $b = d = \mu_{q,1}$, $c = 7$) and see that

$$|L(z)| \leqslant A|z|^3 \exp[\mu_{q,1}\operatorname{Re}(z)] \quad \text{if } \operatorname{Re}(z) \geqslant 0.$$

If one applies lemma 9.2.3 to the function $L(-z)$ (with $M_1 = A$, $a = 3$, $b = d = -\mu_{q,2}$, $c = 7$) one sees that

$$|L(z)| \leqslant A|z|^3 \exp[\mu_{q,2}\operatorname{Re}(z)] \quad \text{if } \operatorname{Re}(z) \leqslant 0.$$

We note that the constant A in these estimates is independent of q and that q can be chosen arbitrarily from the positive or negative integers. We therefore let q tend to $-\infty$, and since $\lim\limits_{q\to-\infty} \mu_{q,r} = 0$ $(r = 1, 2)$ we finally obtain the estimate

$$|L(z)| \leqslant A|z|^3$$

which is valid for all z, so that the entire function $L(z)$ is necessarily a polynomial of degree not exceeding 3. We note that $L(z)$ is real for real z and that $L(0) = 0$; therefore

$$L(z) = \tilde{\delta}z^3 + \tilde{\gamma}z^2 + \tilde{\beta}z,$$

where $\tilde{\beta}$, $\tilde{\gamma}$ and $\tilde{\delta}$ are real constants. We had

$$u(t, y) = \operatorname{Re}[g(t+iy)],$$

so that

$$u(t, 0) - u(t, y) = g(t) - \operatorname{Re}[g(t+iy)]$$

or since $g(z) = \tilde{\phi}(z) + L(z)$

$$u(t, 0) - u(t, y) = \tilde{\phi}(t) - \operatorname{Re}[\tilde{\phi}(t+iy)] + L(t) - \operatorname{Re}[L(t+iy)].$$

It is easily seen that

$$L(t) - \operatorname{Re}[L(t+iy)] = (3\tilde{\delta}t + \tilde{\gamma})y^2.$$

If one of the relations $\tilde{\delta} = 0$, $\tilde{\gamma} \geqslant 0$ were not satisfied then we could find a t such that $3\tilde{\delta}t + \tilde{\gamma} < 0$. We fix such a value of t and see from (9.2.41) that

$$\tilde{\phi}(t) - \operatorname{Re}[\tilde{\phi}(t+iy)] = o(y^2) \quad \text{as } y \to \infty.$$

Hence, for such a fixed t and $y \to \infty$, we would get

$$u(t, 0) - u(t, y) = o(y^2) + (3\tilde{\delta}t + \tilde{\gamma})y^2 \to -\infty.$$

This contradicts (9.2.2) and we see that necessarily $\tilde{\delta} = 0$, $\tilde{\gamma} \geqslant 0$. Therefore

$$g(z) = \sum_{r=1}^{2} \sum_{m=-\infty}^{\infty} \tilde{\lambda}_{m,r}\left(e^{i\mu_{m,r}z} - 1 - \frac{\mu_{m,r}z}{1+\mu^2_{m,r}}\right) + \tilde{\beta}z + \tilde{\gamma}z^2,$$

K

so that the characteristic function $f_1(t)$ belongs to the class $\mathscr{L}$; this means that every factor of $f(t)$ is infinitely divisible, i.e. $f(t) \in I_0$ and theorem 9.2.1 is proved.

Theorem 9.2.1 gives a sufficient condition which assures that a characteristic function $f(t)$ of the class $\mathscr{L}$ belongs to I_0. This condition can be weakened if $f(t)$ belongs to a lattice distribution. I. V. Ostrovskii (1964) obtained the following result:

Theorem 9.2.2. Let $f(t)$ be the characteristic function of a lattice distribution with span ξ and suppose that

   (i) $f(t) \in \mathscr{L}$
   (ii) $\lambda_{m,r} = o(\exp\left[-2\xi^{-1}|\mu_{m,r}|\log(\xi^{-1}|\mu_{m,r}|)\right])$ *as $m \to +\infty$;*
$$r = 1, 2.$$

Then $f(t)$ belongs to I_0.

For the proof we refer to Ostrovskii's paper.

Remark. A. A. Goldberg–I. V. Ostrovskii (1967) constructed an example which shows that there exist characteristic functions which belong to the class $\mathscr{L}$ but not to I_0. This example also indicates that for characteristic functions of lattice distributions of span $\xi = 1$ the condition (ii) of theorem 9.2.2 cannot be replaced by $\lambda_{m,r} = O[\exp(-|\mu_{m,r}|)]$ as $m \to +\infty$, $r = 1, 2$.

9.3 A necessary condition for membership of I_0

We now present a necessary condition which an infinitely divisible characteristic function with Gaussian component[*] must satisfy in order to belong to I_0.

Theorem 9.3.1. If an infinitely divisible characteristic function with Gaussian component belongs to I_0 then it necessarily belongs to the class $\mathscr{L}$.

To prove the theorem we assume that the characteristic function $f(t) \in I_0$ and has a Gaussian component. We show first that $f(t)$ has a finite or denumerable Poisson spectrum. We give an indirect proof and assume therefore that the positive Poisson spectrum has a (non-constant) continuous component,[†] so that

$$f(t) = f_1(t) f_2(t),$$

where

$$f_1(t) = \exp\left\{-\gamma t^2 + \int_{b_1}^{b_2} (e^{itu} - 1)\, dN(u)\right\},$$

---

[*] We say that an infinitely divisible characteristic function has a Gaussian component if $\gamma > 0$.

[†] This means that in the decomposition

$$N(u) = a_1 N_d(u) + a_2 N_c(u) \quad (a_1 \geqslant 0,\ a_2 \geqslant 0,\ a_1 + a_2 = 1)$$

of $N(u)$ into a discrete and a continuous component, $a_2 \neq 0$ and $N_c(u)$ is not constant.

with a continuous spectral function $N(u)$ for which $N(b_2) > N(b_1)$. According to theorem 8.2.9 it is possible to determine positive numbers v and η so small that

$$f_3(t) = \exp\left\{-\gamma t^2 + \int_{b_1}^{b_2} (e^{itu} - 1)\, dN(u) - v(e^{it\eta} - 1)\right\}$$

is a characteristic function. Since $f_3(t)$ is not infinitely divisible it necessarily has an indecomposable factor. Writing

$$f(t) = f_2(t)\, f_3(t) \exp\{v(e^{it\eta} - 1)\},$$

we see that $f(t)$ has an indecomposable factor. This contradicts the assumption $f(t) \in I_0$, so that $N(u)$ cannot have a continuous component. The same argument is used if the negative Poisson spectrum has a non-constant continuous component. We see therefore that $f(t) \in I_0$ implies that the spectrum of $f(t)$ is either denumerable or finite. We can therefore write $\log f(t)$ in the form

$$(9.3.1) \qquad \log f(t) = ait - \gamma t^2 + \sum_{j=1}^{\infty} \lambda_j \left(e^{it\mu_j} - 1 - \frac{it\mu_j}{1 + \mu_j^2}\right)$$
$$+ \sum_{j=1}^{\infty} \lambda_{-j} \left(e^{itv_j} - 1 - \frac{itv_j}{1 + v_j^2}\right),$$

where[*] $\lambda_j \geq 0, \lambda_{-j} \geq 0, \gamma > 0$. If the spectrum is denumerable we assume that the conditions (9.1.3a) and (9.1.3b) are satisfied. Suppose that the positive Poisson spectrum contains at least two points, let μ and $\mu' > \mu$ be two frequencies of the positive spectrum and let λ and λ' be the corresponding energy parameters. We show next that the quotient $\alpha = \mu/\mu'$ is a rational number. The characteristic function $f(t)$ then has a factor

$$f_1(t) = \exp\{-\gamma t^2 + \lambda(e^{it\mu} - 1) + \lambda'(e^{it\mu/\alpha} - 1)\}.$$

If α is irrational then it follows from theorem 8.2.8 that $f_1(t)$, and therefore also $f(t)$, has an indecomposable factor. This contradiction shows that α is necessarily rational, say $\alpha = p/q$, where p and q are integers and can be assumed to be relatively prime, $p < q$. We apply the reasoning used before and use theorem 8.2.7 to conclude that $f_1(t)$, and therefore also $f(t)$, has an indecomposable factor unless $p = 1$. The negative Poisson spectrum is treated in a similar way, so that $f(t)$ belongs to the class $\mathscr{L}$.

Remark. The presence of a Gaussian component is essential since $\gamma > 0$ is necessary for the validity of theorems 8.2.7, 8.2.8 and 8.2.9.

9.4 Infinitely divisible characteristic functions with bounded Poisson spectrum

In this section we study the factorization of infinitely divisible characteristic functions with bounded Poisson spectrum. We also derive sufficient

(*) In order to use (9.3.1) in case of a denumerable as well as a finite spectrum we admit the possibility that only a finite number of energy parameters is positive.

conditions which assure that a characteristic function with bounded spectrum belongs to I_0.

We use for the spectra the notations of Section 3.7 and have to supplement these by introducing a convenient notation for the vectorial sum of identical summands. We define the symbol $(n)A$ recurrently by writing $(1)A = A$ and $(n)A = (n-1)A(+)A$ for $n = 2, 3, \ldots$. We also write

$$(\infty)A = \overset{\infty}{\underset{n=1}{\cup}} (n)A.$$

We need the following lemma:

Lemma 9.4.1.   Let A be a closed set on the real line which is contained in the finite interval $[a, b]$, where $0 < a < b < \infty$. Then $(\infty)A$ is a closed set.

We note that $(n)A \subset [na, nb]$, and since $a > 0$ any finite interval can intersect at most a finite number of the sets $(n)A$. Let $x \in \overline{(\infty)A}$; then there exists a sequence of points $\{x_k\}$ in $(\infty)A$ which converges to x. The interval $(x-1, x+1)$ contains therefore almost all elements of this sequence $\{x_k\}$. However, the interval $(x-1, x+1)$ intersects only a finite number of the sets $(n)A$. Therefore there exists at least one set $(n)A$ which contains an infinite subsequence of the $\{x_k\}$. The set $(n)A$ is closed(†) so that $x \in (n)A$ and therefore also $x \in (\infty)A$; hence $(\infty)A$ is closed.

Theorem 9.4.1.   Let $f(t)$ be an infinitely divisible characteristic function without normal component and which has a Poisson spectrum A such that $0 < a = \underset{t \in A}{\inf} x < b = \underset{x \in A}{\sup} x < \infty$. Then any factor $f_1(t)$ of $f(t)$ has the form

$$f_1(t) = \exp\left[i\gamma t + \int_0^\infty (e^{itu} - 1)\, dN(u)\right],$$

where $N(u)$ is a function of bounded variation which is non-decreasing in the half open interval $[a, 2a)$ and which has a spectrum $S_N \subset [(\infty)A] \cap [a, b]$. The constant γ is real.

Without loss of generality we can assume that $f(t)$ is given by

$$(9.4.1)\qquad f(t) = \exp\left[\int_0^\infty (e^{itu} - 1)\, dN_0(u)\right],$$

where $N_0(u)$ is non-decreasing and has the spectrum $S_{N_0} = A$. Then

$$f(t) = c\left\{1 + \sum_{k=1}^\infty \left[\int_0^\infty e^{itu}\, dN_0(u)\right]^k / k!\right\}$$

where $c = \exp\left[-\int_0^\infty dN_0(u)\right]$. Let $F(x)$ be the distribution function

---

(†) We have seen in Section 3.7, p. 57, that the vectorial sum of two closed and bounded sets is closed.

corresponding to $f(t)$; then

(9.4.2) $\qquad F(x) = c\left\{\varepsilon(x) + \sum_{k=1}^{\infty} N_0^{k*}(x)/k!\right\}.$

Here N_0^{k*} denotes the k-fold convolution of $N_0(x)$ with itself. We see from lemma 3.7.4 that

$$S_{N_0^{k*}} = \overline{(k)S_{N_0}} = \overline{(k)A} = (k)A.$$

It follows from (9.4.1) that

(9.4.3) $\qquad S_F = [(\infty)A] \quad \{0\}$

where $\{0\}$ is the set containing only the point 0.

We assume now that $f(t)$ admits a decomposition

$$f(t) = f_1(t) f_2(t).$$

Then

$$F(x) = F_1(x) * F_2(x),$$

where $F_1(x)$ and $F_2(x)$ are the distribution functions corresponding to $f_1(t)$ and $f_2(t)$ respectively. We see from (9.4.1) and from the assumption concerning the spectrum A of $N_0(u)$ that $\log f(t)$ is an entire function of order 1 and type not exceeding b. Therefore $f(t)$, and hence also $f_1(t)$, is an entire characteristic function without zeros. Moreover, we conclude from corollary 1 to theorem 8.1.3 that $\log f_1(t)$ is an entire function of type not exceeding b.

We see from lemma 3.7.4 that

$$S_F = \overline{S_{F_1}(+)S_{F_2}} \supset S_{F_1}(+)S_{F_2};$$

since $[0, \infty) \supset S_F$ we conclude that S_{F_1} and S_{F_2} are both bounded from the left. It is no restriction(†) to assume that the infimum of S_{F_1} is the point 0. Then $0 \in S_{F_1}$ and $0 \in S_{F_2}$, so that

(9.4.4) $\qquad S_{F_1} \cup S_{F_2} \subset S_{F_1}(+)S_{F_2} \subset S_F.$

We see from (9.4.3) that the point 0 is an isolated point of S_F. Let $a_1 < a$ and write $V = (-a_1, 0) \cup (0, a_1)$ for the union of the two open intervals $(-a_1, 0)$ and $(0, a_1)$. We see from (9.4.3) that V does not contain any points of S_F, therefore $V \subset S_F^c$. We conclude from (9.4.4) that $V \subset S_{F_1}^c$ so that the point 0 is an isolated point of S_{F_1}. This means that F_1 has a discontinuity at the origin. Let d be the saltus of F_1 at 0. Then $F_1(x) = d\varepsilon(x) + G(x)$, where $d > 0$ and where $G(x)$ is a non-decreasing function of bounded variation such that

(9.4.5) $\qquad S_G \subset (\infty)A \subset [a, \infty).$

The characteristic function $f_1(t)$ of $F_1(x)$ is therefore given by

$$f_1(t) = d + \int_a^{\infty} e^{itx} dG(x).$$

(†) This can be shown by replacing $F_1(x)$ by $F_1(x+\delta)$ and $F_2(x)$ by $F_2(x-\delta)$ where $\delta = $ lext $[F_1]$.

We select a positive real number η so large that $\int_a^\infty e^{-\eta x} dG(x) < d$ and write $G_\eta(x) = \int_a^x e^{-\eta y} dG(y)$. Let t be real; then

$$(9.4.6) \qquad \left| \int_a^\infty e^{itx} dG_\eta(x) \right| \leqslant \int_a^\infty dG_\eta(x) < d$$

and we see that $(t, \eta$ real$)$

$$\phi_1(t+i\eta) = \log f_1(t+i\eta) = \log\left\{ d + \int_a^\infty e^{itx} dG_\eta(x) \right\}$$

or

$$(9.4.7) \qquad \phi_1(t+i\eta) = \log d + \sum_{k=1}^\infty (-1)^{k-1} \left[\int_a^\infty e^{itx} dG_\eta(x) \right]^k /(kd^k).$$

Let $G_\eta^{k*}(x)$ be the k-fold convolution of the function $G_\eta(x)$. We see from (9.4.6) that the series $\sum_{k=1}^\infty (-1)^{k-1} G_\eta^{k*}(x)/(kd^k)$ converges for all x. We write $N_\eta(x) = \sum_{k=1}^\infty (-1)^{k-1} G_\eta^{k*}(x)/(kd^k)$. The function $N_\eta(x)$ is a function of bounded variation. Since $S_{G_\eta} = S_G$ we see from (9.4.5) that

$$S_{N_\eta} \subset (\infty)S_G = \bigcup_{k=1}^\infty (k)S_G \subset \bigcup_{k=1}^\infty (k)\left[\bigcup_{n=1}^\infty (n)A \right] = (\infty)A.$$

It follows from (9.4.7) and the definition of the function $N_\eta(x)$ that

$$(9.4.8) \qquad \phi_1(\tau+i\eta) = \log d + \int_0^\infty e^{i\tau x} dN_\eta(x) \quad (\tau, \eta \text{ real}).$$

We mentioned earlier that $\phi_1(z)$ is an entire function of exponential type not exceeding b. According to remark 7 following theorem 7.2.3, the spectrum S_{N_η} is contained in the finite interval $[-b, b]$. Since $\phi_1(z)$ is an entire function, relation (9.4.8) also holds for complex values of τ; we substitute $\tau = t-i\eta$ $(t, \eta$ real$)$ into (9.4.8) and write $N(x) = \int_{-b}^x e^{\eta y} dN_\eta(y)$. In this way we obtain

$$(9.4.9) \qquad \phi_1(t) = \log d + \int_0^\infty e^{itx} dN(x).$$

Here

$$S_N = S_{N_\eta} \subset [(\infty)A] \cap [-b, b] = [(\infty)A] \cap [a, b].$$

We see from (9.4.9) that

$$f_1(t) = \exp[\phi_1(t)] = d \sum_{k=0}^\infty \left[\int_0^\infty e^{itx} dN(x) \right]^k /k!.$$

The corresponding distribution function is given by

$$(9.4.10) \qquad F_1(x) = d\left\{ \varepsilon(x) + \sum_{k=1}^\infty N^{k*}(x)/k! \right\}.$$

Let $H(x) = \sum\limits_{k=2}^{\infty} N^{k*}(x)/k!$ so that

(9.4.11) $F_1(x) = d\{\varepsilon(x)+N(x)+H(x)\}$

where

$$S_H \subset \bigcup_{k=2}^{\infty} (k)S_N \subset [2a, \infty).$$

Let x_1 and x_2 be two points such that

$$a \leqslant x_1 < x_2 < 2a,$$

it follows from (9.4.11) that $0 \leqslant F_1(x_2)-F_1(x_1) = d[N(x_2)-N(x_1)]$, so that $N(x)$ is non-decreasing in the interval $[a, 2a]$. We see further from (9.4.9) that $d = \exp\left[-\int_0^{\infty} dN(x)\right]$; hence $\phi_1(t) = \int_0^{\infty}(e^{itx}-1)\,dN(x)$ so that the theorem is proved.

Theorem 9.4.1 can be used to derive interesting conditions which assure that a characteristic function belongs to the class I_0.

Theorem 9.4.2. *Let $f(t)$ be an infinitely divisible characteristic function without normal component, and suppose that its Poisson spectrum lies in the closed interval $[a, b]$ where $0 < a < b \leqslant 2a$. Then $f(t)$ belongs to I_0.*

The theorem follows from theorem 9.4.1 in the case where $b < 2a$. We must therefore only consider the case $b = 2a$. Let $f_1(t)$ be a factor of $f(t)$. We saw in proving theorem 9.4.1 that $f_1(t)$ is an entire characteristic function without zeros; in view of the statement of theorem 9.4.1 this factor has the form

$$f_1(z) = \exp\left\{i\gamma z + \int_{[a,2a)}(e^{izu}-1)\,dN(u)+\lambda(e^{2iaz}-1)\right\}.$$

Here $z = t+iy$ (t, y real) and $N(u)$ is non-decreasing in the half open interval $[a, 2a)$ over which the integral is taken. We have therefore to prove only that $\lambda \geqslant 0$. We give an indirect proof and assume tentatively that $\lambda < 0$. An elementary computation shows that

$$\left|\frac{f_1(t+iy)}{f_1(iy)}\right| = \exp\left\{\int_{[a,2a)}e^{-yu}(\cos tu-1)\,dN(u)+\lambda\,e^{-2ay}(\cos 2at-1)\right\}.$$

We put here $t = t_0 = \dfrac{\pi}{4a}$ and see that

$$\left|\frac{f_1(t_0+iy)}{f_1(iy)}\right| = \exp\left\{-e^{-2ay}\left[\lambda - \int_{[a,2a)}e^{(2a-u)y}(\cos t_0 u-1)\,dN(u)\right]\right\}.$$

We note that

$$\lim_{y\to-\infty}\int_{[a,2a)}e^{(2a-u)y}(\cos tu-1)\,dN(u) = 0,$$

therefore

$$\left| \frac{f_1(t_0+iy)}{f_1(iy)} \right| = \exp\left\{ -e^{-2ay}[\lambda - o(1)] \right\} \quad \text{as } y \to -\infty.$$

If $\lambda < 0$ this means that $\left| \dfrac{f_1(t_0+iy)}{f_1(iy)} \right| > 1$ for $y < 0$ and $|y|$ sufficiently

large. But this contradicts the ridge property, so that $\lambda \geqslant 0$. Hence the theorem also holds in the case where $b = 2a$.

Remark 1. The assumption that $0 < a$ and $b \leqslant 2a$ is essential. If $a = 0$ or $b > 2a$ then theorem 6.2.3 (respectively theorem 6.2.4) can be used to construct counter-examples.

Remark 2. An analogous result can be obtained for infinitely divisible characteristic functions without normal component with bounded negative Poisson spectrum.

Theorem 9.4.2 has an interesting consequence which illustrates the important role of the class I_0.

Theorem 9.4.3. Every infinitely divisible characteristic function can be represented as a product of at most denumerably many factors belonging to I_0.

Let $f(t)$ be an infinitely divisible characteristic function whose Lévy canonical representation (theorem 5.5.2) is determined by the constants a and σ^2 and the functions $M(u)$ and $N(u)$. We introduce, for $k = 0$, $\pm 1, \pm 2, \ldots$, the functions

$$M_k(u) = \begin{cases} 0 & \text{if } u \leqslant -2^{k+1} \\ M(u) - M(-2^{k+1}) & \text{if } -2^{k+1} \leqslant u \leqslant -2^k \\ M(-2^k) - M(-2^{k+1}) & \text{if } -2^k \leqslant u < 0 \end{cases}$$

and

$$N_k(u) = \begin{cases} 0 & \text{if } 0 < u \leqslant 2^k \\ N(u) - N(2^k) & \text{if } 2^k \leqslant u \leqslant 2^{k+1} \\ N(2^{k+1}) - N(2^k) & \text{if } 2^{k+1} \leqslant u. \end{cases}$$

We write $f_k^{(1)}(t)$ $[f_k^{(2)}(t)]$ for the infinitely divisible characteristic function without normal component whose Lévy canonical representation is determined by $M_k(u)$ $[N_k(u)]$. Then

$$f(t) = \exp\left(iat - \sigma^2 t^2/2\right) \prod_{k=-\infty}^{\infty} f_k^{(1)}(t) f_k^{(2)}(t)$$

and see from theorems 9.4.2 and 8.2.1 that all factors in this representation belong to I_0.

We introduced in Section 8.2 (p. 249) the notion of a finite set of rationally independent numbers. For the next theorem we need an extension of this concept.

A set A of points on the real line is said to be a set with (rationally) independent points if every finite subset of A is a set of rationally independent points.

Theorem 9.4.4.   Let $f(t)$ be an infinitely divisible characteristic function without normal component and suppose that its Poisson spectrum A is positive and forms a closed, bounded set with independent points. Then $f(t)$ belongs to I_0.

Let $a = \inf\limits_{x \in A} x$ and $b = \sup\limits_{x \in A} x$.

As a consequence of our assumption that A is a set with independent points we see easily that the sets $(k)A$ $(k = 1, 2, \ldots)$ are pairwise disjoint. Let n be the largest positive integer such that $na \leqslant b$; then

$$(9.4.12) \qquad [(k)A] \cap [a, b] = \emptyset \quad \text{for } k > n.$$

The characteristic function $f(t)$ satisfies the conditions of theorem 9.4.1. Any factor $f_1(t)$ of $f(t)$ therefore has the form

$$f_1(t) = \exp\left\{i\gamma t + \int_0^\infty (e^{itu} - 1)\, dN(u)\right\}$$

with

$$S_N \subset [\infty(A)] \cap [a, b],$$

In view of (9.4.12) we can write

$$(9.4.13) \qquad S_N \subset \left[\bigcup_{k=1}^n (k)A\right] \cap [a, b].$$

Let $N_m(u)$ be the restriction of $N(u)$ to the set $[(m)A] \cap [a, b]$ $(m = 1, 2, \ldots, n)$ and consider the Fourier–Stieltjes transforms of these functions of bounded variation:

$$\phi_m(t) = \int_{(m)A} e^{itu}\, dN_m(u).$$

Then

$$(9.4.14) \qquad f_1(t) = C \exp\left[i\gamma t + \sum_{m=1}^n \phi_m(t)\right].$$

We see from (9.4.14) that the function $\exp\left[\sum_{m=1}^n \phi_m(t)\right]$ is, except for a constant positive factor, a characteristic function. Therefore there exists a non-decreasing function $G(x)$ of bounded variation defined on $[a, \infty]$ such that

$$\int_a^\infty e^{itx}\, dG(x) = \exp\left[\sum_{m=1}^n \phi_m(t)\right].$$

Hence

$$\int_a^\infty e^{itx} \, dG(x) = \exp \left[\sum_{m=1}^n \int_{(m)A} e^{itu} \, dN_m(u) \right]$$

$$= \sum \frac{1}{k_1! \, k_2! \, \ldots \, k_n!} \left(\int_A e^{itu} \, dN_1(u) \right)^{k_1}$$

$$\times \left(\int_{(2)A} e^{itu} \, dN_2(u) \right)^{k_2} \ldots \left(\int_{(n)A} e^{itu} \, dN_n(u) \right)^{k_n}$$

or

(9.4.15) $$\int_a^\infty e^{itx} \, dG(x) = \sum \frac{1}{k_1! \ldots k_n!} [\phi_1(t)]^{k_1} \ldots [\phi_n(t)]^{k_n}$$

so that

$$G(x) = \sum N_1^{k_1^*} * N_2^{k_2^*} * \ldots N_n^{k_n^*} / (k_1! \, k_2! \ldots k_n!).$$

The function $\prod_{j=1}^n {}^* N_j^{k_j^*}$ has as its spectrum the set

$$(k_1)A(+)(k_2)[(2)A](+) \ldots (+)(k_n)[(n)A] = (k_1 + 2k_2 + \ldots + nk_n)A.$$

If $x \in (m)A$, then

$$k_1 + 2k_2 + \ldots + nk_n = m$$

and we conclude from (9.4.15) and the fact that the sets $(k)A$ are disjoint that

(9.4.16)

$$\int_{(m)A} e^{itx} \, dG(x) = \sum_{k_1 + 2k_2 + \ldots + nk_n = m} [\phi_1(t)]^{k_1} \ldots [\phi_n(t)]^{k_n} / (k_1! \ldots k_n!).$$

We see therefore that the expression on the right of (9.4.16) is the coefficient of y^m in the expansion of

(9.4.17) $$\exp [y\phi_1(t) + y^2 \phi_2(t) + \ldots + y^n \phi_n(t)].$$

It follows that (9.4.17) is, except for a constant positive factor, a characteristic function, provided $y > 0$. We also see from (9.4.16) that

$$\int_A e^{itx} \, dG(x) = \phi_1(t),$$

so that $\phi_1(t)/\phi_1(0)$ is a characteristic function. Since, according to our assumption, $f_1(t)$ is a factor of $f(t)$, there exists a characteristic function $f_2(t)$ such that

(9.4.18) $$f_1(t) f_2(t) = f(t)$$

and we can repeat the earlier reasoning and show that

(9.4.19) $$f_2(t) = C \exp \{i\delta t + \psi_1(t) + \psi_2(t) + \ldots + \psi_n(t)\}.$$

Here C and δ are constants while the functions $\psi_m(t)$ have the form

$$\psi_m(t) = \int_{(m)A \cap [a,b]} e^{itx} \, d\hat{N}(x) \quad (m = 1, 2, \ldots, n),$$

where $\hat{N}$ is a function of bounded variation such that

$$S_{\hat{N}} \subset [a, b] \cap \left[\bigcup_{m=1}^{n} (m)A \right].$$

We see from (9.4.18) that

$$\log f_1(t) + \log f_2(t) = \log f(t)$$

or, in view of (9.4.14) and (9.4.19),

$$[\phi_1(t) + \psi_1(t)] + [\phi_2(t) + \psi_2(t)] + \ldots + [\phi_n(t) + \psi_n(t)] = \log f(t).$$

The spectral function of $f(t)$ has the set A as its spectrum, while $\phi_m(t) + \psi_m(t)$ has $(m)A$ as its spectrum. The sets $(m)A$ are pairwise disjoint, and we conclude easily that

(9.4.20) $\psi_m(t) = -\phi_m(t)$ $(m = 2, 3, \ldots, n).$

As in the case of (9.4.17) we conclude from (9.4.20) that, except for a constant factor,

$$\exp \{y \psi_1(t) - y^2 \phi_2(t) - \ldots - y^n \phi_n(t)\}$$

is a characteristic function, provided $y > 0$. But then the functions

$$y \phi_1(iv) + y^2 \phi_2(iv) + \ldots + y^n \phi_n(iv)$$
$$y \psi_1(iv) - y^2 \phi_2(iv) - \ldots - y^n \phi_n(iv)$$

are convex functions of the real variable v if $y > 0$. This is only possible if

$$\phi_j''(iv) = 0 \quad (j = 2, \ldots, n).$$

Since the entire functions $\phi_j(t)$ are Fourier–Stieltjes transforms of functions of bounded variation we see easily that the functions $\phi_j(t)$ $(j = 2, \ldots, m)$ reduce to constants. We put

(9.4.21) $\phi_j(t) = \phi_j(0) = c_j$ $(j = 2, \ldots, m),$

and substituting (9.4.21) into (9.4.14) we see that

$$f_1(t) = C \exp [i\gamma t + \phi_1(t) + c_2 + \ldots + c_n]$$

or

$$f_1(t) = C_1 \exp [i\gamma t + \phi_1(t)].$$

Similarly we obtain from (9.4.21), (9.4.20) and (9.4.19)

$$f_2(t) = C_2 \exp [i\delta t + \psi_1(t)].$$

The statement of the theorem follows from the fact that the functions $\phi_1(t)$ and $\psi_1(t)$ are, except for a positive constant factor, characteristic functions.

Remark 1.   Theorems 8.2.6 and 8.2.5 are particular cases of theorems 9.4.2 and 9.4.4 respectively.

Remark 2.   Extensions of theorems 9.4.1, 9.4.2 and 9.4.3 can be found in Cuppens (1968) and in I. V. Ostrovskii (1966).

9.5   Theorems concerning certain factorizations

The methods used in the last three sections make it possible to derive results concerning the possible factors of certain infinitely divisible distributions.[*] We list in the following a typical result.

Theorem 9.5.1.   Let $f(t)$ be a characteristic function which admits the representation

$$\log f(t) = \sum_{r=1}^{2} \left\{ \sum_{p=n_r}^{n_r'-1} (a_{pr}+b_{pr}it) \exp{(ip\xi_r t)} + \sum_{m=1}^{\infty} \lambda_{mr} \exp{(iv_{m,r}t)} \right\} + L(it)$$

where the parameters occurring in this representation and the function $L(z)$ satisfy the following conditions:

(a) *$\xi_1 > 0$, $\xi_2 < 0$;*

(b) *n_1 and n_2 are integers such that $-\infty < n_r < \infty$ $(r = 1, 2)$ and $n_1\xi_1 > n_2\xi_2$;*

(c) *n_1' and n_2' are integers, $n_r' \geqslant n_r$ and $n_r' > 0$ $(r = 1, 2)$ [if $n_r' = n_r$ then the sum $\sum_{n_r}^{n_r'-1}$ is omitted];*

(d) *the coefficients a_{pr} and b_{pr} are real, $\lambda_{mr} \geqslant 0$, $v_{m1} > 0$, $v_{m2} < 0$ $(m = 1, 2, \ldots)$. Moreover,*

(d$_1$) *$v_{1r} = n_r'\xi_r$ $(r = 1, 2)$,*

(d$_2$) *$v_{m+1,r}/v_{mr}$ is a natural number greater than 1,*

(d$_3$) *for some $k > 0$ we have $\lambda_{mr} = O[\exp{(-kv_{mr}^2)}]$;*

(e) *$L(z)$ is an entire function which is real for real z and satisfies the estimate (as $|z| \to \infty$)*

$$L(z) = \begin{cases} O\{|z|^2 \exp{[\xi_1' \operatorname{Re}{(z)}]}\} & \text{if } \operatorname{Re}{(z)} \geqslant 0 \\ O\{|z|^2 \exp{[\xi_2' \operatorname{Re}{(z)}]}\} & \text{if } \operatorname{Re}{(z)} \leqslant 0, \end{cases}$$

where ξ_1' and ξ_2' are real numbers such that
$$\max{[n_2\xi_2, (n_1-1)\xi_1]} \leqslant \xi_1' < n_1\xi_1$$
and
$$n_2\xi_2 < \xi_2' \leqslant \min{[(n_2-1)\xi_2, n_1\xi_1]}.$$

Let $f_1(t)$ be a factor of $f(t)$. Then $f_1(t)$ has the form

$$\log f_1(t) = \sum_{r=1}^{2} \left\{ \sum_{p=n_r}^{n_r'-1} (\tilde{a}_{pr}+\tilde{b}_{pr}it) \exp{(ip\xi_r t)} + \sum_{m=1}^{\infty} \tilde{\lambda}_{mr} \exp{(iv_{mr}t)} \right\} + \tilde{L}(it),$$

where the $\tilde{a}_{pr}$ and $\tilde{b}_{pr}$ are real constants and where the coefficients $\tilde{\lambda}_{mr}$ satisfy the inequality $0 \leqslant \tilde{\lambda}_{mr} \leqslant \lambda_{mr}$. The function $\tilde{L}(z)$ is entire, real for real z, and the estimates

$$\tilde{L}(z) = \begin{cases} O\{|z|^3 \exp{[\xi_1' \operatorname{Re}{(z)}]}\} & \text{if } \operatorname{Re}{(z)} \geqslant 0 \\ O\{|z|^3 \exp{[\xi_2' \operatorname{Re}{(z)}]}\} & \text{if } \operatorname{Re}{(z)} \leqslant 0 \end{cases}$$

hold for $|z| \to \infty$.

---

[*] See Yu. V. Linnik (1964), Chapter 9, and I. V. Ostrovskii (1965).

Corollary to theorem 9.5.1.   *Suppose that the conditions of theorem* 9.5.1 *are satisfied and that*

$$L(z) = (\gamma z^2 + \beta z + \alpha) e^{\eta z}$$

with α, β, γ *and* η *real and* $\eta \neq 0$, *where*

$$\max \left[(n_1 - 1)\xi_1, n_2 \xi_2 \right] < \eta < \min \left[(n_2 - 1)\xi_2, n_1 \xi_1 \right].$$

Then the function $\tilde{L}(z)$ *which occurs in the representation of* $f_1(t)$ *is given by* $\tilde{L}(z) = \tilde{a}^{\eta z}$ *with* $\tilde{a} \geqslant 0$.

For the proof of theorem 9.5.1 and its corollary the reader is referred to the paper by I. V. Ostrovskii (1964). In this paper Ostrovskii also considers the case where the constant $\eta = 0$ or where $L(z) \equiv 0$. The same paper contains several theorems similar to theorem 9.5.1.

Theorem 9.5.1 and its corollary can be used to derive conditions which assure that the convolution of Poisson-type characteristic functions belongs to I_0.

Theorem 9.5.2.   *Let*

$$f(t) = \exp \left\{ \sum_{m=1}^{3} \lambda_m \left[\exp \left(i\mu_m t \right) - 1 \right] \right\} \quad (\lambda_m > 0, \mu_1 < \mu_2 < \mu_3)$$

be the characteristic function of the convolution of three Poisson type distributions.[*] *Suppose that one of the following four conditions is satisfied:*

   (i) $\mu_1 < 0, \mu_3 > 0, 0 < \mu_2 < \min (\mu_3, |\mu_1|)$,

   (ii) $\mu_1 < 0, \mu_3 > 0, 0 > \mu_2 > \max (-\mu_3, \mu_1)$,

   (iii) $0 < \mu_1 < \mu_2 < \min (2\mu_1, \mu_3)$,

   (iv) $0 > \mu_1 > \mu_2 > \max (2\mu_3, \mu_1)$.

Then every factor of $f(t)$ *is also a convolution of at most three Poisson-type distributions, so that* $f(t)$ *belongs to* I_0.

We indicate the proof of theorem 9.5.2 in the case when condition (i) is satisfied.

We choose $\xi_1 = \mu_3$, $\xi_2 = \mu_1$, $n_1 = 1$, $n' = 1$, $n_2 = 0$, $n'_2 = 1$ and $a_{02} = -(\lambda_1 + \lambda_2 + \lambda_3)$ and put $b_{02} = \beta$, $\lambda_{11} = \lambda_3$, $\lambda_{12} = \lambda_1$ and $\lambda_{mr} = 0$ (for $m > 1$ and $r = 1, 2$). Let further $L(z) = \lambda_2 e^{\mu_2 z}$. It is then easily seen that the conditions of theorem 9.5.1 are satisfied and that $f(t)$ is the convolution of three Poisson-type characteristic functions. The statement of theorem 9.5.2 follows almost immediately.

In his paper I. V. Ostrovskii indicates a similar result for the convolution of four Poisson-type distributions.

---

[*] It was shown in Section 8.2, p. 252, that such a convolution does not necessarily belong to I_0.

10 α-DECOMPOSITIONS

In this chapter we extend some factorization theorems for analytic characteristic functions. The results presented are, strictly speaking, of an analytical nature but are closely connected with the arithmetic of distribution functions. Most of these studies were originally motivated by other, more penetrating investigations of the theorems of Raikov and Cramér.

We say that a characteristic function $f(t)$ admits a (finite) α-decomposition if there exist characteristic functions $f_1(t), f_2(t), \ldots, f_n(t)$ and positive numbers $\alpha_1, \alpha_2, \ldots, \alpha_n$ such that the relation

$$f(t) = \prod_{j=1}^{n} [f_j(t)]^{\alpha_j}$$

holds either in an interval $|t| < \delta$ on which $f(t)$ is different from zero or on a sequence of points $\{t_k\}$ such that $\lim_{k \to \infty} t_k = 0$. The powers of the characteristic functions $f_j(t)$ are defined by $[f_j(t)]^{\alpha_j} = \exp[\alpha_j \log f_j(t)]$, where we take for $\log f_j(t)$ that branch of the logarithm for which $\log f_j(0) = 0$ and which is continuous. Denumerable α-decompositions are defined in a similar way: the finite product in the representation of the characteristic function $f(t)$ is replaced by an infinite product.

10.1 General theorems on α-decompositions of analytic characteristic functions

The first theorem of this section is related to theorem 8.1.1.

Theorem 10.1.1. *Let $f_1(t), f_2(t), \ldots, f_s(t)$ be arbitrary characteristic functions and let $\alpha_1, \alpha_2, \ldots, \alpha_s$ be positive real numbers. Suppose that $f(t)$ is an analytic characteristic function which has no zeros inside its strip of regularity and that the relation*

(10.1.1) $$\prod_{j=1}^{s} [f_j(t)]^{\alpha_j} = f(t)$$

holds in a neighbourhood of the origin. Then the functions $f_j(t)$ $(j = 1, 2, \ldots, s)$ are analytic characteristic functions and are regular at least in the strip of regularity of $f(t)$ and (10.1.1) is valid in this strip.

In the following we write, as usual, $F_j(x)$ and $F(x)$ for the distribution functions corresponding to $f_j(t)$ and $f(t)$ respectively. We show first that the theorem holds if the distribution functions $F_j(x)$ $(j = 1, 2, \ldots, s)$ and $F(x)$ are symmetric.[*]

---

[*] We will use in the following the properties of symmetric distributions, mainly theorems 3.1.2 and 3.1.3.

We note that it is no restriction to assume that

(10.1.2) $\alpha_j \geqslant 1 \quad (j = 1, 2, \ldots, s).$

This can always be achieved by raising both sides of (10.1.1) to an integer power.

We first prove[(*)] that the second moments of the distribution functions $F_j(x)$ $(j = 1, 2, \ldots, s)$ exist. The characteristic functions $f_j(t)$ are real and

$$f_j(t) = \int_{-\infty}^{\infty} \cos tx \, dF_j(x) = 1 - 2 \int_{-\infty}^{\infty} \sin^2 \frac{tx}{2} \, dF_j(x)$$

so that

$$f_j(t) \leqslant \exp\left\{ -2 \int_{-\infty}^{\infty} \sin^2 \frac{tx}{2} \, dF_j(x) \right\}.$$

Let $\phi(t) = \log f(t)$ be the second characteristic of $F(x)$; we see then from (10.1.1) that

$$\sum_{j=1}^{s} \alpha_j \int_{-\infty}^{\infty} \sin^2 \frac{tx}{2} \, dF_j(x) \leqslant -\tfrac{1}{2}\phi(t)$$

hence

$$\int_{-\infty}^{\infty} \sin^2 \frac{tx}{2} \, dF_j(x) \leqslant -\frac{1}{2\alpha_j} \phi(t) \quad (j = 1, 2, \ldots, s).$$

We write κ_j for the jth cumulant of $f(t)$ and note that $\kappa_{2j-1} = 0$ $(j = 1, 2, \ldots$ ad inf.). It follows from the preceding inequality that

$$\int_{-\infty}^{\infty} \frac{\sin^2 \frac{1}{2}(tx)}{\frac{1}{4}t^2} \, dF_j(x) \leqslant -\frac{2\phi(t)}{t^2 \alpha_j} = \frac{\kappa_2}{\alpha_j} + o(1) \quad \text{as } t \to 0.$$

It follows from Fatou's lemma [see Titchmarsh (1939), section 10.8.1] that the second moments of the distributions $F_j(x)$ $(j = 1, 2, \ldots, s)$ exist.

We show next by induction that the distributions $F_j(x)$ have finite moments of all orders. We assume therefore that the distributions $F_j(x)$ $(j = 1, 2, \ldots, s)$ have moments of order $2k$ and show that this implies the existence of the moments of order $2k+2$. We differentiate equation (10.1.1) $2k$ times and obtain on the left side a sum where each term contains derivatives of the $f_j(t)$. We arrange the terms on the left side into three groups and write

(10.1.3) $S_1(t) + S_2(t) + S_3(t) = f^{(2k)}(t).$

Here

(10.1.4) $S_1(t) = f(t) \sum_{j=1}^{s} \alpha_j \frac{f_j^{(2k)}(t)}{f_j(t)}$

contains all the derivatives of order $2k$ while $S_3(t)$ contains only derivatives of even order not exceeding $2k-2$; the summand $S_2(t)$ consists of all

---

[(*)] The proof was suggested by R. G. Laha.

terms which contain a derivative of odd order. We note that each term of $S_2(t)$ necessarily contains two derivatives of odd order, so that [see statement (i) of the corollary to theorem 3.1.3] $S_2(0) = 0$. We remark further that each term on the left side of (10.1.3) has, except for a constant coefficient, the form

$$f(t) \left[\frac{f_{a_1}^{(r_1)}(t)}{f_{a_1}(t)} \right]^{n_1} \left[\frac{f_{a_2}^{(r_2)}(t)}{f_{a_2}(t)} \right]^{n_2} \cdots \left[\frac{f_{a_m}^{(r_m)}(t)}{f_{a_m}(t)} \right]^{n_m}$$

where each a_j is one of the integers $1, 2, \ldots, s$ and where the positive integers $r_1, r_2, \ldots, r_m$ and $n_1, n_2, \ldots, n_m$ satisfy the relation

$$(10.1.5) \qquad \sum_{j=1}^{m} n_j r_j = 2k.$$

We see easily from (10.1.3) that

$$(10.1.6) \qquad \frac{S_1(t) - S_1(0)}{t^2} + \frac{S_2(t)}{t^2} + \frac{S_3(t) - S_3(0)}{t^2} = \frac{f^{(2k)}(t) - f^{(2k)}(0)}{t^2}.$$

It follows from the corollary to theorem 3.1.3 and from the definition of the functions $S_2(t)$ and $S_3(t)$ that

$$\frac{S_2(t)}{t^2} \quad \text{and} \quad \frac{S_3(t) - S_3(0)}{t^2}$$

tend to finite limits as t goes to zero. Moreover, we conclude from the fact that $f(t)$ is an analytic characteristic function that

$$\lim_{t \to 0} \frac{f^{(2k)}(t) - f^{(2k)}(0)}{t^2}$$

exists and is finite. Hence this is also true for

$$\lim_{t \to 0} \frac{S_1(t) - S_1(0)}{t^2}.$$

We see from (10.1.4) that

$$\frac{S_1(t) - S_1(0)}{t^2} = \sum_{j=1}^{s} \alpha_j \frac{f_j^{(2k)}(t) - f_j^{(2k)}(0)}{t^2} - \sum_{j=1}^{s} \alpha_j f_j^{(2k)}(t) \frac{f_j(t) - f(t)}{t^2 f_j(t)}.$$

It is easy to see that the second sum on the right of this equation tends to a finite limit as t goes to zero; therefore

$$\sum_{j=1}^{s} \alpha_j \frac{f_j^{(2k)}(t) - f_j^{(2k)}(0)}{t^2} = (-1)^{k-1} 2 \sum_{j=1}^{s} \alpha_j \int_{-\infty}^{\infty} x^{2k} \frac{\sin^2 \frac{1}{2} tx}{t^2} dF_j(x)$$

also has a finite limit as t approaches zero. Then this is also true for each summand on the right of this equation and we use again Fatou's lemma to conclude that the moment of order $2k+2$ exists for the distribution function $F_j(x)$ $(j = 1, 2, \ldots, s)$. This completes the induction.

We prove next that the functions $f_j(t)$ are analytic characteristic functions. We raise equation (10.1.1) to the power $2k$ and differentiate it $2k$ times. We write $g(t) = [f(t)]^{2k}$ and obtain

(10.1.7) $\qquad S_1^*(t) + S_2^*(t) + S_3^*(t) = g^{(2k)}(t).$

Here $S_1^*(t)$, $S_2^*(t)$ and $S_3^*(t)$ contain the same kind of terms which we had in $S_1(t)$, $S_2(t)$ and $S_3(t)$ respectively; expressions (10.1.7) and (10.1.3) differ only in the numerical values of the coefficients. This difference is due to the fact that we raised (10.1.1) to the power $2k$. We have then

$$S_1^*(t) = f(t) \sum_{j=1}^{s} 2k\alpha_j \frac{f_j^{(2k)}(t)}{f_j(t)}.$$

Let $G(x)$ be the distribution function which belongs to $g(t)$ and denote the algebraic moments of order r of $G(x)$, $F_1(x)$, ..., $F_s(x)$ by $\alpha_r^{(0)}$, $\alpha_r^{(1)}$ ..., $\alpha_r^{(s)}$, respectively, and put $t = 0$ in equation (10.1.7). Since $S_2^*(0) = 0$ we obtain

(10.1.8) $\qquad S_1^*(0) + S_3^*(0) = (-1)^k \alpha_{2k}^{(0)}$

where

(10.1.9) $\qquad S_1^*(0) = (-1)^k \sum_{j=1}^{s} 2k\alpha_j \alpha_{2k}^{(j)}.$

We conclude from the fact that we raised (10.1.1) to the power $2k$ that

$$S_3^*(0) = (-1)^k C$$

where C is a positive constant. It follows then from (10.1.8) and (10.1.9) that

$$(-1)^k [S_1^*(0) + S_3^*(0)] = \sum_{j=1}^{s} 2k\alpha_j \alpha_{2k}^{(j)} + C = \alpha_{2k}^{(0)}$$

so that

(10.1.10) $\qquad \alpha_{2k}^{(j)} < \alpha_{2k}^{(0)} \quad (j = 1, 2, \ldots, s;\ k = 1, 2, \ldots).$

The number $\alpha_{2k}^{(0)}$ is the $(2k)$th moment of the distribution function belonging to $[f(t)]^{2k}$, that is, of a distribution function which depends on k. It is therefore not possible to conclude from (10.1.10) and the fact that $f(t)$ is an analytic characteristic function that the power-series expansion of $f_j(z)$ converges, at least in the circle of convergence of $f(z)$. Our next aim is to show that the $f_j(z)$ are analytic characteristic functions.

Let R be the radius of convergence of $f(z)$; according to Cauchy's integral formula we have

$$\alpha_{2k}^{(0)} = \frac{d^{2k}}{dt^{2k}} [f(t)]^{2k} \bigg|_{t=0} = \frac{(2k)!}{2\pi i} \int_C \frac{[f(z)]^{2k}}{z^{2k+1}} dz$$

where C is the circle $|z| = R/2$. Let $M_0 = \sup_C |f(z)|$, then

$$\alpha_{2k}^{(0)} \leqslant (2k)!\, M_1^{2k},$$

where $M_1 = 2M_0/R$, and we see from (10.1.10) that

$$\alpha_{2k}^{(j)} < (2k)! \, M_1^{2k} \quad (j = 1, 2, \ldots, s).$$

It follows then that $f_j(z) = f_j(t+iy)$ is an analytic characteristic function which is regular at least in the strip $|\operatorname{Im}(z)| < M_1^{-1}$. One also sees easily that the $f_j(z)$ have no zeros in this strip and that the relation (10.1.1) holds in $|\operatorname{Im}(z)| < M_1^{-1}$.

We introduce the functions

$$g_j(z) = f_j(-iz) = \int_{-\infty}^{\infty} e^{zx} \, dF_j(x) \quad (j = 1, 2, \ldots, s)$$

$$g(z) = f(-iz) = \int_{-\infty}^{\infty} e^{zx} \, dF(x)$$

where $z = t+iy$ (t, y real). The integrals representing the functions $g_j(z)$ converge at least in the circle $|z| < M_1^{-1}$ and the relation

(10.1.1a) $$\prod_{j=1}^{s} [g_j(z)]^{\alpha_j} = g(z)$$

holds in this circle; the function $g(z)$ is regular in the circle $|z| < R$.

In order to prove that the analytic characteristic functions $f_j(z)$ are regular, at least in the strip of regularity of $f(z)$, we must show that the radius of convergence of the series expansion of $f_j(z)$ around the origin is at least equal to R. We carry the proof indirectly and assume that at least one of the series has a radius of convergence inferior to R. It is no restriction to assume that $f_1(z)$ has the smallest radius of convergence $r_1 < R$. Clearly r_1 is also the radius of convergence of $g_1(z)$. We note that the functions $g_j(z)$ have non-negative coefficients and conclude from Prings-heim's theorem[*] that the point $z = r_1$ is a singular point of $g_1(z)$. Let $\Delta < r_1/2$ be a small positive number and put $r_\Delta = r_1 - \Delta$. We see from (10.1.1a) that the relation

(10.1.1b) $$\prod_{j=1}^{s} [g_j(r_\Delta + w)]^{\alpha_j} = g(r_\Delta + w)$$

is valid for sufficiently small $|w|$. The expansion of $g_j(r_\Delta + w)$ according to powers of w has non-negative coefficients and the coefficient of w^n is

$$\frac{1}{n!} \frac{d^n}{dw^n} g_j(r_\Delta + w) \Big|_{w=0}.$$

In order to obtain an estimate for this coefficient we raise (10.1.1b) to the power n, differentiate n times, and put $w = 0$. We can again assume that $\alpha_j > 1$ and therefore obtain a sum of positive terms and conclude that

(10.1.11) $$g(r_\Delta) \sum_{j=1}^{s} \frac{n\alpha_j}{g_j(r_\Delta)} \frac{d^n}{dw^n} g_j(r_\Delta + w) \Big|_{w=0} \leqslant \frac{d^n}{dw^n} [g(r_\Delta + w)]^n \Big|_{w=0}.$$

---

[*] See Titchmarsh (1939), p. 214, or Hille (1962), **1**, p. 133, or Markushevich (1965), **1**, p. 389.

The function $g(r_\Delta + w)$ is regular for $|w| < R - r_1$. We put $\delta = (R - r_1)/2$ and apply Cauchy's integral to estimate the expression on the right of (10.1.11). We see that

$$(10.1.12) \qquad \frac{d^n}{dw^n} [g(r_\Delta + w)]^n \bigg|_{w=0} = \frac{n!}{2\pi i} \int_{|w|=\delta} \frac{[g(r_\Delta + w)]^n}{w^{n+1}} \, dw.$$

Let

$$\rho(r_\Delta) = \sup_{|w|=\delta} |g(r_\Delta + w)|,$$

since $(R + r_1)/2 > r_\Delta + \delta$ we see that

$$\rho(r_\Delta) < C(r_1)$$

where

$$C(r_1) = \sup_{|z|=(R+r_1)/2} |g(z)|$$

is a positive function of r_1 but does not depend on Δ.

It follows then from (10.1.12) that

$$\frac{d^n}{dw^n} [g(r_\Delta + w)]^n \bigg|_{w=0} \leqslant n! \frac{[C(r_1)]^n}{\delta^n} = n! [C_1(r_1)]^n$$

where $C_1(r_1)$ is a function of r_1 and is independent of Δ. The terms on the left of (10.1.11) are all positive, so that

$$\frac{d^n}{dw^n} [g_j(r_\Delta + w)]^n \bigg|_{w=0} \leqslant n! \frac{g_j(r_\Delta)}{g(r_\Delta)} [C_1(r_1)]^n.$$

The radius of convergence of the expansion of $g_j(r_\Delta + w)$ according to powers of w is therefore not less than $[C_1(r_1)]^{-1}$ for any $\Delta \in (0, r_1/2)$. But the function g_1 has a singularity at the point $z = r_1$, so that the radius of convergence of $g_1(r_\Delta + w)$ cannot exceed Δ. Select Δ so small that $\Delta < [C_1(r_1)]^{-1}$. The assumption that $r_1 < R$ then leads to a contradiction. The radius of convergence of $f_j(z)$ around the origin is therefore at least equal to R, so that the characteristic functions $f_j(z)$ are regular, at least in the strip of regularity of $f(z)$. We have therefore established theorem 10.1.1 in the case where the distributions $F(x), F_1(x), \ldots, F_s(x)$ are symmetric, and must now consider the general case.

For this discussion we need the following lemma which is of independent interest.

Lemma 10.1.1. *Let $g(z)$ be an analytic characteristic function which has the strip of regularity $-\alpha < \mathrm{Im}\,(z) < \beta$ and choose a real η such that $-\alpha < \eta < \beta$. Then*

$$h(z) = \frac{g(z + i\eta)}{g(i\eta)}$$

is also an analytic characteristic function which is regular in the strip
$-\alpha - \eta < \text{Im}(z) < \beta - \eta$.

Let $G(x)$ be the distribution function of $g(t)$; the integral

$$C = \int_{-\infty}^{\infty} e^{-\eta x}\, dG(x)$$

exists and is finite and positive. We put

$$H(x) = \frac{1}{C} \int_{-\infty}^{x} e^{-\eta y}\, dG(y);$$

this is a distribution function and we see that

$$h(t) = \frac{1}{C} \int_{-\infty}^{\infty} e^{itx} e^{-\eta x}\, dG(x) = \int_{-\infty}^{\infty} e^{itx}\, dH(x)$$

is its characteristic function. Moreover, it follows from the assumption that $g(z)$ is an analytic characteristic function that $h(t)$ is also analytic and that it has the strip of regularity $-\alpha - \eta < \text{Im}(z) < \beta - \eta$.

We now proceed with the proof of theorem 10.1.1 and suppose that the conditions of the theorem are satisfied by the characteristic functions $f(t), f_1(t), \ldots, f_s(t)$. It follows from equation (10.1.1) that

$$(10.1.13) \qquad \prod_{j=1}^{s} [f_j(t) f_j(-t)]^{\alpha_j} = f(t) f(-t)$$

is also valid. The characteristic functions $[f(t) f(-t)], [f_1(t) f_1(-t)], \ldots,$ $[f_s(t) f_s(-t)]$ belong to symmetric distributions. We apply the result which we obtained for symmetric distributions and see that the characteristic function $f_j(t) f_j(-t)$ is an analytic characteristic function and is regular at least in the strip of regularity of $f(t) f(-t)$. It follows then from theorem 8.1.1 that $f_j(t)$ $(j = 1, 2, \ldots, s)$ is also regular, at least in this strip.

If $f(t)$ is an entire characteristic function then this completes the proof of the theorem, so that we need only consider the case where the strip of regularity of $f(z)$ has one or two horizontal boundary lines. We assume first that $f(z)$ is regular in the strip $-\alpha < \text{Im}(z) < \beta$ where α and β are both finite. The strip of regularity of the analytic characteristic function $f(t) f(-t)$ is then the symmetric strip $|\text{Im}(z)| < \min(\alpha, \beta)$ and it is no restriction to assume that $\alpha < \beta$.

We show this in the case where $\beta < 3\alpha$; if $\beta \geqslant 3\alpha$, the desired result can be obtained by iteration.

We take $\eta_0 = (\beta - \alpha)/2$ and see from lemma 10.1.1 that

$$f(z + i\eta_0)/f(i\eta_0)$$

is an analytic characteristic function which is regular in the strip $|\text{Im}(z)| < (\beta + \alpha)/2$. Moreover it follows from (10.1.1) that

$$\prod_{j=1}^{s} \left[\frac{f_j(t + i\eta_0)}{f_j(i\eta_0)} \right]^{\alpha_j} = \frac{f(t + i\eta_0)}{f(i\eta_0)}$$

and we can conclude that the characteristic functions

$$\frac{f_j(t+i\eta_0)}{f_j(i\eta_0)}$$

$(j = 1, 2, \ldots, s)$ are regular at least in the strip $|\operatorname{Im}(z)| < (\beta+\alpha)/2$. Therefore $f_j(z+i\eta_0)$ is also regular at least in this strip. We write $w = z+i\eta_0$ and see that the analytic characteristic functions $f_j(w)$ $(j = 1, 2, \ldots, s)$ are regular at least in the strip $-\alpha < \operatorname{Im}(w) < \beta$. Theorem 10.1.1 is therefore proved in the case where the strip of regularity of $f(z)$ has two horizontal boundary lines. We consider finally the case where $f(z)$ is regular in the half-plane $\operatorname{Im}(z) > -\alpha$. In this case we can start with the strip $(-\alpha, \alpha)$ and prove by induction that $f_j(z)$ is regular in the strip $-\alpha < \operatorname{Im}(z) < (2^n-1)\alpha$ for any n. Therefore $f_j(z)$ is regular in the half-plane $\operatorname{Im}(z) > -\alpha$ and the proof of the theorem is completed.

Theorem 10.1.1 was modified by Yu. V. Linnik [(1964) theorem 4.2.1] in the following way.

Theorem 10.1.1a. *Let* $f_1(t)$, $f_2(t)$, \ldots, $f_s(t)$ *be arbitrary characteristic functions and let* $\alpha_1, \alpha_2, \ldots, \alpha_s$ *be positive real numbers. Let* $\{t_k\}$ *be a sequence of real numbers such that* $t_k \neq 0$ *and* $\lim_{k\to\infty} t_k = 0$. *Suppose that* $f(z)$ *is an analytic characteristic function which has no zeros in its strip of regularity and that the relation* (10.1.1) *holds at the points of the sequence* $\{t_k\}$. *Then the functions* $f_j(t)$ $(j = 1, 2, \ldots, s)$ *are analytic characteristic functions and are regular, at least in the strip of regularity of* $f(t)$, *and the relation* (10.1.1) *holds in this strip.*

We mention next a theorem which shows that denumerable α-decompositions are possible.

Theorem 10.1.2. *Let* $f_j(t)$ *be a sequence of characteristic functions and let* $\{\alpha_j\}$ *be a sequence of positive numbers which are bounded away from zero (i.e. there exists an* $\alpha_0 > 0$ *such that* $\alpha_j > \alpha_0$ *for all j). Suppose that* $f(t)$ *is an analytic characteristic function which does not have any zeros in its strip of regularity and assume that the relation*

$$(10.1.14) \qquad \prod_{j=1}^{\infty} [f_j(t)]^{\alpha_j} = f(t)$$

holds in a real neighbourhood of the origin. Then the functions $f_j(t)$ *are analytic characteristic functions and are regular, at least in the strip of regularity of* $f(z)$, *and the relation* (10.1.14) *is valid in this strip.*

This theorem also has a modification which corresponds to theorem 10.1.1a.

Theorem 10.1.2a. *Let* $\{f_j(t)\}$ *be a sequence of characteristic functions and let* $\{\alpha_j\}$ *be a sequence of positive numbers which are bounded away from zero.*

Suppose that $f(t)$ is an analytic characteristic function which does not have any zeros in its strip of regularity. Let $\{t_k\}$ be a sequence of real numbers such that $t_k \neq 0$ and $\lim_{k \to \infty} t_k = 0$. Suppose that the relation (10.1.14) holds at the points t_k; then the functions $f_j(t)$ are analytic characteristic functions and are regular, at least in the strip of regularity of $f(t)$, and the relation (10.1.14) is valid in this strip.

The proofs of theorems 10.1.2 and 10.1.2a are very similar to the proof of theorem 10.1.1 and are based on the same idea. One begins by symmetrizing the characteristic functions and proves first that the second moments of the $f_j(t)$ exist and then, by induction, the existence of all moments of the $f_j(t)$. This is done by dividing the $(2k)$th derivative of $f(t)$ into three sums, exactly as in the proof of theorem 10.1.1. The proof of the analyticity is also based on the idea used in the earlier proof and leads to a majoration of the moments as in (10.1.1). The reasoning is, of course, more complicated than in the case of the proof of theorem 10.1.1, since infinite series occur and require a careful consideration of technical detail to justify the necessary operations (such as the term-by-term differentiation of the infinite series). The proof that relation (10.1.14) is valid in the strip of regularity is obvious in the case of theorem 10.1.1 but calls for a more careful discussion in the case of denumerable α-decompositions. In view of the similarity of the demonstrations we omit here the proof of theorems 10.1.2 and 10.1.2a and refer instead to the book of B. Ramachandran (1967) where the proofs are presented in full detail.

The preceding theorems of this section contain the assertion that the characteristic function $f(t)$ on the right-hand side of (10.1.1) and of (10.1.14) does not vanish. It was shown by B. Ramachandran (1965) and by R. Cuppens (1963b) that this restriction is superfluous [see also B. Ramachandran (1967)].

Results which are in some respects similar to theorem 10.1.1a have been obtained by several authors. We mention here a theorem which is due to R. G. Laha (1960).

Theorem 10.1.3. *Let $\{t_k\}$ ($k = \pm 1, \pm 2, \ldots$) be a sequence of real numbers such that $t_k > 0$ while $t_{-k} = -t_k$ for any $k > 0$ and $\lim_{k \to \infty} t_k = 0$. Let $f(t)$ be a characteristic function and let $\psi(z)$ be a function of the complex variable z ($z = t + iy$; t, y real) which is regular in a circle about the origin. Suppose that $f(t_k) = \psi(t_k)$ for all k; then $f(t)$ is an analytic characteristic function and $f(z) = \psi(z)$ in the strip of regularity.*

For the proof we refer the reader to the paper quoted above. The following particular case is sometimes of interest.

Corollary to theorem 10.1.3. *Let $f(t)$ be an even characteristic function and let $\psi(z)$ be a function of the complex variable z ($z = t + iy$; t, y real) which is* *regular in a neighbourhood of the origin and which is even for real values of the argument. Suppose that $\{t_k\}$ is a sequence of real numbers such that $\lim_{k \to \infty} t_k = 0$ and that $f(t_k) = \psi(t_k)$ for all points t_k. Then $f(t)$ is an analytic characteristic function and $f(z) = \psi(z)$.*

10.2 Special results concerning α-decompositions

In Section 10.1 we assumed only that the function subjected to an α-decomposition is an analytic characteristic function. In the present section we consider other assumptions concerning this function. We first treat α-decompositions of entire characteristic functions and then study the α-decomposition of the characteristic functions of lattice distributions and of some infinitely divisible distributions.

Theorem 10.2.1.   If the function $f(t)$ of theorem 10.1.1 or of theorem 10.1.1a is an entire function of finite order ρ, then each function $f_j(t)$ is an entire characteristic function of order not exceeding ρ.

It follows immediately from theorem 10.1.1 that the $f_j(t)$ are entire functions whenever $f(t)$ is an entire characteristic function, so we have only to prove the statement concerning the order of the functions $f_j(t)$. We introduce the symmetric characteristic functions

$$g(t) = f(t) f(-t) \quad \text{and} \quad g_j(t) = f_j(t) f_j(-t)$$

and denote by $\tilde{a}_k^{(j)}$ $(j = 1, 2, \ldots, s)$ the moment of order k of the distribution corresponding to $g_j(t)$. Since $g(z), g_1(z), \ldots, g_s(z)$ are entire functions, equation (10.1.13) holds for all complex z. We can therefore put $z = iy$ (y real) in (10.1.13) and get

$$(10.2.1) \qquad \prod_{j=1}^{s} [g_j(iy)]^{\alpha_j} = g(iy).$$

We note that $g(iy)$ and $g_j(iy)$ are real and that

$$(10.2.2) \qquad g_j(iy) = \sum_{k=0}^{\infty} \frac{\tilde{a}_{2k}^{(j)}}{(2k)!} y^{2k} \geqslant 1.$$

It follows from (10.2.1) and (10.2.2) that

$$(10.2.3) \qquad [g_j(iy)]^{\alpha_j} \leqslant g(iy) \quad (j = 1, 2, \ldots, s).$$

We denote, as usual, by $M(r; g_j)$ and $M(r; g)$ the maximum modulus of the function $g_j(z)$ and $g(z)$ respectively and see from theorem 7.1.2 that

$$(10.2.4) \qquad \begin{cases} M(r; g) = g(ir) = g(-ir) \\ M(r; g_j) = g_j(ir) = g_j(-ir) \quad (j = 1, 2, \ldots, s). \end{cases}$$

It follows from (10.2.3) and (10.2.4) that

$$[M(r; g_j)]^{\alpha_j} \leqslant M(r; g).$$

But this means that the order of $g_j(z)$ cannot exceed the order ρ of $g(z)$. We see finally from theorem 8.1.2 that the order of $f_j(z)$ cannot exceed ρ.

We next consider applications of these results.

Suppose that $f(t) = \exp[i\mu t - \tfrac{1}{2}\sigma^2 t^2]$. It follows then from theorem 10.2.1 that the functions $f_j(t)$ are entire functions of order not exceeding 2. Moreover, one sees from (10.1.1) that the $f_j(t)$ are entire functions without zeros and must therefore have the form

$$f_j(t) = \exp[i\mu_j t - \tfrac{1}{2}\sigma_j^2 t^2] \quad (j = 1, 2, \ldots, s).$$

We have therefore obtained the following theorem:

Theorem 10.2.2. *Let $f_1(t)$, $f_2(t), \ldots, f_s(t)$ be arbitrary characteristic functions and let $\alpha_1, \alpha_2, \ldots, \alpha_s$ be positive real numbers. Suppose that the relation*

$$\prod_{j=1}^{s} [f_j(t)]^{\alpha_j} = \exp[i\mu t - \tfrac{1}{2}\sigma^2 t^2]$$

holds in a neighbourhood of the origin. Then the characteristic functions $f_j(t)$ $(j = 1, 2, \ldots, s)$ belong to normal distributions.

Theorem 10.2.2 is a generalization of theorem 8.2.1 (Cramér's theorem). This extension is due to A. A. Zinger and Yu. V. Linnik. D. Dugué (1957a), (1957c) gave a different proof for theorems 10.1.1 and 10.2.2; he deduced these results from properties of the products of positive powers of absolutely monotonic functions.

We prove next an α-decomposition theorem for lattice distributions. This theorem is an important tool in studying the α-decomposition of the Poisson distribution but has also some independent interest.

Theorem 10.2.3. *Let $f_1(t)$, $f_2(t), \ldots, f_s(t)$ be arbitrary characteristic functions and let $\alpha_1, \alpha_2, \ldots, \alpha_s$ be positive real numbers. Suppose that $f(t)$ is the characteristic function of a lattice distribution $F(x)$ and that the relation*

$$(10.2.5) \qquad \prod_{j=1}^{s} [f_j(t)]^{\alpha_j} = f(t)$$

holds. The characteristic function $f_j(t)$ then belongs also to a lattice distribution $F_j(x)$. Moreover, if $f(x)$ is an entire characteristic function without zeros which belongs to a lattice distribution whose lattice points are the non-negative integers, then each $F_j(x)$ is a one-sided lattice distribution whose discontinuity points are contained in a set of the form $\mu_j + \nu$ $(\nu = 0, 1, 2, \ldots$ ad inf.) where

$$\sum_{j=1}^{s} \alpha_j \mu_j = 0.$$

The first assertion of the theorem is an immediate consequence of theorem 2.1.4. If $f(t)$ is a lattice distribution then there exists a real

$t_0 \neq 0$ such that $|f(t_0)| = 1$. But then necessarily $|f_j(t_0)| = 1$ ($j = 1, 2, \ldots, s$), so that $f_j(t)$ also belongs to a lattice distribution.

To prove the second part of the statement we apply formula (7.2.3a) and see that

(10.2.6) $\qquad$ lext $[F] = -\lim_{y \to \infty} (1/y) \log f(iy) = 0$

where

(10.2.7) $\qquad -(1/y) \log f(iy) = \sum_{j=1}^{s} \alpha_j [-(1/y) \log f_s(iy)].$

The $f_j(t)$ are, according to theorem 10.2.1, entire characteristic functions and

$$\mu_j = -\lim_{y \to \infty} (1/y) \log f_j(iy)$$

is the left extremity of $F_j(x)$. We see from (10.2.6) and (10.2.7) that all μ_j are finite and that

(10.2.8) $\qquad \sum_{j=1}^{s} \alpha_j \mu_j = 0.$

Since $F(x)$ has its discontinuity points at the non-negative integers we have $f(2\pi) = 1$ and therefore also $|f_j(2\pi)| = 1$ ($j = 1, 2, \ldots, s$). It is then easy to see that the discontinuity points of $F_j(x)$ are contained in the set $\mu_j + \nu$, where ν runs through all non-negative integers.

The α-decomposition theorem for the Poisson distribution is an extension of Raikov's theorem (theorem 8.2.2).

Theorem 10.2.4. Let $f_1(t), f_2(t), \ldots, f_s(t)$ be arbitrary characteristic functions and let $\alpha_1, \alpha_2, \ldots, \alpha_s$ be positive numbers. Suppose that the relation

(10.2.9) $\qquad \prod_{j=1}^{s} [f_j(t)]^{\alpha_j} = \exp[\lambda(e^{it}-1)] \quad (\lambda \geq 0)$

holds in a neighbourhood of the origin. Then

$$f_j(t) = \exp[\lambda_j(e^{it}-1) + i\mu_j t]$$

where $\lambda_j \geq 0$ and μ_j are real numbers.

To prove theorem 10.2.4 we set $f(t) = \exp[\lambda(e^{it}-1)]$ in theorem 10.2.3 and conclude that

(10.2.10) $\qquad f_j(t) = e^{it\mu_j} \sum_{\nu=0}^{\infty} p_\nu^{(j)} e^{it\nu}$

where

$$p_\nu^{(j)} \geq 0, \sum_{\nu=0}^{\infty} p_\nu^{(j)} = 1 \quad (j = 1, 2, \ldots, s; \nu = 0, 1, 2, \ldots)$$

and

$$\sum_{j=1}^{s} \alpha_j \mu_j = 0.$$

It follows from the last equation and the assumption (10.2.9) of the theorem that

$$(10.2.11) \qquad \prod_{j=1}^{s} \left[\sum_{\nu=0}^{\infty} p_\nu^{(j)} e^{it\nu} \right]^{\alpha_j} = \exp\left[\lambda(e^{it}-1)\right]$$

holds for real t. We see from theorem 10.1.1 that the functions $f_j(t)$ are entire characteristic functions and conclude from (10.2.11) that they have no zeros. Relation (10.2.11) is therefore valid also for complex values of the variable. We put $w = e^{iz}$ (z complex) and write

$$g_j(w) = \sum_{\nu=0}^{\infty} p_\nu^{(j)} w^\nu$$

and see easily that the $g_j(w)$ are entire functions without zeros. We can then rewrite (10.2.11) in the form

$$(10.2.12) \qquad \prod_{j=1}^{s} [g_j(w)]^{\alpha_j} = \exp\left[\lambda(w-1)\right].$$

The power series for the functions $g_j(w)$ and also for the function $g(w) = \exp[\lambda(w-1)]$ have non-negative coefficients, so that

$$M(r; g_j) = g_j(r)$$

and

$$M(r; g) = g(r).$$

Since for $r > 1$ the functions $g_j(r)$ and $g(r)$ are increasing functions of r, we see that

$$g_j(r) \geqslant g_j(1) = 1$$

and conclude from (10.2.12) that

$$g_j(r) = M(r; g_j) \leqslant \exp\left[\lambda(r-1)\right]$$

for $r \geqslant 1$. The function $g_j(w)$ is therefore an entire function of order not exceeding 1. Since it has no zeros, we conclude from Hadamard's factorization theorem that it has the form

$$g_j(w) = \exp(\lambda_j w + \beta_j)$$

or, since $g_j(1) = 1$,

$$g_j(w) = \exp\left[\lambda_j(w-1)\right].$$

We see finally from (10.2.9) that

$$f_j(t) = \exp\left[\lambda_j(e^{it}-1) + i\mu_j t\right]$$

so that the theorem is proved.

Remark. The statements of theorems 10.2.2, 10.2.3 and 10.2.4 are also valid if one replaces the assumption that (10.2.4) [respectively (10.2.5) or (10.2.9)] is valid in a real interval containing the origin by the assumption that these relations are satisfied in the points of a sequence $\{t_k\}$ such that

$t_k \neq 0$, while $\lim_{k \to \infty} t_k = 0$. It is also possible to derive corresponding denumerable α-decomposition theorems.

Yu. V. Linnik (1959) obtained an α-decomposition theorem for infinitely divisible characteristic functions.

Theorem 10.2.5. *Let* $f_1(t), f_2(t), \ldots, f_s(t)$ *be arbitrary characteristic functions and let* $\alpha_1, \alpha_2, \ldots, \alpha_s$ *be positive numbers. Let* $\{t_k\}$ *be a sequence of real numbers such that* $t_k \neq 0$ *and* $\lim_{k \to \infty} t_k = 0$. *Suppose that* $f(t)$ *is a characteristic function of the class* $\mathscr{L}$ *which has a bounded Poisson spectrum and that the relation*

$$(10.2.13) \qquad \prod_{j=1}^{s} [f_j(t)]^{\alpha_j} = f(t)$$

holds at all points of the sequence $\{t_k\}$. *Then the* $f_j(t)$ *belong also to* $\mathscr{L}$ *and the relation* (10.2.13) *holds for all t. The functions* $f_j(t)$ *are infinitely divisible entire characteristic functions and their spectra are subsets of the spectrum of* $f(t)$.

For the proof we refer to Linnik (1959) or to the monograph of Linnik (1964).

We also note that the proof of theorem 9.2.1 uses only the ridge property of analytic characteristic functions. Using this fact, an α-decomposition theorem corresponding to theorem 9.2.1 can be derived.

We conclude this section by mentioning a few additional results of the type discussed in this chapter.

R. Cuppens (1963b) and B. Ramachandran (1965) have proved a denumerable α-decomposition theorem for the convolution of a binomial and a Poisson distribution with the same span. R. G. Laha and E. Lukacs (1962) considered the situation of theorem 10.1.1 but replaced the assumption that $f(t)$ is an analytic characteristic function by the premise that $f(t)$ has derivatives up to the order $2N$ and obtained a finite α-decomposition theorem. A corresponding denumerable α-decomposition theorem is due to R. Cuppens (1963a).

11 BOUNDARY CHARACTERISTIC FUNCTIONS

In Chapter 7 we introduced analytic characteristic functions and studied their properties. In the present chapter we deal with characteristic functions which are boundary values of analytic functions.

We say that a characteristic function $f(t)$ is the boundary value of an analytic function if there exists a complex-valued function $A(z)$ of the complex variable $z = t+iy$ which is regular in the rectangle

$$\{|t| < \Delta, 0 < y < b\}$$

[respectively in the rectangle $\{|t| < \Delta, -a < y < 0\}$] and has the property that $\lim_{y\to 0} A(t+iy) = f(t)$ for $|t| < \Delta$ and $y > 0$ [respectively for $|t| < \Delta$ and $y < 0$]. The class of characteristic functions just described includes the class of analytic characteristic functions but is more extensive. For the sake of brevity we will call "boundary characteristic functions" those characteristic functions which are boundary values of analytic functions without being analytic characteristic functions. If $f(t)$ is a boundary characteristic function then we can extend its definition to complex values of the variable by writing $f(z) = A(z)$.

11.1 The integral representation

In this section we derive a number of properties of boundary characteristic functions which are similar to results for analytic characteristic functions obtained in Chapter 7. We give first a necessary and sufficient condition which a distribution function must satisfy in order that its characteristic function be a boundary characteristic function.

Theorem 11.1.1. Let $F(x)$ be a distribution function and $f(t)$ be its characteristic function. The function $f(t)$ is the boundary value of an analytic function $A(z)$ ($z = t+iy$; t, y real) which is regular in the rectangle

$|t| < \Delta, 0 < y < b$ *if, and only if, the integral* $\int_{-\infty}^{\infty} e^{-yx} dF(x)$ *exists and is*

finite for $0 \leqslant y < b$ but does not exist for $y < 0$.

We first prove that the condition of the theorem is sufficient and assume therefore that

$$\int_{-\infty}^{\infty} e^{-yx} dF(x)$$

is finite for $0 \leqslant y < b$. Let

$$(11.1.1) \qquad \begin{cases} g_1(z) = \int_{-\infty}^0 e^{izx} \, dF(x) \\ g_2(z) = \int_0^\infty e^{izx} \, dF(x). \end{cases}$$

The function $g_1(z)$ is regular for $\mathrm{Im}\,(z) < b$, while $g_2(z)$ is regular for $\mathrm{Im}\,(z) > 0$. Therefore

$$A(z) = g_1(z) + g_2(z) = \int_{-\infty}^\infty e^{izx} \, dF(x)$$

is regular in the strip $0 < \mathrm{Im}\,(z) < b$; moreover,

$$\lim_{y \downarrow 0} A(t+iy) = \int_{-\infty}^\infty e^{itx} \, dF(x) = f(t).$$

To prove the necessity of the condition we assume that $f(z)$ is a boundary characteristic function. Let $g_1(z)$ and $g_2(z)$ again be given by (11.1.1), then

$$(11.1.2) \qquad f(t) = g_1(t) + g_2(t).$$

The function $f(z)$ is regular in a rectangle, say in $D_1 = \{|t| < \Delta, 0 < y < b\}$, while $g_2(z)$ is regular in the upper half-plane. Therefore $g_1(z)$ is regular in D_1; on the other hand, it follows from the definition of $g_1(z)$ that it is regular in the lower half-plane, so that $g_1(z)$ is regular in the rectangle D_2 which is symmetric to D_1 with respect to the real axis. It follows then from Schwarz's symmetry principle (see Appendix E) that $g_1(z)$ is regular in the rectangle $D = \{|t| < \delta, |y| < b\}$. We first assume that $F(0) \neq 0$ and consider the function

$$\frac{g_1(t)}{F(0)} = \frac{1}{F(0)} \int_{-\infty}^0 e^{itx} \, dF(x).$$

This is an analytic characteristic function whose strip of regularity contains the strip $|\mathrm{Im}\,(z)| < b$. Therefore

$$g_1(iy) = \int_{-\infty}^0 e^{-yx} \, dF(x)$$

exists and is finite for $|y| < b$. Since the integral $\int_0^\infty e^{-yx} \, dF(x)$ exists for $y \geqslant 0$, we see that $\int_{-\infty}^\infty e^{-yx} \, dF(x)$ exists and is finite for $0 \leqslant y < b$, so the necessity of the condition is proved if $F(0) \neq 0$. In the case where $F(0) = 0$ we note that $f(t) = g_2(t)$ and obtain the necessity of the condition.

A criterion analogous to the statement of theorem 11.1.1 holds for characteristic functions which are boundary values of functions regular in a rectangle $\{|t| < \Delta, -a < y < 0\}$ contained in the lower half-plane.

The argument used in the proof of theorem 11.1.1 indicates that a boundary characteristic function can be represented by a Fourier–Stieltjes integral in a horizontal strip. Let $0 < y < \beta$ be the strip of greatest width in which the boundary characteristic function $f(z)$ admits the representation

$$(11.1.2) \qquad f(z) = \int_{-\infty}^{\infty} e^{izx} dF(x) \quad (0 < \mathrm{Im}\,(z) < \beta).$$

The strip $0 < \mathrm{Im}\,(z) < \beta$, in which (11.1.2) is valid, is called the strip of regularity of the boundary characteristic function $f(z)$. The validity of the representation (11.1.2) is the reason for the similarity of many properties of boundary characteristic functions and of analytic characteristic functions.

The discussion of these properties is facilitated by the following lemma:

Lemma 11.1.1. *Let $f(z)$ be a boundary characteristic function with the strip of regularity $0 < \mathrm{Im}\,(z) < \beta$ and choose a real η such that $0 < \eta < \beta$. Then*

$$(11.1.3) \qquad h(z) = \frac{f(z+i\eta)}{f(i\eta)}$$

is an analytic characteristic function which is regular in the strip $-\eta < \mathrm{Im}\,(z) < \beta-\eta$.

Lemma 11.1.1 is analogous to lemma 10.1.1 for analytic characteristic functions and is proved in the same way. The distribution function corresponding to $h(z)$ is

$$(11.1.4) \qquad H(x) = \frac{1}{C} \int_{-\infty}^{x} e^{-\eta y} dF(y),$$

where $C = f(i\eta)$ and $F(x)$ is the distribution function corresponding to $f(z)$.

Corollary 1 to theorem 11.1.1.   The strip of regularity of a boundary characteristic function $f(z)$ has one or two horizontal boundary lines. One of these is always the real axis. The purely imaginary points on the boundary are singular points of $f(z)$.

Corollary 2 to theorem 11.1.1.   Boundary characteristic functions have the ridge property; moreover the zeros and the singular points of boundary characteristic functions are located symmetrically with respect to the imaginary axis.

Corollary 3 to theorem 11.1.1.   A boundary characteristic function has no zeros on the segment of the imaginary axis located in its strip of regularity.

Corollary 4 to theorem 11.1.1.   Let $f(z)$ be a boundary characteristic function whose strip of regularity is $0 < \mathrm{Im}\,(z) = y < \beta$. Then $\log f(iy)$ is convex for $0 < y < \beta$.

Corollary 5 to theorem 11.1.1. Let $F(x)$ be a distribution function which has a boundary characteristic function with strip of regularity $0 < \text{Im}(z) < \beta$. Then

$$\beta = -\limsup_{x \to \infty} \frac{\log F(-x)}{x}.$$

Similarly, if $f(z)$ has $-\alpha < \text{Im}(z) < 0$ as its strip of regularity then

$$\alpha = -\limsup_{x \to \infty} \left\{ \frac{\log [1 - F(x)]}{x} \right\}.$$

These corollaries follow immediately from lemma 11.1.1 and the corresponding theorems of Chapter 7.

Theorem 11.1.2. Let $F(x)$ be a distribution function and $f(t)$ its characteristic function. $F(x)$ is bounded to the left (or right) if, and only if, $f(t)$ is regular in the upper (respectively lower) half-plane and if

$$|f(z)| \leqslant e^{c|z|}$$

for some $c > 0$ and $\text{Im}(z) > 0$ [respectively $\text{Im}(z) < 0$]. The extremity of $F(x)$ is given by $\text{lext }[F] = -\lim_{y \to \infty} y^{-1} \log f(iy)$ *[respectively* $\text{rext }[F] = \lim_{y \to \infty} y^{-1} \log f(-iy)$*].*

The formulae for the extremities were derived in Chapter 7 under the assumption that $f(z)$ is an analytic characteristic function. We now see that they are also valid if this restriction is dropped.

To prove theorem 11.1.2 we first note that the given distribution $F(x)$ and the distribution $H(x)$ which is defined by (11.1.4) have the same extremities. The statement follows immediately from lemma 11.1.1 and from theorem 7.2.2 and its corollary.

Remark. A one-sided distribution function has either an analytic characteristic function or a boundary characteristic function.

We next consider factorizations of boundary characteristic functions.

Lemma 11.1.2. Let $F(x)$, $F_1(x)$ and $F_2(x)$ be distribution functions and $f(t), f_1(t)$ and $f_2(t)$ their characteristic functions. Suppose that $\int_{-\infty}^{\infty} e^{-yx} dF(x)$ exists and is finite for $0 \leqslant y < b$. If $F = F_1 * F_2$ then the integrals $\int_{-\infty}^{\infty} e^{-yx} dF_j(x)$ $(j = 1, 2)$ exist and are finite for $0 \leqslant y < b$, and the relation

$$\int_{-\infty}^{\infty} e^{-yx} dF(x) = \int_{-\infty}^{\infty} e^{-yx} dF_1(x) \int_{-\infty}^{\infty} e^{-yx} dF_2(x)$$

holds for $0 \leqslant y < b$.

The proof of the lemma is completely analogous to the proof of the convolution theorem.

Theorem 11.1.3. *Let $f(t)$ be a boundary characteristic function with strip of regularity $0 < \text{Im}(z) < \beta$. Then any factor $f_1(t)$ of $f(t)$ is regular, at least in the strip of regularity of $f(t)$.*

Since $f_1(t)$ is a factor of $f(t)$, there exists a characteristic function $f_2(t)$ such that $f(t) = f_1(t) f_2(t)$. Let $F(x)$, $F_1(x)$ and $F_2(x)$ be the distribution functions which correspond to $f(x)$, $f_1(x)$ and $f_2(x)$ respectively. Then $F = F_1 * F_2$. We see from theorem 11.1.1 that the integral $\int_{-\infty}^{\infty} e^{-vx} dF(x)$ is finite for $0 < \text{Im}(z) < \beta$, and we conclude from lemma 11.1.2 that the integrals $\int_{-\infty}^{\infty} e^{-vx} dF_j(x)$ $(j = 1, 2)$ are also finite for $0 < \text{Im}(z) < \beta$. Therefore $f_j(z)$ $(j = 1, 2)$ is also regular at least in this strip; moreover we see from lemma 11.1.2 that the equation $f(iy) = f_1(iy) f_2(iy)$ holds in the strip of regularity of $f(z)$. The relation

$$f(z) = f_1(z) f_2(z),$$

valid in the strip $0 \leqslant \text{Im}(z) < \beta$, then follows by analytic continuation.

Theorem 11.1.3 is analogous to theorem 8.1.1 for analytic characteristic functions; it shows that the factors of boundary characteristic functions are either analytic characteristic functions or boundary characteristic functions.

We conclude this section by mentioning another property of boundary characteristic functions noted by A. Zygmund (1951).

Theorem 11.1.4. *Let $\{F_n(x)\}$ be a sequence of distribution functions and let $\{f_n(t)\}$ be the corresponding sequence of characteristic functions. Suppose that the $f_n(t)$ are boundary characteristic functions and that they are regular in a fixed strip (independent of n). The sequence of distribution functions converges weakly to a distribution function $F(x)$ if, and only if, the following two conditions are satisfied: (i) the functions $f_n(t)$ converge to a limiting function $f(t)$ in a fixed interval around the origin; (ii) $f(t)$ is continuous at $t = 0$.*

11.2 Infinitely divisible boundary characteristic functions

In this section we study boundary characteristic functions which are infinitely divisible and one-sided infinitely divisible distributions. As an example of such a characteristic function we mention the stable distribution with parameter $\alpha = \gamma = \frac{1}{2}$, whose frequency function was given by formula (5.8.9).

Lemma 11.2.1. *An infinitely divisible boundary characteristic function has no zeros in the interior of its strip of regularity.*

The lemma corresponds to theorem 8.4.1 and is proved in the same way.

The next theorem shows that a canonical representation of infinitely divisible distributions also holds in the strip of regularity of boundary characteristic functions. This is similar to the statement of theorem 8.4.2. Since a boundary characteristic function does not necessarily have a finite second moment, the representation cannot be the Kolmogorov representation used in theorem 8.4.2. We will use as our starting-point the Lévy canonical representation and will have to modify our reasoning somewhat.

Theorem 11.2.1. Let $f(z)$ be an infinitely divisible boundary characteristic function. Then the canonical representation

$$(11.2.1) \qquad \log f(z) = iza - \frac{\sigma^2}{2} z^2 + \int_{-\infty}^{-0} \left(e^{izu} - 1 - \frac{izu}{1+u^2} \right) dM(u)$$

$$+ \int_{+0}^{\infty} \left(e^{izu} - 1 - \frac{izu}{1+u^2} \right) dN(u)$$

is valid in the interior of the strip of regularity of $f(z)$. The constants a and σ^2 and the spectral functions $M(u)$ and $N(u)$ satisfy the conditions of theorem 5.5.2.

We first assume that $0 < \text{Im}(z) < \beta$ is the strip of regularity of $f(z)$. It follows from lemma 11.2.1 that $\log f(z)$ is regular in $0 < \text{Im}(z) < \beta$ and continuous in $0 \leqslant \text{Im}(z) < \beta$. Since $f(t)$ is infinitely divisible it admits the Lévy representation (11.2.1) for real t. We write for $\text{Im}(z) \geqslant 0$

$$(11.2.2) \qquad \phi_1(z) = \int_{+0}^{\infty} \left(e^{izu} - 1 - \frac{izu}{1+u^2} \right) dN(u).$$

The function $\phi_1(z)$ is regular for $\text{Im}(z) > 0$ and continuous for $\text{Im}(z) \geqslant 0$. We put for $\text{Im}(z) \leqslant 0$

$$(11.2.3) \qquad \phi_2(z) = \int_{-\infty}^{-0} \left(e^{izu} - 1 - \frac{izu}{1+u^2} \right) dM(u);$$

the function $\phi_2(z)$ is regular for $\text{Im}(z) < 0$ and continuous for $\text{Im}(z) \leqslant 0$. Let

$$(11.2.4) \qquad \psi(z) = \log f(z) - iaz - \tfrac{1}{2}\sigma^2 z^2 - \phi_1(z).$$

It follows from our assumptions that $\psi(z)$ is regular for $0 < \text{Im}(z) < \beta$ and continuous for $0 \leqslant \text{Im}(z) < \beta$. Since $f(t)$ is infinitely divisible we see from its Lévy canonical representation that

$$\psi(t) = \phi_2(t)$$

for real t. We conclude then from Schwarz's reflection principle that $\psi(z)$ is the analytic continuation of $\phi_2(z)$, so that $\phi_2(z)$ is regular in $\text{Im}(z) < \beta$. Therefore $\phi_2''(z)$ is regular in $\text{Im}(z) < \beta$. For $\text{Im}(z) < 0$ we have from (11.2.3) the integral representation

$$\phi_2''(z) = -\int_{-\infty}^{-0} e^{izu} u^2 \, dM(u).$$

L

We introduce the non-decreasing function

$$L(u) = \int_{-\infty}^{u} v^2 \, dM(v) \quad (u < 0)$$

and see that

$$\phi''(z) = -\int_{-\infty}^{-0} e^{-izu} \, dL(u).$$

The function $\phi''(z)$ is—except for a constant factor—an analytic characteristic function with strip of regularity Im $(z) < \beta$; therefore its representation by a Fourier integral is valid in this strip. We then see easily that the representation (11.2.3) can be extended and is valid for Im $(z) < \beta$. Since $\psi(z) = \phi_2(z)$ in $0 \leqslant$ Im $(z) < \beta$ we see from the equations (11.2.2), (11.2.3) and (11.2.4) that $\log f(z)$ admits the representation (11.2.1).

The proof follows the same lines if the strip of regularity of $f(z)$ is given by $-\alpha <$ Im $(z) < 0$.

We turn now to the study of infinitely divisible one-sided distributions. In this connection we need the following result:

Lemma 11.2.2. Let $F(x)$ be a distribution function which is bounded from the left (right) and let $f(t)$ be its characteristic function. Then the factors of $f(t)$ belong also to distribution functions which are bounded from the left (right).

The lemma follows easily from theorem 7.2.2 and lemma 11.1.1.

Theorem 11.2.2. Let $f(t)$ be the characteristic function of an infinitely divisible distribution function $F(x)$. The distribution function $F(x)$ is bounded to the left if, and only if, the following three conditions are satisfied:

(i) $\sigma^2 = 0$

(ii) $M(u)$ is constant for $u < 0$

(iii) $\int_0^1 u \, dN(u) < \infty.$

Here σ^2 is the constant, $M(u)$ and $N(u)$ are the spectral functions occurring in the canonical representation (11.2.1) of $f(t)$. If conditions (i), (ii) and (iii) are satisfied, then

$$\text{lext } [F] = a - \int_0^{\infty} \frac{u}{1+u^2} \, dN(u).$$

We first prove that the conditions are necessary.
(i) If $\sigma^2 > 0$, we see from (11.2.1) that

$$f(t) = \exp\left(-\tfrac{1}{2}\sigma^2 t^2\right) g(t)$$

where $g(t)$ is the infinitely divisible distribution without normal factor which is determined by the constant a and the spectral functions $M(u)$ and

$N(u)$. This means that $f(t)$ has a normal factor, in contradiction to lemma 11.2.2.

(ii) If $M(u)$ is not constant for $u < 0$, then there exists a finite interval $[a, b]$, $a < b < 0$ such that $C = M(b) - M(a) > 0$. The function

$$g(z) = \frac{1}{C} \exp\left[\int_a^b (e^{izu} - 1) \, dM(u) \right]$$

is an entire characteristic function which is a factor of $f(z)$. But $g(z)$ cannot satisfy the conditions of theorem 7.2.2, so that $g(t)$ cannot be the characteristic function of a distribution bounded to the left. This contradicts lemma 11.2.2, so that the necessity of (ii) is proved.

For the proof of the necessity of (iii) we can therefore assume that (i) and (ii) are valid, and we see from (11.2.1) that for $y > 0$

$$\log f(iy) = -ay + \int_0^1 (e^{-yu} - 1 + yu) \, dN(u) - y \int_0^1 \frac{u^3}{1 + u^2} \, dN(u)$$
$$+ \int_1^\infty \left(e^{-yu} - 1 + \frac{yu}{1 + u^2} \right) dN(u).$$

We write

$$R(y) = \int_0^1 \frac{e^{-yu} - 1 + yu}{y} \, dN(u)$$

and get

(11.2.5) $\qquad \log f(iy) \geqslant -ay + yR(y) - y \int_0^1 \frac{u^3}{1 + u^2} dN(u) - \int_1^\infty dN(u).$

We give an indirect proof for (iii) and assume tentatively that

(11.2.6) $\qquad \int_0^1 u \, dN(u) = \infty.$

If we can show that (11.2.6) implies

(11.2.7) $\qquad \lim_{y \to \infty} R(y) = \infty$

then it follows from (11.2.5) that $\lim\limits_{y \to \infty} \dfrac{1}{y} \log f(iy) = \infty$. In view of theorem 11.1.2, this contradicts the assumption that $f(t)$ belongs to a distribution bounded from the left. The necessity of (iii) will therefore be established as soon as we show that (11.2.7) follows from (11.2.6).

Let $H(u)$ be defined by

$$H(u) = \int_1^u v \, dN(v) \quad (u > 0).$$

Then $H(u)$ is non-decreasing and we see from (11.2.6) that

(11.2.8) $\qquad H(0) = -\infty.$

It is easily seen that $(e^{-x} - 1 + x)/x$ is positive and non-decreasing in $(0, +\infty)$. Therefore

$$R(y) = \int_0^1 \frac{e^{-yu} - 1 + yu}{yu} \, dH(u) \geqslant \int_1^y \frac{e^{-v} - 1 + v}{v} \, dH\left(\frac{v}{y}\right)$$

so that

$$R(y) \geqslant e^{-1}\left[H(1) - H\left(\frac{1}{y}\right) \right].$$

It follows from (11.2.8) that $\lim_{y \to \infty} R(y) = +\infty$, so that the necessity of (iii) is completely proved.

We prove next the sufficiency of the conditions (i), (ii) and (iii). We assume that these conditions hold, and we obtain, for real t, the canonical representation

$$\log f(t) = iat + \int_0^\infty \left(e^{itu} - 1 - \frac{itu}{1+u^2} \right) dN(u).$$

If we replace in the integral the real variable t by the complex variable $z = t + iy$ then we obtain a function which is regular in the half-plane $y > 0$ and continuous in $y \geqslant 0$. Therefore $f(t)$ is either an analytic characteristic function or a boundary characteristic function, and we see from theorem 11.2.1 that the canonical representation is valid in the upper half-plane. Therefore

$$(11.2.9) \qquad \log f(iy) = -ay + \int_0^\infty \left(e^{-yu} - 1 + \frac{yu}{1+u^2} \right) dN(u) \quad (y \geqslant 0).$$

We put

$$Q(y) = \int_0^\infty \frac{e^{-yu} - 1}{y} \, dN(u)$$

and see from (11.2.9) that

$$(11.2.10) \qquad \log f(iy) = -ay + y \int_0^\infty \frac{u}{1+u^2} \, dN(u) + yQ(y).$$

It follows easily from assumption (iii) of theorem 11.2.2 that

$$\int_0^\infty \frac{u}{1+u^2} \, dN(u) < \infty$$

and that

$$\lim_{y \to \infty} Q(y) = 0.$$

Therefore we conclude from (11.2.10) that

$$\text{lext } [F] = -\lim_{y \to \infty} \frac{1}{y} \log f(iy) = a - \int_0^\infty \frac{u}{1+u^2} \, dN(u),$$

so that the proof of the theorem is completed.

A theorem concerning infinitely divisible distributions which are bounded to the right can be stated and proved in the same way.

12 MIXTURES OF DISTRIBUTION FUNCTIONS AND TRANSFORMATIONS OF CHARACTERISTIC FUNCTIONS

In this chapter we discuss briefly certain integral transforms of distribution functions. These transformations can be used to construct new characteristic functions from given characteristic functions.

12.1 Mixtures of distribution functions

Let $G_1(x)$, $G_2(x)$, $\ldots$, $G_n(x)$ be n distribution functions; we saw in Section 2.1 that

$$F(x) = \sum_{j=1}^{n} a_j G_j(x)$$

is also a distribution function, provided that $a_j \geqslant 0$ $(j = 1, 2, \ldots, n)$ and

$$\sum_{j=1}^{n} a_j = 1.$$

We can regard $F(x)$ as a mixture of the distribution functions $G_1(x)$, $\ldots$, $G_n(x)$ with weights $a_1, \ldots, a_n$. In the present section we consider a more general mixing procedure and apply it also to the corresponding characteristic functions.

Let $G(x, y)$ be a family of functions which has the following properties:

(i) for each value of y the function $G(x, y)$ is a distribution function in x;

(ii) $G(x, y)$ is a measurable function of y.

The functions $G(x, y)$ form a family of distribution functions which depends on a parameter y. In the following we consider only families $\{G(x, y)\}$ of distribution functions which satisfy conditions (i) and (ii). An exhaustive discussion of mixtures of distributions was given by H. Robbins (1948).

Let $H(y)$ be an arbitrary distribution function; we form the expression

$$(12.1.1) \qquad F(x) = \int_{-\infty}^{\infty} G(x, y)\, dH(y)$$

and see easily from the dominated convergence theorem [Loève (1963) pp. 124–127] that $F(x)$ is a distribution function. The corresponding characteristic function is then given by

$$(12.1.2) \qquad f(t) = \int_{-\infty}^{\infty} g(t, y)\, dH(y)$$

where

$$g(t, y) = \int_{-\infty}^{\infty} e^{itx} d_x G(x, y).$$

Mixtures of distributions occur in a great variety of practical applications and were used by W. Feller (1943) to study contagious distributions.

Two particular cases of (12.1.1) are of some interest.

(I) If $G(x, y)$ is a purely discrete distribution,

$$G(x, y) = \sum_v p_v(y)\, \varepsilon(x - \xi_v),$$

then

$$F(x) = \sum_v \left[\int_{-\infty}^{\infty} p_v(y)\, dH(y) \right] \varepsilon(x - \xi_v)$$

is also a discrete distribution. The distribution which is obtained for

$$p_v(y) = e^{-v}\frac{y^v}{v!}, \quad \xi_v = v \ (v = 0, 1, 2, \ldots)$$

is called the compound Poisson distribution.

(II) If

$$H(y) = \sum_v p_v \varepsilon(y - \eta_v)$$

is a purely discrete distribution then (12.1.1) yields

$$F(x) = \sum_v p_v G(x, \eta_v).$$

We put here

$$p_v = e^{-\lambda}\frac{\lambda^v}{v!}, \quad \eta_v = v$$

and let $G(x, v) = [G(x)]^{v*}$ be the v-fold convolution (†) of $G(x)$ with itself ($v = 0, 1, 2, \ldots$). Then

$$F(x) = \sum_{v=0}^{\infty} e^{-\lambda}\frac{\lambda^v}{v!} [G(x)]^{v*}$$

is called the generalized Poisson distribution. Its characteristic function is $f(t) = \exp\{\lambda[g(t) - 1]\}$.

In the following we consider a slightly more general mixture of distribution functions. The process still has the form (12.1.1) but we relax the assumptions concerning the weight function $H(y)$ in so far as we do not require that $H(y)$ be a distribution function. We will only assume that $H(y)$ is a non-decreasing function whose total variation is equal to 1. We

---

(†) Thus $G(x, v)$ is defined by $G(x, 1) = G(x)$ and the relations

$$G(x, v) = \int_{-\infty}^{\infty} G(x - y, v - 1)\, dG(y)$$

for $v = 2, 3, \ldots$.

therefore admit the possibility that $H(-\infty) \neq 0$ and make no assumptions concerning the values of $H(y)$ at its discontinuity points.

Theorem 12.1.1.   *The function*

$$(12.1.3) \qquad F(x) = \int_{-\infty}^{\infty} G(x, y)\, dH(y)$$

is a distribution function whenever $\{G(x, y)\}$ is a family of distribution functions which has the properties (i) *and* (ii) *if, and only if, the conditions*

(a) $H(y)$ *is non-decreasing*

(b) $\int_{-\infty}^{\infty} dH(y) = 1$

are satisfied.
   We note that the characteristic function of $F(x)$ is

$$(12.1.4) \qquad f(t) = \int_{-\infty}^{\infty} g(t, y)\, dH(y),$$

where $g(t, y)$ is the characteristic function of $G(x, y)$.

The sufficiency of the conditions follows easily from the properties of the family $G(x, y)$ and from the dominated convergence theorem. To prove that conditions (a) and (b) are necessary we specialize the family $G(x, y)$. Let η_1 and η_2 be two arbitrary real numbers such that $\eta_1 < \eta_2$ and select

$$G(x, y) = \begin{cases} \varepsilon(x-1) & \text{if } \eta_1 < y \leqslant \eta_2 \\ \varepsilon(x) & \text{if } y \leqslant \eta_1 \quad \text{or} \quad y > \eta_2. \end{cases}$$

It is then easily seen that

$$F(x) = \varepsilon(x-1)[H(\eta_2) - H(\eta_1)] + \varepsilon(x)[1 - H(\eta_2) + H(\eta_1)].$$

If $F(x)$ is a distribution function then we must necessarily have

$$H(\eta_2) - H(\eta_1) \geqslant 0$$

which proves (a). To prove (b) we select $G(x, y) = \varepsilon(x)$ for all y and see that

$$F(x) = \varepsilon(x) \int_{-\infty}^{\infty} dH(y)$$

so that (b) must be satisfied.
   We remark that condition (a) is necessary only to assure that the weight function should produce a distribution function, whatever family, satisfying (i) and (ii), is used in (12.1.3).
   We illustrate this by an example where a non-monotone weight function is used to transform a suitably chosen family into a new distribution. Let

$$H(y) = \frac{1}{\sqrt{(2)}[\sqrt{(2)} - 1]}[\varepsilon(y-1) + \varepsilon(y+1) - \sqrt{(2)}\,\varepsilon(y)]$$

be the weight function and consider the family of normal distributions with mean y and standard deviation $2a$, that is($\dagger$)

$$G(x, y) = \Phi\left(\frac{x-y}{2a}\right).$$

Then

$$F(x) = \frac{1}{\sqrt{(2)}[\sqrt{(2)}-1]}\left[\Phi\left(\frac{x-1}{2a}\right)+\Phi\left(\frac{x+1}{2a}\right)-\sqrt{(2)}\Phi\left(\frac{x}{2a}\right)\right].$$

This is an absolutely continuous function with derivative

$$F'(x) = \frac{1}{2a\sqrt{(4\pi)}[\sqrt{(2)}-1]}$$
$$\times \{\exp\left[-(x-1)^2/8a^2\right]+\exp\left[-(x+1)^2/8a^2\right]-\sqrt{(2)}\exp\left[-x^2/8a^2\right]\}.$$

The function $F(x)$ is a distribution function whenever $F'(x) \geqslant 0$ for all x; it is easy to show that this condition is satisfied if

$$a^2 \geqslant \frac{1}{4\log 2}.$$

The characteristic function of $F(x)$ is, according to (12.1.4), given by

$$f(t) = \left[\frac{\sqrt{(2)}\cos t-1}{\sqrt{(2)}-1}\right]\exp\left(-2a^2t^2\right).$$

12.2   Transformations of characteristic functions

We have already noted that the mixture of distribution functions induces a mixture of the corresponding characteristic functions. We now use the results of Section 12.1 to discuss certain transformations of characteristic functions.

Theorem 12.2.1. *Let $\{f_v(t)\}$ be an arbitrary sequence of characteristic functions and $\{a_v\}$ be a sequence of real numbers. The necessary and sufficient condition that*

$$(12.2.1) \qquad f(t) = \sum_{v=0}^{\infty} a_v f_v(t)$$

should be a characteristic function for every sequence of characteristic functions is that

$$(12.2.2) \qquad a_v \geqslant 0, \ \sum_{v=0}^{\infty} a_v = 1.$$

This follows from theorem 12.1.1 if we put

$$H(y) = \sum_{v=0}^{\infty} a_v \varepsilon(y-v).$$

($\dagger$) Here

$$\Phi(x) = \frac{1}{\sqrt{2\pi}}\int_{-\infty}^{x}\exp\left(-z^2/2\right)dz.$$

Next we let $g(t)$ be an arbitrary characteristic function and write $f_v(t) = [g(t)]^v$ for $v = 0, 1, 2, \ldots$. We obtain immediately the following corollary:

Corollary to theorem 12.2.1. Let $g(t)$ be a characteristic function and let $\Lambda(z)$ be a function of the complex variable z which is regular in $|z| < R$, where $R > 1$. The function $\Lambda[g(t)]$ is also a characteristic function if, and only if, $\Lambda(z)$ has a power series expansion about the origin with non-negative coefficients and if $\Lambda(1) = 1$.

The corollary can also be derived directly from theorem 12.1.1 if we set

$$H(y) = \sum_v a_v \varepsilon(y-v)$$

and $G(x, y) = [G(x)]^{v*}$ for $v \leqslant y < v+1$.

An interesting generalization of the corollary to theorem 12.2.1 has been derived by C. S. Herz (1963) and also by A. G. Konheim–B. Weiss (1965).

Theorem 12.2.2. Let $\Lambda(z)$ be a function of the complex variable z which has the property that $f(t) = \Lambda[g(t)]$ is a characteristic function whenever $g(t)$ is a characteristic function. Then $\Lambda(z)$ can be represented by a series, convergent for $|z| \leqslant 1$, which has the form

$$\Lambda(z) = \sum_{m=0}^{\infty} \sum_{n=0}^{\infty} a_{m,n} z^m \bar{z}^n$$

where the $a_{m,n}$ are real and where $a_{m,n} \geqslant 0$ and $\sum_{m=0}^{\infty} \sum_{n=0}^{\infty} a_{m,n} = 1$.

Clearly the function $\Lambda(z)$ need not be regular; a simple example is the function $\Lambda(z) = |z|^2$. For the proof of theorem 12.2.2 we refer the reader to the papers quoted above.

In a subsequent paper A. G. Konheim–B. Weiss (1968) investigated transformations of non-negative definite functions into infinitely divisible non-negative definite functions.(†) They obtained the following result, formulated here in terms of characteristic functions.

Theorem 12.2.2a. Let $\theta(z)$ be a complex-valued function of the complex variable z. The function $\theta(z)$ has the property that $f(t) = \theta[g(t)]$ is an infinitely divisible characteristic function whenever $g(t)$ is a characteristic function if, and only if, $\theta(z) = \exp[c\Lambda(z)-1]$, where c is a positive constant, while $\Lambda(z)$ is the function defined in theorem 12.2.2.

The sufficiency of the condition follows from theorem 12.2.2 and De Finetti's theorem; for the proof of its necessity the reader is referred to the paper quoted above.

(†) These authors worked in the more general framework of locally compact Abelian groups having elements of arbitrarily high order.

M

Theorem 12.2.3.   *Let $g(t)$ be an arbitrary characteristic function and let p be a real number such that $p > 1$; then*

$$f(t) = \frac{p-1}{p-g(t)}$$

is an infinitely divisible characteristic function.

Let n be an arbitrary integer and put

$$H(y) = \sum_{v=0}^{\infty} a_v \varepsilon(y-v)$$

where

$$a_0 = \left[\frac{p-1}{p}\right]^{1/n} \quad \text{while} \quad a_k = a_0 \frac{(1+n)(1+2n)\ldots[1+(k-1)n]}{(np)^k k!}$$

for $k = 1, 2, \ldots$ and set $G(x, y) = [G(x)]^{v*}$ if $v \leqslant y < v+1$. This shows that

$$f(t) = \left[\frac{p-1}{p-g(t)}\right]^{1/n}$$

is a characteristic function for any positive integer n; in other words, $f(t)$ is an infinitely divisible characteristic function. Theorem 12.2.3 follows also from the corollary to theorem 12.2.1 if we put

$$\Lambda(z) = \left[\frac{p-1}{p-z}\right]^{1/n}$$

and understand that $\Lambda(z)$ is the principal value of this power.

We next discuss a few additional transformations. Let $V(x)$ be a non-decreasing function of bounded variation defined on the interval $[0, M]$ and let

$$g(z) = \int_0^M e^{xz} \, dV(x).$$

Then the function $g(z)/g(1)$ satisfies the conditions of the corollary of theorem 12.2.1. Suppose that $f(t)$ is a characteristic function; then

$$h(t) = \frac{g[f(t)]}{g(1)}$$

is also a characteristic function.

The transformation given by theorem 12.2.1 was derived by using a step function $H(y)$ as the weight function of a mixture. We next specialize $H(y)$ in a different manner and assume that $H(y)$ is a non-decreasing function such that $H(0) = 0$ while $H(1) = 1$. Moreover we suppose that $g(t, y)$ is a function of the product ty so that $g(t, y) = g(ty)$ where $g(u)$ is some characteristic function. We then obtain from theorem 12.1.1 the following result.

*Theorem 12.2.4.   Let g(u) be an arbitrary characteristic function and suppose
that H(y) is a non-decreasing function such that H(y) = 0 if y < 0, while
H(y) = 1 if y > 1. Then*

$$f(t) = \int_0^1 g(ty)\,dH(y) = \int_0^t g(u)\,dH(u/t)$$

is also a characteristic function.

Theorem 12.2.4 can also be used to derive transformations of characteristic functions which are of some interest. We give some applications of
theorem 12.2.4.

*Corollary to theorem 12.2.4.   Let g(u) be an arbitrary characteristic
function and p ⩾ 1 a real number. The function*

$$(12.2.3) \qquad f(t) = \frac{p}{t^p} \int_0^t g(u) u^{p-1}\,du$$

is then a characteristic function.

The corollary follows from theorem 12.2.4 by putting

$$H(y) = \begin{cases} 0 & \text{if } y < 0 \\ y^p & \text{if } 0 \leqslant y < 1 \quad (p \geqslant 1) \\ 1 & \text{if } y \geqslant 1. \end{cases}$$

If we put in the corollary $p = 1$, we see that the function

$$(12.2.3a) \qquad f(t) = \frac{1}{t} \int_0^t g(u)\,du$$

is a characteristic function whenever $g(u)$ is a characteristic function. The
transformations (12.2.3) and (12.2.3a), as well as some generalizations,
were investigated by M. Girault (1954) and by H. Loeffel (1956). A. Ya.
Khinchine was the first to study the transformation (12.2.3a), and his
results have been presented in Section 4.5. We apply the technique of
mixtures to construct operators which transform characteristic functions
into other characteristic functions.

Let $F(x)$ be a distribution function which has a finite second moment

$$\alpha_2 = \int_{-\infty}^{\infty} x^2\,dF(x)$$ and let $f(t)$ be the characteristic function of $F(x)$. Then

$$H(x) = \frac{1}{\alpha_2} \int_{-\infty}^{x} y^2\,dF(x)$$

is also a distribution function. We use in the following $H(x)$ as a weight
function for certain mixtures.

(a) Let $g(u) = \dfrac{e^{iu} - 1}{iu}$ be the characteristic function of a rectangular distribution. Then

$$k(t) = \int_{-\infty}^{\infty} g(tx)\, dH(x) = \frac{1}{\alpha_2} \int_{-\infty}^{\infty} \frac{e^{itx}-1}{itx} x^2\, dF(x)$$

is, according to theorem 12.2.3, a characteristic function. A simple computation shows that

$$k(t) = \frac{f'(t)-f'(0)}{tf''(0)}.$$

(b) Let $g(u) = e^{iu}$; the same procedure shows that

$$k(t) = \int_{-\infty}^{\infty} e^{itx} \frac{x^2}{\alpha_2}\, dF(x) = \frac{f''(t)}{f''(0)}$$

is a characteristic function.

(c) We now modify our assumption and suppose that $F(x)$ is bounded to the left with lext $[F] = 0$ and that the first moment α_1 of $F(x)$ exists. Then

$$H_1(x) = \begin{cases} 0 & \text{if } x < 0 \\ \dfrac{1}{\alpha_1} \displaystyle\int_0^x y\, dF(y) & \text{if } x \geqslant 0 \end{cases}$$

is a distribution function. If we use $H_1(x)$ as a weight function for $g(u) = e^{iu}$, we see that

$$\int_{-\infty}^{\infty} e^{itx}\, dH_1(x) = \frac{1}{\alpha_1} \int_0^{\infty} e^{itx} x\, dF(x) = \frac{f'(t)}{f'(0)}$$

is also a characteristic function.

(d) The function $g(t) = \dfrac{e^{it}-1}{it}$ is the characteristic function of a rectangular distribution over the interval $[0, 1]$. For this distribution the left extremity is zero and the mean equals $\frac{1}{2}$, so that, according to (c),

$$g_1(t) = \frac{g'(t)}{g'(0)} = \frac{2(1+it\, e^{it} - e^{it})}{-t^2}$$

is a characteristic function. Therefore

$$g(t) = e^{it} g_1(-t) = \frac{2(e^{it}-1-it)}{-t^2}$$

is also a characteristic function. We again use $H(x)$ as a weight function and see that

$$k(t) = -\frac{1}{f''(0)} \int_{-\infty}^{\infty} g(tx) x^2\, dF(x) = \frac{2}{t^2 f''(0)} \int_{-\infty}^{\infty} (e^{itx} - 1 - itx)\, dF(x)$$

so that

$$k(t) = \frac{2}{t^2 f''(0)} [f(t) - 1 - tf'(0)]$$

is a characteristic function.

We summarize these results.

Theorem 12.2.5. Let T_1, T_2, T_3 and T_4 be operators defined by

(a) $T_1 f(t) = \dfrac{f'(t) - f'(0)}{tf''(0)}$

(b) $T_2 f(t) = \dfrac{f''(t)}{f''(0)}$

(c) $T_3 f(t) = \dfrac{f'(t)}{f'(0)}$

(d) $T_4 f(t) = \dfrac{2}{t^2 f''(0)} [f(t) - 1 - tf'(0)].$

Suppose that the domains of these operators are characteristic functions $f(t)$ which satisfy the following conditions:

In cases (a), (b) *and* (d), *the $f(t)$ are characteristic functions whose distributions have finite second moments; in case* (c), *the $f(t)$ belong to distributions with finite first moment and left extremity at the point 0.*

These operators transform characteristic functions satisfying these conditions into other characteristic functions.

Remark. If we apply an operator T_i ($i = 1, 2, 3, 4$) to an analytic characteristic function contained in its domain, then the transformed function is also in the domain of T_i, so that its application can be iterated.

As an example we consider the characteristic function $f(t) = e^{-t^2/2}$. The functions

$$h_{2k}(t) = T_2^k e^{-t^2/2} = \frac{(-1)^k}{\alpha_{2k}} H_{2k}(t) e^{-t^2/2}$$

and

$$h_{2k-1}(t) = T_1 T_2^{k-1} e^{-t^2/2} = \frac{(-1)^k}{\alpha_{2k}} \frac{H_{2k-1}(t)}{t} e^{-t^2/2}$$

are then characteristic functions. Here $H_k(x)$ is the Hermite polynomial of degree k defined by the relation

$$H_k(x) = e^{x^2/2} \frac{d^k}{dx^k} (e^{-x^2/2}),$$

while $\alpha_{2k} = (2k)!/2^k k!$ is the $(2k)$th moment of the normal distribution with mean zero and variance 1.

The characteristic functions $h_{2k}(t)$ are indecomposable, while the $h_{2k-1}(t)$ are decomposable and always have a normal factor. The functions $h_{2k}(t)$ and $h_{2k-1}(t)$ belong to the class of entire characteristic functions of order 2 which have only a finite number of zeros. The factorizations of this class are completely known [see E. Lukacs (1967)].

We mention two other transformations which are obtained as mixtures of characteristic functions.

Theorem 12.2.6. *Let $F(x)$ be a distribution function with characteristic function $f(t)$. Suppose that $F(x)$ is bounded to the left and that* lext $[F] \geqslant 0$. *If* exp $[\psi(t)]$ *is the characteristic function of an infinitely divisible distribution and if λ is a positive number, then $g(t) = f[-i\lambda\psi(t)]$ is a characteristic function.*

Since $f(u) = \displaystyle\int_0^\infty e^{iuy}\, dF(y)$ we see that

$$g(t) = f[-i\lambda\psi(t)] = \int_0^\infty \exp\,[\lambda y\psi(t)]\, dF(y).$$

According to our assumption, exp $[\lambda y\psi(t)]$ is a characteristic function for $y > 0$, so that $g(t)$ is a mixture of characteristic functions, and the statement follows from theorem 12.1.1.

A particular case of some interest is obtained by putting $\psi(t) = h(t) - 1$ where $h(t)$ is an arbitrary characteristic function. It follows from lemma 5.4.1 and theorem 12.2.6 that $f(t) = f[i(1 - h(t))]$ is a characteristic function, provided that the distribution which belongs to $f(t)$ satisfies the conditions of theorem 12.2.6.

Theorem 12.2.7. *Let $f(\sqrt{iz})$ be an analytic characteristic function and suppose that the corresponding distribution function $F(x)$ is bounded to the left and that* lext $[F] = 0$; *then $f(iz)$ is also a characteristic function.*

Let $F(x)$ be the distribution function of $f(\sqrt{iz})$. Then

$$p^*(y) = \int_0^\infty \frac{1}{2\sqrt{\pi x}} \exp\left(-\frac{y^2}{4x}\right) dF(x)$$

is the frequency function of a mixture of normal frequency functions. Let

$$\alpha_s^* = \int_{-\infty}^\infty y^s\, p^*(y)\, dy$$

be the moments of this mixture. Then

$$\alpha_{2k-1}^* = 0$$

while

$$\alpha_{2k}^* = 2 \int_0^\infty \int_0^\infty y^{2k} \frac{1}{2\sqrt{\pi x}} \exp\left(-\frac{y^2}{4x}\right) dF(x)\, dy.$$

We change the variable of integration by putting $y = u\sqrt{2x}$ and see, after an elementary computation, that

$$(12.2.4) \qquad \alpha_{2k}^* = \frac{(2k)!}{k!}\, \alpha_k,$$

where α_k is the moment of order k of $F(x)$. The characteristic function $f(\sqrt{iz})$ has the expansion

$$f(\sqrt{iz}) = \sum_{k=0}^{\infty} \frac{i^k \alpha_k}{k!} z^k$$

so that

$$f(u) = \sum_{k=0}^{\infty} \frac{\alpha_k}{k!} u^{2k}.$$

Therefore

$$f(iz) = \sum_{k=0}^{\infty} \frac{(-1)^k \alpha_k}{k!} z^{2k}$$

and we see from (12.2.4) that

$$f(iz) = \sum_{k=0}^{\infty} \frac{(-1)^k \alpha_{2k}^*}{(2k)!} z^{2k}.$$

Since this is the characteristic function which belongs to the frequency function $p^*(y)$, the statement is proved.

As an example we mention the characteristic function

$$f(t) = \frac{\sqrt{iz}}{\sin \sqrt{iz}}.$$

D. Dugué (1966) has shown that this is the characteristic function of a distribution which is closely related to the distribution function of Kolmogorov's statistic used extensively in the theory of non-parametric statistical tests.

We conclude this chapter with the discussion of transformations which are not the result of mixtures of distributions.

Let $g(t)$ be an arbitrary characteristic function and denote its distribution function by $G(x)$. Then

$$h(u) = \int_0^u g(y) \, dy = \int_0^u \int_{-\infty}^{\infty} e^{ivx} \, dG(x) \, dy.$$

It is easily seen that the order of the two integrations can be exchanged, so that

$$h(u) = \int_{-\infty}^{\infty} \frac{e^{iux} - 1}{ix} \, dG(x).$$

We introduce the integral

(12.2.5) $\phi(t) = -\int_0^t \int_0^u g(y) \, dy \, du$

so that

$$\phi(t) = -\int_0^t h(u) \, du = \int_0^t \int_{-\infty}^{\infty} \frac{1 - e^{iux}}{ix} \, dG(x) \, du.$$

It is again possible to exchange the order of the integrations and one obtains

$$\phi(t) = \int_{-\infty}^{\infty} (e^{itx} - 1 - itx) \frac{dG(x)}{x^2}.$$

The last formula agrees with the Kolmogorov canonical representation (theorem 5.5.3) and we conclude that the function $\phi(t)$, as defined by (12.2.5), is the logarithm of an infinitely divisible characteristic function which has a finite second moment. We have therefore obtained the following result:

Theorem 12.2.8. *Let $g(y)$ be an arbitrary characteristic function; then*

$$(12.2.6) \qquad f(t) = \exp\left\{ -\int_0^t \int_0^u g(y)\,dy\,du \right\}$$

is the characteristic function of an infinitely divisible distribution with finite second moment.

As an example we consider the characteristic function $g(t) = e^{-|t|}$ of the Cauchy distribution. The corresponding function (12.2.6) is then

$$(12.2.7) \qquad f_1(t) = \exp\left(-|t| + 1 - e^{-|t|}\right);$$

this is an infinitely divisible characteristic function with finite second moment. The function $f_2(t) = \exp(e^{-|t|} - 1)$ is also (lemma 5.4.1) an infinitely divisible characteristic function, and we obtain from (12.2.7) the relation

$$e^{-|t|} = f_1(t)\,f_2(t).$$

This indicates that it is possible to decompose the Cauchy distribution in such a way that both factors are infinitely divisible but do not belong to stable distributions.

APPENDIX A

The notations O and o

A.1 *The notation O.* Let $f(x)$ and $g(x)$ be two functions and assume that $g(x)$ is positive for sufficiently large x. We say that $f(x)$ is at most of the order of $g(x)$ as x tends to infinity and write

$$f(x) = O[g(x)] \quad \text{as } x \to \infty$$

if there exists a value x_0 and a constant $A > 0$ such that

$$|f(x)| < Ag(x) \quad \text{for } x \geqslant x_0.$$

Thus $f(x) = O[g(x)]$ means that the quotient $|f(x)|/g(x)$ is bounded for sufficiently large x.

Examples. $\sqrt{x} = O(x)$, $x+1 = O(x)$, $\exp(itx) = O(1)$, $\exp(\sqrt{\log x}) = O(x)$, $1/x^2 = O(x^{-3/2})$, $x \sin x = O(x)$. In all these examples we have taken for granted that the statement holds as $x \to \infty$.

We write $f(x) = O(1)$ to express that $f(x)$ is bounded as x increases. We list a few rules for the use of these notations.

  (I) $f_1(x) = O[g_1(x)]$, $f_2(x) = O[g_2(x)]$ imply that $f_1(x)+f_2(x) = O[g_1(x)+g_2(x)]$.

  (II) If $a > 0$ is a constant then $f(x) = O[ag(x)]$ implies $f(x) = O[g(x)]$.

  (III) If $f_1(x) = O[g_1(x)]$ and $f_2(x) = O[g_2(x)]$ then $f_1(x) f_2(x) = O[g_1(x) g_2(x)]$.

A.2 *The symbol "o".* Let $f(x)$ and $g(x)$ be both defined and positive for sufficiently large x. We say that $f(x)$ is of smaller order than $g(x)$ as $x \to \infty$ and write

$$f(x) = o[g(x)] \quad \text{as } x \to \infty$$

if

$$\lim_{x \to \infty} \frac{f(x)}{g(x)} = 0.$$

Examples. $\log x = o(x)$, $x = o(x^{3/2})$, etc.

We list a few properties of this symbol.

  (I) $f(x) = o[g(x)]$ implies $f(x) = O[g(x)]$.

  (II) If $f_1(x) = O[g_1(x)]$ and $f_2(x) = o[g_2(x)]$ then $f_1(x) f_2(x) = o[g_1(x) g_2(x)]$.

We write $f(x) = o(1)$ to indicate that $f(x)$ tends to zero.

The same symbols O and o are used if x does not tend to infinity but to some finite value; it is also possible to use this notation if the variable assumes only integer values as it tends to infinity. This cannot lead to any misunderstanding since the context will always indicate the variable and the limit which it approaches.

APPENDIX B

Schwarz's inequality

We prove this inequality in the form in which we need it: namely as an inequality which refers to Lebesgue–Stieltjes integrals with respect to a distribution function.

Let $F(x)$ be a distribution and consider two real-valued functions $g(x)$ and $h(x)$ and suppose that $g^2(x)$ and $h^2(x)$ are both integrable with respect to $F(x)$ over $(-\infty, +\infty)$. Then

$$\int_{-\infty}^{\infty} [u\,g(x)+v\,h(x)]^2\,dF(x)$$

is a non-negative quadratic form in the variables u and v, so that the discriminant of this form is non-negative. This yields

$$\left[\int_{-\infty}^{\infty} g(x)\,h(x)\,dF(x)\right]^2 \leqslant \int_{-\infty}^{\infty} [g(x)]^2\,dF(x) \int_{-\infty}^{\infty} [h(x)]^2\,dF(x)$$

which is the desired inequality.

APPENDIX C

Weierstrass' approximation theorem

We need here only the trigonometric approximation theorem of Weierstrass and introduce the following notation.

We denote by C_L the class of all continuous functions $f(x)$, defined for all real x, which are periodic with period L. We define trigonometric polynomials $T_n(x)$ of period 2π and degree n

$$T_n(x) = \sum_{v=0}^{n} (\alpha_v \cos vx + \beta_v \sin vx).$$

It is sometimes convenient to write these in complex form as

$$T_n(x) = \sum_{v=-n}^{+n} a_v\,e^{ivx}$$

where the a_v can easily be expressed in terms of the α_v and β_v. If $T_n(x)$ is a trigonometric polynomial with period 2π then $T_n(2\pi x/L)$ is a trigonometric polynomial with period L.

Weierstrass' (trigonometric) approximation theorem. Let $f(x) \in C_{2\pi}$; then for every $\varepsilon > 0$ there exists a trigonometric polynomial $T_n(x)$ (of period 2π) such that $|f(x) - T_n(x)| < \varepsilon$ for all real x.

If $f(x) \in C_L$ then $f[Ly/(2\pi)] \in C_{2\pi}$ so that one obtains essentially the same approximation theorem for the functions of C_L; the approximating trigonometric polynomials then have necessarily the period L.

A convenient proof of the theorem may be found in I. P. Natanson (1955) [see § 2] or in N. I. Achieser (1956) [see § 22].

APPENDIX D

Order and type of entire functions

Let $f(z) = \sum\limits_{k=0}^{\infty} c_k z^k$ be an entire function.

We denote by

(D.1) $M(r; f) = \max\limits_{|z| \leqslant r} |f(z)|$

the maximum modulus of $f(z)$ in the circle $|z| \leqslant r$. This value is assumed on the perimeter of the circle.

The order ρ of an entire function $f(z)$ is defined as

(D.2) $\rho = \limsup\limits_{r \to \infty} \dfrac{\log \log M(r; f)}{\log r}.$

One has $0 \leqslant \rho \leqslant \infty$. In this monograph we are in general not interested in functions of order inferior to 1; if $\rho < \infty$ then we say that $f(z)$ is an entire function of finite order.

An entire function $f(z)$ of finite order ρ is said to be of type τ if

(D.3) $\limsup\limits_{r \to \infty} \dfrac{\log M(r; f)}{r^\rho} = \tau.$

An entire function $f(z)$ of finite order ρ is said to be of minimal type if $\tau = 0$, of normal (or intermediate) type if $0 < \tau < \infty$, and of maximal type if $\tau = \infty$.

Entire functions of order 1 and finite type ($\tau < \infty$) or of order inferior to 1 are called entire functions of exponential type.

Order and type of an entire function can be expressed in terms of its coefficients; one has

$$(D.4) \qquad \rho = \limsup_{k \to \infty} \frac{k \log k}{\log |c_k|^{-1}}$$

and, if $0 < \rho < \infty$,

$$(D.5) \qquad \tau = \frac{1}{e\rho} \limsup_{k \to \infty} k |c_k|^{\rho/k}.$$

For the proof of these statements we refer the reader to E. Hille (1962) [see pp. 182–188] or A. I. Markushevich (1965) [see vol. II, Chapter 9].

APPENDIX E

Proof of lemmas needed in Chapter 9

E.1   *Proof of lemma* 9.1.1.

We note that

$$\int_0^z (e^m - zw)\, dw = e^z - z - 1$$

and introduce the function

$$k(z) = \frac{e^z - z - 1}{z^2} = z^{-2} \int_0^z e^w (z - w)\, dw.$$

It is easily seen that $|k(z)| \leqslant 1$ for $|z| \leqslant 1$. We write $z = x + iy$ (x, y real) and consider the case $|z| > 1$. Since

$$k(z) = z^{-2} \int_0^x (z - u)e^u\, du + iz^{-2} e^x \int_0^y (z - x - iv)e^{iv}\, dv,$$

we see that

$$|k(z)| \leqslant |z|^{-2} \{|(e^x - 1)z| + e^x |y|^2\} \leqslant 2e^x + 1.$$

Therefore

$$|k(z)| \leqslant 1 + 2 \exp[\operatorname{Re}(z)] \quad \text{for all } z.$$

Since

$$(E.1.1) \qquad \left| e^{zu} - 1 - \frac{zu}{1+u^2} \right| = \left| (zu)^2 k(zu) + \frac{zu^3}{1+u^2} \right|$$

$$\leqslant 2u^2 (1 + e^{u \operatorname{Re}(z)})(|z|^2 + |z|),$$

we conclude that the assumption $\int_{+0}^a u^2\, dN(u) < \infty$ implies the uniform convergence of the integral defining $f(z)$ on every bounded z-set. The function $f(z)$ is therefore an entire function. We see from (E.1.1) that

$$|f(z)| \leqslant \begin{cases} 4|z|^2(1+e^{a\,\mathrm{Re}\,(z)}) \displaystyle\int_{+0}^{a} u^2\,dN(u) & \text{if } |z| > 1 \text{ and Re}\,(z) > 0 \\ 8|z|^2 \displaystyle\int_{+0}^{a} u^2\,dN(u) & \text{if } |z| > 1 \text{ and Re}\,(z) \leqslant 0. \end{cases}$$

The estimate of the lemma follows immediately.

E.2 *Proof of lemmas* 9.1.2A *and* 9.1.2B

Let $f(z) = \displaystyle\sum_{p=0}^{\infty} d_p \exp\left(\frac{2\pi p}{T} z\right)$ where the coefficients satisfy the estimate

(E.2.1) $\quad d_p = O[\exp(-kp^2)] \quad (p \to \infty)$.

Condition (E.2.1) ensures that the series for $f(z)$ converges absolutely and uniformly in every bounded set of the z-plane. Therefore $f(z)$ is an entire function which obviously has the period iT. We write $x = \mathrm{Re}\,(z)$ and see that

$$|f(z)| \leqslant \sum_{p=0}^{\infty} |d_p| \exp\left(\frac{2\pi p x}{T}\right) = O\left\{ \sum_{p=0}^{\infty} \exp\left(-kp^2 + \frac{2\pi p x}{T}\right)\right\}$$

$$= O\left\{ \exp\left(\frac{\pi^2 x^2}{kT^2}\right) \sum_{p=-\infty}^{\infty} \exp\left[-k\left(p - \frac{\pi x}{kT}\right)^2\right]\right\}$$

$$= O\left[\exp\left(\frac{\pi^2 x^2}{kT^2}\right)\right].$$

The last estimate follows from the fact that $\displaystyle\sum_{p=-\infty}^{\infty} \exp\left[-k\left(p - \frac{\pi x}{kT}\right)^2\right]$ is a continuous periodic function of x with real period kT/π and is therefore bounded. If $x = \mathrm{Re}\,(z) \leqslant 0$ we see that $|f(z)| \leqslant \displaystyle\sum_{p=0}^{\infty} |d_p| = O(1)$ and lemma 9.1.2A is proved.

We proceed to the proof of lemma 9.1.2B.

We assume that the entire function $f(z)$ is periodic with period iT and that the estimates (9.1.7) hold.

We expand $f(iy)$ into a Fourier series,

$$f(iy) = \sum_{p=-\infty}^{\infty} d_p \exp\left(\frac{2\pi i p y}{T}\right) \quad (-\infty < y < \infty)$$

where

(E.2.2) $\quad d_p = \dfrac{1}{T} \displaystyle\int_0^T f(iy) \exp\left(-\frac{2\pi i p y}{T}\right) dy \quad (p = 0, \pm 1, \pm 2, \ldots)$.

Let ζ be a complex variable and consider the entire function $\lambda(\zeta) = f(i\zeta)\exp(-2i\pi p\zeta/T)$. [For real ζ this is the integrand in (E.2.2).] We integrate $\lambda(\zeta)$ around the rectangle whose vertices are the four points 0, $i\theta$, $i\theta + T$ and T (θ real). According to Cauchy's theorem this integral is zero. Since the function $\lambda(\zeta)$ is periodic with period T, the integrals along the vertical sides of the rectangle cancel, and we see that

$$d_p = \frac{1}{T} \int_0^T f(iy - \theta) \exp\left[-\frac{2\pi i p}{T}(y + i\theta) \right] dy.$$

It follows that

(E.2.3) $$|d_p| \leqslant \exp\left(\frac{2\pi p \theta}{T}\right) \max_{0 \leqslant y \leqslant T} f(iy - \theta).$$

Suppose that $\theta > 0$; we see then from (9.1.7) that

$$|d_p| \leqslant \exp\left[\frac{2\pi p}{T}\theta + O(\log \theta)\right].$$

We let θ tend to $+\infty$ and see that $d_p = 0$ for $p < 0$. If $\theta < 0$ we obtain from (E.2.3) and (9.1.7) the estimate

$$d_p = O\left[\exp\left(\frac{2\pi p}{T}\theta + N\theta^2\right)\right].$$

We put $\theta = -\dfrac{\pi p}{NT}$ and get the desired estimate

$$d_p = O(-kp^2)$$

where $k = -\dfrac{\pi^2}{NT^2}$.

E.3 *Proof of lemma 9.2.3*

Let $z = t + iy$ (t, y real); we show first that the function $\theta(z) = (z+1)^{-c} e^{-bz} f(z)$ is bounded in the half-plane $\mathrm{Re}\,(z) \geqslant 0$. We select a point $z_0 = t_0 + iy_0$ in the first quadrant; i.e. $z_0 \in [(t, y): t > 0,\ y > 0]$. Let $\mathfrak{D}_\varepsilon$ be the angle formed by the rays $\ell = [(t, y): y = 0,\ t \geqslant 0]$ and $\ell_\varepsilon = \left[(t, y): y = \dfrac{dt}{2\varepsilon},\ t \geqslant 0\right]$. We select $\varepsilon > 0$ so that $z_0 \in \mathfrak{D}_\varepsilon$.

We put $\theta_\varepsilon(z) = \theta(z) \exp(i\varepsilon z^2)$, then for $z \in \mathfrak{D}_\varepsilon$ we have

$$|\theta_\varepsilon(z)| = |\theta(z)| \exp(-2\varepsilon t y) \leqslant M_3 \exp(dt^2 - 2\varepsilon t y) \leqslant M_3 \exp(d|z|^2).$$

Moreover, $|\theta_\varepsilon(z)| \leqslant |\theta(z)| \leqslant M_2$ on the ray ℓ and $|\theta_\varepsilon(z)| \leqslant M_3$ on the ray ℓ_ε. We can therefore apply lemma 8.2.1 with $\mathfrak{D} = \mathfrak{D}_\varepsilon$, $M = \max(M_2, M_3)$, $\beta = \dfrac{\pi}{2} > \alpha = \arctan \dfrac{d}{2\varepsilon}$ and $\rho = 2 < \pi/\beta$.

Then

$$|\theta_\varepsilon(z)| \leqslant M \quad \text{for } z \in \mathfrak{D}_\varepsilon$$

and

$$|\theta(z_0)| \leqslant \max(M_2, M_3) \exp(2\varepsilon t_0 y_0).$$

We let ε tend to zero and see that

$$|\theta(z_0)| \leqslant \max(M_2, M_3).$$

The point z_0 is an arbitrary point of the first quadrant, so that $\theta(z)$ is bounded in the closed first quadrant. In a similar way[*] one shows that $\theta(z)$ is also bounded in the closed fourth quadrant $[(t, y): t \geqslant 0, y \leqslant 0]$ and therefore in the half-plane Re $(z) \geqslant 0$. We consider the function

$$\theta_1(z) = (z+1)^{-a} e^{-bz} f(z) = (z+1)^{c-a} \theta(z).$$

On the boundary of the half-plane Re $(z) \geqslant 0$ we have

$$|\theta_1(z)| \leqslant M_1$$

while in the half-plane Re $(z) \geqslant 0$

$$\theta_1(z) = O[|z+1|^{c-a}].$$

The assumptions of lemma 8.2.1 are again satisfied if we identify $\mathfrak{D}$ with the half-plane Re $(z) \geqslant 0$ and put $f(z) = \theta_1(z)$, $M = M_1$, $\alpha = -\pi/2$, $\beta = \pi/2$ and $\rho = \frac{1}{2}$. We see then that for Re $(z) \geqslant 0$

$$|\theta_1(z)| \leqslant M_1,$$

or

$$|f(z)| \leqslant M_1|z+1|^a \exp[b \text{ Re}(z)],$$

as stated in lemma 9.2.3.

E.4   *Proof of lemma 9.2.4*

Let $f_1(z) = f(z+iT) - f(z)$; the function $f_1(z)$ is entire and

(E.4.1) $|f_1(z)| \leqslant \exp\{k \text{ Re}(z) + O(\log|z|)\}$ [Re $(z) \geqslant 0$].

It follows from the representation of $f(z)$ that

$$f_1(iy) = \sum_{j=-\infty}^{\infty} (iTb_j) \exp\left(\frac{2\pi ijy}{T}\right).$$

According to the assumption of the lemma, this series converges uniformly on the interval $0 \leqslant y \leqslant T$ and is therefore the Fourier series of its sum $f(iy)$. We repeat the reasoning which led from formula (E.2.2) of Appendix E.2 to (E.2.3) and see that

(E.4.2) $|iTb_j| \leqslant \exp\left(\dfrac{2\pi j\theta}{T}\right) \max\limits_{0 \leqslant y \leqslant T} |f_1(iy-\theta)|.$

For $\theta < 0$ we can apply the estimate (E.4.1) and get

$$|b_j| \leqslant \exp\left[\frac{2\pi j\theta}{T} - k\theta + O(\log|\theta|)\right].$$

We let θ tend to $-\infty$ and conclude that

(E.4.3) $b_j = 0$ for $j > \omega = [kT/(2\pi)]$.

---

[*] To show this we consider instead of $\theta_\varepsilon(z)$ the function $\theta(z) \exp(-i\varepsilon z^2)$.

We next put

$$f_2(z) = f(z) - \sum_{j=-\infty}^{\omega} (a_j + b_j z) \exp\left(\frac{2\pi j z}{T}\right) = \sum_{j=\omega+1}^{\infty} (a_j + b_j z) \exp\left(\frac{2\pi j z}{T}\right).$$

In view of (E.4.3) we have

$$f_2(iy) = \sum_{j=\omega+1}^{\infty} a_j \exp\left(\frac{2\pi i j y}{T}\right) \quad (-\infty < y < \infty).$$

Moreover

$$|f_2(z)| \le \exp\{k \operatorname{Re}(z) + O(\log|z|)\} \quad [\operatorname{Re}(z) \ge 0].$$

Using the same argument as before, we see that

$$|a_j| \le \exp\left(\frac{2\pi j \theta}{T}\right) \max_{0 \le y \le T} |f_2(iy - \theta)|.$$

The estimate for $f_2(z)$ yields, for $\theta < 0$, the inequality

$$|a_j| \le \exp\left[\frac{2\pi j \theta}{T} - k\theta + O(\log|\theta|)\right].$$

We let $\theta \to -\infty$ and see that $a_j = 0$ for $j > \omega = [kT/(2\pi)]$. This completes the proof of lemma 9.2.4.

APPENDIX F

Schwarz's reflection principle

Let D_1 and D_2 be two domains such that $D_1 \cap D_2 = \emptyset$ while $\overline{D}_1 \cap \overline{D}_2$ is an interval γ on the real axis. Let $f_1(z)$ be regular in D_1 and continuous in $D_1 \cup \gamma$ and let $f_2(z)$ be regular in D_2 and continuous in $D_2 \cup \gamma$. Suppose that for $\xi \in \gamma$

$$\lim_{z \to \xi} f_1(z) = \lim_{z \to \xi} f_2(z) = h(\xi)$$

where the approach is from D_1 in the first and from D_2 in the second limit. Then there exists a function $f(z)$ regular in $D_1 \cup D_2 \cup \gamma$ which coincides with $f_1(z)$ in D_1 and with $f_2(z)$ in D_2.

For the proof we refer to Hille (1959), p. 184. In Chapter 11 we used for D_1 the interior of a rectangle located in the upper half-plane and for D_2 the interior of the rectangle which is located symmetrically to D_1 with respect to the real axis.

LIST OF EXAMPLES OF
CHARACTERISTIC FUNCTIONS[*]

[*] Abbreviations used: c.f. = characteristic function(s), d. = distribution(s),
d.f. = distribution function(s), i.d. = infinitely divisible.

REFERENCES

ACHIESER, N. I. (1956). *Theory of Approximation*. Transl. from Russian, New York, Frederick Ungar. [Russian originally published by Ogiz, Moscow–Leningrad (1947).]

AKUTOWICZ, E. J. (1959). On extrapolating a positive definite function from a finite interval. *Mathematica Scandinavica*, **7**, 157–169.

AKUTOWICZ, E. J. (1960). Sur l'approximation par certaines fonctions entières. *Ann. Scientifiques École Normale Supérieure* (3e série), **77**, 281–301.

BERGSTRÖM, H. (1952). On some expansions of stable distributions. *Arkiv for Matematik*, **2**, 375–378.

BLUM, J.–ROSENBLATT, M. (1959). On the structure of infinitely divisible distributions, *Pacific J. Math.*, **9**, 1–7.

BOAS, R. P. (1967). Lipschitz behaviour and integrability of characteristic functions. *Ann. Math. Statist.*, **38**, 32–36.

BOCHNER, S. (1932). *Vorlesungen über Fourier'sche Integrale*. Leipzig, Akademische Verlagsgesellschaft. Reprinted by Chelsea Publishing Co., New York, N.Y. (1948). English transl.: *Lectures on Fourier Integrals*, Annals of Math. Studies, No. 42, Princeton University Press, Princeton, N.J. (1959).

BOHR, H. (1932). *Fastperiodische Funktionen*. Ergebnisse d. Mathematik I/4, Berlin, J. Springer. English transl. (1947): *Almost periodic functions*, Chelsea Publishing Co., New York, N.Y.

CAIROLI, R. (1964). Sur les fonctions caractéristiques des lois de probabilité. *Publ. Inst. Statist. Univ. Paris*, **13**, 45–53.

CHRISTENSEN, I. F. (1962). Some further extensions of a theorem of Marcinkiewicz. *Pacific J. Math.*, **12**, 59–67.

CHUNG, K. L. (1953). Sur les lois de probabilité unimodales. *C.R. Acad. Sci. Paris*, **236**, 583–584.

COPSON, E. T. (1935). *An Introduction to the Theory of Functions of a Complex Variable*. Oxford, Clarendon Press.

CRAMÉR, H. (1939). On the representation of a function by certain Fourier integrals. *Trans. Amer. Math. Soc.*, **46**, 191–201.

CRAMÉR, H. (1964). *Mathematical Methods of Statistics*. Princeton University Press, Princeton, N.J.

CRUM, M. M. (1956). On positive definite functions. *Proc. London Math. Soc.*, **(3)**, **6**, 548–560.

CUPPENS, R. (1963a). Sur la décomposition d'une fonction 2q fois dérivable à l'origine en produit infini des fonctions caractéristiques. *C.R. Acad. Sci. Paris*, **256**, 3806–3808.

CUPPENS, R. (1963b). Sur un théorème de Mamay. *C.R. Acad. Sci. Paris*, **257**, 586–588.

CUPPENS, R. (1969). On the decomposition of infinitely divisible probability laws without normal factor. *Pacific J. Math.*, **28**, 61–76.

DUGUÉ, D. (1955). Sur l'approximation d'une fonction caractéristique par sa série de Fourier. *C.R. Acad. Sci. Paris*, **240**, 151–152.

DUGUÉ, D. (1957a). Résultats sur les fonctions absolument monotones et applications à l'arithmétique des fonctions de type positif. *C.R. Acad. Sci. Paris*, **244**, 715–717.

DUGUÉ, D. (1957b). Arithmétique des lois de probabilités. *Mémorial des Sciences Math.*, **137**. Paris, Gauthier-Villars.

DUGUÉ, D. (1957c). Sur le théorème de Lévy–Cramér. *Publ. Inst. Statist. Univ. Paris*, **6**, 213–225.

DUGUÉ, D. (1966). Sur les lois de Kolmogoroff et de von Mises. *C.R. Acad. Sci. Paris*, **262**, 999–1000.

DUGUÉ, D.–GIRAULT, M. (1955). Fonctions convexes de Pólya. *Publ. Inst. Statist. Univ. Paris*, **4**, 3–10.

ESSEEN, C. G. (1944). Fourier analysis of distribution functions. *Acta Mathematica*, **77**, 1–125.

EVANS, G. C. (1957). *Calculation of moments for a Cantor–Vitali function*. Herbert Ellsworth Slought Memorial paper No. 6, Supplement to *Amer. Math. Monthly*, **64**, No. 8, 22–27.

FELLER, W. (1943). On a general class of "contagious" distributions. *Ann. Math. Statist.*, **14**, 389–400.

FELLER, W. (1952). On a generalization of Marcel Riesz' potentials and the semigroups generated by them. *Medd. Lunds Univ. Mat. Sem.*, *Tome Supplémentaire Marcel Riesz*, 73–81.

FISZ, M.–VARADARAJAN, V. S. (1963). A condition for absolute continuity of infinitely divisible distribution functions. *Z. f. Wahrscheinlichkeitstheorie*, **1**, 335–339.

GIL-PELAEZ, J. (1951). Note on the inversion theorem. *Biometrika*, **38**, 481–482.

GIRAULT, M. (1954). Les fonctions caractéristiques et leurs transformations. *Publ. Inst. Statist. Univ. Paris*, **4**, 223–299.

GIRAULT, M. (1955). Analyticité et périodicité des fonctions caractéristiques. *Publ. Inst. Statist. Univ. Paris*, **5**, 91–94.

GNEDENKO, B. V.–KOLMOGOROV, A. N. (1954). *Limit distributions for sums of independent random variables*. (Transl. from Russian by K. L. Chung), Cambridge, Mass., Addison–Wesley Publishing Co.

GOLDBERG, A. A.–OSTROVSKII, I. V. (1967). An application of a theorem of W. K. Hayman to a problem in the theory of the decomposition of probability laws. *Ukrain. Mat. Žurnal*, **19**, 104–106. [А. А. Гольдберг.–И. В. Островский. Применение теоремы У. К. Хеймана к одному вопросу теорий разложений вероятностных законов. Украинский Мат. Журнал, **19** (1967), 104–106.]

HAHN, H.–ROSENTHAL, A. (1948). *Set Functions*. Albuquerque, N. M., Univ. of New Mexico Press.

HALMOS, P. R. (1950). *Measure Theory*. D. Van Nostrand Co., New York.

HARDY, G. H. (1963). *A Course in Pure Mathematics* (10th edn), Cambridge, Univ. Press.

HARDY, G. H.–LITTLEWOOD, J. E.–PÓLYA, G. (1934). *Inequalities*. Cambridge, Univ. Press.

HARTMAN, P.–WINTNER, A. (1942). On the infinitesimal generators of integral convolutions. *Amer. J. Math.*, **64**, 273–298.

HAUSDORFF, F. (1927). *Mengenlehre* (2nd rev. edn). Berlin–Leipzig, Walter de Gruyter & Co.

HERZ, C. S. (1963). Fonctions opérant sur les fonctions définies positives. *Annales de l'Institut Fourier*, **13**, 161–180.

HILLE, E. (1959, 1962). *Analytic Function Theory*, vol. I (1959), vol. II (1962). Ginn & Co., Boston, Mass.

HOBSON, E. W. (1927). *The theory of functions of a real variable*, I, II. Cambridge, Univ. Press; reprinted by Dover Publications, New York (1957).

IBRAGIMOV, I. A. (1956a). On the composition of unimodal distributions. *Teoriya veroyatnostei i ee primeneniya*, **1**, 283–288. English transl.: *Theory of probability and its applications*, **1**, 255–260.

IBRAGIMOV, I. A. (1956b). A theorem in the theory of infinitely divisible laws. *Teoriya veroyatnostei i ee primeneniya*, **1**, 485–489. English transl.: *Theory of probability and its applications*, **1**, 440–444.

IBRAGIMOV, I. A. (1957). Remark on a probability distribution of class *L*. *Teoriya veroyatnostei i ee primeneniya*, **2**, 121–124. English transl.: *Theory of probability and its applications*, **2**, 117–119.

IBRAGIMOV, I. A.–LINNIK, YU. V. (1965). Independent and stationary dependent variables. Moscow, *Izdat. Nauka*. [И. А. Ибрагимов–Ю. В. Линник. Независимые и стационарно связанные величины. Москва (1965), Іздат. Наука.]

INGHAM, A. I. (1936). A note on Fourier transforms. *J. London Math. Soc.*, **9**, 27–32.

JESSEN, B.–WINTNER, A. (1935). Distribution functions and the Riemann Zeta function. *Trans. Amer. Math. Soc.*, **38**, 48–88.

JOHANSEN, S. (1966). An application of extreme point methods to the representation of infinitely divisible distributions. *Z. f. Wahrscheinlichkeitstheorie*, **5**, 304–316.

JORDAN, C. (1950). *Calculus of Finite Differences*. New York, Chelsea Publishing Co.

KAWATA, T. (1940). On the division of probability laws. *Proc. Imp. Acad. Tokyo*, **16**, 249–254.

KERSHNER, R. (1936). On singular Fourier transforms. *Amer. J. Math.*, **58**, 450–453.

KERSHNER, R.–WINTNER, A. (1935). On symmetric Bernoulli convolutions. *Amer. J. Math.*, **57**, 541–545.

KONHEIM, A. G.–WEISS, B. (1965). Functions which operate on characteristic functions. *Pacific J. Math.*, **15**, 1279–1293.

KONHEIM, A. G.–WEISS, B. (1968). A note on functions which operate. *Pacific J. Math.*, **24**, 297–302.

KRASNER, M.–RANULAC, B. (1937). Sur une propriété des polynômes de la division du cercle. *C.R. Acad. Sci. Paris*, **204**, 397–399.

KREIN, M. G. (1940). Sur le problème du prolongement des fonctions hermitiennes positives et continues. *C.R. (Doklady) Acad. Sci. USSR*, **26**, 17–20.

KREIN, M. G. (1943). On the representation of functions by Fourier–Stieltjes integrals. *Ucenie Zapiski Kuibishevskogo Gosud. Pedag. i Ucitelskogo Inst.*, **7**, 123–148 [М. Г. Крейн. О Представлении функций интегралами фурье Стилтьеса. Ученые Записки Куйбышевского Госуд. Педагогического и Учительского Института, **7**, 123–148.]

KUBIK, L. (1961/62). A characterization of the class *L* of probability distributions. *Studia Math.*, **21**, 254–252.

KUBIK, L. (1962/63). Some analogies between the class of infinitely divisible distributions and the class *L* of distributions. *Studia Math.*, **22**, 197–209.

KURATOWSKI, C. (1952). *Topologie*, vol. I (3rd edn). Monografie Matematyczne XX: Polska Akademia Nauk, Warszawa.

LAHA, R. G. (1960). On a property of positive definite functions. *Bull. Amer. Math. Soc.*, **66**, 388–391.

LAHA, R. G.–LUKACS, E. (1962). On a factorization of characteristic functions which have a finite number of derivatives at the origin. *Publ. Inst. Statist. Univ. Paris*, **11**, 221–224.

LETTA, G. (1963). Eine Bemerkung zur Kennzeichnung der charakteristischen Funktionen. *Z. f. Wahrscheinlichkeitstheorie*, **2**, 69–74.

LEVIN, B. YA. (1964). *Distribution of zeros of entire functions*. Amer. Math. Soc., Providence, R.I. [Russian original published Moscow, 1956.]

LEVINSON, N. (1936). On a class of non-vanishing functions. *Proc. London Math. Soc.*, (2), **41**, 393–407.

LEVINSON, N. (1938). A theorem relating to non-vanishing and analytic functions. *J. Math. Phys.*, **16**, 185–190.

LÉVY, P. (1931). Sur les séries dont les termes sont des variables éventuelles indépendantes. *Studia Math.*, **3**, 119–155.

LÉVY, P. (1937a). *Théorie de l'addition des variables aléatoires*. Paris, Gauthier-Villars. [2nd edn, Paris, 1954.]

LÉVY, P. (1937b). Sur les exponentielles de polynômes. *Ann. Scientifiques École Normale Supérieure* (3e série), **73**, 231–292.

LÉVY, P. (1937c). L'arithmétique des lois de probabilité et les produits finis des lois de Poisson. *C.R. Acad. Sci. Paris*, **204**, 944–946.

LÉVY, P. (1938a) L'arithmétique des lois de probabilité. *J. Math. Pures et Appl.*, **103**, 17–40.

LÉVY, P. (1938b). L'arithmétique des lois de probabilité et les produits finis des lois de Poisson. *Actualités Scientifiques et Industrielles*, No. 736 (Colloque de Genève III), 25–59. Hermann, Paris.

LÉVY, P. (1939). Sur certains processus stochastiques homogènes. *Compositio Mathematica*, **7**, 283–339.

LÉVY, P. (1952). Sur une classe des lois de probabilité indécomposables. *C.R. Acad. Sci. Paris*, **235**, 489–491.

LÉVY, P. (1961). Quelques problèmes non résolus de la théorie des fonctions caractéristiques. *Annali Mat. Pura e Appl.* (ser. 4), **53**, 315–332.

LÉVY, P. (1962). Extensions d'un théorème de D. Dugué et M. Girault. *Z. f. Wahrscheinlichkeitstheorie*, **1**, 159–173.

LEWIS, T. (1967). The factorization of the rectangular distribution. *J. Applied Prob.*, **4**, 529–542.

LINNIK, YU. V. (1953). Linear forms and statistical criteria: I, II. *Ukrain Mat. Ž.*, **5**, 207–243, 247–290. English transl. in *Selected Translations Math. Statist. and Prob.*, **3**, 1–40, 41–90. Amer. Math. Soc., Providence, R.I. (1962).

LINNIK, YU. V. (1957). On the decomposition of the convolution of Gaussian and Poissonian laws. *Teoriya veroyatnostei i ee primeneniya*, **2**, 34–59. English transl.: *Theory of probability and its applications*, **2**, 31–57.

LINNIK, YU. V. (1959). On "α-factorizations" of infinitely divisible probabilistic laws. *Vestnik Leningrad Univ.* (1959), 14–23. English transl. in *Selected translations Math. Statist. and Prob.*, **2**, 159–169. Amer. Math. Soc., Providence, R.I.

LINNIK, YU. V. (1964). *Decomposition of Probability Distributions*. Oliver and Boyd, Edinburgh–London. [Russian original published Leningrad, 1960.]

LOEFFEL, H. (1956). Beiträge zur Theorie der charakteristischen Funktionen. *Mitt. Verein. Schweiz. Versich. Math.*, **56**, 337–381.

LOÈVE, M. (1955). *Probability Theory*. D. Van Nostrand, New York (3rd edn, 1963).

LUKACS, E. (1958). Some extensions of a theorem of Marcinkiewicz. *Pacific J. Math.*, **8**, 487–501.

LUKACS, E. (1964). A linear mapping of the space of distribution functions onto a set of bounded continuous functions. *Z. f. Wahrscheinlichkeitstheorie*, **3**, 1–6.

LUKACS, E. (1967). On the arithmetic properties of certain entire characteristic functions. *Proc. 5th Berkeley Symp. Math. Statist. and Prob.*, **2**, Part I, 401–414. Univ. of Calif. Press, Berkeley and Los Angeles.

LUKACS, E.–SZÁSZ, O. (1954a). Certain Fourier transforms of distributions: II. *Canad. J. Math.*, **5**, 186–189.

LUKACS, E.–SZÁSZ, O. (1954b). Non-negative trigonometric polynomials and certain rational characteristic functions. *J. Research Nat. Bureau Standards*, **52**, 153–160.

MARCINKIEWICZ, J. (1938). Sur une propriété de la loi de Gauss. *Math. Zeitschr.*, **44**, 612–618. Reprinted in J. Marcinkiewicz, *Collected Papers*. Panstwowe wydawnictwo Naukowe Warszawa, 1964.

MARKUSHEVICH, A. I. (1965–67). *Theory of Functions of a Complex Variable*, vol. I, II (1965), III (1967). Transl. from Russian by R. A. Silvermann. Englewood Cliffs, N.Y., Prentice Hall.

MEDGYESSY, P. (1956). Partial differential equations for stable density functions and their applications. *Magyar Tud. Akad. Mat. Kutató Intéz. Közl.*, **1**, 489–518.

MEDGYESSY, P. (1963). On the interconnection between the representation theorems of characteristic functions of unimodal distributions and of convex characteristic functions. *Magyar Tud. Akad. Mat. Kutató Intéz. Közl.*, **8**, 425–430.

MILLER, H. D. (1967). Generalization of a theorem of Marcinkiewicz. *Pacific J. Math.*, **20**, 261–274.

NATANSON, I. P. (1955). *Konstruktive Funktionentheorie*. Berlin, Akademie Verlag. [Russian original published by Ogiz, Moscow–Leningrad, 1951.]

NOACK, A. (1950). A class of variables with discrete distributions. *Ann. Math. Statist.*, **21**, 127–132.

OSTROVSKII, I. V. (1963). Entire functions satisfying some special inequalities connected with the theory of characteristic functions of probability laws. *Kharkovskogo Univ. Mat. Obshestva*, **29**, 145–168. English transl. in *Selected Translations Math. Statist. and Prob.*, **7**, 203–234. Amer. Math. Soc., Providence, R.I.

OSTROVSKII, I. V. (1964). On the decomposition of infinitely divisible lattice laws. *Vestnik Leningrad Univ.*, **19**, 51–60. [И. В. Островский. О разложениях решетчатых безгранично делимых законов. Вестник Ленинградского Университета, **19**, 51–60 (1964).]

OSTROVSKII, I. V. (1965). Some theorems on the decomposition of probability laws. *Trudi Mat. Inst. Steklova*, **79** (1965), 198–235. English transl.: *Proceedings of the Steklov Institute of Mathematics*, No. 79 (1965), 221–259. Amer. Math. Soc., Providence, R.I. (1966).

OSTROVSKII, I. V. (1966). On the factorization of multidimensional infinitely divisible probability laws without Gaussian component. *Vestnik Kharkovskogo Gosud. Univ. (Ser. Meh.-Mat.)*, **32**, 51–72. [И. В. Островский. О разложениях многмерных везгранично делемых законов без гауссовой компоненты. Вестник Харковского Госуд. Унив. Сер. Мех.-Мат., **32**, 51–72.]

PALEY, R. E. A. C.–WIENER, N. (1934). *Fourier transforms in the complex domain*. Amer. Math. Soc. Colloquium Publ. No. 19, Amer. Math. Soc., New York, N.Y.

PITMAN, E. J. G. (1956). On the derivation of a characteristic function at the origin. *Ann. Math. Statist.*, **27**, 1156–1160.

PITMAN, E. J. G. (1961). Some theorems on characteristic functions of probability distributions. *Proc. 4th Berkeley Symp. Math. Statist. and Prob.*, **2**, 393–402. Univ. of Calif. Press, Berkeley and Los Angeles.

PÓLYA, G.–SZEGÖ, G. (1925). *Aufgaben und Lehrsätze aus der Analysis*, I. J. Springer, Berlin. American Edition: Dover Publications, New York (1945).

RAIKOV, D. A. (1938). On the decomposition of Gauss and Poisson laws. *Izvest. Akad. Nauk SSSR (Ser. Mat.)*, **2**, 91–124. [Д. А. Райков. О разложении законов Гаусса и Пуассона. Известия Акад. Наук. СССР, Сер. Мат., **2**, 91–124.]

RAIKOV, D. A. (1940). On positive definite functions. *Doklady Akad. Nauk SSSR,* **26,** 857–862. [Д. А. Райков. О положительно определенных функциях. Доклады Акад. Наук СССР, **26,** 857–862.]

RAMACHANDRAN, B. (1962). On the order and type of entire characteristic functions. *Ann. Math. Statist.,* **33,** 1238–1255.

RAMACHANDRAN, B. (1965). An extension of a theorem of Mamay with application. *Sankhyā,* **A, 27,** 303–310.

RAMACHANDRAN, B. (1967). *Advanced Theory of Characteristic Functions.* Statistical Publishing Society, Calcutta.

RIESZ, F. (1933). Über Sätze von Stone und Bochner. *Acta Univ. Szeged,* **6,** 184–198.

RIESZ, M.–LIVINGSTONE, A. E. (1955). A short proof of a classical theorem in the theory of Fourier integrals. *Amer. Math. Monthly,* **62,** 434–437.

ROBBINS, H. (1948). Mixture of distributions, *Ann. Math. Statist.,* **19,** 360–369.

ROSSBERG, H. J. (1966). Wachstum und Nullstellenverteilung ganzer charakteristischer Funktionen. *Monatsberichte Deutsch. Akad. Wiss. Berlin,* **8,** 275–286.

ROSSBERG, H. J. (1967a). Der Zusammenhang zwischen einer ganzen charakteristischen Funktion einer verfeinerten Ordnung und ihrer Verteilungsfunktion. *Czechoslovak Math. J.,* **17(92),** 317–334.

ROSSBERG, H. J. (1967b). Ganze charakteristische Funktionen mit vollkommen regulärem Wachstum. *Czechoslovak Math. J.,* **17(92),** 335–346.

SALEM, R. (1943). On some singular monotonic functions which are strictly increasing. *Trans. Amer. Math. Soc.,* **53,** 427–439.

SAPOGOV, N. A. (1951). The stability problem for a theorem of Cramér. *Izvest. Akad. Nauk SSSR (Ser. Mat.),* **15,** 205–218. English transl. in *Selected Translations Math. Statist. and Prob.,* **1,** 41–53. Amer. Math. Soc., Providence, R.I.

SCHMETTERER, L. (1965). Some theorems on the Fourier analysis of positive definite functions. *Proc. Amer. Math. Soc.,* **16,** 1141–1146.

SCHWARTZ, L. (1941). Sur le module de la fonction caractéristique du calcul des probabilités. *C.R. Acad. Sci. Paris,* **212,** 418–421.

SHIMIZU, R. (1964). On the decomposition of infinitely divisible characteristic functions with a continuous Poisson spectrum. *Ann. Inst. Statist. Math.,* **16,** 387–407.

SHOHAT, J. A.–TAMARKIN, J. D. (1943). *The Problem of Moments.* (Mathematical Surveys, 1.) Amer. Math. Soc., New York, N.Y.

SKOROHOD, A. V. (1954). Asymptotic formulas for stable distribution laws. *Doklady Akad. Nauk SSSR (N. S.),* **98,** 731–734. English transl. in *Selected Translations Math. Statist. and Prob.,* **1,** 157–161. Amer. Math. Soc., Providence, R.I.

SUN, T. C. (1967). A note on the unimodality of distribution functions of the class *L*. *Ann. Math. Statist.,* **38,** 1296–1299.

TAKANO, K. (1951). Certain Fourier transforms of distributions. *Tohoku Math. J.,* **(2), 3,** 306–315.

TEICHER, H. (1954). On the factorization of distributions. *Ann. Math. Statist.,* **25,** 769–774.

TITCHMARSH, E. C. (1937). *Introduction to the Theory of Fourier Integrals.* Oxford, Clarendon Press.

TITCHMARSH, E. C. (1939). *The Theory of Functions* (2nd edn). Oxford, Univ. Press.

TUCKER, H. G. (1962). Absolute continuity of infinitely divisible distributions. *Pacific J. Math.,* **12,** 1125–1129.

TUCKER, H. G. (1964). On continuous singular infinitely divisible distribution functions. *Ann. Math. Statist.*, **35**, 330–335.

TUCKER, H. G. (1965). On a necessary and sufficient condition that an infinitely divisible distribution be absolutely continuous. *Trans. Amer. Math. Soc.*, **118**, 316–330.

WIDDER, D. V. (1946). *The Laplace Transform.* Princeton, Univ. Press.

WINTNER, A. (1936). On a class of Fourier transforms. *Amer. J. Math.*, **58**, 45–90.

WINTNER, A. (1938). *Asymptotic distributions and infinite convolutions* (planographed lecture notes). Edwards Brothers, Ann Arbor, Michigan.

WINTNER, A. (1947). *The Fourier Transforms of Probability Distributions.* Baltimore, Md (published by the author).

WINTNER, A. (1956). Cauchy's stable distributions and an "explicit formula" of Mellin. *Amer. J. Math.*, **78**, 819–861.

ZEMANIAN, A. H. (1959). On the pole and zero location of rational Laplace transformations of non-negative functions. *Proc. Amer. Math. Soc.*, **10**, 868–872.

ZEMANIAN, A. H. (1961). On the pole and zero locations of rational Laplace transformations of non-negative functions, II. *Proc. Amer. Math. Soc.*, **12**, 870–874.

ZINGER, A.–LINNIK, YU. V. (1957). On a class of differential equations and its application to some questions of regression theory. *Vestnik Leningrad Univ.*, **12**, 121–130. English transl. in *Selected Translations Math. Statist. and Prob.*, **3**, 181–190. Amer. Math. Soc., Providence, R.I.

ZOLOTAREV, V. M. (1954). Expression of the density of a stable distribution with exponent α greater than 1 by means of a density with exponent $1/\alpha$. *Doklady Akad. Nauk SSSR*, **98**, 735–738. English transl. in *Selected Translations Math. Statist. and Prob.*, **1**, 163–167. Amer. Math. Soc., Providence, R.I.

ZOLOTAREV, V. M. (1956). On analytic properties of stable distribution laws. *Vestnik Leningrad Univ.*, **11**, No. 1, 49–52. English transl. in *Selected Translations Math. Statist. and Prob.*, **1**, 207–211. Amer. Math. Soc., Providence, R.I.

ZOLOTAREV, V. M. (1963). Analytical structure of the infinitely divisible laws of the L-class. *Litovskii Mat. Sbornik*, **3**, 123–124. [В. М. Золотарев. Аналитическое строение безгранично делемых законов класса L. Литовский Математический Сборник, **3**, 123–124.]

ZOLOTAREV, V. M. (1964). On the representation of stable laws by integrals. *Trudi Mat. Inst. Steklova*, **71** (1964), 46–50. English transl. in *Selected Translations Math. Statist. and Prob.*, **6**, 84–88. Amer. Math. Soc., Providence, R.I.

ZYGMUND, A. (1947). A remark on characteristic functions. *Ann. Math. Statist.*, **18**, 272–276.

ZYGMUND, A. (1951). A remark on characteristic functions. *Proc. 2nd Berkeley Symp. Math. Statist. and Prob.*, 369–372. Berkeley, Univ. of California Press.

ZYGMUND, A. (1952). *Trigonometrical Series* (2nd edn, corrected reprint of 1st edn, Monographie Mat. 5, Warszawa, 1935). Chelsea Publishing Co., New York, N.Y.

INDEX*

---

* The following abbreviations are used in the index: c.f. = characteristic function; a.c.f. = analytic characteristic function; d = distribution; d.f. = distribution functions; f. = function; i.d. = infinitely divisible; i.d.d. = infinitely divisible distribution.

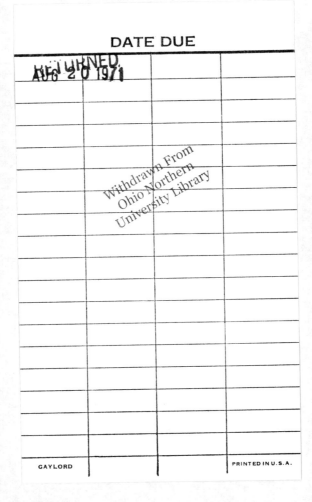